D1603419

Revised Second Edition

Field Theory, the Renormalization Group, and Critical Phenomena

DANIEL J. AMIT
Racah Institute of Physics
The Hebrew University of Jerusalem
Israel

World Scientific
Singapore • New Jersey • London • Hong Kong

05642279

PHYSICS

REpl B000228062

Published by

World Scientific Publishing Co. Pte. Ltd.
P O Box 128, Farrer Road, Singapore 9128
USA office: Suite 1B, 1060 Main Street, River Edge, NJ 07661
UK office: 73 Lynton Mead, Totteridge, London N20 8DH

FIELD THEORY, THE RENORMALIZATION GROUP, AND
CRITICAL PHENOMENA

First edition published by McGraw-Hill, Inc., 1978.
This revised edition by World Scientific Publishing Co. Pte. Ltd.
Reprinted 1989, 1993.

ISBN   9971-966-10-7
ISBN   9971-966-11-5 (pbk)

Printed in Singapore.

To **Paris**
to **Saclay**

CONTENTS

PART II   FURTHER APPLICATIONS AND DEVELOPMENTS

PREFACE

The methods and the applications of the renormalization group in the areas of statistical mechanics and high energy physics have ceaselessly continued to expand since the appearance of the first edition of this book. In retrospect one may say that particle physicists have shown greater openness to adopt creatively concepts of condensed matter physics, than that shown by solid state physicists towards the ideas of field theory. Yet no one lost ground. The wealth of the subject has been such that no reckoning has been called for.

It therefore appears quite appropriate to publish the second edition of this book, firstly because the first has disappeared, and new generations of physicists are entering a scene dominated by this language. Secondly it is an opportunity to expand and enlarge the scope of the book, to express some of the additional riches of the subject.

Once again one feels almost embarrassed realizing how many topics remain unmentioned. Moreover, the two main directions in which the book has been expanded had been invented prior to the appearance of the first edition. Those are the Coleman-Weinberg mechanism, which provides a description of *first order phase transitions induced by fluctuations*, and the systematic treatment of systems near their *lower critical dimension*. Both have moved closer to center-stage and are frequent participants in discussions of lattice gauge theories, of models of the inflationary universe, of disordered systems and of spin-glasses.

The main new features of the new edition are represented in the restructuring of the old Chapter 10 into a Part II of six chapters. In dealing with the approach to scaling we have included the field theoretic treatment of *finite size scaling*. Universality has become a chapter which includes the demonstration of the independence of physical quantities of the renormalization procedure. The Coleman-Weinberg mechanism is described in the context of a chapter describing the rich world systems with more than one coupling constant. Crossover phenomena have also become a chapter, which includes the treatment of dilution of magnetic systems. Finally, the ordered state of the $O(M)$-symmetric magnet is described in detail, as a field theory near two dimensions.

Jerusalem, June 1984

GENERAL SOURCES AND REFERENCES

1. E. S. Abers and B. W. Lee, *Physics Reports*, **9**, 1 (1973) to be referred to as AL.
2. N. N. Bogoliubov and D. V. Shirkov, *Introduction to the Theory of Quantized Fields* (Interscience, N.Y. 1959) to be referred to as BS.
3. E. Brézin, J. C. Le Guillou and J. Zinn-Justin, in *Phase Transitions and Critical Phenomena*, Vol. VI, C. Domb and M. S. Green, eds. (Academic Press, N.Y., 1976.) To be referred to as BLZ.
4. C. Domb and M. S. Green, eds., *Phase Transitions and Critical Phenomena*, Vol. VI (Academic Press, N.Y., 1976) to be referred to as DG.
5. J. Illiopoulos, C. Itzykson and A. Martin, *Reviews of Modern Physics*, **47**, 165 (1975), to be referred to as IIM.
6. C. Itzykson and J. B. Zuber, *Quantum Field Theory* (McGraw-Hill International, 1980). To be referred to as IZ.
7. S. K. Ma, *Modern Theory of Critical Phenomena* (Benjamin, N.Y., 1976).
8. K. Symanzik, "Small Distance Behavior in Field Theory" in *Particles, Quantum Fields and Statistical Mechanics*, M. Alexanian and A. Zepeda, eds. (Springer Verlag, Berlin, 1975). To be referred to as KS.
9. G. 't Hooft and M. Veltman, "Diagrammar", CERN report 73-9 (1973).
10. G. Toulouse and P. Pfeuty, *Introduction au Groupe de Renormalization et à ses Application* (Presses Universitaire de Grenoble, 1975).
11. F. Wegner "Critical Phenomena and the Renormalization Group" Lectures at the VIII Finnish Summer School (1973). To be referred to as FW.
12. K. G. Wilson and J. B. Kogut, *Physics Reports*, **12c**, 77 (1974), to be referred to as WK.
13. W. Zimmermann, "Local Operator Products and Renormalization" in *Lectures on Elementary Particle Physics and Quantum Field Theory* S. Deser et al., eds. (MIT Press, Cambridge, Mass., 1971).

PART I

BASIC IDEAS AND TECHNIQUES

PERTINENT CONCEPTS AND IDEAS IN THE THEORY OF CRITICAL PHENOMENA

1-1 DESCRIPTION OF CRITICAL PHENOMENA

There is a rich variety of systems which exhibit second order phase transitions. By a second order transition we mean one in which the system approaches, continuously, a state at which the scale of correlations becomes unbounded. In the language of field theory, one is approaching a zero mass theory. At such points the first derivatives of the free energy – like entropy, volume, magnetization, etc. – behave continuously. The name phase transition stems probably from the fact that often there is a change in symmetry occurring at the same point – as, for example, in the magnetic cases, or in changes of crystal structures, superconductivity, superfluidity, etc. But the classic second order transition – that of the critical point of the gas–liquid transition – involves no symmetry change at all.

One notices the large scale correlations by observing, for example, critical opalescence at the gas–liquid critical point. The dramatic increase in the scattering of light is a direct result of the fact that regions of the size of microns – the wavelength of visible light – are fluctuating coherently. The divergence of the susceptibility in ferromagnets reflects the long-range nature of correlations, since, as we shall see, the susceptibility is given by the integral of the correlation function (see Sec. 2-5).

Various physical quantities either vanish or diverge as one approaches the transition point. We have mentioned already the correlation length and magnetic susceptibility. Thus, if the correlation function of the fluctuating quantity at two different points is

$$\langle \delta s(x)\delta s(0) \rangle \underset{|x| \to \infty}{\sim} \exp(-x/\xi) \qquad (1\text{-}1)$$

then we define the asymptotic behaviour of the correlation length ξ, as a function of the temperature by:

$$\xi = \frac{f_+(T - T_c)^{-\nu}}{f_-(T - T_c)^{-\nu'}} \qquad \begin{matrix} T > T_c \\ T < T_c \end{matrix} \qquad (1\text{-}2)$$

For magnets $s(x)$ is the local magnetic moment, and δs is its value relative to its average. For antiferromagnets $s(x)$ is the local sum of spins added with a positive sign if on one lattice, and with a negative sign if on the other. For a liquid $s(x)$ is the difference between the local density at x and the mean density at the critical point. For systems like superfluids the fluctuating field is not directly observable. It is a complex order parameter. The behaviour of the correlation length can be deduced using Josephson's[1] relation which states that the exponent of the superfluid density is equal to ν.

But despite the great variety of physical systems one can use a unified language, based on some order-parameter field, whose identification may at times require much ingenuity. This order parameter may have one component, as in the Ising model, or 3 as in the Heisenberg model, or perhaps 18 as in the He^3 superfluid transition.

Within this unified language we define a susceptibility

$$\chi \sim \frac{C_+ |T - T_c|^{-\gamma}}{C_- |T - T_c|^{-\gamma'}} \qquad \begin{matrix} T > T_c \\ T < T_c \end{matrix} \qquad (1\text{-}3)$$

χ is the response of the system — the change in the average order parameter — when an infinitesimal external field which couples linearly to the order parameter, is applied.

Again there may be a variety of situations. In the liquid χ is the compressibility; in the antiferromagnet it is the response to a staggered field; in a superfluid it is not a physical quantity; in a Heisenberg system there may be a susceptibility tensor, with longitudinal and transverse components, etc.

If one is right at the critical temperature, $T = T_c$, then the correlation function generally decreases as a power. Thus we define

$$\langle \delta s(x) \delta s(0) \rangle \underset{|x| \to \infty}{\sim} |x|^{-(d-2+\eta)} \qquad (1\text{-}4)$$

where d is the number of space dimensions.

The specific heat is described asymptotically by:

$$C \sim \begin{array}{ll} A_+ |T - T_c|^{-\alpha} & T > T_c \\ A_- |T - T_c|^{-\alpha'} & T < T_c \end{array} \qquad (1\text{-}5)$$

where $\alpha = 0$ implies at times a discontinuity, and more recently a logarithmic behaviour.

In many systems one can measure a coexistence curve, the term being borrowed from the liquid–gas system, where it describes the thermodynamic subspace in which gas and liquid coexist in equilibrium. In a magnetic system it is the behaviour of the magnetization as a function of temperature at zero external field. One uses the magnetic notation, writing

$$M \sim (T_c - T)^\beta \qquad (1\text{-}6)$$

Another exponent is defined by considering the approach to the transition at $T = T_c$, but with external field, $h \neq 0$. The magnetization can be described as

$$M \sim h^{1/\delta} \qquad (1\text{-}7)$$

Similarly, this will describe the approach to the liquid critical point at $T = T_c$, but the pressure $p \neq p_c$.

The various quantities and exponents have to be interpreted anew for every system. We have used the simplest illustrations but the concepts have been applied successfully to a whole variety of transitions – including polymers, percolation problem, liquid crystals, helical magnets, ferroelectrics, etc., . . . and four pages of etc., . . . [2]

1-2 SCALING AND HOMOGENEITY

The idea of scaling, as first conjectured by Widom,[3] consists of writing the asymptotic, sometimes called singular, part of the free energy, or the equation of state as a homogeneous function of the variables. For example, the equation of state describes a relation between the magnetization, the temperature and the magnetic field. In general we could write:

$$h = M^\delta f(M, t) \qquad t = |T - T_c| \qquad (1\text{-}8)$$

Instead, Widom proposed that f should depend on a single variable. Thus we can write

$$h = M^\delta f(t/M^{1/\beta}) \qquad (1\text{-}9)$$

This type of relation seemed to be obeyed quite well experimentally. It was also verified in various approximations and models, such as the mean-field approximations, the droplet model, and the spherical model. Similarly, one writes for the singular part of the free energy

$$F(t,h) = t^{2-\alpha}\varphi(t/h^{1/\beta\delta}) \qquad (1\text{-}10)$$

and for the correlation function, at $M = h = 0$, for example,

$$G(r,t) = |r|^{-(d-2+\eta)}g(r/t^{-\nu}) \qquad (1\text{-}11)$$

From these homogeneous relations one can derive what are called "scaling laws," or relations among exponents. Thus, one finds easily that:

$$2\beta + \gamma = 2 - \alpha$$
$$2\beta\delta - \gamma = 2 - \alpha$$
$$\gamma = \nu(2 - \eta)$$
$$\nu d = 2 - \alpha \qquad (1\text{-}12)$$

Furthermore, one finds that the exponents are symmetrical about the transition. Consequently, if scaling really holds, one needs to know only two exponents in order to know them all. These relations are exactly obeyed by the two-dimensional Ising model, and by the spherical model. Both experimental results and numerical studies of various models support them strongly. The idea of scaling was injected with a very creative intuitive insight by Kadanoff[4] and formulated by Patashinskii and Pokrovskii.[5] The phenomenological aspect of this idea has been developed extensively by Fisher,[6] and brought to its logical and aesthetic extreme by Griffiths.[7]

1-3 COMPARISON OF VARIOUS RESULTS FOR CRITICAL EXPONENTS

In several cases self-consistent approximations were developed for the description of critical phenomena. For example, the Van der Waals equation of state was devised for the gas–liquid transition. The Weiss theory was developed for ferromagnetism, and the Curie–Weiss theory for antiferromagnetism, etc. Landau, in 1937, unified all theories of this type under what has since been called Landau theory.[8] Basically, all these theories assume that the interacting system can be replaced by a system in an external field, if only that field is properly chosen. A non-interacting system in an external field can be exactly solved, and

Table 1-1   Values of critical exponents

Exponent	Mean field theory	Ising model $d = 2$	Ising model $d = 3^{\dagger}$	Heisenberg model $d = 3^{\dagger}$	Spherical model $\epsilon > 0$
α α'	0	0 0	0.12	-0.06	$-\dfrac{\epsilon}{2-\epsilon}$
β	$\frac{1}{2}$	$\frac{1}{8}$	0.31		$\frac{1}{2}$
γ γ'	1	$\frac{7}{4}$	1.25	1.38 not defined	$\dfrac{2}{2-\epsilon}$
ν ν'	$\frac{1}{2}$	1	0.64	0.7	$\dfrac{1}{2-\epsilon}$
δ	3	15	5.0		$\dfrac{6-\epsilon}{2-\epsilon}$
η	0	$\frac{1}{4}$	0.04	0.05	0

†Approximate results from numerical extrapolations of high-temperature and low-temperature series. The uncertainties are higher for $n - 3$ than $n = 1$ and for the primed indices.

then the field is determined by a variational calculation. This is called a *mean field theory*. It is equivalent, as we shall see later, to selecting out of all possible configurations only the one which gives the largest term in the partition sum. Thus all fluctuations are ignored. In the language of field theory this is the classical, or tree, approximation.

The result is that the free energy is an analytic function of the thermodynamic variables, and a set of universal exponents ensues. They are represented by the first column of Table 1-1, and are callled either mean field, Landau, or classical exponents. Landau simply circumvented the specificity of the system, and wrote directly a power expansion, with analytic coefficients for the free energy. Since one assumes that near the transition there are small quantities like t, and M or $\rho - \rho_c$, one can obtain directly a universal theory for the critical region. And, as so often in the history of physics, the material state of the art, i.e., the experimentation, was crude enough to allow for the introduction of such universal descriptions.

This type of theory, though quantitatively wrong, is quite often a very reliable qualitative guide, and is always a good starting point for more sophisticated approaches which consider fluctuations.

As experimental techniques were improved it could be seen unambiguously that there are deviations from mean field exponents. By 1944 the thermodynamics of an interacting system was solved exactly for the first time. The two-dimensional Ising model was solved by Onsager,[9] and while a mean field calculation would have predicted for it the same exponents as for any other system, the results were dramatically different.

There is no exact solution for the thermodynamic properties of a three-dimensional interacting system. But a whole industry of numerical calculations was developed by Domb, Fisher and others,[10] to produce increasingly accurate values for the critical exponents in three dimensions for a variety of systems. Some results are listed in Table 1-1. It can be seen that the dependence on dimensionality is quite significant.

What all this indicated, beyond the numerical discrepancies in exponents, was that something fundamental was missing in the understanding of critical phenomena. While mean field theory was wrong, scaling and scaling laws still were obeyed. Thus, it was felt that a unifying theory for all critical phenomena with rather simple features should exist.

The nine exponents β, α, α', γ, γ', δ, ν, ν', η are listed in Table 1-1 for a few cases.

1-4 UNIVERSALITY – DIMENSIONALITY, SYMMETRY

We have used the concept of universality a few times in a rather colloquial sense. In the context of a mean field theory, or a Landau theory, the critical behaviour is universal in the trivial sense that it depends on none of the characteristics of the system. It does not depend on whether it is an Ising or Heisenberg magnet, or a superfluid, whether as a Heisenberg ferromagnet it is isotropic or not. It does not depend on the type of interactions in the system, nor on the number of space dimensions of the system.

Now, the independence of the critical exponents of the strength and range of the interactions is supported by solutions of two-dimensional Ising models with various strengths, lattice structures and ranges – as long as they are finite. In other words, a *universality*, in the sense of independence of any microscopic details, has survived the scrutiny of recent investigations, both experimental and calculational. As we shall see, this type of universality can be understood within the theory, once fluctuations are treated properly.

On the other hand, the exponents show a very marked dependence on *symmetry* and on the number of *space dimensions*. What is meant here by symmetry is the internal spin symmetry. Thus, an Ising model has a discrete symmetry of two elements – changing the sign of all spins. The Helium superfluid transition or the superconducting transition, which have a complex order parameter, have a continuous symmetry of multiplication by a phase, i.e., a gauge symmetry of the first kind. This is equivalent to expressing the theory in terms of two real fields, possessing a symmetry of rotations in the two-

dimensional *spin* space. The Heisenberg isotropic ferromagnet has a three component spin, and is invariant under $O(3)$, while if anisotropy is introduced its
symmetry is reduced to $O(2)$, or to the Ising symmetry.

The number of space dimensions is independent of the number of dimensions of the spin discussed in the previous paragraph. One knows, for
example, that if there is a continuous symmetry, no long-range order, or broken
symmetry, will occur at any finite temperature, in a system in two space
dimensions.[11] If the symmetry is discrete, long-range order may appear, as in
the Ising model, even in two dimensions. But beside these qualitative changes the
exponents also depend quantitatively on d, the number of dimensions.

EXERCISES

1-1 Given that the equation of state is of the homogeneous form

$$h = M^{\delta} F(t/M^{1/\beta})$$

show that

(a) β and δ have the meaning defined by the critical exponents with the same
names;

(b) $\gamma = \gamma' = \beta(\delta - 1)$.

1-2 Given that the free energy has the homogeneous form

$$F = t^{2-\alpha}\varphi(t/h^{1/\beta\delta})$$

show that

(a) α β, δ have the same meaning as the corresponding critical exponents;

(b) $\alpha = \alpha'$;

(c) $2 - \alpha = \beta(\delta + 1)$.

1-3 If the correlation function has the form

$$G(r, t) = |r|^{-(d-2+\eta)}g(r/t^{-\nu})$$

and g has a finite range, show that

$$\gamma = \nu(2 - \eta)$$

REFERENCES

1. B. D. Josephson, *Physics Letters*, **21**, 608 (1966).
2. The classic review on this matter is P. Heller, "Experimental Investigation of Critical
   Phenomena", *Reports on Progress in Physics*, Vol. XXX, 731 (1967).
3. B. Widom, *Journal of Chemical Physics*, **43**, 3898 (1965).

4. L. P. Kadanoff, *Physics,* **2**, 263 (1966).
5. A. Z. Patashinskii and V. L. Pokrovskii, *Z.E.T.F.,* **50**, 439 (1966). [English translation: *Soviet Physics – J.E.T.P.,* **23**, 292 (1966).]
6. See e.g., M. E. Fisher, "The Theory of Equilibrium Critical Phenomena", *Reports on Progress in Physics,* Vol. XXX, 615 (1967). See also L. P. Kadanoff et al., *Reviews of Modern Physics,* **39**, 395 (1967).
7. R. B. Griffiths, *Physical Review,* **158**, 176 (1967).
8. L. D. Landau in *Collected Papers of L. D. Landau,* D. Ter Haar, ed. (Pergamon, London, 1956) and L. D. Landau and E. M. Lifshitz, *Statistical Physics* (Pergamon, Oxford, 1968), Chap. 13.
9. L. Onsager, *Physical Review*, **65**, 117 (1944).
10. See, e.g., C. Domb and M. S. Green, eds., *Phase Transitions and Critical Phenomena,* Vol. III (Academic Press, N.Y., 1974).
11. N. D. Mermin and H. Wagner, *Physical Review Letters,* **17**, 1133 (1966). See also S. Coleman, *Communications in Mathematical Physics,* **31**, 259 (1973).

FORMULATION OF THE PROBLEM OF PHASE TRANSITIONS IN TERMS OF FUNCTIONAL INTEGRALS

2-1 INTRODUCTION

As was discussed in the previous chapter a continuous phase transition is characterized by strong fluctuations in some field, usually called the order parameter. Thus, in order to be able to treat the problem systematically, a procedure for calculating averages, fluctuations, correlations, etc., is needed. One such procedure, is to define a statistical weight for a given spatial distribution of the *order parameter field*, to define a measure over the space of these distributions, and then to proceed to calculate all the consequences of the theory.

The first problem is connected with the identification of the order parameter field. Clearly, there is nothing automatic about it, since the same microscopic system can undergo many types of phase transitions. One given mixture of protons, neutrons and electrons can undergo a gas—liquid transition, a ferromagnetic or antiferromagnetic transition, a liquid—solid transition, many structural transitions, a superconducting transition, or a metal—insulator transition, a superconducting transition, or a metal—insulator transition, etc. . . . A good deal of ingenuity has to be invested in deciding how to restrict attention to the most relevant features of a given phase transition. The main task being the physical interpretation of the order parameter and its internal symmetry.

2-2 CONSTRUCTION OF THE LAGRANGIAN

One way to proceed, after the order parameter and its symmetry have been determined, is to construct from the field and its derivatives all possible invariants of the symmetry group, and then to add them with arbitrary coefficients to make a "Lagrangian" density, $\mathscr{L}(\phi)$, taking care of the obvious symmetries of space–time. To clarify this point we consider a few examples.

2-2-1 The Real Scalar Field

Considering a system such as a uniaxial ferromagnet or a liquid, the order parameter will be a real scalar field $\phi(x)$ with no internal symmetry. In such a case one would construct $\mathscr{L}[\phi(x)]$ as a general polynomial in ϕ, and in $(\nabla\phi)^2$. If, as is the case for the Ising model, for example, there is a symmetry with respect to the direction of the axis, i.e. $\phi \to -\phi$, then only even powers will appear in the polynomial.

Thus, one has an infinite number of terms in $\mathscr{L}$, and the weight corresponding to this distribution is

$$W\{\phi\} = \exp\left\{-\int dx \, \mathscr{L}[\phi(x)]\right\} \qquad (2\text{-}1)$$

Further considerations are introduced to restrict the number of terms in $\mathscr{L}$. These considerations are consistent with the results of the renormalization group analysis, and indicate that, in the generic case, one needs include only $(\nabla\phi)^2$, ϕ^2 and ϕ^4, with arbitrary coefficients. Other monomials are irrelevant, in a sense which will become clear as we go along.

If a magnetic field is applied then a term linear in $\phi(x)$ will appear in $\mathscr{L}$. The result can be written in the form:

$$\mathscr{L}[\phi(x)] = A_0(\nabla\phi)^2 + A_1\phi^2(x) + A_2\phi^4(x) + h\phi(x) \qquad (2\text{-}2)$$

2-2-2 Complex Field

For systems such as He^4, at the superfluid transition, or for some material near its superconducting transition, one argues that a complex field, ψ, plays the role of the order parameter. The overall phase of this field is unobservable and arbitrary. One has a gauge-invariance of the first kind, the group being $U(1)$ or $O(2)$.

$\mathscr{L}[\psi]$ has to be constructed as a polynomial in $|\psi|^2$ and in $|\nabla\psi|^2$.

Arguments of relevance restrict the list to

$$\mathcal{L}[\psi(x)] = A_0 |\nabla \psi|^2 + A_1 |\psi|^2 + A_2 |\psi|^4 \tag{2-3}$$

In this way we exhibit the $U(1)$ symmetry. But we can, of course, write $\psi(x)$ in terms of two real fields

$$\psi(x) = \phi_1 + i\phi_2 \tag{2-4}$$

and the $U(1)$ symmetry becomes an $O(2)$ symmetry in the (ϕ_1, ϕ_2)-plane. Equation (2-3) can be written as:

$$\mathcal{L}[\phi_1, \phi_2] = A_0 [(\nabla\phi_1)^2 + (\nabla\phi_2)^2]$$
$$+ A_1 [\phi_1^2(x) + \phi_2^2(x)] + A_2 [\phi_1^2 + \phi_2^2]^2 \tag{2-5}$$

2-2-3 A Hypercubic n-Vector Model

Consider a system with an order parameter which has n real components

$$\boldsymbol{\phi} = [\phi_1(x), \ldots, \phi_n(x)] \tag{2-6}$$

Assume that the system is invariant under reflections, $\phi_i \to -\phi_i$, and under the permutations of the ϕ_i's. This is a typical case of a system with n-dimensional cubic symmetry, where the ϕ_i's are along the axes of the hypercube. A special example is a Heisenberg ferromagnet, for which $n = 3$, in a cubic crystal.

Now, as previously, we have just one quadratic invariant

$$\sum_{i=1}^{n} \phi_i^2 \equiv \boldsymbol{\phi}^2$$

but there are two quartic invariants. Namely,

$$(\boldsymbol{\phi}^2)^2 \quad \text{and} \quad \sum_{i=1}^{n} \phi_i^4$$

If we ignore the fact that the ϕ_i's are actually related to physical spatial axes in the crystal, and that consequently one can construct invariants by using the fact that the coordinates have a vector structure related to that of the ϕ's, then $\mathcal{L}$ will be written as:

$$\mathcal{L}[\boldsymbol{\phi}(x)] = A_0(\nabla\boldsymbol{\phi})^2 + A_1\boldsymbol{\phi}^2(x) + A_2[\boldsymbol{\phi}^2(x)]^2 + A_3\sum_i \phi_i^4(x) \tag{2-7}$$

in which

$$(\nabla\boldsymbol{\phi})^2 \equiv \sum_{i=1}^{n} (\nabla\phi_i)^2 \tag{2-8}$$

Rather general n-vector models describe situations in which there is a transition at finite momentum, as for an antiferromagnet. In such a case a whole star of k's becomes unstable.[1]

2-2-4 Two Coupled Fluctuating Fields

We mentioned above the possibility of introducing an external field. Such a field does not fluctuate, and is kept at some prescribed value. There are situations where two different fluctuating fields are interacting near the transition.

One may consider a competition between a ferromagnetic and a ferroelectric transition, each fluctuating in its own right. One can then include in $\mathscr{L}$ invariants composed of both fields. Another interesting case is the superconductor. There, the fluctuations of the complex order parameter are accompanied by fluctuations of the internal electromagnetic field. When one takes both into account one can write[2]

$$\mathscr{L} = A_0 \, | \, (\nabla - ie\mathbf{A})\psi \, |^2 + A_1 \, | \, \psi \, |^2 + A_2 \, | \, \psi \, |^4$$
$$+ A_3 \sum_{i>j} (\nabla_j A_i - \nabla_i A_j)^2 \qquad (2\text{-}9)$$

where $\mathbf{A}$ is the electromagnetic field, which is just the Lagrangian for scalar electrodynamics.[3] This coupling to the electromagnetic field changes the superconducting transition into a first order one. A similar phenomenon occurs in liquid crystals.

2-3   THE PARAMETERS APPEARING IN $\mathscr{L}$

The procedure for constructing $\mathscr{L}$, outlined in the previous section, has the apparent drawback that the parameters are arbitrary. There are a few comments that should be made concerning this point. Firstly, as far as what has come to be considered as the central problem of critical phenomena, namely, the calculation of critical exponents, the explication of universality, etc., the values of the initial parameters are immaterial. This is the content of universality, and it takes all the power of the renormalization analysis to bring it to the surface.

In certain cases, as we shall see in Sec. 2-5, transformations have been devised to pass from a discrete spin system, or from a quantum mechanical system, to a representation in terms of continuous classical fields. As far as a real physical system is concerned, the associated Ising model is not clearly a more faithful representation than the $\mathscr{L}$ we have constructed. But, what is perhaps more cogent, there are usually snags in these transformations which obscure the connection between the values of the parameters in the microscopic model Hamiltonian, and the ones appearing in the corresponding $\mathscr{L}$. Neither do these procedures limit the number of terms appearing in $\mathscr{L}$.

Nevertheless, something can be said about the parameters introduced in the phenomenological way since when one moves away from the critical point, fluctuations become less important, and $\mathscr{L}$ itself makes for a lowest order approximation to the free energy in a systematic expansion in the fluctuations. This subject is discussed in Chap. 6. Here we will add that this approximation is simply the Landau approximation. Consequently, one can obtain approximate values for the parameters, either by comparing the Landau theory with experiments performed at a safe distance from the critical point, or by performing a mean field calculation on a model Hamiltonian representing the same system. One important consequence of this type of identification is the realization that the size of the coefficient of the quadratic term, denoted in the present section by A_1, is a linear measure of the temperature.

But a word of caution is necessary. If the transition indicated either by the Landau theory or by the mean field calculation is a discontinuous one, the relation between the two is apt to be wrong. The reason is that while the mean field approximation gives a free energy which behaves linearly for asymptotically large values of the order parameter, the Landau approximation behaves as a high power.

Another parameter appearing in the theory is a cutoff. One has to introduce either a lower limit on the length scale over which the order parameter field can vary, or an upper limit to the wave number of the Fourier components of the field. Otherwise, infinities are incurred in the calculation of the various correlation functions, as is the case in quantum field theory. In relativistic quantum field theory a special procedure has to be introduced to define the finite part of the various quantities. In statistical physics problems the cutoff is rather natural, but as we shall see later on, the logic of the problem involves an elimination of the cutoff near a critical point, and the methods of quantum field theory have to be introduced.

For example, in a localized magnet the lattice spacing is a natural spatial cutoff; in a superfluid the thermal wavelength $(\hbar^2/mkT)^{1/2}$ can serve. Again, formal transformations on microscopic Hamiltonians do not give a much better definition of this cutoff. Fortunately, as in the case of the other parameters, critical exponents and other universal quantities are independent of the cutoff, as a result of the long-range nature of fluctuations near the critical point.

2-4   THE PARTITION FUNCTION, OR THE GENERATING FUNCTIONAL

Once the Lagrangian has been chosen the probability distribution is written as in Eq. (2-1), namely

$$W\{\phi, A\} = \exp\left\{-\int dx\, \mathscr{L}[\phi, A]\right\}$$

In addition we introduce a source $\mathbf{h}$, or an external field, which couples linearly to all the relevant fields. The source appears in $\mathscr{L}$ as a term of the form:

$$-h(x) \cdot \phi(x) = - \sum_{i=1}^{n} h_i(x) \, \phi_i(x) \qquad (2\text{-}10)$$

If $W\{\phi, \mathbf{h}\}$ gives the probability distribution in function space, then we can write down a generating functional for all the correlation functions of the order parameter. It is given by:

$$Z\{h\} = \int \mathscr{D}\phi \, W\{\phi, h\} \qquad (2\text{-}11)$$

where we have omitted $\mathbf{A}$ from the notation. Z is, of course, the partition function in the presence of an external field.

$\mathscr{D}\phi$ in Eq. (2-11) is a rather schematic notation. To make it clearer we write explicitly

$$\mathscr{D}\phi = \prod_{i=1}^{n} \mathscr{D}\phi_i \qquad (2\text{-}12)$$

which is clear since there is a finite number of ϕ_i's. As far as $\mathscr{D}\phi_i$, the measure in function space, is concerned, one often finds the following specification:

Divide the volume V of the system into cubes of size a^d. Denote the center of the cube by an integer lattice vector $\mathbf{l}$, of which there is a finite set when the volume is finite. Then define,

$$\mathscr{D}\phi = \prod_{l} d\phi(l) \qquad (2\text{-}13)$$

and at the same time express $\mathscr{L}$ in terms of $\phi(\mathbf{l})$ and its finite differences. The formal properties of the measure obtained in this way are not very clear, although it is intuitively very attractive.

In practice one rarely uses this type of definition. Instead, one specifies the set of continuous distributions one would like to include. This set is properly parametrized, and then the integration is carried out over the parameters.

The most common procedure, since one usually considers translationally invariant systems, is to decompose $\phi(x)$ into Fourier components via

$$\phi(x) = \frac{1}{\sqrt{V}} \sum_{k} \phi_k \exp(-ikx) \qquad (2\text{-}14)$$

This choice gives a set of distributions with nice continuity and differentiability properties. Furthermore, as long as the volume is finite, the k's are discrete, and the functions satisfy periodic boundary conditions. The coarse graining is introduced by including the condition

$$|\mathbf{k}| < \Lambda \approx \frac{1}{a}$$

If $\phi(x)$ is a real field then

$$\phi_{\mathbf{k}} = \phi^*_{-\mathbf{k}} \qquad (2\text{-}15)$$

and the space of distribution is covered by letting the amplitudes $\phi_{\mathbf{k}}$, where $\mathbf{k}$ is restricted to half space, vary over all complex values. The measure is then written as

$$\mathscr{D}\phi = \prod_{\mathbf{k}>0;\, |\mathbf{k}|<\Lambda} d^2 \phi_{\mathbf{k}} \qquad (2\text{-}16)$$

This procedure can be generalized to descriptions in terms of other bases of the space of distributions, if the latter is taken as a Hilbert space. More general measures can be defined over these spaces, but since we will not make use of any such more sophisticated methods we will not go into any detail.[4]

Once the question of a measure is settled one can proceed to the task of calculating $Z\{\mathbf{h}\}$ of Eq. (2-11). The importance of the functional Z is that its derivatives with respect to the sources $h_i(x)$ give all the correlation functions and averages of the field $\boldsymbol{\phi}$. Thus:

$$\langle \phi_i(x_1) \rangle = Z^{-1} \frac{\delta Z\{\mathbf{h}\}}{\delta h_i(x_1)} \qquad (2\text{-}17)$$

If the system is translationally invariant then $\langle \phi_i(\mathbf{x}) \rangle$ is independent of $\mathbf{x}$. If, in addition, the system possesses an internal symmetry — such as $\phi \rightarrow -\phi$ in an Ising system, or some rotation of the $\boldsymbol{\phi}$-field vector — then $\langle \phi_i \rangle = 0$, when the sources $h_i = 0$. This will hold true unless a situation of *broken symmetry* arises.

A situation of a *spontaneously broken symmetry* will arise in the sense that

$$\lim_{h_i \to 0} \lim_{V \to \infty} \langle \phi_i(x) \rangle \neq 0 \qquad (2\text{-}18)$$

This corresponds to the intuitive picture in which for some values of the parameters the statistical weight develops maxima at non-zero values of the order parameter field. But it still preserves the symmetry of the problem, and thus the maxima appear for all values of the order parameter field which transform into each other under the action of the symmetry group. The field h_i breaks this symmetry and makes one of the maxima higher. If the volume is held fixed and h_i is made to vanish, all maxima will become equally probable, and $\langle \phi_i \rangle \to 0$. On the other hand, if for small but finite field, h_i, $V \to \infty$, two situations may arise:

(i) The interaction between different points is strong enough so that the logarithm of the statistical weight will be higher for the direction selected by h_i, by a term which diverges with V faster than the first power. In this case, as $V \to \infty$, all other directions will be suppressed, and as $h_i \to 0$, $\langle \phi_i \rangle$ will have the value of ϕ which maximizes the weight.

(ii) The interactions are weak, and do not prefer aligned distributions of $\phi(x)$. Then, after $V \to \infty$, as $h_i \to 0$, the various maxima disappear and $\langle \phi_i \rangle \to 0$.[5]
A correlation function is given by:

$$G_{ij}^{(2)}(\mathbf{x} - \mathbf{y}) = \langle \phi_i(\mathbf{x}) \, \phi_j(\mathbf{y}) \rangle = Z^{-1} \left. \frac{\delta^2 Z}{\delta h_i(\mathbf{x}) \, \delta h_j(\mathbf{y})} \right|_{b=0} \qquad (2.19)$$

and in general

$$G_{i_1 \ldots i_n}^{(n)}(\mathbf{x}_1, \ldots, \mathbf{x}_n) = Z^{-1} \left. \frac{\delta^n Z}{\delta h_{i_1}(\mathbf{x}_1) \ldots \delta h_{i_n}(\mathbf{x}_n)} \right|_{b=0} \qquad (2.20)$$

Note that we may choose to incorporate an external field in $\mathscr{L}$, and consider $\mathbf{h}$ as a purely formal tool for the generation of distributions. Eqs. (2-20) can be summarized by writing:

$$\frac{Z\{h\}}{Z\{0\}} = 1 + \sum_{N=1}^{\infty} \frac{1}{N!} \sum_{i_1 \ldots i_N} \int dx_1 \ldots dx_N h_{i_1}(x_1) \ldots$$

$$\ldots h_{i_N}(x_N) G_{i_1 \ldots i_N}^{(N)}(x_1 \ldots x_N) \qquad (2-21)$$

2-5 REPRESENTATION OF THE ISING MODEL IN TERMS OF FUNCTIONAL INTEGRALS

In this section we will follow one example from its microscopic formulation to its representation as a functional integral over continuous fields. We will use the simplest example, namely, the Ising model for magnetism.[6] But, the technique can be applied in much more general cases. See Examples 2-3 and 2-5. On the other hand the Ising model exhibits most of the interesting features of critical phenomena.

2-5-1 Definition of the Model and its Thermodynamics

In order to define the model we consider a lattice, in any number of dimensions, and on each site i we place a two-valued variable $s_i = \pm 1$. To a given configuration of the spins, of which there are 2^N (where N is the number of sites) we ascribe an energy

$$E\{s_i\} = - \sum_{i,j} J_{ij} s_i s_j - \sum_i h_i s_i \qquad (2-22)$$

Positive values of J give lower energies to configurations with parallel spins (equal sign) – ferromagnetic coupling. While negative values of J prefer antiparallel configurations, i.e. antiferromagnetic coupling. The variable h_i is the value of an external magnetic field at the site i.

The probability of a state, or a configuration, is proportional to

$$P\{s_i\} = \exp[-\beta E\{s_i\}] \equiv \exp\left(\sum_{ij} K_{ij}s_i s_j + \sum H_i s_i\right) \qquad (2\text{-}23)$$

and the partition function, which is the generating function, is given by the sum of P over the 2^N configurations

$$Z\{H_i\} = \sum_{\{s_i\}} \exp[-\beta E\{s_i\}] \qquad (2\text{-}24)$$

We have introduced the notation

$$\beta = (kT)^{-1}$$

and $K_{ij} = \beta J_{ij}$, $H_i = \beta h_i$. The symbol k is Boltzmann's constant, and T is the temperature.

In this discrete model $Z\{H_i\}$ generates all the correlation functions. Namely:

$$M_i = \langle s_i \rangle_{H_i=0} = Z^{-1} \left.\frac{\partial Z}{\partial H_i}\right|_{H=0} \qquad (2\text{-}25)$$

is the average magnetization at site i. The symmetry of the energy under $s_i \rightarrow -s_i$, when $H = 0$, implies $M = 0$, as was discussed in the previous section. Unless, again, one encounters spontaneously broken symmetry.

If

$$J_{ij} = J_{i-j} \qquad (2\text{-}26)$$

then, when $H_i = H$, the system is translationally invariant. Consequently

$$\langle s_i \rangle = \langle s \rangle$$

independent of i, and we can write M in terms of a derivative with respect to the uniform field H as:

$$M(H) = \frac{1}{N} Z^{-1} \frac{\partial Z}{\partial H} = \frac{1}{N} \sum_i \langle s_i \rangle \qquad (2\text{-}27)$$

The susceptibility is given as

$$\chi(H) = \frac{\partial M}{\partial H} \qquad (2\text{-}28)$$

and χ will in general differ from zero as H vanishes, whether or not there is a persistent magnetization. Thus:

$$\chi = \frac{\partial M}{\partial H}\bigg|_{H=0} = \frac{1}{N} \sum_{ij} (\langle s_i s_j \rangle - \langle s_i \rangle \langle s_j \rangle)$$

$$= \frac{1}{N} \sum_{ij} \langle (s_i - M)(s_j - M) \rangle \qquad (2\text{-}29)$$

The terms in the sum are the correlation functions

$$g(r_i - r_j) = \langle (s_i - \langle s_i \rangle)(s_j - \langle s_j \rangle) \rangle$$

$$g(\mathbf{r}_i - \mathbf{r}_j) = Z^{-1} \frac{\partial^2 Z}{\partial H_i \partial H_j} - \left(Z^{-1} \frac{\partial Z}{\partial H_i} \right)^2 \qquad (2\text{-}30)$$

Since we have translational invariance we can rewrite (2-29) as

$$\chi = \sum_{\mathbf{R}} g(\mathbf{R}) \qquad (2\text{-}31)$$

where $\mathbf{R}$ are all the vectors of the lattice relative to one given site.

In addition to the magnetization and the susceptibility we can also identify at this stage the two properties connected to the correlation function. Namely, the correlation length ξ and the anomalous exponent η associated with the behavior of g at T_c.

The specific heat is given in terms of derivatives with respect to β. The mean energy is

$$\langle E \rangle = - \frac{\partial}{\partial \beta} \ln Z\{0\} \qquad (2\text{-}32)$$

and the specific heat

$$C = \frac{1}{N} \frac{\partial \langle E \rangle}{\partial T} = - \frac{1}{N} \beta^2 \frac{\partial}{\partial \beta} \langle E \rangle = \frac{1}{N} \beta^2 \frac{\partial^2}{\partial \beta^2} \ln Z\{0\} \qquad (2\text{-}33)$$

where we have set $k = 1$. If Z is expressed in terms of K, as in Eq. (2-23), then in order to regain C one replaces $K_{ij} \rightarrow \lambda K_{ij}$ and

$$C = \frac{1}{N} \frac{\partial^2}{\partial \lambda^2} \ln Z\{0\} \bigg|_{\lambda=1} \qquad (2\text{-}34)$$

The critical singular behavior of the specific heat can, like that of the susceptibility, be related to a long-range behavior of a correlation function. For a given configuration one can associate with the point $\mathbf{r}_i$ an energy

$$E_i = - \sum_j J_{ij} s_i s_j \qquad (2\text{-}35)$$

and an average energy per site

$$\langle E_i \rangle = \left\langle -\sum_j J_{ij} s_i s_j \right\rangle = \frac{1}{N} \langle E \rangle \qquad (2\text{-}36)$$

where we have used translational invariance. Writing (2-33) explicitly we have

$$C = \frac{1}{N} \beta^2 \left[\left\langle \left(\sum_{ij} J_{ij} s_i s_j \right) \left(\sum_{kl} J_{kl} s_k s_l \right) \right\rangle - \left\langle \sum_{ij} J_{ij} s_i s_j \right\rangle^2 \right]$$

$$= \frac{1}{N} \beta^2 \left[\sum_{ik} \langle\!\langle (E_i - \langle E_i \rangle)(E_k - \langle E_k \rangle) \rangle\!\rangle \right] \qquad (2\text{-}37)$$

and using translational invariance again we can write

$$C = \beta^2 \sum_R g_E(R) \qquad (2\text{-}38)$$

where $g_E(R)$ is the energy–energy correlation function, given by

$$g_E(R) = \langle (E_0 - \langle E_0 \rangle)(E_R - \langle E_R \rangle) \rangle \qquad (2\text{-}39)$$

2-5-2 The Gaussian Transformation

The identity

$$\int_{-\infty}^{\infty} \exp \left(-\frac{1}{4a^2} x^2 + sx \right) \, dx = \text{Constant} \times \exp(a^2 s^2) \qquad (2\text{-}40)$$

can be generalized to read

$$\int_{-\infty}^{\infty} \prod_{i=1}^{N} dx_i \exp \left(-\frac{1}{4} x_i V_{ij}^{-1} x_j + s_i x_i \right)$$

$$= \text{Constant} \times \exp(s_i V_{ij} s_j) \qquad (2\text{-}41)$$

where summation over repeated indices is implied, and V is any symmetric positive definite matrix.[7]

Thus the generating function, Eq. (2-24), can be rewritten as:

$$Z\{H_i\} = \sum_{\{s_i\}} \exp(s_i K_{ij} s_j + H_i s_i)$$

$$= \sum_{\{s_i\}} \int_{-\infty}^{\infty} \prod_{i=1}^{N} d\phi_i \exp \left[-\frac{1}{4} \phi_i K_{ij}^{-1} \phi_j + (\phi_i + H_i) s_i \right]$$

$$= \int_{-\infty}^{\infty} \prod_{i=1}^{N} d\phi_i \exp \left[-\frac{1}{4} (\phi_i - H_i) K_{ij}^{-1} (\phi_j - H_j) \right]$$

$$\times \sum_{\{s_i\}} \exp(\phi_i s_i) \qquad (2\text{-}42)$$

The sum over configurations can be carried out, since the spins are now independent. Thus:

$$\sum_{\{s_i\}} \exp(\phi_i s_i) = \prod_i (2 \cosh \phi_i) = \text{Constant} \times \exp\left[\sum_i \ln(\cosh \phi_i)\right]$$
(2-43)

At this stage, if we set $H_i = 0$ in Eq. (2-42), we recover a partition function similar to the ones we considered in Sec. 2-2 of this chapter. The term $\phi_i K_{ij}^{-1} \phi_j$ gives the part of $\mathscr{L}$ which depends on derivatives, while $\Sigma_i \ln(\cosh \phi_i)$ gives a power series in ϕ_i, which is local. However, we still have to find out how one calculates the thermodynamic quantities of the Ising model, which are defined as derivatives with respect to H or β.

To make this relationship simpler we perform another linear transformation on the fields

$$\psi_i = \tfrac{1}{2} K_{ij}^{-1} \phi_j \qquad (2\text{-}44)$$

then

$$Z\{H_i\} \propto \exp\left(-\frac{1}{4} H_i K_{ij}^{-1} H_j\right)$$

$$\times \int \mathscr{D}\psi \exp\left\{-\psi_i K_{ij} \psi_j + H_i \psi_i + \sum_i \ln[\cosh(2K_{ij}\psi_j)]\right\} \qquad (2\text{-}45)$$

We see, therefore, that except for the trivial prefactor, the external field H plays exactly the role of the source in the generating functional.

2-5-3 The Free Part

Since any further progress is made by expansions around bilinear forms we have to study first of all the structure of the bilinear part of the exponent in Eq. (2-45).

We transform to Fourier space by writing:

$$\psi_i \equiv \psi(\mathbf{r}_i) = \frac{1}{\sqrt{N}} \sum_{\mathbf{k}} \exp(-i\mathbf{k} \cdot \mathbf{r}_i) \psi(\mathbf{k}) \qquad (2\text{-}46)$$

where the $\mathbf{k}$'s are the reciprocal lattice vectors lying in the first Brillouin zone. Similarly,

$$K_{ij} \equiv K(\mathbf{r}_i - \mathbf{r}_j) = \frac{1}{N} \sum_{\mathbf{k}} \exp[-i\mathbf{k} \cdot (\mathbf{r}_i - \mathbf{r}_j)] K(\mathbf{k}) \qquad (2\text{-}47)$$

Equation (2-44) takes the simple form:

$$\phi(\mathbf{k}) = 2K(\mathbf{k})\psi(\mathbf{k}) \qquad (2\text{-}48)$$

There are two contributions to the bilinear part:

$$\psi_i K_{ij} \psi_j = \sum_{\mathbf{k}} K(\mathbf{k}) \psi(\mathbf{k}) \psi(-\mathbf{k}) \qquad (2\text{-}49)$$

and one coming from the expansion of the ln cosh. This expansion reads

$$\ln \cosh x = \tfrac{1}{2} x^2 - \tfrac{1}{12} x^4 + \ldots \qquad (2\text{-}50)$$

and its contribution to the bilinear term is:

$$2 \sum_i (K_{ij} \psi_j)^2 = 2 \sum_{\mathbf{k}} K(\mathbf{k}) \psi(\mathbf{k}) K(-\mathbf{k}) \psi(-\mathbf{k}) \qquad (2\text{-}51)$$

The free part of $\mathscr{L}$ in (2-45) is:

$$\int \mathscr{L}_0 \, dx = \sum_{\mathbf{k}} [K(\mathbf{k}) - 2 \mid K(\mathbf{k}) \mid^2] \, \psi(\mathbf{k}) \psi(-\mathbf{k}) \qquad (2\text{-}52)$$

Next the coefficient is expanded to second order in $\mid k \mid$. The justification is provided a posteriori by showing, as was already mentioned in Sec. 2-2, that the higher order terms are irrelevant. One writes:

$$K(\mathbf{k}) = K_0 (1 - \rho^2 k^2) \qquad (2\text{-}53)$$

where, using the inverse of (2-47), namely,

$$K(\mathbf{k}) = \sum_{\mathbf{R}} K(\mathbf{R}) \exp(i\mathbf{k} \cdot \mathbf{R}) \qquad (2\text{-}54)$$

we find that

$$K_0 = \sum_{\mathbf{R}} K(\mathbf{R}) = \gamma \beta J_0 \qquad (2\text{-}55)$$

The last equality assumes that there are only nearest neighbor interactions and that each spin has γ nearest neighbors. The same assumptions will give for the k^2 term

$$K_0 \rho^2 k^2 = \frac{1}{2} \sum_{\mathbf{R}} K(\mathbf{R}) (\mathbf{k} \cdot \mathbf{R})^2 \approx K_0 a^2 k^2 \qquad (2\text{-}56)$$

which implies that $\rho \approx a$ – the lattice constant.

Inserting (2-53) in (2-52) and keeping terms up to order k^2 we find:

$$\int dx \ \mathscr{L}_0 = \sum_{\mathbf{k}} \psi(\mathbf{k}) \psi(-\mathbf{k}) K_0 [(1 - 2K_0) + (4K_0 - 1) \rho^2 k^2] \qquad (2\text{-}57)$$

Recall that $K_0 = \gamma \beta J_0$, and hence as T decreases K_0 increases and at some value the k-independent term in (2-57) will vanish. That will happen for

$$T_0 = 2\gamma J_0 \qquad (2\text{-}58)$$

At this temperature the field amplitude with $k = 0$ becomes unstable. Nothing in the probability distribution restricts it from growing arbitrarily large. At the same temperature the coefficient of k^2 is exactly ρ^2, thereby rendering the amplitudes $\psi(\mathbf{k})$ stable.

One should not be misled by the fact that at high temperatures, and small K_0, the coefficient of k^2 becomes negative; this is an artifact of our expansion superposed on a real ambiguity in the transformation. The coefficient in (2-52) can be written as

$$K(\mathbf{k}) \, [1 - 2K(-\mathbf{k})]$$

This term can change its sign at finite k in one of two situations – either $K(k)$ changes sign, or $K(k)$ has a maximum at some $k \neq 0$. The second possibility has a real physical significance, and it gives rise to phase transitions with finite wave-vectors such as the antiferromagnetic one, where $K(\mathbf{k})$ is maximum at the zone boundary and minimum at $k = 0$. In the ferromagnetic Ising case the maximum is at $k = 0$.

If, on the other hand, $K(k)$ were to change sign, then the transformation is ill defined. In order to see this one has simply to realize that $K(k)$ are the eigenvalues of the matrix K_{ij}. Thus, if for some k, $K(k) < 0$ the matrix is not positive definite and our transformation (2-41) is undefined. Unfortunately, the matrix K for the Ising model always has negative eigenvalues, since all its diagonal elements are zero and thus the sum of its eigenvalues vanishes.

The remedy has been suggested a long time ago.[8] Since $s_i^2 = 1$, we can add an arbitrary scalar matrix AI to J, and the energy changes by a trivial constant amount $A \cdot N$. This trick, which is exact, makes the value of K_0 in (2-57) arbitrary. Also the connection with mean field theory becomes more problematic. In fact, the temperature given by (2-58) is exactly equal to that at which the transition occurs in mean field theory.

Another comment that should be made at this point is that, while the range of wave-vectors (momenta) appearing in (2-47) covers the whole Brillouin zone, once the quadratic approximation is used this is no longer the case. The momentum cutoff becomes also arbitrary, though still of order a^{-1}.

Thus, as was mentioned in Sec. 2-2, the microscopic theory does not solve the problem of the identification of the parameters in the functional integral.

We write $\mathcal{L}_0$, Eq. (2-57), as an expansion in the neighborhood of T_0, Eq. (2-58), the point at which the free theory becomes unstable. In this region we can write

$$1 - 2K_0 = \frac{T - T_0}{T_0} + 0(T - T_0)^2 \qquad (2\text{-}59)$$

$$4K_0 - 1 = 1 + 0(T - T_0) \qquad (2\text{-}60)$$

$$K_0 = \tfrac{1}{2} + 0(T - T_0) \qquad (2\text{-}61)$$

and

$$\int dx \, \mathscr{L}_0 = \frac{1}{2} \sum_k \left(\frac{T - T_0}{T_0} + \rho^2 k^2 \right) \psi(\mathbf{k}) \psi(-\mathbf{k}) \qquad (2\text{-}62)$$

Finally, to make the theory look even more like a *Euclidean* quantum field theory (see next section) we write

$$\phi = \rho \psi \qquad (2\text{-}63)$$

$$\mu^2 \equiv \frac{1}{\rho^2} \frac{T - T_0}{T_0} \qquad (2\text{-}64)$$

and then,

$$\int dx \, \mathscr{L}_0 = \frac{1}{2} \sum_k (k^2 + \mu^2) \phi(\mathbf{k}) \phi(-\mathbf{k}) \qquad (2\text{-}65)$$

where the square of the *free mass*, to use the language of field theory, is a linear measure of the temperature. In the process our field ϕ acquires dimensions of length,

$$[\phi] = L^1 \qquad (2\text{-}66)$$

The representation of the theory in terms of continuous distributions in coordinate space is achieved by writing

$$\bar\phi(\mathbf{r}) = \frac{1}{\sqrt{V}} \sum_k \exp(-i\mathbf{k} \cdot \mathbf{r}) \phi(\mathbf{k}) \qquad (2\text{-}67)$$

with $|k| < \Lambda$, and then

$$\int dx \, \mathscr{L}_0 = \frac{1}{2} \int dx \, [(\nabla \bar\phi)^2 + \mu^2 \bar\phi^2] \qquad (2\text{-}68)$$

$\bar\phi(r)$ is not exactly $\phi(r_i)$, as a transform of the type (2-46) would have given. Comparison of the two relations, (2-46) and (2-67), gives:

$$\bar\phi(\mathbf{r}) = \left(\frac{N}{V} \right)^{1/2} \phi(\mathbf{r}_i) = a^{-d/2} \phi(\mathbf{r}_i) \qquad (2\text{-}69)$$

which has just the necessary factor for converting the sum over sites into an integral, with a^d being the volume of the unit cell in d dimensions, i.e.,

$$\sum_i F(\phi(r_i)) = \int dx \, a^{-d} F[\phi(x)] \qquad (2\text{-}70)$$

The dimension of $\bar\phi(\mathbf{r})$ can be evaluated either by using (2-66) and (2-69), or, which is a procedure independent of the contortions that we have undergone to reach (2-68), by noting that in the latter equation

$$\int dx (\nabla \bar{\phi})^2$$

is dimensionless. Thus,

$$[\bar{\phi}(\mathbf{r})] = L^{1-d/2} \qquad (2\text{-}71)$$

These simple comments about dimensions are introduced because, as we shall see later on, dimensional considerations are very useful in dealing with renormalized perturbation theory. From (2-65) we see also that μ^2 has the same dimensions as k^2,

$$[\mu^2] = L^{-2} \qquad (2\text{-}72)$$

2-5-4 Some Properties of the Free Theory — a Free Euclidean Field Theory in Less than Four Dimensions

From (2-65) we see immediately that when $\mu^2 \to 0$ the field amplitude with $k = 0$ becomes unstable. In fact, when $\mu^2 < 0$, the free theory is undefined. We can calculate the correlation function

$$G_0(\mathbf{k}) = \langle \phi(\mathbf{k})\phi(-\mathbf{k}) \rangle_0$$

$$= \frac{\int \mathscr{D}\phi \, \phi(\mathbf{k})\phi(-\mathbf{k}) \exp[-\Sigma_k \frac{1}{2}(k^2 + \mu^2)\phi(\mathbf{k})\phi(-\mathbf{k})]}{\int \mathscr{D}\phi \, \exp(-\int \mathscr{L}_0)} \qquad (2\text{-}73)$$

Note that $G_0(\mathbf{k})$ is, with the definition (2-67) of the Fourier transform, the Fourier transform of the spatial correlation function, namely,

$$G_0(r) = \langle \phi(\mathbf{r})\phi(0) \rangle_0 = \frac{1}{V} \sum_{\mathbf{k}} \exp(-i\mathbf{k} \cdot \mathbf{r}) G_0(\mathbf{k}) \qquad (2\text{-}74)$$

which, when $V \to \infty$, becomes:

$$G_0(\mathbf{k}) = \int \frac{dk}{(2\pi)^d} \exp(-i\mathbf{k} \cdot \mathbf{r}) G_0(r) \qquad (2\text{-}75)$$

As was discussed in Sec. 2-3, the correlation functions are most naturally obtained from the generating functional as derivatives with respect to the source. To obtain $G_0(\mathbf{k})$ we add to $\mathscr{L}^0$ a term

$$\sum_{\mathbf{k}} \phi(\mathbf{k})h(-\mathbf{k})$$

and then

$$G_0(\mathbf{k}) = \frac{1}{Z^0\{h\}} \frac{\partial^2 Z^0\{h\}}{\partial h(\mathbf{k})\partial h(-\mathbf{k})} \bigg|_{h=0} \qquad (2\text{-}76)$$

The generating functional in the presence of the source term looks like

$$Z^0\{h\} = \int \mathscr{D}\phi \exp\left\{ -\sum_k \left[\frac{1}{2}(k^2 + \mu^2)\,\phi(\mathbf{k})\phi(-\mathbf{k}) + \phi(\mathbf{k})h(-\mathbf{k})\right]\right\}$$

$$= \left[\int \mathscr{D}\phi \exp\left\{ -\frac{1}{2}\sum_k \phi(\mathbf{k})(k^2 + \mu^2)\phi(-\mathbf{k})\right\}\right]$$

$$\times \exp\left\{ \frac{1}{2}\sum_k h(\mathbf{k})(k^2 + \mu^2)^{-1}h(-\mathbf{k})\right\} \qquad (2\text{-}77)$$

where (2-77) was derived by a shift of the integration variable

$$\phi(\mathbf{k}) \to \phi(\mathbf{k}) - (k^2 + \mu^2)^{-1}h(\mathbf{k})$$

The integral does not have to be performed since it cancels against the denominator in (2-76). We immediately conclude that

$$G_0(\mathbf{k}) = (k^2 + \mu^2)^{-1} \qquad (2\text{-}78)$$

The susceptibility, as given by Eq. (2-31), can be written in terms of $G_0(\mathbf{k})$:

$$\chi = G_0(k = 0) = \mu^{-2} \qquad (2\text{-}79)$$

It diverges when $\mu \to 0$. At that point

$$G_0(k) = k^{-2} \qquad (2\text{-}80)$$

and $\eta = 0$. Also, Eq. (2-79), together with the definition of μ^2, Eq. (2-64), gives $\gamma = 1$.

If the correlation length is defined by:

$$\xi^2 = \frac{\int r^2 G(r)\,dr}{\int G(r)\,dr} \qquad (2\text{-}81)$$

it can be expressed in terms of $G(k)$ as:

$$\xi^2 = \left[-\frac{\partial}{\partial k^2} G(k)\right]\bigg/ G(k)\bigg|_{k=0} \qquad (2\text{-}82)$$

Inserting G_0, we find

$$\xi^2 = 2\mu^{-2}$$

and $\nu = \frac{1}{2}$.

Notice that at this level none of the quantities required any knowledge of the cutoff. No momentum integrals enter. They make their first appearance in the computation of the specific heat. For this calculation the Gaussian integral in (2-77) has to be carried out. The result is

$$\ln Z^0 = -\frac{1}{2}\sum_{k} \ln(k^2 + \mu^2) + \frac{1}{2}\sum_{k} h(k)G_0^{-1}(k)h(-k) + \text{constant} \qquad (2\text{-}83)$$

Setting $h = 0$, and using the prescription (2-34) to calculate the specific heat, we find for the leading term in $T - T_0$

$$C = \frac{1}{2}\left(\frac{V}{N}\right)\int^{\Lambda} \frac{dk}{(k^2 + \mu^2)^2} \qquad (2\text{-}84)$$

Below four dimensions the specific heat diverges, due to the infrared singularity, and

$$\alpha = \tfrac{1}{2}\,(4 - d) \qquad (2\text{-}85)$$

There is no divergence when $d > 4$. But following the constant term, there may be a non-analytic term.

It is easy to see that the leading term in the specific heat would come from:

$$C = -\frac{1}{N}\left(\frac{\partial}{\partial\mu^2}\right)^2 \ln Z^0 = -\frac{1}{N}\left[\left\langle \frac{1}{2}\int \phi^2(r)\frac{1}{2}\int \phi^2(r)\right\rangle - \left\langle \frac{1}{2}\int \phi^2(r)\right\rangle^2\right] \qquad (2\text{-}86)$$

In field theory, this dependence of the specific heat on the cut-off, is reflected in the fact that the $\phi^2 - \phi^2$ Green function is divergent, even in zeroth order in perturbation theory. This fact introduces additive renormalization in addition to the multiplicative renormalization (see, e.g., Sec. 8-10).

2-6   CORRELATION FUNCTIONS INCLUDING COMPOSITE OPERATORS

From the discussion in the previous section it follows that derivatives of averages, or of correlation functions with respect to temperature, are essentially derivatives with respect to μ^2. In order to obtain the scaling behavior near a critical point such derivatives are necessary, as was the case for the calculation of the specific heat at the end of the previous section. But, more generally, if one wants to find the correlations between the energy density at various points and the magnetization one has to consider averages of the type

$$G_{i_1\ldots i_N, j_1\ldots j_L}^{(N,L)}(x_1\ldots x_N, y_1\ldots y_L)$$

$$= (\tfrac{1}{2})^L \langle \phi_{i_1}(x_1)\phi_{i_2}(x_2)\ldots\phi_{i_N}(x_N)\phi_{j_1}^2(y_1)\ldots\phi_{j_L}^2(y_L)\rangle \qquad (2\text{-}87)$$

The specific heat, for example, will be given by:

$$C = - \int d(y_1 - y_2)[G^{(0,2)}(y_1, y_2) - G^{(0,1)}(y_1)G^{(0,1)}(y_2)] \qquad (2\text{-}88)$$

Compare with Sec. 2-5-4.

A glance at (2-87) leads to the conclusion that this type of correlation function can also be generated by a source. This can be done by adding to the Lagrangian density, in addition to (2-10) also a term of the form:

$$-\frac{1}{2} \sum_j t_j(y) \phi_j^2(y) \qquad (2\text{-}89)$$

Then

$$G^{(N,L)}_{i_1 \ldots i_N, j_1 \ldots j_L}(x_1 \ldots x_N, y_1 \ldots y_L)$$

$$= Z^{-1} \frac{\delta^{N+L} Z}{\delta h_{i_1}(x_1) \ldots \delta h_{i_N}(x_N) \delta t_{j_1}(y_1) \ldots \delta t_{j_L}(y_L)} \Bigg|_{h=t=0} \qquad (2\text{-}90)$$

As we shall see in later chapters, *composite operators* like ϕ^2 have an independent existence when fluctuations become important. Namely, when the theory has to be renormalized (to remove divergences or uninteresting dependence on the cutoff Λ) Green functions with ϕ^2's in them exhibit singularities which cannot be cured by treating $G^{(N,0)}$ and then identifying some pairs of coordinates.

One can consider other composite operators such as any monomial in the fields at a given point, $\phi^s(x)$, or any product of derivatives of the field multiplied by powers of the field —

$$\frac{\partial \phi(x)}{\partial x_1} \ldots \frac{\partial \phi(x)}{\partial x_t} \phi^s(x)$$

In general, correlation functions which include these operators will have to be studied independently. (See, e.g., Sec. 10-3).

Of course, $G^{(N,L)}$ can be obtained from $(\frac{1}{2})^L G^{(N+2L)}$ by identifying the coordinates of the last $2L$ points in pairs. As long as we have a finite momentum cutoff, and we keep away from critical points, we can write

$$G^{(N,L)}(x_1, \ldots, x_N, y_1, \ldots, y_L)$$

$$= (\tfrac{1}{2})^L G^{(N+2L)}(x_1, \ldots, x_N, y_1, y_1, y_2, y_2, \ldots, y_L, y_L) \qquad (2\text{-}91)$$

But if one thinks of $G^{(N,L)}$ in terms of $G^{(N+2L)}$ it is important to realize that translational invariance would now imply, for the last $2L$ coordinates, an independence of the coordinates of pairs of ϕ's, rather than of those of single

ϕ's. The full meaning of this difference will become clearer from Chapter 4 onward.

The last point to be mentioned here is that in the limit in which $t(y)$ becomes independent of y, it can be considered as a variation of the mass, or the temperature. Thus the functions $G^{(N,L)}$ can be used as coefficients in an expansion of $G^{(N)}$ about a certain value of the temperature. Namely:

$$G^{(N)}(x_1, \ldots, x_N) = \sum_{L=0}^{\infty} \frac{1}{L!} (\delta t)^L \int dy_1 \ldots dy_L G^{(N,L)}(x_1, \ldots, x_N, y_1, \ldots, y_L)$$

(2-92)

where $G^{(N)}$ is the Green function calculated with $\mu^2 + \delta t$ as the coefficient of the quadratic term in the Lagrangian, while $G^{(N,L)}$ has μ^2 for the corresponding coefficient. As we shall see, this is an important tool for obtaining the dependence of $G^{(N)}$ on $T - T_c$.

EXERCISES

2-1 Construct the invariants up to 4th degree in the following cases:

(a) A system with an order parameter with 6 real components, which has reflection symmetry in the components and rotation symmetry in the 6-dimensional spin space. The spin rotations are independent of the space transformations.

(b) A system with 2 order parameters, each with 3 real components. The symmetry is under the three-dimensional rotations of each order parameter separately. Spin and space are independent.

(c) A system as in (b) but where the two order parameters always rotate together.

(d) A system as in (b) but where the rotations of the order parameters are induced by the rotation of the coordinates.

2-2 If the order parameter is proportional to a local quadrupole moment, as it often is in liquid crystals, then it has 5 real components. If one assumes symmetry under space rotations what invariants are needed for the construction of $\mathscr{L}$?[9]

2-3 Spins are situated on a lattice, s_i at site i

$$s_i^2 = n$$

where n is the number of components of s_i. Each spin is free to rotate on the sphere of radius $\sqrt{n}$.

The energy of a given configuration is

$$E = - \sum_{ij} J_{ij} s_i \cdot s_j$$

This is the generalized classical Heisenberg model for which the partition function is

$$Z = Tr \exp(-\beta E) \equiv \int \prod_i d\Omega_n^{(i)} \exp(-\beta E)$$

where $d\Omega_n^{(i)}$ is the solid angle on the ith sphere, given by:

$$d\Omega_n = \sin^{n-2}\theta_{n-1} d\theta_{n-1} \sin^{n-3}\theta_{n-2} d\theta_{n-2} \ldots d\theta_1$$
$$(0 \leqslant \theta_1 \leqslant 2\pi; 0 \leqslant \theta_k \leqslant \pi)$$

(a) What would be the representation of this problem in terms of continuous fields?[10]
(b) Compare your answer with the result you would have obtained by using symmetry considerations alone.
(c) Show that when $n = 1$ you recover the Ising model.
(d) What happens when $n \to 0$?[11]

2-4 Perform the calculation of Z in problem 2-3 using the mean field approximation. Calculate the free energy, $\ln Z$, as a function of the mean field. Compare with results of (2-3(a)).

2-5 Another extension of the Ising model is the Potts model. Assume that at every site there are three states, and that the energy of two sites depends only on whether they are in the same state or not.

(a) Show that one can represent the energy of this system by:

$$E = \sum_{ij} J_{ij} s_i \cdot s_j$$

where s_i is a two-dimensional vector assigned to site i. Give an explicit representation of these vectors.[12]
(b) Using the Gaussian transform obtain the relevant terms of $\mathcal{L}$, in a formulation in terms of continuous fields.
(c) Could you obtain this $\mathcal{L}$ by symmetry considerations alone?
(d) Try to generalize to an n states Potts model.[13]

2-6 Calculate the average of ϕ in the presence of a uniform field, for a free theory. What is δ?

2-7 Calculate the partition function in the free case.

2-8 Calculate the specific heat using the derivatives with respect to λ.

2-9(a) Calculate $G^{(4,0)}(x_1, \ldots, x_N)$, $G^{(2,1)}(x_1, x_2; y_1)$ and $G^{(0,2)}(y_1, y_2)$ in the free theory.
(b) Calculate their Fourier transforms.

REFERENCES

1. D. Mukamel, *Physical Review Letters*, **34**, 482 (1975).
2. B. I. Halperin, T. C. Lubensky and S. K. Ma, *Physical Review Letters*, **32**, 292 (1974).
3. S. Coleman and E. Weinberg, *Physical Review*, **D7**, 1888 (1973).
4. I. M. Gelfand and A. M. Yaglom, *Journal of Mathematical Physics*, **1**, 48 (1960); E. Nelson, *Dynamical Theories of Brownian Motion* (Princeton University Press, N.J. 1967). See also the reviews by S. Albeverio and R. Höegh-Krohn, Oslo University preprint ISBN-82-553-0193-3 (1974) and F. Guerra, L. Rosen and B. Simon, *Annals of Mathematics*, **101**, 111 (1975).
5. H. Wagner, *Zeitschrift für Physik*, **195**, 273 (1966), and references cited therein.
6. E. Ising, *Zeitschrift für Physik*, **31**, 253 (1925). An exact solution in absence of a field was found by L. Onsager, Ref. 1.8. See also T. Schultz, D. Mattis and E. Lieb, *Review of Modern Physics*, **36**, 856 (1964).
7. T. H. Berlin and M. Kac, *Physical Review*, **86**, 821 (1952); R. L. Stratonovich, *Doklady Akad. Nauk SSR*, **115**, 1097 (1957) [English translation: *Soviet Physics-Doklady*, **2**, 416 (1958)]; J. Hubbard, *Physical Review Letters*, **3**, 77 (1958); G. A. Baker, *Physical Review*, **126**, 2071 (1962). For an application to liquids see J. Hubbard and P. Schofield, *Physics Letters*, **40A**, 245 (1972).
8. See, e.g., Berlin and Kac, Ref. 7.
9. P. G. De Gennes, *Physics Letters*, **30A**, 454 (1969).
10. H. J. F. Knops, *Physics Letters*, **45A**, 217 (1974).
11. P. G. De Gennes, *Physics Letters*, **38A**, 339 (1972). See also J. Des Cloizeaux, *Journal de Physique*, **36**, 281 (1975).
12. J. Ashkin and E. Teller, *Physical Review*, **64**, 178 (1943); R. B. Potts, *Proceedings of the Cambridge Philosophical Society*, **48**, 106 (1952).
13. R. K. P. Zia and D. J. Wallace, *Journal of Physics*, **A8**, 1495 (1975).

FUNCTIONAL INTEGRALS IN QUANTUM FIELD THEORY

3-1 INTRODUCTION

In this section we will briefly describe the procedure by which one deduces that in quantum field theory the main quantities of interest, the Green functions, are the analogues of the correlation functions discussed in the previous chapter, in the context of statistical mechanics. These Green functions can be expressed in terms of the variations with respect to sources of a generating functional analogous to the one defined in Sec. 2-2. There are, of course, major differences hidden beyond the analogies.

There is no cutoff in the relativistic quantum field theory and thus, strictly speaking, the theory is not well defined in four dimensions. This difficulty is handled by treating the perturbation theory as a formal structure, which gives rise to diagrams, etc., and then defining the physical quantities by a procedure which extracts the finite part of every term in the perturbation series. This process is the regularization and renormalization program, associated with the names of Dyson, Gell-Man, Low and others.

The relativistic Lagrangian has a part quadratic in the derivatives of the fields, but its form is

$$\mathscr{L}_0 = -\tfrac{1}{2}(\partial_\mu \phi \partial^\mu \phi + \mu^2 \phi^2) \qquad (3\text{-}1)$$

where ∂^μ are 4-derivatives. The square of the time derivative ∂^0 enters with the opposite sign to the spatial derivatives. Thus one encounters singularities in the free theory.

Furthermore, as we shall see, $\mathscr{L}$ enters in the exponential of the generating functional as

$$i \int \mathscr{L}(\phi) \, d^4 x$$

If one replaces t by $-i\tau$, the derivative part of $\mathscr{L}$ becomes a sum of squares, i.e. it is Euclidean, and the i is replaced by a minus sign, completing the analogy with statistical mechanics presented in Sec. 2-2. This procedure is called a Wick rotation. The physical quantities which are calculated for real times are obtained as analytic continuations of the Euclidean ones. We will start by illustrating the process in the framework of the quantum mechanics of a system with a single degree of freedom, following Abers and Lee.[1]

3-2 FUNCTIONAL INTEGRALS FOR A QUANTUM-MECHANICAL SYSTEM WITH ONE DEGREE OF FREEDOM

3.2.1 Schwinger's Transformation Function

Denote by $Q(t)$ the position operator in the Heisenberg picture, and by $|q, t\rangle$ its eigenstates:

$$Q(t)|q,t\rangle = q|q,t\rangle \qquad (3\text{-}2)$$

The probability amplitude that a particle which was at q at time t will be at q' at time t', also called the Schwinger transformation function, is

$$F(q't';qt) = \langle q't' | qt \rangle \qquad (3\text{-}3)$$

In the Schrödinger picture, Q_s is time-independent, and is related to $Q(t)$ by

$$Q(t) = \exp(iHt)Q_s \exp(-iHt) \qquad (3\text{-}4)$$

where we have taken the Hamiltonian H to be time-independent. Q_s has time-independent eigenstates

$$Q_s|q\rangle = q|q\rangle \qquad (3\text{-}5)$$

The relation between the eigenstates is

$$|q\rangle = \exp(-iHt)\,|q,t\rangle \qquad (3\text{-}6)$$

and in terms of the states $|q\rangle$

$$F(q't';qt) = \langle q'\,|\exp[iH(t-t')]\,|q\rangle \qquad (3\text{-}7)$$

In order to express F as a path integral we divide the time interval into $n+1$ intervals:

$$t = t_0, t_1, \ldots, t_{n+1} = t'; \quad t_k = t_0 + k\epsilon$$

Then

$$F(q't';qt) = F(q't+(n+1)\epsilon;qt) = \langle q't+(n+1)\epsilon\,|\,qt\rangle$$

$$= \int dq_1 \ldots dq_n \, \langle q't'\,|\,q_n t_n\rangle\langle q_n t_n\,|\,q_{n-1}t_{n-1}\rangle$$

$$\times \langle q_{n-1}t_{n-1}\,|\,q_{n-2}t_{n-2}\rangle \ldots \langle q_1 t_1\,|\,qt\rangle \qquad (3\text{-}8)$$

ϵ can be made arbitrarily small by increasing n, thus

$$\langle q_l t_l\,|\,q_{l-1}t_{l-1}\rangle = \langle q_l\,|\exp(-i\epsilon H)\,|\,q_{l-1}\rangle$$

$$= \delta(q_l - q_{l-1}) - i\epsilon\,\langle q_l\,|\,H\,|\,q_{l-1}\rangle + 0(\epsilon^2) \qquad (3\text{-}9)$$

If

$$H = \frac{p^2}{2} + V(Q) \qquad (3\text{-}10)$$

then the matrix element on the r.h.s. of (3-9) can be written as

$$\langle q_l\,|\,H\,|\,q_{l-1}\rangle = \int_{-\infty}^{\infty} \frac{dp}{2\pi} \exp[ip(q_l - q_{l-1})] \left[\frac{p^2}{2} + V(q_l)\right]$$

$$= \int_{-\infty}^{\infty} \frac{dp}{2\pi} \exp[ip(q_l - q_{l-1})]\, H\left(p, \frac{q_l + q_{l-1}}{2}\right) \qquad (3\text{-}11)$$

The δ-function in Eq. (3-9) can also be Fourier transformed, giving for the matrix element:

$$\langle q_l t_l\,|\,q_{l-1}t_{l-1}\rangle = \int \frac{dp}{2\pi} \exp\left\{i\left[p(q_l - q_{l-1}) - \epsilon H\left(p, \frac{q_l + q_{l-1}}{2}\right)\right]\right\} + 0(\epsilon^2)$$

$$(3\text{-}12)$$

and Schwinger's function becomes:

$$F(q't'; qt) = \lim_{n \to \infty} \int \prod_{i=1}^{n} dq_i \int_{-\infty}^{\infty} \prod_{i=1}^{n+1} \frac{dp_i}{2\pi}$$

$$\exp\left\{i \sum_{j=1}^{n+1} \left[p_j(q_j - q_{j-1}) - \frac{t'-t}{n+1} H\left(p_j, \frac{q_j + q_{j-1}}{2}\right) \right]\right\} \qquad (3\text{-}13)$$

which in the limit $n \to \infty$ is an operational definition of the path integral:

$$F = \int \frac{\mathscr{D}p\,\mathscr{D}q}{2\pi} \exp\left\{i \int_t^{t'} [p\dot{q} - H(p, q)]\, dt\right\} \qquad (3\text{-}14)$$

where one sums over all $p(t), q(t)$, such that

$$q(t) = q; \quad q(t') = q'$$

If, furthermore, H is quadratic in the momenta, as we assumed in (3-10), then the integral over p in (3-13) can be performed using the Fresnel integral

$$\int_{-\infty}^{\infty} \frac{dp}{2\pi} \exp\left[i\epsilon \left(p\dot{q} - \frac{p^2}{2}\right)\right] = \frac{1}{\sqrt{2\pi i \epsilon}} \exp\left(\frac{1}{2} i\epsilon \dot{q}^2\right) \qquad (3\text{-}15)$$

leading to

$$F = \lim_{n \to \infty} \int \prod \frac{dq_i}{\sqrt{2\pi i \epsilon}} \exp\left[i\epsilon \sum_{i=1}^{n+1} \frac{1}{2}\dot{q}_i^2 - V\left(\frac{q_i + q_{i-1}}{2}\right)\right]$$

$$\equiv \int \frac{\mathscr{D}q}{\sqrt{2\pi i \epsilon}} \exp\left[i \int_t^{t'} \mathscr{L}(q, \dot{q})\, dt\right] \qquad (3\text{-}16)$$

and $\mathscr{L}$ is the Lagrangian.

This procedure has a heuristic value but is far from rigorous. For the type of system discussed above, rigorous formulations have been developed by Nelson, Simon and others.[2] Furthermore, if the potentials are velocity dependent, matters become even more complicated, and one has to devise effective Lagrangians case by case.[3]

The main advantage is that in (3-16) there are no more operators, and $\mathscr{L}$ is the classical Lagrangian. Hence using this representation, one can study the effects of the symmetries of the classical Lagrangian on quantum-mechanical objects.

3-2-2 Matrix Elements — Green Functions

If we choose t_0 such that $t \leqslant t_0 \leqslant t'$, we can identify t_0 with an end of one of the intervals t_i, denoted by t_{i0}. We have

$$Q(t_0) \, |q_{i0}t_{i0} \rangle = q_{i0} \, |q_{i0}t_{i0} \rangle$$

Thus, in the decomposition (3-8) we can insert $Q(t_0)$ just in front of $|q_{i0}t_{i0} \rangle$, and obtain

$$\langle q't' \, | Q(t_0) \, |qt \rangle = \int \frac{\mathscr{D}p \, \mathscr{D}q}{2\pi} \, q(t_0) \exp \left\{ i \int_t^{t'} [p\dot{q} - H(p, q)] \, dt \right\} \qquad (3\text{-}17)$$

where $q(t_0) = q_{i0}$. When H is quadratic in p, the integration over p proceeds as before.

Next we consider two times $t_1 t_2$, such that

$$t < t_2 < t_1 < t'$$

Identifying $t_1 = t_{i1}$ and $t_2 = t_{i2}$ we can proceed to write

$$\langle q't' \, | Q(t_1)Q(t_2) \, |qt \rangle = \int \frac{\mathscr{D}q \, \mathscr{D}p}{2\pi} \, q(t_1)q(t_2) \exp \left\{ i \int_t^{t'} (p\dot{q} - H) \, dt \right\} \qquad (3\text{-}18)$$

On the right-hand side of the last equation the order of the two q's is irrelevant. But this expression is equal to a matrix element of the operators with the indicated order. The only thing which is important on the right-hand side is the fact that $t_1 > t_2$. For $t_1 < t_2$ the right-hand side is equal to the matrix element of the two operators multiplied in the opposite order.

If we define a time-ordering operator T by:

$$TQ(t_1)Q(t_2) = \begin{cases} Q(t_1)Q(t_2) & (t_1 > t_2) \\ Q(t_2)Q(t_1) & (t_2 > t_1) \end{cases} \qquad (3\text{-}19)$$

then for $t < t_i < t'$:

$$\langle q't' \, | T[Q(t_1)\dots Q(t_n)] \, |qt \rangle = \int \frac{\mathscr{D}p \, \mathscr{D}q}{2\pi} \, q(t_1)\dots q(t_n) \exp \left\{ i \int_t^{t'} (p\dot{q} - H) \, dt \right\}$$

$$(3\text{-}20)$$

Thus all expectation values of time-ordered products are expressed in terms of moments of distributions of classical fields.

3-2-3 The Generating Functional

Usually, in quantum field theory, one is interested in the expectation values of time-ordered products of operators in the vacuum state. These suffice to give the S-matrix (Sec. 3-3-4). In the present case the vacuum is the ground state.

Using (3-20) we can write:

$$\langle 0 \mid T[Q(t_1)\dots Q(t_n)] \mid 0 \rangle = \int dq \; dq' \Phi_0(q't')\Phi_0^*(qt)$$

$$\times \int \frac{\mathscr{D}p\mathscr{D}q}{2\pi}\, q(t_1)\dots q(t_n) \exp\left\{ i \int_t^{t'} (p\dot{q} - H)\, dt \right\} \qquad (3\text{-}21)$$

where

$$\Phi_n(q,t) = \langle n \mid qt \rangle \qquad (3\text{-}22)$$

$\mid n \rangle$ being energy eigenstates, namely,

$$H \mid n \rangle = E_n \mid n \rangle \qquad (3\text{-}23)$$

The times t and t' in (3-21) are arbitrary, but they have to satisfy the condition $t < t_i < t'$.

The right-hand side of Eq. (3-21) can be generated by adding to H a term

$$H_{\text{ext}} = - \int_t^{t'} J(t)q(t)\, dt \qquad (3\text{-}24)$$

or to the operator Hamiltonian, a term $-JQ$. The steps of Sec. 3-2-1 can now be retraced to calculate $\langle q't' \mid qt \rangle^J$ which is the same function as (3-3), but calculated in the presence of the source. Then, the functional

$$Z\{J\} = \int dq \; dq' \; \Phi_0^*(q't')\langle q't' \mid qt \rangle^J \Phi_0(q,t) \qquad (3\text{-}25)$$

will generate the quantities on the right-hand side of (3-21) via

$$(i)^n \langle 0 \mid T[Q(t_1)\dots Q(t_n)] \mid 0 \rangle = \frac{\delta^n Z\{J\}}{\delta J(t_1)\dots \delta J(t_n)}\bigg|_{J=0} \qquad (3\text{-}26)$$

We now use the fact that the source J vanishes for times outside the interval (t, t') to obtain an expression for Z in terms of the asymptotic behavior of transformation functions at large times. If $T' > t' > t > T$, then:

$$\langle Q'T' \mid QT \rangle^J = \int dq \; dq' \langle Q'T' \mid q't' \rangle\langle q't' \mid qt \rangle^J \langle qt \mid QT \rangle \qquad (3\text{-}27)$$

where the first and last factors in the integrand are independent of J. In fact, we know from (3-7) that:

$$\langle qt|QT\rangle = \langle q|\exp[-iH(t-T)]|Q\rangle = \sum_n \Phi_n^*(q)\Phi_n(Q)\exp[-iE_n(t-T)]$$

(3-28)

$$\Phi_n(q) = \langle n|q\rangle \qquad (3\text{-}29)$$

In order to project the ground state we continue T to the imaginary axis and then

$$\lim_{T\to i\infty} \exp(-iE_0 T)\langle qt|QT\rangle = \Phi_0(q)\Phi_0^*(Q)\exp(-iE_0 t)$$

$$= \Phi_0(q,t)\Phi_0^*(Q) \qquad (3\text{-}30)$$

which leads to

$$Z\{J\} = \lim_{\substack{T'\to -i\infty \\ T\to i\infty}} \frac{\langle Q'T'|QT\rangle^J}{\exp[-iE_0(T'-T)]\Phi_0(Q')\Phi_0^*(Q)} \qquad (3\text{-}31)$$

Furthermore, one is usually interested in time-ordered products of operators divided by $\langle 0|0\rangle$, and hence any factor in Eq. (3-31) which is independent of J can be ignored. $Z\{J\}$ is written as:

$$Z\{J\} = \lim_{\substack{T\to i\infty \\ T'\to -i\infty}} \int \mathscr{D}q \exp\left\{ i\int_T^{T'} [\mathscr{L}(q,\dot q) + Jq]\, dt \right\} \qquad (3\text{-}32)$$

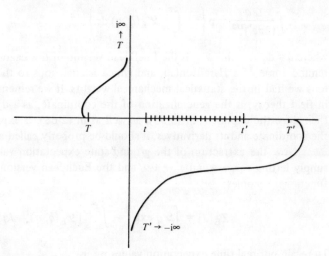

FIGURE 3-1
Time path used for the calculation of Z — the generating functional for real times — in the complex time plane. The source $J \neq 0$ only on an interval on the real axis.

One should keep in mind that it is only outside the interval (t, t') that we continue to the imaginary time axis. Because there $J = 0$, and hence we know the time-dependence explicitly (Eq. (3-28); see Fig. 3-1).

3-2-4   Analytic Continuation in Time — the Euclidean Theory

The apparent inconvenience, implied by the awkward path in the complex time plane, can be turned into an advantage by continuing all times to the imaginary axis — i.e., by performing a Wick rotation. All we have to do is to define time-ordering for imaginary times, and this we do by defining

$$t_i = -i\tau_i \qquad (3\text{-}33)$$

so that the τ_i's can be ordered along the imaginary axis — to later t_i's correspond "later" τ_i. The only change that will occur in the previous discussion is that

$$\epsilon = \frac{t' - t}{n + 1} \to \epsilon' = \frac{\tau' - \tau}{n + 1} = i\epsilon \qquad (3\text{-}34)$$

and we have to add a boundary condition insuring that the solutions of the Schrödinger equation for large imaginary times will remain finite. Effectively we are converting the Schrödinger equation into a diffusion equation.

The transformation function, Eq. (3-16), takes on the form

$$
\begin{aligned}
F &= \lim_{n \to \infty} \int \Pi \frac{dq_i}{(2\pi\epsilon')^{1/2}} \exp\left\{ -\epsilon' \sum_{n=1}^{n+1} \left[\frac{1}{2}\dot{q}^2 + V\left(\frac{q_i + q_{i-1}}{2}\right) \right] \right\} \\
&= \int \frac{\mathscr{D}q}{(2\pi\epsilon')^{1/2}} \exp\left\{ -\int_{\tau}^{\tau'} \mathscr{L}_E(\dot{q}, q)\, d\tau \right\}
\end{aligned}
\qquad (3\text{-}35)
$$

where $\dot{q} = dq/d\tau$, and $\mathscr{L}_E$ is the Euclidean version of the Lagrangian, which may remind some of a Hamiltonian, and which is analogous to the type of expressions we had in the statistical mechanical weights. If we remember that the field, in field theory, is the generalization of the coordinate, as a dynamical variable, then since the exponent in (3-35), as well as in (2-68), is expressed in terms of the coordinate and its derivatives, it should be properly called a Lagrangian.

Now the extraction of the ground state expectation value is obtained by simply letting $\tau \to -\infty$ and $\tau' \to +\infty$, and the Euclidean version of the generating functional becomes:

$$Z_E\{J\} = \int \mathscr{D}q \exp\left\{ -\int_{-\infty}^{\infty} [\mathscr{L}_E(\dot{q}, q) - Jq]\, d\tau \right\} \qquad (3\text{-}36)$$

To regain our real time expectation values we use

$$\frac{1}{Z\{J\}} \frac{\delta^n Z}{\delta J(t_1) \ldots \delta J(t_n)}\Bigg|_{J=0} = \frac{(\mathrm{i})^n}{Z_E} \frac{\delta^n Z_E}{\delta J(\tau_1) \ldots \delta J(\tau_n)}\Bigg|_{\substack{J=0 \\ \tau_i = it_i}} \qquad (3\text{-}37)$$

Had we generated the Green functions in "momentum" space, which in the present case means frequency, then the analytic continuation to *the causal* functions would have been obtained by:

$$\frac{1}{Z\{J\}} \frac{\delta^n Z}{\delta J(k_1) \ldots \delta J(k_n)}\bigg|_{J=0} = \frac{(i)^n}{Z_E} \frac{\delta^n Z_E}{\delta J(K_1) \ldots \delta J(K_n)}\bigg|_{\substack{J=0 \\ K_i = ik_i \\ \omega^2 = \omega^2 - i\epsilon}} \tag{3-38}$$

where ω^2 is the coefficient of q^2 in the Lagrangian.

Exercises 3-1 and 3-2 are illustrations of the mechanisms discussed above, in the case of the harmonic oscillator. There the original Lagrangian is

$$\mathscr{L} = \tfrac{1}{2}\dot{q}^2 - \tfrac{1}{2}\omega^2 q^2 \tag{3-39}$$

and its Euclidean version

$$\mathscr{L}_E = \tfrac{1}{2}\dot{q}^2 + \tfrac{1}{2}\omega^2 q^2 \tag{3-40}$$

The Euclidean two-point Green functions in frequency and in time are, respectively (see Exercise 3-2)

$$\langle 0 \mid q(K)q(-K) \mid 0 \rangle \propto \frac{1}{K^2 + \omega^2} \tag{3-41}$$

$$\langle 0 \mid q(\tau_1)q(\tau_2) \mid 0 \rangle \propto -\frac{1}{2\omega} \exp(-\omega \mid \tau_1 - \tau_2 \mid) \tag{3-42}$$

The analytic continuation in time as given by (3-37) leads to:

$$\langle 0 \mid q(t_1)q(t_2) \mid 0 \rangle \propto$$

$$-\frac{1}{2\omega}\left\{ \theta(t_1 - t_2)\exp[-i\omega(t_1 - t_2)] + \theta(t_2 - t_1)\exp[i\omega(t_1 - t_2)] \right\} \tag{3-43}$$

The continuation in Fourier space gives:

$$\langle 0 \mid q(k_1)q(-k_1) \mid 0 \rangle \propto \frac{1}{-k_1^2 + \omega^2 - i\epsilon} \tag{3-44}$$

which is the Fourier transform of (3-43). The boundary conditions imposed on the Euclidean theory determine those of the real time theory and fix the solution of the homogeneous equation.

3-3 FUNCTIONAL INTEGRALS FOR THE SCALAR BOSON FIELD THEORY

3-3-1 Introduction

In the present section we will consider, rather briefly and schematically, the procedure by which the quantities of main interest in quantum field theory are expressed in terms of functional integrals. These quantities are the Green functions, or time-ordered products of interacting fields, averaged in the vacuum state. The S-matrix, describing all possible scattering processes, is expressed in terms of these Green functions with their variables set on the mass shell and the part corresponding to stable incoming particles extracted.

On the one hand it is rather interesting to see the extent of the analogy between the formulation of a statistical mechanical problem given in Chapter 2, and the formulation of quantum field theory. On the other, in all situations of interest in the latter case, namely when infinities arise, the manipulations are of a purely formal character. The theory is then supplemented by additional prescriptions which render it finite in a systematic way, but most of the structure used in the derivation is lost.† The complications involved in resurrecting such things as field equations, interpolating fields, etc. have been discussed at length by Zimmermann (Brandeis Lecture Notes). Perhaps the most rational attitude is that of t'Hooft and Veltman (Diagrammar) in which the theory is postulated in terms of its regularized perturbation expansion. So there seems little point in giving a lengthy exposition.

Here we will follow the presentation of Fried[4] which in turn follows Symanzik. The logic is as follows:

(1) For an interacting bose field $\Phi(x)$ we can define the operator

$$T\{J\} = T \exp\left[i \int_{-\infty}^{\infty} J(x)\Phi(x)\, d^4x \right] \qquad (3\text{-}45)$$

where $J(x)$ is a c-number source, and T is the time-ordering operator. The vacuum expectation values of time ordered products of Φ-fields are generated by

$$Z\{J\} = \langle 0 \,|T\{J\}|\, 0 \rangle \qquad (3\text{-}46)$$

(2) If the dynamics of the field is described by a Lagrangian

$$\mathscr{L} = \mathscr{L}^{(0)}(\Phi) + \mathscr{L}_{\text{Int}}(\Phi) \qquad (3.47)$$

then

$$Z\{J\} = \mathscr{N}^{-1} \exp\left\{ i \int \mathscr{L}_{\text{Int}} \left[i\frac{\delta}{\delta J(x)} \right] d^4x \right\} Z^0\{J\} \qquad (3\text{-}48)$$

with Z^0 the generating functional for the non-interacting theory. Z can be written also as:

$$Z\{J\} = \mathscr{N}^{-1} \int \mathscr{D}\phi \exp\left\{ i \int [\mathscr{L}(\phi) + J\phi]\, d^4x \right\} \qquad (3\text{-}49)$$

with ϕ a c-number field.

---

† The reasons which make this strange logical procedure of Symanzik work are discussed by Lowenstein.[5]

(3) Finally one shows that, apart from a phase factor, the S-matrix is given by

$$S = : \exp\left[\int \Phi_{IN}(x) K_x \frac{\delta}{\delta J(x)} d^4x\right] : Z\{J\}\Big|_{J=0} \qquad (3\text{-}50)$$

where Φ_{IN} is the incoming field at $t \to -i\infty$, K is the Klein–Gordon operator (it would have been the Dirac operator for fermions), and : : implies normal ordering – i.e., destruction operators to the right of the creation operators.

If the incoming fields are chosen to have the observed mass of the particles, then K_x plays the role of selecting out of any matrix element of S that part which corresponds to the poles associated with the incoming or outgoing real particles.

3-3-2 The Generating Functional for Green Functions

As implied in the previous section, we will consider the case of the scalar boson field. We denote the interacting field in the Heisenberg picture by $\Phi(x)$, where x is a space–time four-vector. If a term $\int J\Phi$ is added to the Lagrangian the additional time-dependence is generated by the operator

$$T_{t_1 t_2}\{J\} = T \exp\left[i \int_{t_1}^{t_2} J(x)\Phi(x) \, d^4x\right] \qquad (3\text{-}51)$$

with T on the right-hand side indicating time-ordering. $J(x)$ is a c-number source, which has to be replaced by an anticommuting c-number in the case of fermions.

Taking functional derivatives with respect to $J(x)$ gives (see, e.g., Exercise 3-4)

$$\delta T_{t_1 t_2}\{J\}/\delta J(x) = 0$$

if x_0 is outside the interval (t_1, t_2) and

$$\delta T_{t_1 t_2}\{J\}/\delta J(x) = T[i\Phi(x)T_{t_1 t_2}\{J\}] \qquad (3\text{-}52)$$

Denoting by T the limit

$$T\{J\} = \lim_{\substack{t_1 \to -\infty \\ t_2 \to +\infty}} T_{t_1 t_2}\{J\}$$

we have

$$\delta^n T\{J\}/\delta J(x_1)\ldots\delta J(x_n) = T[(i)^n\Phi(x_1)\ldots\Phi(x_n)T\{J\}] \qquad (3\text{-}53)$$

where it has been assumed that $T\{J\}$ will not be confused with the time-ordering operator.

It follows immediately that if $|0\rangle$ is the vacuum state, or, at this stage, any other state, we will have

$$(i)^n \langle 0 | T[\Phi(x_1) \ldots \Phi(x_n)] | 0 \rangle = \delta^n \langle 0 | T\{J\} | 0 \rangle / \delta J(x_1) \ldots \delta J(x_n) \Big|_{J=0}$$

$$(3\text{-}54)$$

which establishes that

$$Z\{J\} = \langle 0 | T\{J\} | 0 \rangle$$

is the generating functional for time-ordered vacuum expectation values.

3-3-3 The Generating Functional as a Functional Integral

If the Lagrangian density of our scalar boson field theory is split according to Eq. (3-47) with

$$\mathcal{L}_0(\Phi) = -\tfrac{1}{2}(\mu^2 \Phi^2 + \partial_\mu \Phi \partial^\mu \Phi) \qquad (3\text{-}55)$$

then the equations of motion of the field, obtained by varying the action $\int \mathcal{L}$, take the form

$$K_x \Phi(x) = \frac{\partial \mathcal{L}_{\text{Int}}(\Phi)}{\partial \Phi} \qquad (3\text{-}56)$$

where

$$K_x = \mu^2 - (\nabla^2 - \partial_0^2) \equiv \mu^2 - \partial^2 \qquad (3\text{-}57)$$

This equation is purely formal, since products of operators at the same point are problematic even for free fields. Nevertheless, we will not be discouraged by such trifles, and we proceed to calculate

$$K_x \langle 0 | T[\Phi(x)T\{J\}] | 0 \rangle = K_x \cdot \delta Z / i\delta J(x)$$

Two terms appear in the derivative. One comes from the space–time variation of $\Phi(x)$, and the other from the time-ordering. The first is given by:

$$\langle 0 | T[K_x \Phi(x)T\{J\}] | 0 \rangle = \langle 0 | [T \frac{\partial \mathcal{L}_{\text{Int}}}{\partial \Phi} T\{J\}] | 0 \rangle$$

$$= \mathcal{L}'_{\text{Int}}[-i\delta/\delta J(x)]Z\{J\} \qquad (3\text{-}58)$$

where we have used Eq. (3-56) and introduced the notation

$$\mathcal{L}'(A) = \frac{\partial \mathcal{L}}{\partial A}$$

The second term comes only from the time derivative present in K_x. It is left as an exercise (3-7) to show that this term can be written as:

$$-i \int d^3x' J(x', x_0) \langle 0 \mid T[\Phi(x', x_0), \dot{\Phi}(x, x_0)] T\{J\} \mid 0 \rangle$$

The equal time commutation relation between Φ and $\dot{\Phi}$ is like that between a coordinate and a momentum, namely:

$$[\Phi(x', x_0), \dot{\Phi}(x, x_0)] = i\delta^3(x' - x) \qquad (3\text{-}59)$$

Thus we find

$$K_x \delta Z / i\delta J(x) = J(x)Z + \mathcal{L}'_{Int}[-i\delta/\delta J(x)]Z \qquad (3\text{-}60)$$

If the theory were free, i.e. $\mathcal{L}_{Int} = 0$, then with the same source we would have had

$$K_x \delta Z^0 / i\delta J(x) = J(x)Z^0 \qquad (3\text{-}61)$$

where Z^0 is the generating functional for the free theory. Using the identity

$$\left[\exp\left\{ i \int F[-i\delta/\delta J(y)] d^4y \right\}, J(x) \right] = F'[-i\delta/\delta J(x)] \exp\left\{ i \int F[-i\delta/\delta J] \right\} \qquad (3\text{-}62)$$

the proof of which is left as Exercise 3-8, one finds that the solution of Eq. (3-60) can be written in terms of $Z^0\{J\}$ as:

$$Z\{J\} = \exp\left\{ i \int \mathcal{L}_{Int}[-i\delta/\delta J(x)] d^4x \right\} Z^0\{J\} \qquad (3\text{-}63)$$

Applying K_x to $\delta Z\{J\}/i\delta J(x)$, and using (3-61) and (3-62), gives:

$$\exp\left\{ i \int \mathcal{L}_{Int}[-i\delta/\delta J(x)] d^4x \right\} K_x \delta / i\delta J(x) Z^0\{J\}$$

$$= \exp\left\{ i \int \mathcal{L}_{Int}[-i\delta/\delta J(x)] d^4x \right\} J(x) Z^0\{J\}$$

$$= J(x)Z\{J\} + \left[\exp\left\{ i \int \mathcal{L}_{Int}[-i\delta/\delta J(x)] d^4x \right\}, J(x) \right] Z^0\{J\}$$

$$= J(x)Z\{J\} + \mathcal{L}'_{Int}[-i\delta/\delta J(x)]Z\{J\}$$

Equation (3-60) determines Z up to a multiplicative constant which we choose by imposing the condition

$$Z\{J = 0\} = 1 \qquad (3\text{-}64)$$

To complete the calculation of Z we still have to solve (3-61) for $Z^0\{J\}$.

It is rather easy to guess the form of the solution of (3-61); it must be

$$Z^0\{J\} = \exp\left\{\frac{i}{2} \int J(x)\Delta(x - y)J(y)\, d^4x\, d^4y\right\} \qquad (3\text{-}65)$$

in which Δ is a solution of the inhomogeneous Klein–Gordon equation

$$K_x\Delta(x - y) = \delta(x - y) \qquad (3\text{-}66)$$

But this equation admits many solutions depending on the choice of the solution of the homogeneous part, or, correspondingly, on the choice of boundary conditions. In our case the choice has been made by the requirement (3-54), i.e., that we generate time-ordered products.

We know on the one hand, from (3-65), that

$$\delta^2 Z^0/\delta J(x)\delta J(y)\,|_{J=0} = i\Delta(x - y) \qquad (3\text{-}67)$$

On the other hand, using (3-54)

$$\delta^2 Z^0/\delta J(x)\delta J(y)\big|_{J=0} = -\langle 0\mid T[\Phi^0(x)\Phi^0(y)]\mid 0\rangle \qquad (3\text{-}68)$$

where Φ^0 denotes the free field. The vacuum expectation value of free fields is easy to calculate. All one has to do is to have the creation operators to the right, and if Φ^0 is written as

$$\Phi^0(x) = \Phi^+(x) + \Phi^-(x) \qquad (3\text{-}69)$$

with the destruction operators included in Φ^+ and the creation operators in Φ^-. Then

$$\Delta(x - y) = i\langle 0\mid \Phi^+(x)\Phi^-(y)\mid 0\rangle\, \theta\,(x_0 - y_0)$$

$$+ i\langle 0\mid \Phi^+(y)\Phi^-(x)\mid 0\rangle\theta(y_0 - x_0)$$

$$\equiv \Delta_c(x - y) = \int \frac{d^4k}{(2\pi)^4}\, \frac{\exp[ik(x - y)]}{k^2 + \mu^2 - i\epsilon} \qquad (3\text{-}70)$$

where $k^2 = \mathbf{k}^2 - k_0^2$. This is conventionally called the causal function. For more details the reader is referred to Bjorken and Drell[6] or Fried,[4] etc., and Exercises 3-9 to 3-13.

In Eq. (3-60) there are no operators and we can try to solve it without invoking any. Consider, for example, the functional

$$\bar{Z} = \int \mathscr{D}\phi \exp\left\{i \int [\mathscr{L}(\phi) + J\phi]\, d^4x\right\} \qquad (3\text{-}71)$$

in which ϕ is, of course, a c-number function.

Then, just as for a usual integral, we have

$$\int \mathscr{D}\phi \, \frac{\delta}{\delta\phi(x)} \exp\left\{ i \int [\mathscr{L}(\phi) + J\phi] \, d^4x \right\} = 0 \qquad (3\text{-}72)$$

Performing the differentiation under the integral sign one finds

$$\int \mathscr{D}\phi \, i \, \frac{\partial \mathscr{L}(\phi) d^4x}{\partial\phi(x)} \exp\left\{ i \int [\mathscr{L}(\phi) + J\phi] \, d^4x \right\} + iJ(x)\bar{Z} = 0 \qquad (3\text{-}73)$$

But $\partial\mathscr{L}/\partial\phi$ is a polynomial in ϕ which can be generated by functional derivatives with respect to $J(x)$. In particular, the term $\partial\mathscr{L}_{\mathrm{Int}}/\partial\phi(x)$ can be written as:

$$\mathscr{L}'_{\mathrm{Int}}[-i\delta/\delta J(x)]$$

$\mathscr{L}^0$ is quadratic in ϕ, and thus $\partial\mathscr{L}^0/\partial\phi$ is linear. But because $\mathscr{L}^0$ includes derivatives of the field we have to exercise some caution in performing the functional derivative. The explicit calculation reads:

$$-\frac{i\delta}{\delta\phi(x)} \int d^4y \, \frac{1}{2} \, [m^2\phi^2(y) + \partial_\mu\phi\partial^\mu\phi] = -i \int d^4y \, [m^2\phi(y) + \partial_\mu\phi\partial^\mu\phi] \, \delta(x - y)$$

$$= -i[m^2\phi(x) - \partial_\mu\partial^\mu\phi(x)] = -iK_x\phi(x)$$

Inserting it all back in (3-73) one finds that $\bar{Z}$ satisfies Eq. (3-60). If in addition we normalize $\bar{Z}$ in the same way in which we normalized Z, and write $m^2 - i\epsilon$ instead of m^2, then $\bar{Z}^0 = Z^0$ and $\bar{Z} = Z$.

What has been achieved, apart from showing that the generating functional in quantum field theory can be written in terms of a functional integral analogous to the ones appearing in statistical mechanics, is the derivation of Eqs. (3-63) and (3-65), which we recapitulate:

$$Z\{J\} = \exp\left\{ i \int \mathscr{L}_{\mathrm{Int}}[-i\delta/\delta J(x)] \, dx \right\} \exp\left\{ \frac{i}{2} \int J(x)\Delta_c(x - y)J(y) \, dx \, dy \right\} \qquad (3\text{-}74)$$

This form applies to the Euclidean theory as well, and is very useful in generating the perturbation expansion, which is an expansion in the parameters of $\mathscr{L}_{\mathrm{Int}}$. As we show in the next chapter.

3-3-4 The S-Matrix Expressed in Terms of the Generating Functional

For completeness we include a brief description, along traditional lines, of the procedure by which the S-matrix is expressed in terms of the generating functional Z.

As the Schrödinger states of the interacting system are extrapolated to times at $-\infty$ and at $+\infty$, they tend to free particle states called, respectively, the

IN and OUT states, which are denoted, respectively, $|\rangle_{IN}$ and $|\rangle_{OUT}$. These two complete sets of free states are constructed as a Fock space by the free field operators $\Phi_{IN}(x)$ and $\Phi_{OUT}(x)$. The S-matrix is defined as the unitary operator which connects the two complete sets. Namely,

$$\Phi_{OUT}(x) = S^+ \Phi_{IN}(x)S \qquad (3\text{-}75)$$

and correspondingly

$$|\rangle_{OUT} = S^+ |\rangle_{IN} \qquad (3\text{-}76)$$

In addition, asymptotic conditions are imposed. They read:

$$\lim_{x_0 \to \mp \infty} [\langle a | \Phi(x) | b \rangle - \langle a | \Phi_{IN \atop OUT} | b \rangle] = 0 \qquad (3\text{-}77)$$

for any pair of normalizable states.

Two comments are in place here. Firstly, the imposition of strong asymptotic conditions, i.e., on the operators themselves, leads to the result that there is no scattering. Secondly, if one insists that the equal time commutation relation of the Φ's — the interacting field — be normalized to a δ function, as in (3-59), then another constant should be multiplying one of the matrix elements in (3-77). We leave this factor out. Furthermore, we will disregard the distinction between strong and weak asymptotic conditions in intermediate steps, and instead we will avoid using it where the weak condition does not suffice.

Since the field satisfies the field equation (3-56) we can write

$$\Phi(x) = \Phi_{IN}(x) + \int d^4 y \Delta_R(x - y) \frac{\partial \mathscr{L}_{Int}(\Phi)}{\partial \Phi}$$

$$= \Phi_{IN}(x) + \int d^4 y \Delta_R(x - y) K_y \Phi(y) \qquad (3\text{-}78)$$

where Φ_{IN} is a solution of the homogeneous equation and Δ_R is the Green function of the Klein–Gordon equation, which vanishes when its time argument is negative. Similarly, we can write

$$\Phi(x) = \Phi_{OUT}(x) + \int d^4 y \Delta_A(x - y) K_y \Phi(y) \qquad (3\text{-}79)$$

Multiplying Eqs. (3-78) and (3-79) by $T\{J\}$ and by the operator of time-ordering, keeping in mind that Φ_{IN} is $\Phi(x)$ at $t = -\infty$ and Φ_{OUT} is $\Phi(x)$ at $t = +\infty$, we have, using (3-52),

$$\delta T / \delta J(x) = i T\{J\} \Phi_{IN}(x) + \int d^4 y \Delta_R(x - y) K_y \delta T\{J\} / \delta J(y) \qquad (3\text{-}80a)$$

$$\delta T / \delta J(x) = i \Phi_{OUT}(x) T\{J\} + \int d^4 y \Delta_A(x - y) K_y \delta T\{J\} / \delta J(y) \qquad (3\text{-}80b)$$

from which it follows that

$$(\Phi_{OUT}T - T\Phi_{IN}) = i \int d^4y\Delta(x - y)K_y\delta T\{J\}/\delta J(y) \qquad (3\text{-}81)$$

where

$$\Delta(x) = \Delta_A(x) - \Delta_R(x) \qquad (3\text{-}82)$$

The relations of the various Δ's are left as exercises (see, e.g., Exercise 3-13).

Next, multiplying both sides of (3-81) by S and using (3-75) one finds:

$$[\Phi_{IN}(x), ST] = i \int d^4y\Delta(x - y)K_y\delta (ST)/\delta J(y) \qquad (3\text{-}83)$$

since S is independent of J.

Using the identity (see Exercise 3-15)

$$[A, e^B] = [A, B]e^B \qquad (3\text{-}84)$$

for operators A and B whose commutator is a c-number, we have

$$\left[\Phi_{IN}(x), \exp\left\{\int \Phi_{IN}^-(x)f(x)\,dx\right\}\exp\left\{\int \Phi_{IN}^+(x)f(x)\,dx\right\}\right]$$
$$= i \int \Delta(x - y)f(y)\,d^4y \exp\left\{\int \Phi_{IN}^-(x)f(x)\,dx\right\}\exp\left\{\int \Phi_{IN}^+(x)f(x)\,dx\right\}$$
$$(3\text{-}85)$$

in which $\Phi_{IN}^-(x)$ is the part of Φ_{IN} which creates particles, while Φ^+ destroys them. Φ_{IN} is decomposed via

$$\Phi_{IN}(x) = \Phi_{IN}^+(x) + \Phi_{IN}^-(x) \qquad (3\text{-}86)$$

(see also Exercises 3-9 and 3-14), and using the definition of the normal product:

$$\exp\left\{\int \Phi_{IN}^-(x)f(x)\,dx\right\}\exp\left\{\int \Phi_{IN}^+(x)f(x)\,dx\right\} \equiv : \exp\left\{\int \Phi_{IN}(x)f(x)\,dx\right\} :$$

the solution of Eq. (3-83) is now straightforward. It is given by

$$ST = C : \exp\left\{\int \Phi_{IN}(x)K_x\delta/\delta J(x)\,dx\right\} : Z\{J\} \qquad (3\text{-}87)$$

as can be verified by calculating $[\Phi_{IN}, ST]$ and using (3-85). C is an arbitrary constant.

Taking the vacuum expectation value of (3-87), and noting that

$$_{IN}\langle 0 | : e^R : | 0 \rangle_{IN} = 1 \qquad (3\text{-}88)$$

for any operator R, we find that

$$_{\text{IN}}\langle 0 \mid ST\{J\} \mid 0 \rangle_{\text{IN}} = CZ\{J\} \qquad (3\text{-}89)$$

And since $T\{J\} \to 1$ as $J \to 0$, we have that

$$S = C : \exp \left\{ \int \Phi_{\text{IN}}(x) K_x \delta/\delta J(x) \right\} : Z\{J\} \Big|_{J=0} \qquad (3.90)$$

If, furthermore, there are no external fields, $S^\dagger \mid 0 \rangle_{\text{IN}} = e^{i\Phi} \mid 0 \rangle_{\text{IN}}$ and (3-89) implies that C is simply this phase factor.

EXERCISES

3-1 Calculate the Euclidean generating functional of the harmonic oscillator directly, in terms of a time-dependent as well as a frequency-dependent source.

3-2 Calculate the Euclidean two-point function.

(a) What equation does it satisfy?

(b) What boundary conditions have been assumed?

3-3 Show that the analytic continuation in time and frequency space are Fourier transforms of each other. Compare with the solution of Feynman and Hibbs.[7]

3-4 If $F\{J\}$ is a functional of J, then the functional derivative of F, $\delta F/\delta J(x)$ is defined by:

$$F\{J + \delta J\} - F\{J\} = \int dx \left(\frac{\delta F}{\delta J(x)} \right) \delta J(x) + 0(\delta J^2)$$

Using the fact that for bosons:

$$T(AB) = T(BA)$$

prove Eqs. (3-52) and (3-53).

3-5 Just as in usual integration we have

$$\int_{-\infty}^{\infty} dx \, \frac{d}{dx} f(x) = 0$$

if f is integrable, we have for functional integrals

$$\int \mathcal{D}\phi \, \frac{\delta}{\delta\phi(x)} F\{\phi\} = 0$$

By considering the expression

$$\int \mathcal{D}\phi \; \phi(x) \frac{\delta}{\delta\phi(y)} \exp\left\{-\int \mathcal{L}[\phi] \, dx\right\}$$

derive an equation for

$$\langle \, \phi(x) \, \phi(y) \, \rangle$$

assuming that

$$\mathcal{L}(\phi) = \tfrac{1}{2} (\partial\phi)^2 + P(\phi^2)$$

where P is a polynomial.

3-6 What would this equation read for the harmonic oscillator in Euclidean and real time?

What is the correspondence between the solutions?

3-7 Show that

$$\partial_0^2 \langle \, 0 \mid T[\Phi(x)T\{J\}] \mid 0 \, \rangle - \langle \, 0 \mid T[\partial_0^2\Phi(x)]T\{J\}] \mid 0 \, \rangle$$

$$= -i \int d^3x' J(x', x_0) \langle \, 0 \mid T[\Phi(x', x_0), \dot\Phi(x, x_0)]T\{J\} \mid 0 \, \rangle$$

3-8 Using the fact that

$$[\delta/\delta J(y), J(x)] = \delta(x - y)$$

prove identity (3-62).

3-9 The destructive and creative parts of the free field can be written as:

$$\Phi^+(x) = \frac{1}{(2\pi)^{3/2}} \int d^4 k a(k) \exp(ikx)\theta(k_0)\delta(k_0^2 - k^2 - m^2)$$

$$\Phi^-(x) = \frac{1}{(2\pi)^{3/2}} \int d^4 k a^+(k) \exp(-ikx)\theta(k_0)\delta(k_0^2 - k^2 - m^2)$$

with

$$[a(k), a(k')] = 0, \quad [a(k), a^+(k')] = \delta(k - k')$$

show that

$$[\Phi^+(x), \Phi^-(y)] = i\Delta^+(x - y)$$

$$= -\frac{i}{(2\pi)^3} \int d^4k \, \delta(k^2 + m^2)\theta(k_0) \exp(ikx)$$

and that Δ^+ satisfies the homogeneous Klein–Gordon equation.

3-10 Show that

$$\Delta_c(x - y) = -\theta(x_0 - y_0)\Delta^+(x - y) - \theta(y_0 - x_0)\Delta^+(y - x)$$

is the Green function for the Klein–Gordon equation.

3-11 By making a Fourier decomposition of the θ-functions show that

$$\Delta_c = \int \frac{d^4k}{(2\pi)^4} \frac{\exp[ik(x - y)]}{k^2 + m^2 - i\epsilon}$$

3-12 Show that in coordinate space Δ_c has the form

$$\Delta_c(x) = \frac{1}{4\pi}\delta(x^2) + \frac{im}{4\pi^2}\frac{\theta(x^2)}{\sqrt{x^2}}K_1(m\sqrt{x^2}) - \frac{m}{8\pi}\frac{\theta(-x^2)}{\sqrt{-x^2}}H_1^{(2)}(m\sqrt{-x^2})$$

where K and H are the conventional Bessel functions. Use this form to rationalize the name "causal" attached to this function.

3-13 Show that

$$\Delta_R(x) = -\theta(x_0)\Delta(x) \quad \text{(retarded)}$$
$$\Delta_A(x) = \theta(x_0)\Delta(x) \quad \text{(advanced)}$$

where $\Delta(x) = \Delta^+(x) - \Delta^+(-x)$, are Green functions of the Klein–Gordon equation.

3-14 Show, using results of Exercise 3-9, that

$$\langle 0 | [\Phi_{IN}(x), \Phi_{IN}(y)] | 0 \rangle = i\Delta(x - y)$$

3-15 Using the Baker–Housdorf formula

$$\exp(A + B) = \exp A \exp B \exp(-\tfrac{1}{2}[A,B])$$

where $[A,B]$ is a c-number, show that

$$[A, e^B] = [A, B]e^B$$

REFERENCES

1. E. S. Abers and B. W. Lee, *Physics Reports*, **9C**, 1 (1973).
2. Cf. Ref. 4, Chap. 2.
3. T. D. Lee and C. N. Yang, *Physical Review*, **128**, 885 (1962).
4. H. M. Fried, *Functional Methods and Models in Field Theory* (M.I.T. Press, Cambridge, Mass., 1972).
5. J. Lowenstein, *Physical Review*, **D4**, 2281 (1970). See also W. Zimmermann (Brandeis Lectures).
6. J. D. Bjorken and S. D. Drell, *Relativistic Quantum Fields* (McGraw-Hill, N.Y., 1965).
7. R. P. Feynman and A. R. Hibbs, *Quantum Mechanics and Path Integrals* (McGraw-Hill, N.Y., 1965).

PERTURBATION THEORY AND FEYNMAN GRAPHS

4-1 INTRODUCTION

The main tool for the manipulation of a field theory is an expansion in powers of coupling constants about some quadratic form, which is exactly soluble. Unfortunately, too many interesting results lie beyond any finite power expansion, especially if the parameters of the problem make the individual terms become very large. Nevertheless, perturbation expansions do not lose their usefulness, as the remaining chapters will try to show.

Traditionally one tried to leap beyond finite power expansions by identifying — either by force of physical argument or, as often, by mathematical ability — an infinite subset of the series, which can be summed in some region of the parameter space. Then the result was continued to other regions. Various results of this type come under the names of Hartree Approximation, the Random Phase Approximation, the Shielded Potential Approximations, etc.

Another great leap beyond perturbation theory was pioneered by Dyson, Gell-Man, Low, Bogoliubov, Symanzik, Callan and others. Their approach investigates the properties of a general term in the perturbation series and then arrives at equations — the Renormalization Group Equations — for the quantity expanded. The equations are assumed to be valid beyond the perturbation expansion, and the solutions often have properties which do not show in any finite order.

The recent developments of Wilson's ideas have followed two major trends. One, which was the later one, lies within the scope of manipulations of perturbation series. This has been initiated by Wilson[1] himself and developed by Brézin, Le Guillou and Zinn-Justin,[2] by Di Castro and Jona-Lasinio[3] and by Schröer and Jegerlehner.[4] But even the other trend, that of iterations and recursion relations, when systematically developed, relies heavily on diagrammatic perturbation expansions about a Gaussian theory.

In keeping track of the multitude of terms generated by perturbation theory, Feynman graphs serve as an invaluable device. All the terms in the expansion of any physical quantity can be mapped onto an easily definable set of graphs. Given a graph, one can easily reconstruct the algebraic expression, with its combinatorial coefficient. One can develop intuitions about the graphs, and draw many conclusions by studying their topological structure.

The present chapter is dedicated to some elementary ideas about perturbation theory and graphs. The argument is carried mainly by reference to some simple examples. Though in what follows we will mainly use graphs in momentum space, we start by developing the theory in coordinate space. This is, of course, the natural framework for the study of general spatially varying situations. Since our main concern will be with translationally invariant problems, momentum space has its obvious advantages.

4-2   PERTURBATION EXPANSION IN COORDINATE SPACE

We will restrict ourselves to a Euclidean field theory. As we have seen in Sec. 3-3-3, the generating functional, Eq. (2-11) can be expressed (up to a normalization factor) as

$$Z\{J\} = \mathcal{N}^{-1} \exp\left\{-\int dx\, \mathcal{L}_{\text{Int}}(\delta/\delta J(x))\right\} \exp\left\{\frac{1}{2}\int dx\, dy\, J(x)G_0(x-y)J(y)\right\} \tag{4-1}$$

where we have further restricted the discussion to a single scalar field, and G_0 is the Fourier transform of (2-78). Some generalizations will be discussed in later sections and in the exercises. $\mathcal{N}$ is determined by the normalization condition

$$Z\{J=0\} = 1 \tag{4-2}$$

Furthermore, all Green functions of a product of any number of fields at different points, are expressed as functional derivatives of Z with respect to J,

$$G^{(N)}(x_1, x_2, \ldots, x_N) = \delta^N Z\{J\}/\delta J(x_1) \ldots \delta J(x_N) \big|_{J=0} \tag{4-3}$$

The conjunction of (4-3) with (4-1) implies that it all reduces to the calculation of many derivatives of the Gaussian form, at the origin. Clearly a derivative of the exponential brings down a factor of J. Thus, if the term is not to vanish when J is set to zero, another derivative must act to eliminate this factor. Consequently, if a string of derivatives acts on the free part and we set $J = 0$, the derivative terms must group in pairs – in all possible ways. For each such pair there will appear a factor $G_0(x - y)$, where x and y are the coordinates of the J's in the pair.

The result of the operation of an odd number of derivatives on Z^0 at $J = 0$ vanishes.

The above simple considerations are the expression and the proof of *Wick's theorem.*

The form of the general term in the expansion of (4-3) in powers of the coupling constants appearing in $\mathscr{L}_{Int}$ is an integral over the coordinates, originating from the integral over $\mathscr{L}_{Int}$, of a product of G_0's, with $x_1, \ldots, x_N$ unintegrated.

Examples

(i) *The two point function in a ϕ^4 theory*   We have:

$$\mathscr{L}_{Int} = \frac{\lambda}{4!} \phi^4 \qquad (4\text{-}4)$$

Expanding $Z\{J\}$ in powers of λ gives:

$$Z\{J\} = \mathscr{N}^{-1} \sum_0^\infty \frac{1}{n!} \left(\frac{-\lambda}{4!} \right)^n$$

$$\int dx_1 \ldots dx_n \left[\frac{\delta}{\delta J(x_1)} \right]^4 \left[\frac{\delta}{\delta J(x_2)} \right]^4 \cdots \left[\frac{\delta}{\delta J(x_n)} \right]^4 Z^0\{J\} \qquad (4\text{-}5)$$

$\mathscr{N}$ is equal to the sum on the right-hand side, evaluated at $J = 0$, and as such it also depends on λ. A word of caution is, however, in place here. Due to the special way in which spontaneous symmetry breaking enters – Sec. 2-4 – the application of Eq. (4-5) should be restricted to the symmetric state. The reason is that Z^0 is symmetric, and no perturbation theory around it will produce $\langle \phi \rangle \neq 0$. Broken symmetry will be discussed in Sec 5-5, where vertices in the state of broken symmetry are expressed in terms of symmetric vertices.

In principle, in order to calculate $G^{(N)}$ to order n in λ one has to operate with the derivatives on the first $n + 1$ members in the sum, then multiply by the normalization factor calculated to that order, and retain all terms up to order λ^n.

To zeroth order we find

$$G_0^{(2)}(x_1, x_2) = G_0(x_1 - x_2) = \int \frac{dp}{(2\pi)^d} \frac{\exp[ip(x_1 - x_2)]}{p^2 + \mu^2} \qquad (4\text{-}6)$$

To this order $\mathscr{N} = 1$.

The first order term is:

$$G_1^{(2)} = \left(\frac{-\lambda}{4!}\right) \frac{\delta}{\delta J(x_1)} \frac{\delta}{\delta J(x_2)} \int dx' \left[\frac{\delta}{\delta J(x')}\right]^4 \exp\left\{\frac{1}{2} \int J(x)G^0(x-y)J(y)\right\}\bigg|_{J=0}$$
$$+ \mathcal{N}_1 G_0(x_1 - x_2) \tag{4-7}$$

where $\mathcal{N}_1$ is the first order term in the normalization factor.

Wick's theorem tells us that the six derivatives in the first term on the right-hand side of the last equation have to be paired. The pairings can be done in the following ways:

(a) $J(x_1)$ paired with $J(x_2)$ and the four J's in the interaction paired among themselves.

(b) $J(x_1)$ and $J(x_2)$ are paired with J's in the interaction.

In (a) there are three different possibilities of pairing the four J's. The result for this part is:

$$(a) \quad -\frac{\lambda}{8} G_0(x_1 - x_2) \int dx' G_0(x' - x')G_0(x' - x') \tag{4-8}$$

In (b) there are 12 possibilities of pairing $J(x_1)$ and $J(x_2)$ with the four J's in the interaction. Thus, this part contributes:

$$(b) \quad -\frac{\lambda}{2} \int dx' G_0(x_1 - x')G_0(x' - x_2)G_0(x' - x') \tag{4-9}$$

The term (a) has a form just like that of the second term in (4-7). Namely, $G_0(x_1 - x_2)$ multiplied by a factor independent of the coordinates x_1 and x_2. In fact, as is shown in Exercise 4-3, these two terms cancel. This is a special case of a general theorem which we prove below. The result for the first order term in $G^{(2)}$ is given by (4-9).

To each one of the terms (4-8) and (4-9) we assign a graph by drawing a point for every external coordinate and for every interaction. Each point is labeled by its coordinate. For every $G_0(x - y)$ we draw a line between the points labeled x and y. Thus to (4-8) will correspond graph (a) of Fig. 4-1 and graph (b) to (4-9).

A graph which has a part with no external coordinates is called a vacuum graph. It appears in the algebraic expression as a factor which is independent of

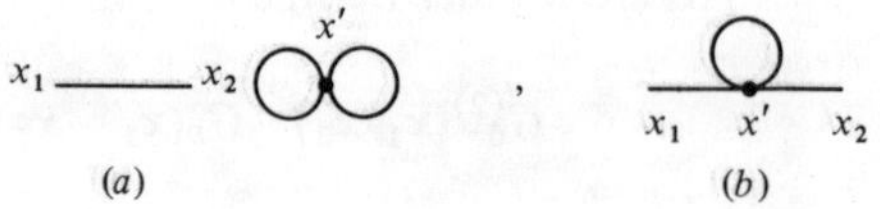

FIGURE 4-1
First order graphs of $G^{(2)}$.
(a)   (b)

the external coordinates. Clearly, all graphs corresponding to terms in $\mathcal{N}$ are of this type.

Given any of these graphs we can reconstruct the algebraic expression by writing a product which consists of:

1. A factor $(-\lambda/4!)$ for every point which is not an external point.
2. A factor $G_0(x - y)$ for any line between x and y.

This product has to be integrated over all coordinates which are not external. Finally, it has to be multiplied by two more factors. One comes from the factorials in the expansion (4-5). If, as we shall show the case to be, terms which mix different orders from the numerator and denominator all cancel, then this factor is simply $1/n!$. The second is the intrinsic symmetry factor of the term, which gives the number of ways in which the pairings can be affected so as to give the particular graph. These are the factors 3 and 12 encountered in the previous example.

If we consider terms of second order we have

$$
G_2^{(2)} = \frac{1}{2!}\left(\frac{-\lambda}{4!}\right)^2 \int dx_1'\, dx_2'\, \frac{\delta}{\delta J(x_1)}\, \frac{\delta}{\delta J(x_2)} \left[\frac{\delta}{\delta J(x_1')}\right]^4 \left[\frac{\delta}{\delta J(x_2')}\right]^4
$$

$$
\exp\left\{\frac{1}{2}\int J(x)G^0(x-y)J(y)\right\}\Bigg|_{J=0} \mp \mathcal{N}_1 G_1^{(2)} \mp \mathcal{N}_2 G_0^{(2)} \tag{4-10}
$$

The pairings fall into three main categories:

1. x_1 and x_2 are paired.
2. Both x_1 and x_2 are paired with either x_1' or x_2'.
3. x_1 is paired with x_1' and x_2 with x_2' (or vice versa) and x_1' is paired with x_2'.

The terms produced in 1. and in 2. cancel the last two terms in (4-10) (see Exercise 4-3). There are three such terms in 1. They are represented in Fig. 4-2. The expressions corresponding to the three graphs in this figure are:

$$
4\text{-}2(a) \quad \frac{1}{2!}\, 9\left(\frac{\lambda}{4!}\right)^2 G_0(x_1-x_2) \int dx_1' G_0^2(x_1'-x_1') \int dx_2' G_0^2(x_2'-x_2') \tag{4-11}
$$

$$
4\text{-}2(b) \quad \frac{1}{2!}\, 72\left(\frac{\lambda}{4!}\right)^2 G_0(x_1-x_2) \int dx_1'\, dx_2' G_0(x_1'-x_1') G_0^2(x_1'-x_2') G_0(x_2'-x_2') \tag{4-12}
$$

$$
4\text{-}2(c) \quad \frac{1}{2!}\, 24\left(\frac{\lambda}{4!}\right)^2 G_0(x_1-x_2) \int dx_1'\, dx_2' G_0^4(x_1'-x_2') \tag{4-13}
$$

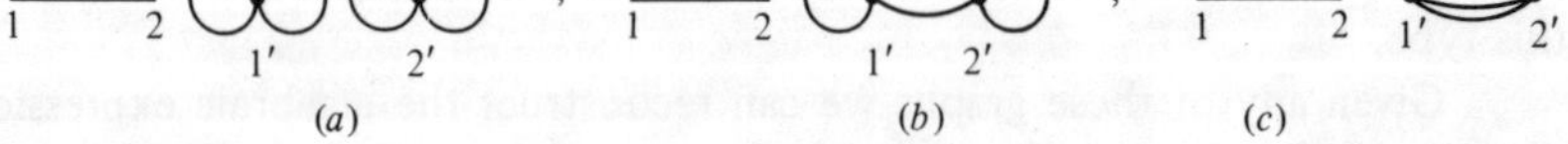

FIGURE 4-2
Second order graphs of $G^{(2)}$ which belong to $\mathcal{N}_2 G_0^{(2)}$.

All of these include vacuum parts. There is one term in 2., namely:

$$\frac{1}{2!} 36 \times 2 \left(\frac{\lambda}{4!}\right)^2 \int dx_1' G_0(x_1 - x_1') G_0(x_1' - x_1') G_0(x_1' - x_2) \int dx_2' G_0^2(x_2' - x_2')$$

$$(4\text{-}14)$$

and we represent it in Fig. 4-3.

FIGURE 4-3
Terms of $G^{(2)}$ belonging to $\mathcal{N}_1 G_1^{(2)}$.

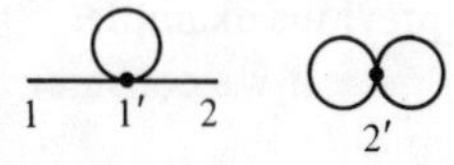

All the terms of type 3. survive. These three terms (see Fig. 4-4) are given by:

$$4\text{-}4(a) \quad \frac{1}{2!} 144 \times 2 \left(\frac{\lambda}{4!}\right)^2 \int dx_1' \, dx_2' G_0(x_1 - x_1') G_0(x_1' - x_2) G_0^2(x_1' - x_2')$$

$$G_0(x_2' - x_2') \quad (4\text{-}15)$$

$$4\text{-}4(b) \quad \frac{1}{2!} 96 \times 2 \left(\frac{\lambda}{4!}\right)^2 \int dx_1' \, dx_2' G_0(x_1 - x_1') G_0^3(x_1' - x_2') G_0(x_2' - x_2) \quad (4\text{-}16)$$

$$4\text{-}4(c) \quad \frac{1}{2!} 144 \times 2 \left(\frac{\lambda}{4!}\right)^2 \int dx_1' \, dx_2' G_0(x_1 - x_1') G_0(x_1' - x_1') G_0(x_1' - x_2')$$

$$G_0(x_2' - x_2') G_0(x_2' - x_2) \quad (4\text{-}17)$$

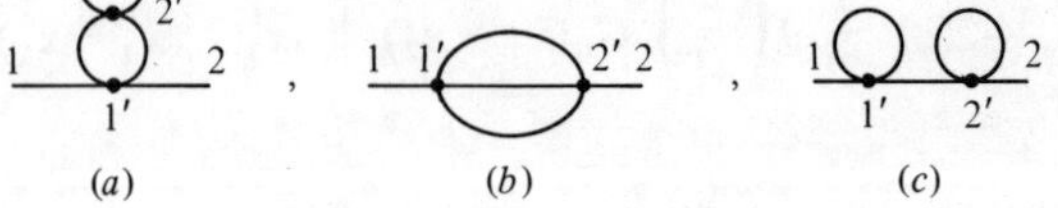

FIGURE 4-4
Second order graphs of $G^{(2)}$ without vacuum parts.

Notice that in the last four terms we have included an explicit factor of 2, which corresponds to the permutation of interaction vertices. Another feature is that all surviving terms are connected. In terms of the graphs it means that they are made of one piece. In terms of the algebraic expressions, all coordinates are connected by the integrations. This is a special feature of the two point function in a ϕ^4 theory. In a ϕ^3 theory, for example, $G^{(2)}$ will have disconnected terms. If one calculates $G^{(4)}$ in a ϕ^4 theory such terms also appear as we proceed to show.

(ii) *The four-point function in a ϕ^4 theory*   At zeroth order we have

$$G_0^{(4)}(x_1, \ldots, x_4) = \frac{\delta}{\delta J(x_1)} \cdots \frac{\delta}{\delta J(x_4)} \exp\left\{\frac{1}{2} \int J(x) G_0(x - y) J(y)\right\}\bigg|_{J=0}$$

$$= G_0(x_1 - x_2) G_0(x_3 - x_4) + G_0(x_1 - x_3) G_0(x_2 - x_4)$$
$$+ G_0(x_1 - x_4) G_0(x_2 - x_3) \tag{4-18}$$

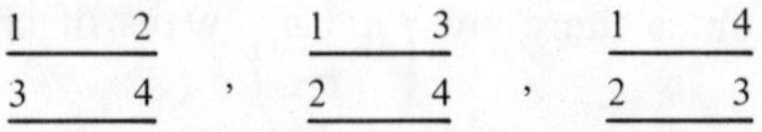

FIGURE 4-5
Zeroth order term of $G^{(4)}$.

$$\frac{1 \quad\quad 2}{3 \quad\quad 4} \quad , \quad \frac{1 \quad\quad 3}{2 \quad\quad 4} \quad , \quad \frac{1 \quad\quad 4}{2 \quad\quad 3}$$

The graphs for this term are depicted in Fig. 4-5, they are all disconnected but include no vacuum parts. Notice that we have made the change in notation $x_i \to i$.

In first order there are three possible terms (see Fig. 4-6) for which we write the expression:

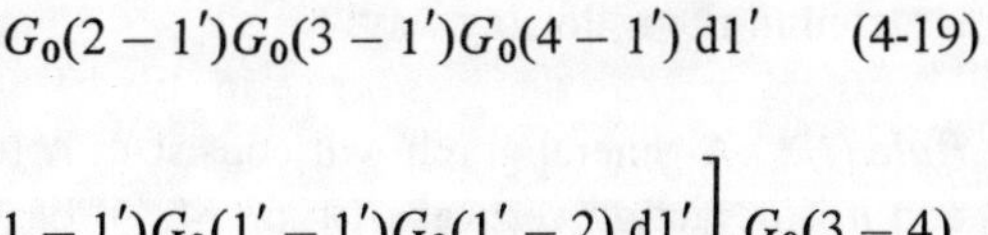

FIGURE 4-6
First order terms of $G^{(4)}$.   (a)   (b)   (c)

$$4\text{-}6(a) = \left(\frac{-\lambda}{4!}\right) 24 \int G_0(1 - 1') G_0(2 - 1') G_0(3 - 1') G_0(4 - 1') \, d1' \tag{4-19}$$

$$4\text{-}6(b) = \left(\frac{-\lambda}{4!}\right) 12 \left[\int G_0(1 - 1') G_0(1' - 1') G_0(1' - 2) \, d1'\right] G_0(3 - 4)$$
$$+ 5 \text{ permutations} \tag{4-20}$$

$$4\text{-}6(c) = \left(\frac{-\lambda}{4!}\right) 3 \left[\int d1' G_0^2(1' - 1')\right] G_0(1 - 2) G_0(3 - 4)$$
$$+ 2 \text{ permutations} \tag{4-21}$$

4-6(a) is a connected graph; 4-6(b) is a disconnected graph; and 4-6(c) is a disconnected graph with a vacuum part. This last term is cancelled by the normalization.

4-3 THE CANCELLATION OF VACUUM GRAPHS

Before proceeding to the general rules for the expansion in terms of graphs, we demonstrate that the cancellation of graphs with vacuum parts is a general feature.

The proof can be carried through for a general $\mathscr{L}_{Int}(\phi)$ which we multiply by λ for counting purposes. Consider a general term in the numerator of some Green function. Let it be of order $n + p$ in λ, and let it have a vacuum part of order p. The combinatorial factor of this graph will be

$$\frac{1}{(n + p)!} \binom{n + p}{p} = \frac{1}{n!p!}$$

since there are $\binom{n + p}{p}$ ways of choosing the p factors of $\mathscr{L}_{Int}$ in the vacuum part. Hence the expression for this graph becomes a product of the expression for the vacuum part, with its correct factorial denominator $p!$, and the expresssion for the non-vacuum part with its $1/n!$. Summing over all p we obtain the nth order contribution, to the Green function, without vacuum parts, multiplied by the sum of all vacuum graphs. But that last sum is just the normalization coefficient. So it cancels.

4-4 RULES FOR THE COMPUTATION OF GRAPHS[5]

Let us first consider a scalar field, and let

$$\mathscr{L}_{Int} = \sum_r \frac{\lambda_r}{r!} \phi^r \qquad (4\text{-}22)$$

In the expansion of $G^{(N)}(x_1, \ldots, x_N)$ we will have all possible graphs constructed in the following way:

Rule (i)   A general graph will consist of N (external) points marked $1, \ldots, N$, and n_r interaction vertices of type r-(ϕ^r). Each vertex is represented by a point

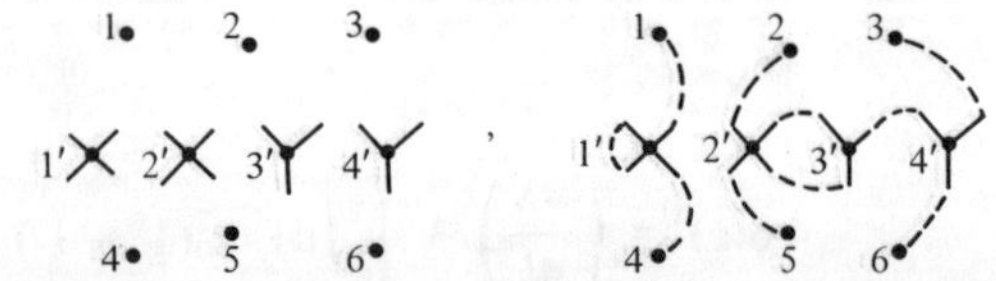

FIGURE 4-7
Constructing a graph from external points and vertices.

with a coordinate, out of which emanate r lines. All lines have to be connected either to other lines or to the external points. In order to avoid vacuum parts the connection has to be made in such a way that every interaction is connected directly or indirectly to an external point.

In Fig. 4-7 one way of creating a graph of $G^{(6)}$ is indicated.

In order to calculate the numerical value of the term in the perturbation series, which corresponds to a given graph, one has the self evident rule:

Rule (ii)   A product including the following factors should be formed:

for every internal point of type r a factor $(-\lambda_r/r!)$;
for every line a factor G_0 (of the difference of the coordinates at its ends);
an overall $1/n_2! \, n_2! \ldots$ where n_r is the number of points of type r;
an overall symmetry factor, which counts the number of ways in which the lines could have been connected in Rule (i) to give the same topological structure;
all internal coordinates should be integrated over.

We will not include a general proof of this rule here. In fact, rules of this type are most convincing when assimilated in private. We will present two examples:

Example (1)   In Fig. 4-8 a graph of $G^{(3)}$ is depicted. The expression corresponding to it is:

$$\left(-\frac{\lambda_3}{3!}\right)^3 \int G_0(1-1')G_0(2-2')G_0(3-3')G_0(1'-2')G_0(2'-3')G_0(3'-1')$$

$$\times \frac{1}{3!} \times \text{(symmetry factor)} \qquad (4\text{-}23)$$

FIGURE 4-8
A third order graph of $G^{(2)}$ in a ϕ^3 theory. All primed coordinates are integrated over.

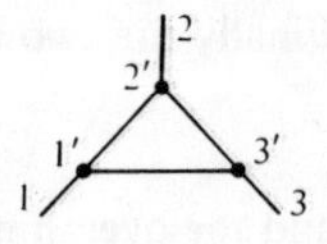

All primed coordinates are integrated over.

Next we compute the symmetry factor. There are 3 vertices and 3 external points, as shown in Fig. 4-9.

FIGURE 4-9
Elements for the construction of the graph in Fig. 4-8.

FIGURE 4-10
After external points have been attached.

The first external point can be attached in 9 ways, the second — which has to be attached to a different vertex if the same topological structure is to result — can be attached in 6 ways, and the third in 3 ways. Now the situation is as shown in Fig. 4-10. A given line of the vertex with 1 can be attached to one of the two lines of the two vertices 2 or 3. The other line of 1 has to be attached to one of the two lines of the remaining vertex. Hence:

$$\text{Symmetry factor} = 9 \times 6 \times 3 \times 2 \times 2 \times 2 = (3!)^4$$

and the overall numerical factor in Eq. (4-23) is 1.

Example (2)   We consider a graph of $G^{(2)}$ (see Fig. 4-11) in a theory with ϕ^4 and ϕ^3 interactions. The expression corresponding to it is

FIGURE 4-11
A graph of $G^{(2)}$ in a ϕ^4, ϕ^3 theory.

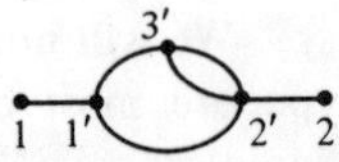

$$\left(-\frac{\lambda_3}{3!}\right)^2 \left(-\frac{\lambda_4}{4!}\right) \int G_0(1 - 1')G_0(2 - 2')G_0(1' - 3')G_0(1' - 2')G_0^2(2' - 3')$$

$$\times \frac{1}{2!1!} \times (\text{symmetry factor}) \qquad (4\text{-}24)$$

There are 6×4 possibilities for attaching the external points. After they have been attached we have Fig. 4-12. One of *three* remaining lines of $2'$ will attach to one out of *two* remaining lines of $1'$. One of *three* lines of $3'$ will attach to $1'$. Finally the two remaining lines of $2'$ and $3'$ can combine in *two* ways. Thus,

$$\text{Symmetry factor} = 6 \times 4 \times 3 \times 2 \times 3 \times 2 = (3!)^2 (4!)$$

and the overall numerical factor in Eq. (4-24) is $\frac{1}{2}$.

FIGURE 4-12
After external points have been attached.

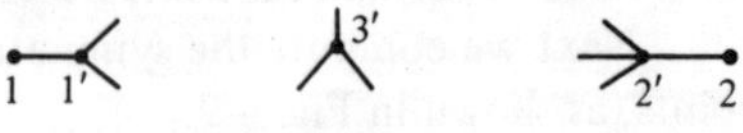

In fact, the $1/r!$ denominators in Eq. (4-22) are so chosen that if a graph possesses no symmetry which allows an exchange of lines, or vertices, keeping all connections intact, to map the graph on itself, then its numerical factor is unity. In the second example, that of Fig. 4-11, the loop between $2'$ and $3'$ has a symmetry which introduces a factor of $\frac{1}{2}$.

4-5 MORE GENERAL CASES

4-5-1 The M-vector theory

We have M boson fields or an M-dimensional spin on a lattice site. The free Lagrangian may be

$$\mathcal{L}_0 = \frac{1}{2} \sum_{i=1}^{M} (\partial_\mu \phi_i \partial^\mu \phi_i + \mu_i^2 \phi_i^2) \qquad (4\text{-}25)$$

and the interaction may have the form, for example,

$$\mathcal{L}_{\text{Int}} = \frac{1}{4!} \lambda F_{ijkl} \phi_i \phi_j \phi_k \phi_l \qquad (4\text{-}26)$$

in which a summation over repeated indices is implied (see, e.g., Exercise 4-8).

The generating functional is obtained by adding a term

$$\mathcal{L}_s = -J_i \phi_i \qquad (4\text{-}27)$$

which leads, in the free case, to

$$Z^0\{J\} = \exp\left\{ \frac{1}{2} \int \sum_i J_i(x) G_{0i}(x-y) J_i(y) \right\} \qquad (4\text{-}28)$$

where G_{0i} is given by an expression like (4-6) with μ_i^2 replacing μ^2. In order to derive Eq. (4-28) one simply notes that $\mathcal{L}_0$ is a sum of independent terms for each i, and hence Z^0 is a product.

In order to obtain the Green functions in the interacting theory we should calculate $Z\{J_i\}$, and then:

$$
\begin{aligned}
G_{i_1}^{(N)} \cdots {}_{i_N}(x_1, \ldots, x_N) &= \langle \phi_{i_1}(x_1) \phi_{i_2}(x_2) \ldots \phi_{i_N}(x_N) \rangle \\
&= \frac{\delta^N Z\{J_i\}}{\delta J_{i_1}(x_1) \delta J_{i_2}(x_2) \ldots \delta J_{i_N}(x_N)} \bigg|_{J_i=0}
\end{aligned}
\qquad (4\text{-}29)
$$

On the other hand, it is easy to show (see Exercise 4-9) that

$$Z\{J_i\} = \exp\left\{ -\int \mathcal{L}_{\text{Int}} \left[\frac{\delta}{\delta J_i(x)} \right] dx \right\} Z^0\{J_i\} \qquad (4\text{-}30)$$

Thus, once again, the problem of calculating $G^{(N)}$ in any given order of perturbation theory is reduced to the calculation of many derivatives of Z^0 with respect to $J_i(x)$, at $J_i = 0$. The additional feature here is that in the process of pairing the derivatives, the two derivatives will be forced to have the same index i.

Consider the first order term in $G^{(2)}_{i_1 i_2}$. It will be

$$\sum_{ijkl} F_{ijkl} \frac{\delta}{\delta J_{i_1}(x_1)} \frac{\delta}{\delta J_{i_2}(x_2)} \left(\frac{-\lambda}{4!} \right) \int dx' \frac{\delta}{\delta J_i(x')} \frac{\delta}{\delta J_j(x')} \frac{\delta}{\delta J_k(x')} \frac{\delta}{\delta J_l(x')} Z^0 \bigg|_{J=0}$$

Keeping only the term without a vacuum part, we find:

$$-\frac{\lambda}{2} \sum_k F_{i_1 i_2 kk} \int d1' \, G_{0i_1}(1 - 1') G_{0i_2}(2 - 1') G_{0k}(1' - 1') \qquad (4\text{-}31)$$

where we have assumed that F is symmetric in its indices. This term can again be represented by the graph in Fig. 4-13. We could have drawn it in the following way: each of the external points has an index; apart from the coordinate, the vertex has an index with each of its lines (see Fig. 4-14). In the process of matching lines against lines, or against external points, the two indices are set equal. The combinatorial factor is identical to the one obtained in the theory with a single field, since it just counts the number of ways a contraction of a certain type can be made.

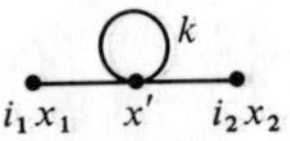

FIGURE 4-13

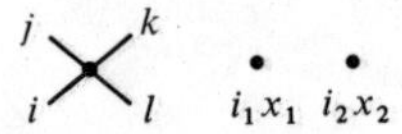

FIGURE 4-14
Elements for the construction of $G^{(2)}$.

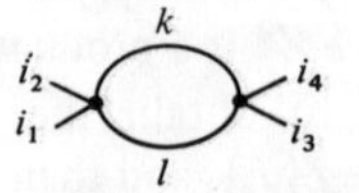

FIGURE 4-15
A second order graph of $G^{(4)}$.

If we calculate the second order term in $G^{(4)}_{i_1 \ldots i_4}(x_1, \ldots, x_4)$, one type of contraction will have the form shown in Fig. 4-15. As far as the tensorial structure is concerned we will have

$$\sum_{k,l} F_{i_1 i_2 kl} F_{kl i_3 i_4} \qquad (4\text{-}32)$$

The integral is, or course,

$$\frac{1}{2!} \left(\frac{\lambda}{4!} \right)^2 \int d1' \, d2' \, G_{0i_1}(1 - 1') G_{0i_2}(2 - 1') G_{0k}(1' - 2') G_{0l}(1' - 2')$$

$$G_{0i_3}(2' - 3) G_{0i_4}(2' - 4) \qquad (4\text{-}33)$$

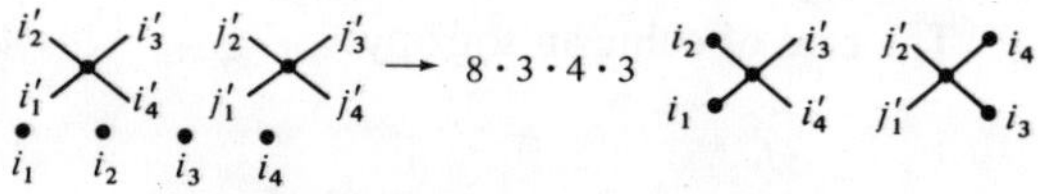

FIGURE 4-16
The construction of the graph Fig. 4-15.

Finally, we have to count the number of ways in which the pairing (Fig. 4-15) can be affected. The process is represented in Fig. 4-16. The symmetry factor is 8 x 3 x 4 x 3 x 2. Hence the numerical factor in front of the integral is

$$\frac{\lambda^2}{2} F_{i_1 i_2 kl} F_{kli_3 i_4} \qquad (4\text{-}34)$$

Two very popular cases are:

1. The $O(M)$ symmetric case. Since the only quadratic $O(M)$ invariant is ϕ^2, all bare masses are equal $-\mu_i^2 = \mu^2$, and the interaction will be of the form:

$$\mathscr{L}_{\text{Int}} = \frac{\lambda}{4!} \left(\sum_i \phi_i^2 \right)^2 \qquad (4\text{-}35)$$

In that case all $G_{0i} = G_0$, and the tensor F has the form:

$$S_{ijkl} = \tfrac{1}{3}(\delta_{ij}\delta_{kl} + \delta_{ik}\delta_{jl} + \delta_{il}\delta_{jk}) \qquad (4\text{-}36)$$

Inserting (4-36) in (4-31) the result is:

$$\sum_k S_{i_1 i_2 kk} = \frac{M+2}{3} \delta_{i_1 i_2} \qquad (4\text{-}37)$$

which gives the dependence on M, as well as the fact that the two-point function is diagonal in the field indices. And Eq. (4-32) now reads:

$$\sum_{kl} S_{i_1 i_2 kl} S_{kli_3 i_4} = \frac{1}{9}\left[(M+4)\delta_{i_1 i_2}\delta_{i_3 i_4} + 2\delta_{i_1 i_3}\delta_{i_2 i_4} + 2\delta_{i_1 i_4}\delta_{i_2 i_3} \right]. \qquad (4\text{-}38)$$

which, when the two additional permutations are added, gives:

$$\frac{M+8}{3} S_{i_1 i_2 i_3 i_4} \qquad (4\text{-}39)$$

provided, of course, that the variables x_i are chosen such that $G^{(4)}$ is symmetric under their interchange.

In fact, for an interaction tensor of the type (4-36) one can show that the terms in the two-point function are proportional to $\delta_{i_1 i_2}$, at all orders in perturbation theory, and that the terms in the four point function at a symmetric momentum point are all proportional to S_{ijkl}. We leave the demonstration to Exercises 4-10 to 4-12.

2. The case of cubic anisotropy:

$$\mathscr{L}_{\text{Int}} = \frac{\lambda}{4!} \sum_i \phi_i^4 \qquad (4\text{-}40)$$

and $\mu_i^2 = \mu^2$. In this case tensor F has the form:

$$F_{ijkl} = \delta_{ij}\delta_{ik}\delta_{il} \qquad (4\text{-}41)$$

which is symmetric under the interchange of any two indices. Computing the expressions corresponding to (4-31) and (4-33) (see Figs. 4-13 and 4-15, respectively), one finds

$$\text{Fig. (4.13)} \quad -\frac{\lambda}{2} \sum_k F_{i_1 i_2 k k} \int d1' G_0(1-1')G_0(1'-2)G_0(1'-1')$$

$$= -\frac{\lambda}{2} \delta_{i_1 i_2} \times \text{integral} \qquad (4\text{-}42)$$

$$\text{Fig. (4.15)} \quad \frac{\lambda^2}{2}(F_{i_1 i_2 kl}F_{kli_3 i_4} + 2 \text{ permutations}) \times \text{integral}$$

$$= \frac{3}{2}\lambda^2 F_{i_1 i_2 i_3 i_4} \times \text{integral} \qquad (4\text{-}43)$$

Again the two point function is diagonal and the four point function at the symmetric point is proportional to F_{ijkl}. And, as in the $0(M)$ symmetric case, these statements can be generalized to all orders.

The difference between the two cases is that the $0(M)$ symmetry implies a diagonal free part in $\mathscr{L}_0$. The cubic symmetry allows for a term of the form $\Sigma_{ij}\phi_i\phi_j$, which can lead to additional terms in the expansion of $G^{(2)}$ and $G^{(4)}$. Both types of interactions may be present in the same single model (see, e.g., Sec. 10-8).

To summarize we note that the rules (i) and (ii) of the previous section have to be slightly modified. Modifications to Rule (i):

1.   The external points have to be marked by an index $i_1, \ldots, i_N$.
2.   The lines emanating from each vertex have to be marked by indices $j_1, \ldots, j_r$ for a vertex of type r.
3.   Indices of lines which have been connected should be identified.

Modifications to Rule (ii):

1.   For every internal point associate a tensor $F_{j_1 \cdots j_r}$.
2.   For every internal line with index i associate a term G_{0i}.
3.   Sum over all internal indices.

4-5-2   Comments on Fields with Higher Spin

Below we will make but a few comments about spinors, vector fields, etc. An extensive discussion of the diagrammatic rules for these fields can be found in "Diagrammar".

Spin $\frac{1}{2}$ fermions   The free Lagrangian is:

$$\mathscr{L}_0 = -\overline{\psi}(\gamma^\mu \partial_\mu + \mu_0)\psi \qquad (4\text{-}44)$$

Hence the free Green function is:

$$G_0(x) = \int \frac{dk}{(2\pi)^d} \frac{-i\gamma_\mu k^\mu + \mu_0}{k^2 + \mu_0^2 - i\epsilon} \exp(ikx) \qquad (4\text{-}45)$$

which is, of course, a matrix.

The interesting point to notice, as far as our discussion will be concerned, is that for large space-like momenta ($k^2 = \Sigma k_i^2$) the Fourier transform of $G_0(x)$ decreases as $|k|^{-1}$. This should be compared with the fact that for the spin-0 bosons it decreased as $|k|^{-2}$.

A massive vector field   The free Lagrangian is

$$\mathscr{L}_0 = -\left[\frac{1}{4}(\partial_\mu A_\nu - \partial_\nu A_\mu)(\partial^\mu A^\nu - \partial^\nu A^\mu) + \frac{\mu_0^2}{2} A_\mu A^\mu \right]$$

$$= -\frac{1}{2} A^\mu [(\partial^2 + \mu_0^2)g_{\mu\nu} - \partial_\mu \partial_\nu] A^\nu + \text{divergence} \qquad (4\text{-}46)$$

From this expression the free Green function can be derived as the inverse matrix to the one in square brackets. $g_{\mu\nu}$ is the metric tensor given by ($\mu, \nu = 0, 1, 2, 3$):

$$g_{\mu\nu} = \begin{pmatrix} -1 & & & \\ & 1 & & 0 \\ & & 1 & \\ 0 & & & 1 \end{pmatrix} \qquad (4\text{-}47)$$

One finds

$$G_0^{\mu\nu}(x) = \int \frac{dk}{(2\pi)^d} \exp(ikx) \left(g^{\mu\nu} - \frac{k^\mu k^\nu}{\mu_0^2} \right) \Big/ (k^2 + \mu_0^2 - i\epsilon) \qquad (4\text{-}48)$$

In this case the free propagator does not decrease at all as $k \to \infty$ in a space-like direction.

The limit of a vector field with zero mass is not obtained from (4-48) in a simple way. But once gauge invariance is taken into account, it can be shown that the free propagator will decrease again as $|k|^{-2}$.[6]

4-6 DIAGRAMMATIC EXPANSION IN MOMENTUM SPACE

As was mentioned earlier, the Lagrangian is invariant under spatial translations and thus all expressions simplify when Fourier transformed. This statement is, of course, false when a spatially varying external field is present in $\mathscr{L}$. The translational invariance manifests itself in the Green function by the fact that $G^{(N)}$ depends on $N-1$ coordinate differences, rather than on all N coordinates. This can be checked explicitly in the examples of Sec. 4-4 in which $G^{(2)}$ and $G^{(4)}$ were evaluated to second order. In the present section we will discuss a perturbation expansion directly in momentum space, where the form of the free Green functions is simple, and translational invariance is reflected in momentum conservation. We will limit ourselves to the scalar field.

In Sec. 2-4 the free generating functional Z^0 was discussed in the Euclidean version of the theory. There it was seen that

$$Z^0\{J\} = \int \mathscr{D}\phi \exp\left\{-\sum_k \left[\frac{1}{2}\phi(k)(k^2+\mu^2)\phi(-k) - J(k)\phi(-k)\right]\right\} \qquad (4\text{-}49)$$

where $\phi(k)$ is related to $\phi(x)$ via

$$\phi(x) = \frac{1}{\sqrt{V}}\sum_k \exp(-ikx)\phi(k) \qquad (4\text{-}50)$$

and

$$J(x) = \frac{1}{\sqrt{V}}\sum_k \exp(-ikx)J(k) \qquad (4\text{-}51)$$

But in a similar way we can express every term in the Lagrangian in terms of $\phi(k)$. Since we have discussed mainly polynomials, we only have to study the expression for

$$\mathscr{L}_r = \int \phi^r(x)\, dx$$

If Eq. (4-50) is inserted for $\phi(x)$ one obtains

$$\mathscr{L}_r\{\phi\} = V^{-r/2} \sum_{k_1\ldots k_r} \phi(k_1)\ldots\phi(k_r) \int dx \exp\left(-i\sum_i k_i\right)x$$

$$= V^{-r/2+1} \sum_{k_1\ldots k_r} \delta^K(\Sigma k_i)\phi(k_1)\ldots\phi(k_r) \qquad (4\text{-}52)$$

where we have used the fact that as long as the volume V is finite

$$\int \exp(ikx)\, dx = V\delta^K(k) \qquad (4\text{-}53)$$

and, since the k's are discrete, the δ^K is a Kronecker function. As the volume tends to infinity the k's become continuous, and

$$V\delta^K(\mathbf{k}) \to (2\pi)^d \delta(\mathbf{k}) \qquad (4\text{-}54)$$

where δ is Dirac's δ-function. In that limit sums over $\mathbf{k}$ become integrals according to:

$$\sum_{\mathbf{k}} f(\mathbf{k}) \to \frac{V}{(2\pi)^d} \int d\mathbf{k} f(\mathbf{k}) \qquad (4\text{-}55)$$

The interaction Lagrangian becomes:

$$\int \mathscr{L}_I(\phi)\, dx = \sum_r \frac{\lambda_r}{r!} V^{-r/2+1} \sum_{\mathbf{k}_1 \dots \mathbf{k}_r} \phi(\mathbf{k}_1) \dots \phi(\mathbf{k}_r) \delta\left(\sum_1^r \mathbf{k}_i\right) \qquad (4\text{-}56)$$

With (4-56) we arrive at a situation which is very similar to the one described in Sec. 4-5, in which we had a field with many components. Now the k_i serves as a label of the field and we have a tensor of coefficients

$$F(\mathbf{k}_1, \dots, \mathbf{k}_r) = V^{-r/2+1} \delta(\Sigma \mathbf{k}_i) \qquad (4\text{-}57)$$

The Green functions can be expressed in terms of corresponding averages in momentum space, namely, using (4-50) we can write

$$G^{(N)}(x_1, \dots, x_N) = V^{-N/2} \sum_{k_1 \dots k_N} \exp[-i(k_1 x_1 + \dots + k_N x_N)] G^{(N)}(k_1, \dots, k_N)$$
$$(4\text{-}58)$$

where

$$G^{(N)}(k_1, \dots, k_N) = \langle \phi(k_1) \dots \phi(k_N) \rangle \qquad (4\text{-}59)$$

The average in the last equation is the usual one given by:

$$\langle \phi(k_1) \dots \phi(k_N) \rangle = \mathscr{N}^{-1} \int \mathscr{D}\phi \, \phi(k_1) \dots \phi(k_N) \exp\left[-\int \mathscr{L}(\phi)\, dx\right] \qquad (4\text{-}60)$$

which yields immediately:

$$G^{(N)}(k_1, \dots, k_N) = V^{N/2} \left. \frac{\delta^N Z\{J\}}{\delta J(-k_1) \dots \delta J(-k_N)} \right|_{J=0} \qquad (4\text{-}61)$$

Comment The volume factors which appear everywhere are a consequence of our definitions (4-50) and (4-51). This notation is close to the one commonly used in the solid state literature, but it can be avoided by defining Fourier transforms directly in terms of integrals. Here we will proceed using the discrete representation, but the factors of the volume will be omitted. They can be reconstituted by dimensional analysis.

An important property of $G^{(N)}(k_i)$, which corresponds to translational invariance is revealed by shifting all x_i to $x_i + a$. Using (4-58), one finds that

$$G^{(N)}(x_i) \rightarrow \sum_{k_1 \ldots k_N} \exp(-ia\Sigma k_i)\exp(-i\Sigma k_i x_i)G^{(N)}(k_i)$$

Thus, if $G^{(N)}(x_i)$ is not to be changed by the translation $\mathbf{a}$, we must have†:

$$G^{(N)}(k_i) = \bar{G}^{(N)}(k_i)\delta(\Sigma k_i) \qquad (4\text{-}62)$$

The last step which is needed in order to develop the perturbation expansion is the analog of (4.1), which is quite easily established. It has the form:

$$Z\{J\} = \mathcal{N}^{-1} \exp\left\{-\sum_r \frac{\lambda_r}{r!} \sum_{k_1 \ldots k_r} \delta(\Sigma k_i) \frac{\delta}{\delta J(-k_1)} \cdots \frac{\delta}{\delta J(-k_r)}\right\}$$

$$\times \exp\left\{\frac{1}{2} \sum_k J(k)G_0(k)J(-k)\right\} \qquad (4\text{-}63)$$

in which

$$G_0(k) = (k^2 + \mu^2)^{-1} \qquad (4\text{-}64)$$

The k_i's appearing in $G^{(N)}$ are called the external momenta. The J's associated with them will have to be paired with other derivatives connected to external points or to ones appearing in $\mathcal{L}_{\text{Int}}$. Again, only completely paired products will survive in the expansion of (4-61) in powers of the λ_r's. The pairings have to match a k with a $-k$ because of the special form of Z^0 which is diagonal in k-space. $\mathcal{N}$ will cancel all terms which have vacuum parts.

Let us consider the calculation of the second order term in the expansion of $G^{(4)}(k_1, \ldots, k_4)$, when $\mathcal{L}_{\text{Int}} = (\lambda/4!)\phi^4$

$$G_2^{(4)}(k_1 \ldots k_4) = \frac{1}{2!} \frac{\delta}{\delta J(-k_1)} \cdots \frac{\delta}{\delta J(-k_4)} \left[\frac{\lambda}{4!} \sum_{q_1 \ldots q_4} \delta(\Sigma q_i) \frac{\delta}{\delta J(-q_1)} \cdots \frac{\delta}{\delta J(-q_4)}\right]$$

$$\times \left[\frac{\lambda}{4!} \sum_{p_1 \ldots p_4} \delta(\Sigma p_i) \frac{\delta}{\delta J(-p_1)} \cdots \frac{\delta}{\delta J(-p_4)}\right]$$

$$\times \exp\left\{\frac{1}{2} \sum_k J(k)G_0(k)J(-k)\right\}\bigg|_{J=0} \qquad \text{(omit vacuum graphs)} \qquad (4\text{-}65)$$

We will select the special term in which two of the external derivatives pair with two of one vertex, and the other two pair with the other vertex. The two remaining derivatives in each vertex pair between the vertices. Schematically, the term we are selecting corresponds to the graph in Fig. 4-15.

There are three different ways of choosing which pairs of external derivatives will go together. We choose 1 and 2 to contract with the same vertex. The other choices correspond to permutations of the external indices.

†The special notation for vector momenta will be omitted, unless ambiguities will arise.

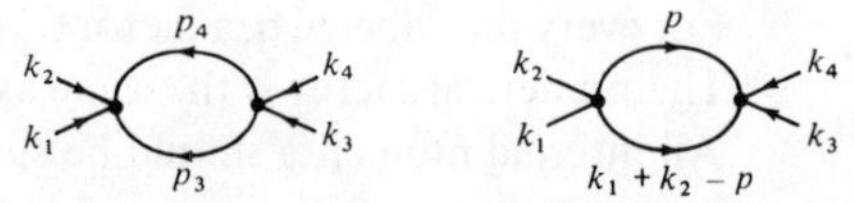

FIGURE 4-17
Graphs of $\Gamma^{(4)}$ in momentum space.   (a)   (b)

The counting proceeds just like in Sec. 4-2, namely, k_1, can choose among *eight* factors to its right to pair with. Leaving *three* choices for k_2, *four* for k_3 and *three* for k_4. Finally, the two leftovers in each vertex can join in *two* different ways. Altogether there is a numerical factor of $\frac{1}{2}$.

After we introduce the contractions $q_1 = -k_1$, $q_2 = -k_2$, $p_1 = -k_3$, $p_2 = -k_4$ and $q_3 = -p_3, q_4 = -p_4$, the expression reduces to:

$$\frac{\lambda^2}{2} G_0(k_1)G_0(k_2)G_0(k_3)G_0(k_4)$$

$$\sum_{p_3 p_4} \delta(k_1 + k_2 + p_3 + p_4)\delta(-k_3 - k_4 + p_3 + p_4)G_0(p_3)G_0(p_4) \qquad (4\text{-}66)$$

and performing the sum over p_4 one finds:

$$\frac{\lambda^2}{2} G_0(k_1) \ldots G_0(k_4) \sum_p G_0(p)G_0(k_1 + k_2 - p)\delta(\Sigma k_i) \qquad (4\text{-}67)$$

In addition there are the two permutations in which $k_1 + k_2$ is replaced by $k_1 + k_3$, or by $k_1 + k_4$.

One can now draw a graph corresponding to (4-66) or to (4-67). In the first case we would draw Fig. 4-17a and interpret it as a product of $G_0(k)$ for any line labeled by k and $(-\lambda/4!)\delta(\Sigma k_i)$ for every vertex which is reached by k_i. All internal momenta are to be summed (or integrated) over. The arrows indicate our choice of momentum flows. They, thus, prescribe the momentum combinations in the δ-functions in (4-66). In the second case we can draw the graph Fig. 4.17b. There is a $G_0(k)$ for every line, as before. But, there are no δ-functions apart from the overall one. The lines are marked by arrows, which indicate whether the momentum carried by the line goes into the vertex or leaves it. Internal momenta are eliminated by requiring that the total momentum leaving (or entering) each vertex, vanish.

The general rules can now be stated:

Rule (iii)   construction of graphs   A general graph will consist of N external points from each of which emanates one line marked $k_i(i = 1, \ldots, N)$ and of n_r vertices of type r, represented by points from which emanate r lines marked $q_1^{(i)} \ldots q_r^{(i)}$ (i runs over all the interaction vertices). All lines have to be connected by pairs, the indices of a paired couple of lines should be set equal. No graphs with vacuum parts need be considered.

Rule (iv)   evaluation of a graph   For every internal point of type r, a factor, $-(\lambda_r/r!)\delta(\Sigma q_i)$, where q_i are the momenta of the lines starting at the point.

For every line labeled q, a factor $G_0(q)$.
The numerical factor is the same as in Sec. 4-4.
All internal momenta should be summed over.

One can now sum over as many internal momenta as there are vertices, since each vertex has a δ function. But, since one δ function, the overall momentum conserving one, remains, it means that if there are n vertices, only $n - 1$ internal sums can be eliminated.

4-7   PERTURBATION EXPANSION OF GREEN FUNCTIONS WITH COMPOSITE OPERATORS[7]

4-7-1   In Coordinate Space

We have mentioned already in Sec. 2-7 that $G^{(N,L)}$, in which there are L operators $\frac{1}{2}\phi^2(y)$, can be obtained in the cutoff theory from $G^{(N+2L)}$ by matching the last $2L$ coordinates in pairs. Thus, to obtain the perturbation expansion of $G^{(N,L)}$ one can proceed to calculate $G^{(N+2L)}$ and then to identify pairs of coordinates.

For example, in Sec. 4-2 $G^{(4)}(x_1, \ldots, x_4)$ was calculated to first order in the ϕ^4-coupling constant. Using the results we can directly write $G^{(2,1)}(x_1, x_2, y)$ by setting $x_3 = x_4 = y$ in Eqs. (4-18) through (4-21), and by multiplying the result by $\frac{1}{2}$. It reads:

$$G^{(2,1)}(x_1, x_2, y) = \frac{1}{2} G_0(x_1 - x_2) G_0(y - y) + G_0(x_1 - y) G_0(x_2 - y)$$

$$- \frac{\lambda}{2} \int dx' G_0(x_1 - x') G_0(x_2 - x') [G_0(y - x')]^2$$

$$- \frac{\lambda}{4} \int dx' G_0(x_1 - x') G_0(x' - x') G_0(x' - x_2) G_0(y - y)$$

$$- \frac{\lambda}{2} \int dx' G_0(x_1 - x') G_0(x' - x') G_0(x' - y) G_0(y - x_2)$$

$$- \frac{\lambda}{2} \int dx' G_0(x_2 - x') G_0(x' - x') G_0(x' - y) G_0(x_1 - y)$$

$$- \frac{\lambda}{4} \int dx' [G_0(y - x')]^2 G_0(x' - x') G_0(x_1 - x_2)$$

$$- \frac{\lambda}{16} \int dx' [G_0(x' - x')]^2 G_0(x_1 - x_2) G_0(y - y)$$

$$- \frac{\lambda}{8} \int dx' [G_0(x' - x')]^2 G_0(x_1 - y) G_0(x_2 - y) \qquad (4\text{-}68)$$

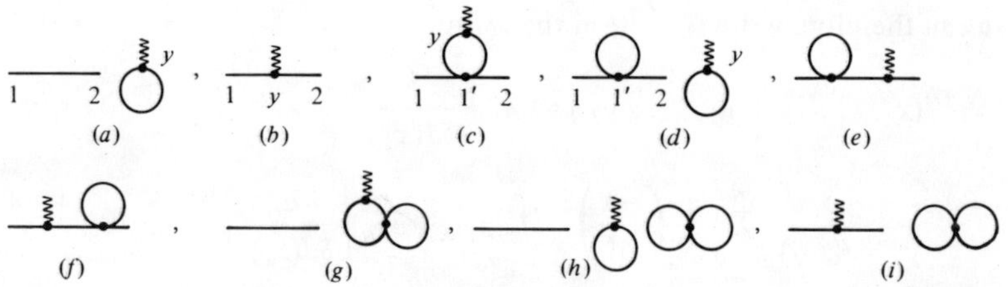

FIGURE 4-18
Diagrams of $G^{(2,1)}$ to first order in the coupling constant.

The various permutations of the variables have been made explicit, since some of them become identical after x_3 and x_4 are made equal to y.

The graphs corresponding to the 9 terms in Eq. (4-68) are drawn in Fig. 4-18 in the same order. In drawing these diagrams we have used a new convention in which the coordinate into which the two external legs have been collapsed is denoted by a wiggly line to differentiate it from an external leg. In fact, the point y plays exactly the role of an interaction vertex — having two legs in the particular example — except for the fact that it is not integrated over. The choice of the factor $1/2!$ in the definition of the composite operator ϕ^2 insures that the symmetry factor of a graph can be deduced by considering the point y as a vertex, and then determining the symmetry operations which map the graph on itself. Thus, an inspection of the graphs in Fig. 4-17 would have immediately produced the coefficients in Eq. (4-68).

But this is a general feature. If the ϕ^2 insertions are generated by a term

$$\frac{1}{2!} t(x)\phi^2(x)$$

we can include this part of $\mathscr{L}$ in the interaction Lagrangian. Then $Z\{J, t\}$, which will generalize Eq. (4-5), will read:

$$Z\{J, t\} = \mathscr{N}^{-1} \sum_{n=0}^{\infty} \sum_{l=0}^{\infty} \frac{1}{n!l!} \left(\frac{-\lambda}{4!}\right)^n \int dx_1 \ldots dx_n \left(\frac{1}{2!}\right)^l \int dy_1 \ldots dy_l$$

$$t(y_1)\ldots t(y_l) \left[\frac{\delta}{\delta J(x_1)}\right]^4 \cdots \left[\frac{\delta}{\delta J(x_n)}\right]^4 \left[\frac{\delta}{\delta J(y_1)}\right]^2 \cdots \left[\frac{\delta}{\delta J(y_l)}\right]^2 Z^0\{J\}$$

$$(4\text{-}69)$$

Using Eq. (2-90) for $G^{(N,L)}$ one finds that the L derivatives with respect to $t(y_i)$ at $t = 0$ will simply choose one term out of the sum over l — the term with $l = L$ — and they will suppress the integrals over y. $\mathscr{N}$ is independent of J or t and will not be affected by the derivatives.

We can therefore write $G^{(N,L)}$ in the form:

$$G^{(N,L)}(x_1, \ldots, x_N, y_1, \ldots, y_L) = \mathcal{N}^{-1} \frac{\delta}{\delta J(x_1)}$$

$$\cdots \frac{\delta}{\delta J(x_N)} \sum_{n=0}^{\infty} \frac{1}{n!} \left(\frac{-\lambda}{4!} \right)^n \int dz_1 \ldots dz_n \left[\frac{\delta}{\delta J(z_1)} \right]^4$$

$$\cdots \left[\frac{\delta}{\delta J(z_n)} \right]^4 \left(\frac{1}{2} \right)^L \left[\frac{\delta}{\delta J(y_1)} \right]^2 \cdots \left[\frac{\delta}{\delta J(y_L)} \right]^2 Z^0\{J\} \bigg|_{J=0} \qquad (4\text{-}70)$$

Thus the nth order terms in the perturbation expansion of $G^{(N,L)}$ are calculated like the terms of $G^{(N)}$ which are of nth order in the usual interaction vertices, and of *first* order in L vertices with two legs, which are *different*, and which are not integrated over. In other words, there is no $(L!)^{-1}$ multiplying the expression corresponding to the graph.

Example The second order graph in $G^{(2,2)}(x_1, x_2, y_1, y_2)$ shown in Fig. 4-19

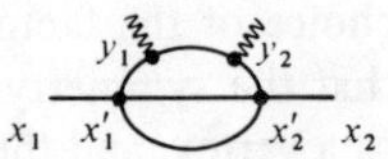

FIGURE 4-19
Second order graph in $G^{(2,2)}(x_1, x_2, y_1, y_2)$.

is calculated by multiplying $(-\lambda/4!)$ for each ϕ^4 vertex, by $1/2$ for each ϕ^2 insertion, by $1/2!$ because it is second order in λ (and *no* $1/2!$ for the two ϕ^2's). Then counting the number of ways in which this particular graph can be constructed one finds a symmetry factor of $1/2$, which could have been guessed by noting that the graph is symmetric under the interchange of its bottom two lines.

The final expression is

$$\frac{\lambda^2}{2} \int dx_1' \, dx_2' G_0(x_1 - x_1') G_0^2(x_1' - x_2') G_0(x_1' - y_1)$$
$$G_0(y_1 - y_2) G_0(y_2 - x_2') G_0(x_2' - x_2)$$

$$(4\text{-}71)$$

The elimination of vacuum graphs proceeds just as before since $\mathcal{N}$ is unchanged. This implies that out of the graphs in Fig. 4-18 only (h) and (i) are cancelled.

4-7-2 In Momentum Space
The effect of identifying two coordinates in $G^{(N+2)}$ to produce $G^{(N,1)}$ is seen more clearly in the momentum representation. The Fourier transform of $G^{(N,1)}$

is defined by

$$G^{(N,1)}(x_1, \ldots, x_N, y) = \sum_{k_i, p} G^{(N,1)}(k_1, \ldots, k_N, p) \exp[-i(k_i x_i + py)]$$
(4-72)

By analogy with (4-58) and (4-59)

$$G^{(N,1)}(k_1, \ldots, k_N, p) = \frac{1}{2} \langle \phi(k_1) \ldots \phi(k_N) \phi^2(p) \rangle \qquad (4\text{-}73)$$

where $\phi^2(p)$ is defined by

$$[\phi(x)]^2 = \sum_p \exp(-ipx)\phi^2(p) \qquad (4\text{-}74)$$

In (4-74) we can insert on the left-hand side the Fourier transform of $\phi(x)$, and then it follows that[†]:

$$\phi^2(\mathbf{p}) = \sum_k \phi(\mathbf{k})\phi(\mathbf{p} - \mathbf{k}) \qquad (4\text{-}75)$$

Thus,

$$G^{(N,1)}(k_1, \ldots, k_N, p) = \frac{1}{2} \sum_k G^{(N+2)}(k_1, \ldots, k_N, k, p - k) \qquad (4\text{-}76)$$

The composite operator $\phi^2(x)$ implies a summation over the momenta of two of the $N + 2$ momentum variables in $G^{(N+2)}$, with their sum kept fixed. This relation provides one way of computing the perturbation theory for $G^{(N,1)}$ in momentum space out of that of $G^{(N+2)}$.

Another way is to follow the procedure at the end of Sec. 4-7-1, namely, to consider the ϕ^2's as interaction vertices. Then $G^{(N,L)}(k_1, \ldots, k_N, p_1, \ldots, p_L)$ at nth order in the usual interactions is first order in L ϕ^2-interactions, i.e., no $(L!)^{-1}$. Furthermore, while all interactions have the form

$$\frac{\lambda_r}{r!} \sum_{k_i} \phi(k_1) \ldots \phi(k_r) \delta(\Sigma k_i)$$

the ϕ^2 one has the form

$$\phi^2(p) = \frac{1}{2!} \sum_{k_1, k_2} \phi(k_1)\phi(k_2)\delta(k_1 + k_2 - p) \qquad (4\text{-}77)$$

Thus the rules can be taken over from Sec. 4-6, namely, for the calculation of a graph of $G^{(N,L)}$ apply the rules for the calculation of $G^{(N)}$ at the same order in the usual interactions and first order in L interactions of the type (4-77). At the ϕ^2 interaction vertices there will be a δ-function which makes the sum of the two incoming momenta equal p_i.

[†]For factors of the volume consult comment on page 69.

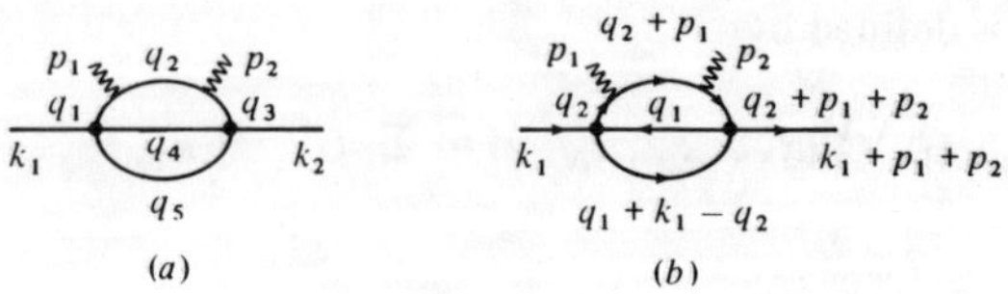

FIGURE 4-20
Second order graphs of $G^{(2,2)}(k_1, k_2, p_1, p_2)$.

Example The graph shown in Fig. 4-19 looks in momentum space as in Fig. 4-20. Graph 4-20(a) has five internal momenta. In 4-20(b) the momentum δ-functions have been taken into account. Clearly $k_1 - k_2 + p_1 + p_2 = 0$ as a result of overall momentum conservation.

The expression corresponding to graph 4-20(b) is

$$\frac{\lambda^2}{2} \frac{1}{k_1^2 + \mu^2} \frac{1}{k_2^2 + \mu^2}$$

$$\times \int \frac{1}{(q_1^2 + \mu^2)(q_2^2 + \mu^2)[(k_1 + q_1 - q_2)^2 + \mu^2][(q_2 + p_1)^2 + \mu^2][(q_2 + p_1 + p_2)^2 + \mu^2]}$$

$$\times (2\pi)^d \delta(k_1 - k_2 + p_1 + p_2) \frac{dq_1}{(2\pi)^d} \frac{dq_2}{(2\pi)^d} \qquad (4\text{-}78)$$

4-7-3 Insertion at Zero Momentum

What corresponds to the integration over y_1 and y_2 is the limit $p_1, p_2 \to 0$. But this will produce out of (4-78) an expression similar to that of the second order graph of $G^{(2)}$, Fig. 4-21, which is:

$$\frac{\lambda^2}{6} \frac{1}{k_1^2 + \mu^2} \frac{1}{k_2^2 + \mu^2} \int \frac{1}{(q_1^2 + \mu^2)(q_2^2 + \mu^2)[(k_1 + q_1 - q_2)^2 + \mu^2]}$$

$$\times (2\pi)^d \delta(k_1 - k_2) \qquad (4\text{-}79)$$

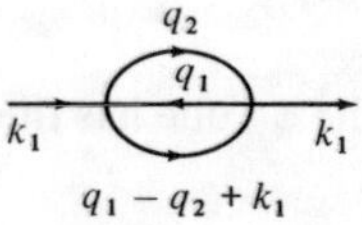

FIGURE 4-21

The difference is only in that $1/2$ replaces $1/6$, and one denominator becomes cubed.

This difference is rather easy to understand. Inserting one integrated ϕ^2-operator in the graph in Fig. 4-21 is equivalent to taking a derivative with respect to $(-\mu^2)$. This produces three terms, in which the internal lines are affected. They are all equal, which explains the change of $1/6$ into $1/2$. Taking a second derivative with respect to $(-\mu^2)$, to produce the graph of Fig. 4-19, one has to differentiate the same internal line that was differentiated before. So there is only one possibility. Except that the denominator now derived is already squared and gives another factor of two and becomes cubed. Finally, instead of (4-78) with $p_1 = p_2 = 0$, we obtain twice this value. This corresponds to the fact that we had another graph of the form in Fig. 4-19 but with p_1 and p_2 interchanged.

EXERCISES

4-1 Calculate $\mathcal{N}$ to second order in λ for a ϕ^4 theory.

4-2 Calculate $\mathcal{N}$ to fourth order in λ if $\mathcal{N}_{Int} = (\lambda/3!)\phi^3$. Altogether there are seven different types of terms.

4-3 Show that the normalization factor in the ϕ^4 theory cancels the vacuum graphs to order λ^2 in $G^{(2)}$.

4-4 Exhibit the cancellation of vacuum graphs to order λ^3 in a ϕ^3 theory, in $G^{(1)}$.

4-5 Calculate $G^{(2)}$ to order λ^2 in a ϕ^3 theory. Show that there are disconnected graphs which do not include vacuum parts.

4-6 Draw the graphs of fourth order in λ for $G^{(2)}$ in a ϕ^3 theory.

4-7 Calculate the symmetry factors, and the overall numerical factors in Fig. 4-22.

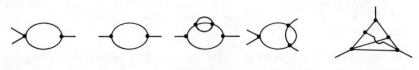

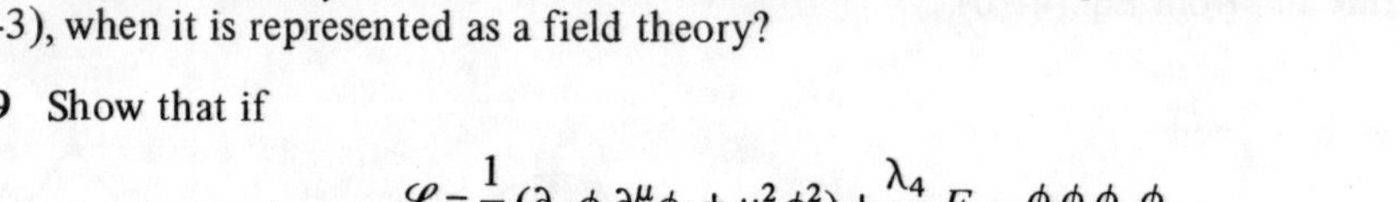

FIGURE 4-22

4-8 What tensor F_{ijkl} is obtained for the classical Heisenberg model, Exercise (2-3), when it is represented as a field theory?

4-9 Show that if

$$\mathcal{L} = \frac{1}{2}(\partial_\mu \phi_i \partial^\mu \phi_i + \mu_i^2 \phi_i^2) + \frac{\lambda_4}{4!} F_{ijkl}\phi_i\phi_j\phi_k\phi_l$$

then the generating functional, defined by

$$Z\{J_i\} = \mathcal{N}^{-1}\int \mathcal{D}\,\phi \exp\left\{-\int[\,\mathcal{L}(\phi) - J_i\phi_i]\,dx\right\}$$

is given by:

$$Z\{J_i\} = \mathcal{N} \exp\left\{-\int \mathcal{L}_{\text{Int}}\left[\frac{\delta}{\delta J_i}\right] dx\right\} Z^0\{J_i\}$$

4-10 Write down the expressions corresponding to the graphs shown in Fig. 4-23.

FIGURE 4-23

4-11 Write down the expression for the graphs in Fig. 4-24 with a symmetric distribution of external momenta, in an $O(M)$-symmetric theory. Try to generalize the tensorial structure to all orders.[8]

FIGURE 4-24

4-12 Show that the general term in the two-point function is proportional to $M + 2$.[9]

4-13 Obtain the remaining non-vacuum second order terms in $G^{(4)}(k_1, \ldots, k_4)$ for a ϕ^4 interaction.

4-14 Draw the diagrams of $G^{(4)}$ in second order in λ. Obtain $G^{(2,1)}(x_1, x_2, y)$ to this order.

4-15 Show that a computation of $G^{(2)}$ to second order in λ and to first order in $\frac{1}{2}\phi^2(y)$, leads to the result of Exercise 4-14.

4-16 Calculate the expressions corresponding to the graphs in Fig. 4-25 by the rule and from Eq. (4-70).

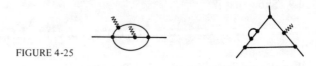

FIGURE 4-25

4-17 Prove that if Eq. (4-71) is integrated over y_1 and y_2 it is exactly equal to one of the terms appearing in the second derivative of $G^{(2)}$, with respect to μ^2.

FIGURE 4-26

4-18 Calculate the expressions corresponding to the graphs shown in Fig. 4-26 in momentum space. Compare with μ^2 derivatives of the corresponding Green functions.

FIGURE 4-27

4-19 Calculate the symmetry factors of the graphs shown in Fig. 4-27 in an $0(M)$-symmetric theory.

REFERENCES

1. K. G. Wilson, *Physical Review Letters*, **28**, 548 (1972); E. Brézin, D. J. Wallace and K. G. Wilson, *Physical Review Letters*, **29**, 591 (1972).
2. E. Brézin, J. C. Le Guillou and J. Zinn-Justin, *Physical Review*, **D8**, 434 (1973) and **D8**, 2418 (1973). This approach is summarized in BLZ.
3. C. Di Castro, *Lettere al Nuovo Cimento*, **5**, 69 (1972) and C. Di Castro, G. Jona-Lasinio and L. Peliti, *Annals of Physics*, **87**, 327 (1974).
4. B. Schröer, *Physical Review*, **B8**, 4200 (1973), and F. Jegerlehner and B. Schröer, *Acta Physica Austriaca Supplement*, **11**, 389 (1973).
5. 't Hooft, "Diagrammar".
6. See, e.g., E. Brézin, J. Iliopoulos, C. Itzykson and R. Stora, *Theorie des Champs-Gif 73*, Part 2 (Institute National de Physique Nucleaire et de Physique des Particules, 1973).
7. J. Zinn-Justin, "Wilson Theory of Critical Phenomena and Renormalized Theory". Lectures delivered at the Cargése Summer School 1973. K. Symanzik, op. cit. and KS.
8. R. K. P. Zia and D. J. Wallace, *Journal of Physics*, **A8**, 1089 (1975).
9. R. Balian and G. Toulouse, *Physical Review Letters*, **30**, 544 (1973). See also M. E. Fisher, *Physical Review Letters*, **30**, 679 (1973).

5

VERTEX FUNCTIONS AND SYMMETRY BREAKING

5-1 INTRODUCTION

As one starts to consider the perturbation series for any given theory, one notices quickly that there are two features which increase the number of terms very considerably without adding any new intrinsic properties. The first is the appearance of disconnected graphs, like those at the end of Sec. 4-2. Clearly, the properties of a disconnected graph are identical with those of the product of the disjoint parts. Thus one is naturally tempted to look for a way of reconstructing the full Green function given only its connected graphs. This is done in Sec. 5-2.

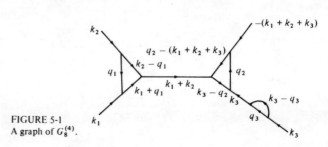

FIGURE 5-1
A graph of $G_8^{(4)}$.

The next feature is sometimes called "one-particle-reducibility." Consider, in a ϕ^3 theory, the eighth order graph of the four point function (see Fig. 5-1). According to the rules of the previous chapter the algebraic expression corresponding to this graph, apart from numerical factors, is:

$$G_0(k_1)G_0(k_2) \left[\int dq_1 G_0(q_1)G_0(k_1+q_1)G_0(k_2-q_1) \right]$$

$$\times\ G_0(k_1+k_2) \left[\int dq_2 G_0(q_2)G_0(k_3-q_2)G_0(q_2-k_1-k_2-k_3) \right]$$

$$\times\ G_0(k_1+k_2+k_3)G_0(k_3) \left[\int dq_3 G_0(q_3)G_0(k_3-q_3) \right] G_0(k_3) \qquad (5\text{-}1)$$

The overall δ function has been divided out. The relevant feature for our present discussion is that parts which are connected by single lines are simply multiplied, apart from some intervening G_0 factors. There are no momentum integrations joining them.

Thus, in order to find the dependence on k_1, k_2 and k_3 of the graph in Fig. 5-1 it would suffice to know $G_0(k)$ and the two functions represented in Fig. 5-2, which are constructed by our usual rules, except that the G_0's which correspond to the crossed lines should be omitted. If the graph in Fig. 5-1 is denoted by $G_8^{(4)}(k_1,k_2,k_3)$ and the two graphs (a) and (b) in Fig. 5-2 by $\Gamma_3^{(3)}(k_1,k_2)$ and $\Gamma_2^{(2)}(k)$, correspondingly, then we can write:

$$G_8(k_1,k_2,k_3) = G_0(k_1)G_0(k_2)[\Gamma_3^{(3)}(k_1,k_2)]G_0(k_1+k_2)[\Gamma_3^{(3)}(k_1+k_2,k_3)]$$

$$\times\ G_0(k_1+k_2+k_3)G_0(k_3)[\Gamma_2^{(2)}(k_3)]G_0(k_3) \qquad (5\text{-}2)$$

In (5-2) square brackets are inserted so that $\Gamma_3^{(3)}$ and $\Gamma_2^{(2)}$ can be defined by comparison with (5-1).

The absence of integrals in (5-2) is due to the fact that there should be no integrals. Every time that a graph can be separated into two graphs by severing a single internal line, the momentum of the severed line is fixed by the momenta of the external lines attached to either of the two parts. This assertion follows simply from the fact that momentum is conserved at every vertex, and so the momentum flowing out along any external line is the sum of the momenta coming in along the other external lines of the same graph. Thus, the absence of

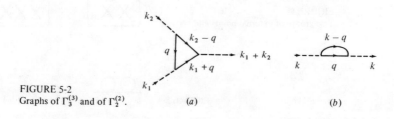

FIGURE 5-2
Graphs of $\Gamma_3^{(3)}$ and of $\Gamma_2^{(2)}$.   (a)   (b)

integrations on variables attached to single lines, which make a graph "one-particle-reducible", is a general feature. It is not true, of course, if the graph is separated in two by cutting more than one line (see Exercise 5-1).

Again, considering only *one-particle-irreducible* $-$ 1PI $-$ graphs diminishes the number of graphs considerably. The question, whether the theory can be systematically reconstructed from the knowledge of the sums of the 1PI graphs of each function is treated in Sec. 5-3. It turns out that not only can the theory be reconstructed, but the formulation of the theory in terms of the 1PI parts, or *vertex functions*, is very elegant and provides the natural tool for the study of broken symmetries in interacting field theories. The vertex functions are also the natural candidates for the study of renormalization questions since they are not encumbered by internal lines which are not integrated over, and thus are irrelevant to the divergences introduced by fluctuations (radiative corrections). But, this will be discussed in later chapters.

5-2   CONNECTED GREEN FUNCTIONS AND THEIR GENERATING FUNCTIONAL

From the rules of the construction of graphs it follows that the N external points can be divided into r groups each of which includes N_i points, and the n interactions can also be grouped into r groups each including n_i interactions. Then, one can make connections inside each group separately. This will give rise to a set of disconnected graphs contributing to the nth order term of $G^{(N)}$.

For example, for the fifth order term of $G^{(6)}$, in a ϕ^4 theory, we can form the two groups of external points and vertices represented in Fig. 5-3. In the first we can make the contractions as shown in Fig. 5-4. In the second there are contractions such as those shown in Fig. 5-5.

All possible products between terms in the two sets, give disconnected graphs of $G^{(6)}$. In addition, there are connected graphs, of course.

The contractions in each group of external points and vertices constitute graphs of $G^{(N_i)}$ of order n_i. Thus, in the example considered above, the graphs in Fig. 5-4 are second order graphs of $G^{(2)}$. While those in Fig. 5-5 are third

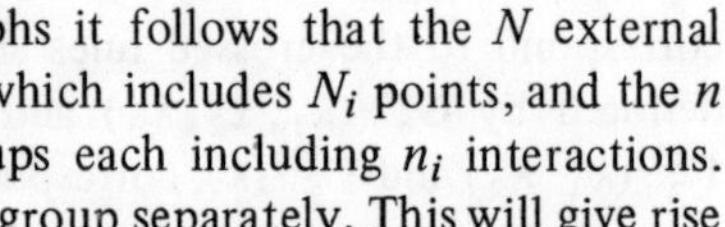

FIGURE 5-3
Two groups of external points and vertices.

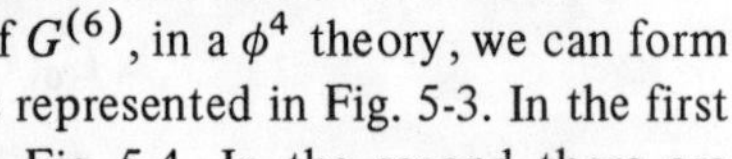

FIGURE 5-4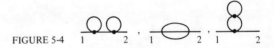

FIGURE 5-5

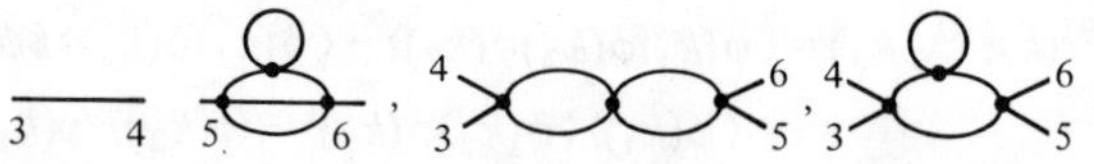

order graphs of $G^{(4)}$. The question is whether, having taken into account all the possible ways of distributing the vertices among the groups of external points, the product of the $G^{(N_i)}$, with the external indices distributed in a specific way, accounts for all the disconnected terms with the same distribution of external labels. It is simply a question of combinatorics. The answer is positive and the proof proceeds along the same lines as the elimination of vacuum graphs. Here it is left as Exercise 5-3.

We know that $Z\{J\}$ generates the Green functions. Namely,

$$G^{(N)}(k_1, \ldots, k_N) = \frac{\delta^N Z\{J\}}{\delta J(-k_1) \ldots \delta J(-k_N)} \bigg|_{J=0}$$

This implies that $Z\{J\}$ can be written as a Taylor series in the J's,

$$Z\{J\} = 1 + \sum_{N=1}^{\infty} \frac{1}{N!} \sum_{k_1 \ldots k_N} G^{(N)}(k_1 \ldots k_N) J(-k_1) \ldots J(-k_N) \qquad (5\text{-}3)$$

Using the results of Exercise 5-4 one concludes that if a functional $F\{J\}$ is defined via:

$$F\{J\} = \sum_{N=1}^{\infty} \frac{1}{N!} \sum_{k_1 \ldots k_N} G_c^{(N)}(k_1 \ldots k_N) J(-k_1) \ldots J(-k_N) \qquad (5\text{-}4)$$

where $G_c^{(N)}$ are the connected parts of the $G^{(N)}$'s, then,

$$Z\{J\} = e^{F\{J\}} \qquad (5\text{-}5)$$

It is furthermore clear that F is the generating functional for the connected Green functions $G_c^{(N)}$. Namely,

$$G_c^{(N)}(k_1, \ldots, k_N) = \frac{\delta^N F\{J\}}{\delta J(-k_1) \ldots \delta J(-k_N)} \bigg|_{J=0} \qquad (5\text{-}6)$$

In the context of statistical mechanics Z is identified as a partition function and F is the free energy, apart from a sign.

Using Eqs. (5-6) and (5-5) we can write

$$G_c^{(1)}(k_1) = \langle \phi(k_1) \rangle = G^{(1)}(k_1) \qquad (5\text{-}7)$$

$$G_c^{(2)}(k_1, k_2) = \langle \phi(k_1)\phi(k_2) \rangle - \langle \phi(k_1) \rangle \langle \phi(k_2) \rangle$$
$$= G^{(2)}(k_1, k_2) - G^{(1)}(k_1)G^{(1)}(k_2) \qquad (5\text{-}8)$$

$$
\begin{aligned}
G_c^{(3)}(k_1, k_2, k_3) &= \langle \phi(k_1)\phi(k_2)\phi(k_3) \rangle - \langle \phi(k_1)\phi(k_2) \rangle \langle \phi(k_3) \rangle \\
&\quad - \langle \phi(k_1) \rangle \langle \phi(k_2)\phi(k_3) \rangle - \langle \phi(k_2) \rangle \langle \phi(k_1)\phi(k_3) \rangle \\
&\quad + 2 \langle \phi(k_1) \rangle \langle \phi(k_2) \rangle \langle \phi(k_3) \rangle \\
&= G^{(3)}(k_1, k_2, k_3) - G^{(1)}(k_1)G^{(2)}(k_2, k_3) - G^{(1)}(k_2)G^{(2)}(k_1, k_3) \\
&\quad - G^{(1)}(k_3)G^{(2)}(k_1, k_2) + 2G^{(1)}(k_1)G^{(1)}(k_2)G^{(1)}(k_3) \qquad (5\text{-}9)
\end{aligned}
$$

The functions on the right-hand side are often called cumulants.

The inversion of (5-7) through (5-9) gives:

$$
G^{(1)}(k_1) = G_c^{(1)}(k_1) \qquad (5\text{-}10)
$$

$$
G^{(2)}(k_1, k_2) = G_c^{(2)}(k_1, k_2) + G_c^{(1)}(k_1)G_c^{(1)}(k_2) \qquad (5\text{-}11)
$$

$$
\begin{aligned}
G^{(3)}(k_1, k_2, k_3) &= G_c^{(3)}(k_1, k_2, k_3) + G_c^{(1)}(k_1)G_c^{(2)}(k_2, k_3) + G_c^{(1)}(k_2)G_c^{(2)}(k_1, k_3) \\
&\quad + G_c^{(1)}(k_3)G_c^{(2)}(k_1, k_2) + G_c^{(1)}(k_1)G_c^{(1)}(k_2)G_c^{(1)}(k_3)
\end{aligned}
$$

$$
(5\text{-}12)
$$

etc.

To summarize:

1. Based on Exercise 5-4 the conclusion is that given the connected parts of the Green functions we can easily reconstruct the full functions.
2. Since the $G_c^{(N)}$'s are cumulants, given either by (5-6), or by (5-7)–(5-9), etc., when two sets of coordinates are separated from each other by a large distance, the connected functions vanish. This follows from the fact that all possible factorizations have been subtracted (see also Exercise 5-5).

One would naturally use $G_c^{(2)}$ for the calculation of the susceptibility. In the disordered (symmetric) state

$$
\langle \phi(x) \rangle = 0
$$

and thus

$$
G^{(2)}(1, 2) = G_c(1, 2) \xrightarrow[|1-2| \to \infty]{} 0 \qquad (5\text{-}13)
$$

On the other hand in the ordered—broken symmetry—state

$$
G^{(2)}(1, 2) \xrightarrow[|1-2| \to \infty]{} \langle \phi(1) \rangle \langle \phi(2) \rangle = \langle \phi \rangle^2 \qquad (5\text{-}14)
$$

If $G^{(2)}(1, 2)$ is now integrated over in order to compute the susceptibility χ, according to Eq. (2-31):

$$
\chi = \int dx\, G^{(2)}(x) \qquad (5\text{-}15)
$$

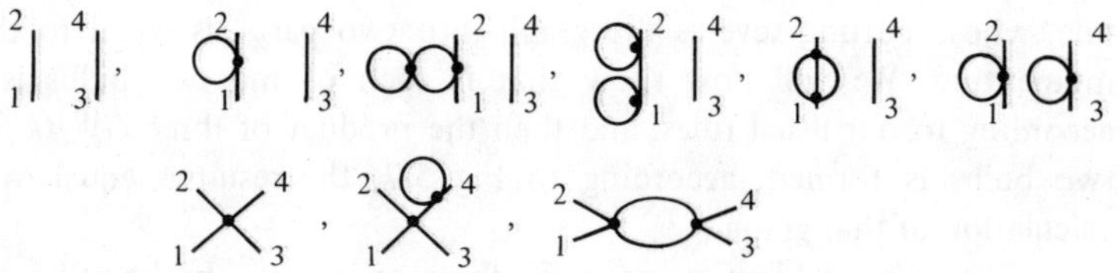

FIGURE 5-6
Connected and disconnected graphs of $G^{(4)}$.

we will obtain a finite, meaningful result in the symmetric state, and infinity below. This does not represent the response to a field, but simply the fact that the symmetry has been broken. It is, of course, $G_c^{(2)}$ which should be integrated in order to obtain the response (cf. Eq. (2-29)).

3.   The number of graphs at every order is reduced. For example, to second order in a ϕ^4 theory, one has for the four-point function the graphs appearing in Fig. 5-6. All the graphs in the first line of Fig. 5-6 are included in $G^{(2)}(1, 2) G^{(2)}(3, 4)$ + permutations, and thus do not appear in $G_c^{(4)}$. Only the last three graphs remain.

5-3 THE MASS OPERATOR

In order to discuss the second problem mentioned in the introduction, namely, that of vertex parts, or one-particle reducibility, it is convenient to start by considering the two-point function. Among the graphs of $G_c^{(2)}$ one would encounter, for example,

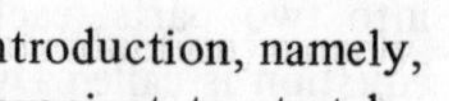

which can be considered in the same manner as the graph in Sec. 5-1. One would find that it can be written as a product of $G^{(0)}(k)$ and of

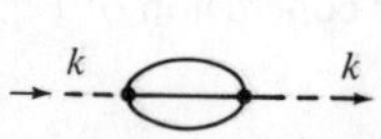

Assume now that we consider a situation with one type of interaction, one monomial in ϕ. Consider the graph given in Fig. 5-7 where the bulbs are some general connected graphs, the bulb number 1 is of order n_1 in the interaction, and number 2 is of order n_2. The order of the total graph is $n_1 + n_2$. The same argument which we used in Sec. 5-1, implies here that the momentum of the

FIGURE 5-7
Self-energy parts.

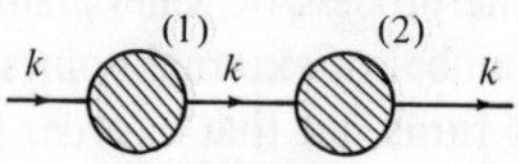

line, whose cutting severes the graph into two parts, is equal to the external momentum. We will now show that if each of the two bulbs is calculated according to our usual rules, and then the product of three $G_c^{(0)}(k)$ and of the two bulbs is formed, according to Fig. 5-7, the result is equal to the direct calculation of that graph.

The only problem is one of combinatorics again. In the full graph we have a factor of $[(n_1 + n_2)!]^{-1}$, while in the bulbs we have a factor $(n_1!)^{-1}$ and $(n_2!)^{-1}$, respectively. The full graph can then be computed by first considering in how many ways can the $n_1 + n_2$ identical vertices be distributed among the two bulbs. The rest of the combinatorics continues inside each bulb, and is taken care of by the calculation of the bulbs themselves. Thus $[(n_1 + n_2)!]^{-1}$ has to be multiplied by $(n_1 + n_2)!/(n_1!n_2!)$, which gives exactly the result of the calculation via the two separate bulbs. The generalization to more general interactions is left as Exercise 5-6.

It now follows that if we denote by $\Sigma(k)$ the sum of all graphs of $G_c^{(2)}(k)$, calculated by the usual rules, which are one-particle irreducible and without the two external legs, then $G_c^{(2)}(k)$ can be written as

$$G_c^{(2)}(k) = G_0(k) + G_0(k)\Sigma(k)G_0(k) + G_0(k)\Sigma(k)G_0(k)\Sigma(k)G_0(k) + \ldots$$

$$= [G_0^{-1}(k) - \Sigma(k)]^{-1} \qquad (5\text{-}16)$$

Irreducibility will be restricted hereafter to the impossibility of cutting the graph into two parts, each containing external legs of the original graph. This last equation is called Dyson's equation, and $\Sigma(k)$ is called the *mass operator*, or the self energy.

Again, to second order in a ϕ^4 interaction only, the graphs in Fig. 5-8 appear in $\Sigma(k)$ (see also Exercises 5-7–5-8).

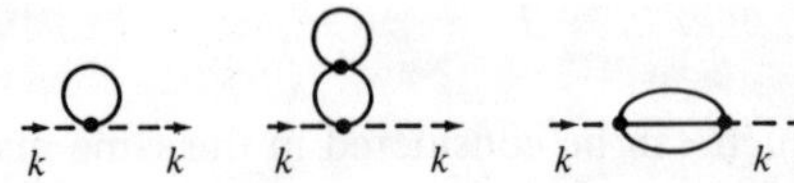

FIGURE 5-8
Graphs of Σ.

Another conclusion of Eq. (5-16) is that

$$[G_c^{(2)}(k)]^{-1} = G_0^{-1}(k) - \Sigma(k) \qquad (5\text{-}17)$$

indicating that the inverse of the two-point connected function contains only 1PI graphs. This is the first instance of a vertex function, which we will now proceeed to generalize.

5-4 THE LEGENDRE TRANSFORM AND VERTEX FUNCTIONS

The process of generalizing the concept of vertex functions to include any given number of external points takes us through a very beautiful formal development. It turns out that in order to obtain the generating functional for the vertex (1PI) functions one needs only perform a Legendre transform of $F\{J\}$ with respect to the expectation value $\langle \phi(k) \rangle$. The development, associated with the names of Schwinger,[1] De Dominicis and Martin,[2] and Jona-Lasinio,[3] then produces extra benefits such as the very useful identities of Ward and Takahashi;[4] the Goldstone theorem, and a systematic way of treating problems with broken symmetry in the presence of interactions.[5]

Basically, the idea is to express the thermodynamic potential $F\{J\}$, which is a functional of the spatially varying external field $J(k)$, in terms of the corresponding magnetization – to use the language of statistical physics. This type of transformation plays a central role in the development of the theory of thermodynamics[6] as well as in classical mechanics.[7]

Since the momentum index and the component label play a very similar role in the theory, when the free part of the Lagrangian is diagonal in both, we can include both in a single index. Thus we will write

$$\langle \phi(i) \rangle \equiv \langle \phi_{\alpha_i}(k_i) \rangle \equiv \bar{\phi}(i) = \frac{\delta F\{J\}}{\delta J\{i\}} \qquad (5\text{-}18)$$

The transform Γ, which is defined via:

$$\Gamma\{\bar{\phi}\} + F\{J\} = \sum_i \bar{\phi}(i) J(i) \qquad (5\text{-}19)$$

is a function of $\bar{\phi}$ after J has been eliminated from (5-19) by the use of (5-18).

The transform is inverted algebraically by noting that

$$\frac{\delta \Gamma\{\bar{\phi}\}}{\delta \bar{\phi}(i)} = -\sum_j \frac{\delta F\{J\}}{\delta J(j)} \frac{\delta J(j)}{\delta \bar{\phi}(i)} + \sum_j \bar{\phi}(j) \frac{\delta J(j)}{\delta \bar{\phi}(i)} + \sum_j J(j) \delta(i,j) = J(i) \qquad (5\text{-}20)$$

This equation replaces (5-18) in transforming Γ into $F\{J\}$ via Eq. (5-19). But it has another interesting property. If a symmetry is spontaneously broken, then

$$\bar{\phi}_i\{J\} = \frac{\delta F\{J\}}{\delta J(i)} \xrightarrow[J \to 0]{} v(i) \neq 0 \qquad (5\text{-}21)$$

In terms of Γ, the condition for a broken symmetry is:

$$\left. \frac{\delta \Gamma}{\delta \bar{\phi}(i)} \right|_{\bar{\phi}(i) = v(i)} = 0 \qquad (5\text{-}22)$$

That is, $\Gamma\{\bar{\phi}\}$ has an extremum at $\bar{\phi}(i) = v(i)$ – sometimes called the classical field.

Let us now differentiate Eq. (5-18) with respect to $\bar{\phi}(j)$. We find

$$\delta(i,j) = \frac{\delta^2 F\{J\}}{\delta J(i) \delta \bar{\phi}(j)} = \sum_k \frac{\delta^2 F\{J\}}{\delta J(i) \delta J(k)} \frac{\delta J(k)}{\delta \bar{\phi}(j)}$$

$\delta J/\delta\bar\phi$ can be obtained by differentiating Eq. (5-20), which gives

$$\sum_k \frac{\delta^2 F}{\delta J(i)\delta J(k)} \frac{\delta^2 \Gamma}{\delta\bar\phi(k)\delta\bar\phi(j)} = \delta(i,j) \qquad (5\text{-}23)$$

As $J \to 0$

$$\frac{\delta^2 F}{\delta J(i)\delta J(k)} \to G_c^{(2)}(i,k) \qquad (5\text{-}24)$$

and Eq. (5-23) implies that

$$\left. \frac{\delta^2 \Gamma\{\bar\phi\}}{\delta\bar\phi(i)\delta\bar\phi(j)} \right|_{J=0} \equiv \Gamma^{(2)}(i,j) \qquad (5\text{-}25)$$

is the inverse, in the matrix sense, of the connected two-point Green function. In other words, it is the vertex of the two-point function, which is 1PI (cf. Eq. (5-17)). It is important to note that Eq. (5-23) holds also when $J \neq 0$.

One can now take another derivative of (5-23) with respect to $J(l)$. Since the right-hand side is independent of J, one finds:

$$\sum_k \frac{\delta^3 F}{\delta J(l)\delta J(i)\delta J(k)} \frac{\delta^2 \Gamma}{\delta\bar\phi(k)\delta\bar\phi(j)} = -\sum_k \frac{\delta^2 F}{\delta J(i)\delta J(k)} \frac{\delta^3 \Gamma}{\delta J(l)\delta\bar\phi(k)\delta\bar\phi(j)} \qquad (5\text{-}26)$$

which holds for any value of J. The right-hand side can be further rewritten as

$$-\frac{\delta^2 F}{\delta J(i)\delta J(k)} \frac{\delta^3 \Gamma}{\delta\bar\phi(m)\delta\bar\phi(k)\delta\bar\phi(j)} \frac{\delta\bar\phi(m)}{\delta J(l)}$$

in which summation over repeated indices is implied. Using (5-18), (5-24) and (5-23), and taking the limit $J \to 0$ leads to:

$$G_c^{(3)}(i_1, i_2, i_3) = -G_c^{(2)}(i_1, j_1)G_c^{(2)}(i_2, j_2)G_c^{(2)}(i_3, j_3)\Gamma^{(3)}(j_1, j_2, j_3) \qquad (5\text{-}27)$$

where $\Gamma^{(3)}$ is defined via:

$$\Gamma^{(3)}(i_1, i_2, i_3) \equiv \left. \frac{\delta^3 \Gamma\{\bar\phi\}}{\delta\bar\phi(i_1)\delta\bar\phi(i_2)\delta\bar\phi(i_3)} \right|_{J=0} \qquad (5\text{-}28)$$

and we have used equation (5-23) to divide the left-hand side of (5-26) by the matrix $\delta^2 \Gamma/\delta\bar\phi(i)\delta\bar\phi(j)$.

Note that Eq. (5-23) can be written in a form analogous to (5-27), namely:

$$G_c^{(2)}(i_1, i_2) = G_c^{(2)}(i_1, j_1) G_c^{(2)}(i_2, j_2) \Gamma^{(2)}(j_1, j_2) \qquad (5\text{-}29)$$

The functions $G_c^{(2)}$ and $G_c^{(3)}$ have a special feature. For any type of interaction, if a graph is one-particle reducible, one of the two parts is a graph of a two-point function connected to an external point. Pictorially, one is simply

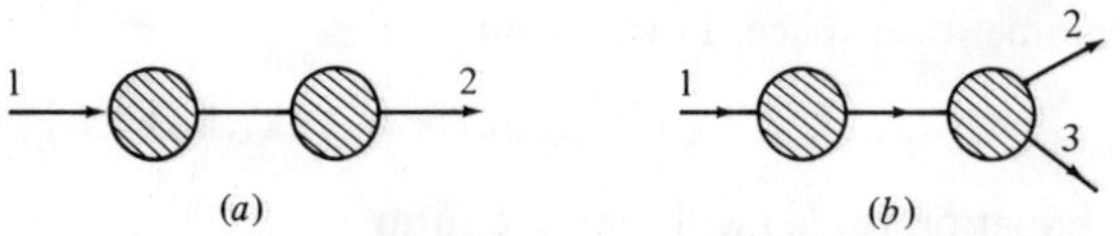

FIGURE 5-9
One particle reducible graphs of $G_c^{(2)}$ and $G_c^{(3)}$.

saying that a typical one-particle reducible graph for the two- and three-point functions has the form of Fig. 5-9a and 5-9b, respectively, provided the restriction following Eq. (5-16) is respected.

Equation (5-29) states that in order to obtain all connected graphs of $G^{(2)}$ we have to attach to $\Gamma^{(2)}$, which is the sum of all 1PI terms, the full connected two-point functions. Using Eq. (5-27) one can conclude that $\Gamma^{(3)}$ as defined by (5-28) is *minus* the 1PI part of $G_c^{(3)}$ or of $G^{(3)}$.

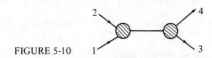

FIGURE 5-10

In general the reduction by one particle can happen in places other than an external propagator. For example, if a ϕ^3 interaction is present the graph of Fig. 5-10 will appear in $G^{(4)}$. Its reduction leads to two graphs of a three-point function (see, e.g., Exercise 5-9).

The definitions (5-25) and (5-26) can nevertheless be generalized. Defining

$$\Gamma^{(N)}(1,\ldots,N) \equiv \frac{\delta^N \Gamma\{\bar{\phi}\}}{\delta\bar{\phi}(1)\ldots\delta\bar{\phi}(N)}\bigg|_{J=0} \qquad (5\text{-}30)$$

one can express the connected N-point function for $N > 2$ as:

$$G_c^{(N)}(1,\ldots,N) = -G_c^{(2)}(1,1')G_c^{(2)}(2,2')$$

$$\ldots G_c^{(2)}(N,N')\Gamma^{(N)}(1',\ldots,N') + Q^{(N)}(1,\ldots,N) \qquad (5\text{-}31)$$

The content of (5-31) is the fact that the first term contains all graphs of $G_c^{(N)}$ which are one-particle reducible *only* by cutting an external line — all of which are explicitly written. $Q^{(N)}$ includes the terms which are one-particle reducible by body cuts. Thus, $\Gamma^{(N)}$ is 1PI. The proof of this statement is left as Exercise 5-10.

To bring our notation back to earth we consider again the typical situation, in which we have an M-component boson field which is studied in momentum space. In that case

$$G^{(2)}(1, 2) \to G^{(2)}_{i_1 i_2}(\mathbf{k}_1, \mathbf{k}_2) = G^{(2)}_{i_1 i_2}(\mathbf{k}_1)\delta^K(\mathbf{k}_1 + \mathbf{k}_2) \qquad (5\text{-}32)$$

Equation (5-23) will take the form

$$\sum_{\mathbf{k}_3, i_3} G^{(2)}_{ci_1 i_3}(\mathbf{k}_1, \mathbf{k}_3)\Gamma^{(2)}_{i_3 i_2}(-\mathbf{k}_3, \mathbf{k}_2) = \delta^K(\mathbf{k}_1 + \mathbf{k}_2)\delta_{i_1 i_2} \qquad (5\text{-}33)$$

Using (5-32) one finds that

$$\Gamma^{(2)}_{i_1 i_2}(\mathbf{k}_1, \mathbf{k}_2) = \Gamma^{(2)}_{i_1 i_2}(\mathbf{k}_1)\delta^K(\mathbf{k}_1 + \mathbf{k}_2) \qquad (5\text{-}34)$$

which would have followed by translational invariance. And,

$$\sum_{i_3} G^{(2)}_{ci_1 i_3}(k)\Gamma^{(2)}_{i_3 i_2}(k) = \delta_{i_1 i_2} \qquad (5\text{-}35)$$

If the two-point functions are diagonal in the field index, then

$$G^{(2)}_{ci_1 i_2}(k) = G^{(2)}_c(k)\delta_{i_1 i_2}$$

and we will have

$$\Gamma^{(2)}_{i_1 i_2}(k) = \Gamma^{(2)}(k)\delta_{i_1 i_2}$$

with

$$\Gamma^{(2)}(k) = [G^{(2)}_c(k)]^{-1} \qquad (5\text{-}36)$$

In terms of continuous momenta, (5-33) reads:

$$\int \frac{dk_3}{(2\pi)^d} \sum_{i_3} G^{(2)}_{ci_1 i_3}(\mathbf{k}_1, \mathbf{k}_3)\Gamma^{(2)}_{i_3 i_2}(-\mathbf{k}_3, \mathbf{k}_2) = (2\pi)^d \delta(\mathbf{k}_1 + \mathbf{k}_2)\delta_{i_1 i_2} \qquad (5\text{-}37)$$

Translational invariance implies that

$$G^{(2)}_c(k_1, k_2) = (2\pi)^d \delta(k_1 + k_2)G^{(2)}_c(k_1) \qquad (5\text{-}38)$$

$$\Gamma^{(2)}(k_1, k_2) = (2\pi)^d \delta(k_1 + k_2)\Gamma^{(2)}(k_1) \qquad (5\text{-}39)$$

and (5-36).

Matrix products, like that in the first term in (5-31), become simple products as far as the momentum variable is concerned. Thus

$$G^{(N)}_c(\mathbf{k}_1, \ldots, \mathbf{k}_N) = -G^{(2)}_c(\mathbf{k}_1) \ldots G^{(2)}_c(\mathbf{k}_N)\Gamma^{(N)}(\mathbf{k}_1, \ldots, \mathbf{k}_N) + Q^{(N)} \qquad (5\text{-}40)$$

The field indices still play a role of matrix indices, unless, for some reason such as a symmetry, the $G^{(2)}$'s are diagonal.

Finally, to obtain all the graphs of $\Gamma^{(N)}$ one has to draw all 1PI graphs of $G^{(N)}_c$. In computing the terms, one gives each graph its *usual weight* according to the rules for the construction of $G^{(N)}$, and omits the external lines.

5-5 THE GENERATING FUNCTIONAL AND THE POTENTIAL

The definition (5-30), beyond defining the vertex function $\Gamma^{(N)}$, is a statement that Γ — the Legendre transform of F — is the generating functional for the $\Gamma^{(N)}$'s. This implies that the N-point vertex functions can be used as expansion coefficients for $\Gamma\{\bar{\phi}\}$ in analogy with the expansions for $Z\{J\}$ and $F\{J\}$ in Sec. 5-2. But while the expansions in Sec. 5-2 were expansions in J and the coefficients — Eq. (5-6), for example — were evaluated at $J = 0$, here the coefficients are still evaluated at $J = 0$, but the expansion variable is $\bar{\phi}$. Consequently, the expansion will be about that value of $\bar{\phi}$ — the classical field — which is obtained as $J \to 0$. Namely, in a situation where $\bar{\phi} = v \neq 0$ as $J = 0$, the expansion will be about a non-zero value of $\bar{\phi}$. The vector notation is used here for field components only.

Thus:

$$\Gamma\{\bar{\phi}\} = \sum_{N=1}^{\infty} \frac{1}{N!} \sum_{i_1 \dots i_N} \int dx_1 \dots dx_N \, \Gamma^{(N)}_{i_1 \dots i_N}(x_1, \dots, x_N; v)$$

$$\times [\bar{\phi}_{i_1}(x_1) - v_{i_1}] \dots [\bar{\phi}_{i_N}(x_N) - v_{i_N}] \qquad (5\text{-}41)$$

where

$$v_i = \lim_{J \to 0} \bar{\phi}_i \qquad (5\text{-}42)$$

If the source vanishes, the sum will start at $N = 2$, since for $J = 0$ the first term

$$\Gamma^{(1)} = \frac{\delta \Gamma}{\delta \bar{\phi}} = J = 0 \qquad (5\text{-}43)$$

Note also that in the $\Gamma^{(N)}$'s appearing in Eq. (5-42) we have inserted an explicit dependence on v. The reason for that is of course that the $\Gamma^{(N)}$'s are defined at $J = 0$, where we may have $v \neq 0$. This is especially important in situations with spontaneously broken symmetry.

But if a function $f(x)$ has a Taylor expansion

$$f(x) = \sum_{n=0}^{\infty} \frac{1}{n!} f^{(n)}(a)(x - a)^n$$

then it has an expansion about $x = 0$ which reads

$$f(x) = \sum_{n=0}^{\infty} \frac{1}{n!} f^{(n)}(0) x^n$$

Thus (5-41) can be rewritten as

$$\Gamma\{\bar{\phi}\} = \sum_{N=1}^{\infty} \frac{1}{N!} \sum_{i_1 \dots i_N} \int dx_1 \dots dx_N \, \Gamma^{(N)}_{i_1 \dots i_N}(x_1, \dots, x_N) \bar{\phi}_{i_1}(x_1) \dots \bar{\phi}_{i_N}(x_N)$$

$$(5\text{-}44)$$

in which the $\Gamma^{(N)}$'s are evaluated with $v = 0$, i.e., *in the symmetric theory*. The question as to whether the symmetry is, or is not, spontaneously broken is answered by studying the equation

$$\frac{\delta \Gamma\{\bar{\phi}\}}{\delta \bar{\phi}} = 0 \qquad (5\text{-}45)$$

and searching for solutions with $\bar{\phi} \neq 0$. Namely, broken symmetry is discovered as an extremum property of $\Gamma\{\phi\}$.

Furthermore, since

$$\frac{\delta^2 \Gamma}{\delta \bar{\phi}(1) \delta \bar{\phi}(2)} = [G_c^{(2)}]^{-1}(1, 2)$$

and since

$$G_c^{(2)}(1, 2) = \langle (\phi(1) - v_1)(\phi(2) - v_2) \rangle$$

which is a positive semi-definite matrix, the extremum is a minimum.

Another useful function is Γ for a uniform distribution $\bar{\phi} = \Phi$

$$\Gamma\{\Phi\} = \sum_{N=2}^{\infty} \frac{1}{N!} \sum_{i_1 \ldots i_N} \left[\int dx_1 \ldots dx_N \Gamma_{i_1 \ldots i_N}^{(N)}(x_1, \ldots, x_N) \right] \Phi_{i_1} \ldots \Phi_{i_N} \quad (5\text{-}46)$$

If we define the Fourier transform of $\Gamma^{(N)}$ directly in the infinite volume limit via

$$\Gamma^{(N)}(x_1, \ldots, x_N) = \int \frac{dk_1}{(2\pi)^d} \cdots \frac{dk_N}{(2\pi)^d} \Gamma^{(N)}(k_1, \ldots, k_N) \exp\{-i\Sigma k_i x_i\} \quad (5\text{-}47)$$

then translational invariance implies that

$$\Gamma^{(N)}(k_1, \ldots, k_N) = (2\pi)^d \delta(\Sigma k_i) \bar{\Gamma}^{(N)}(k_1, \ldots, k_N) \qquad (5\text{-}48)$$

as in (4-63), and (5-46) can be written as:

$$\Gamma\{\Phi\} = \sum_{N=1}^{\infty} \frac{1}{N!} \sum_{i_1 \ldots i_N} \bar{\Gamma}_{i_1 \ldots i_N}^{(N)}(0, \ldots, 0) \Phi_{i_1} \ldots \Phi_{i_N} \cdot (2\pi)^d \delta(0)$$

$$\equiv (2\pi)^d \delta(0) U(\Phi) \qquad (5\text{-}49)$$

The appearance of $(2\pi)^d \delta(0)$ implies simply that the quantity is proportional to the volume of the system. $U(\Phi)$ is called the *potential* or effective potential.

Symmetry breaking is obtained by finding minima of $U(\Phi)$ for $\Phi \neq 0$. This is the function which corresponds to the free energy as a function of the magnetization. The Landau theory, for example, is a special approximation to this function. An approximation which we shall study in the next chapter.

One can further identify the source J with the *physical* external field. This field can be taken to be uniform and $U(\Phi)$, for the corresponding uniform Φ, can be written down. The average Φ is calculated by using

$$\frac{\partial U(\Phi)}{\partial \Phi_i} = J_i \qquad (5\text{-}50)$$

Using the equation corresponding to (5-49) for $J \neq 0$, one finds

$$J_i = \sum_{N=1}^{\infty} \frac{1}{N!} \sum_{i_1 \dots i_N} \bar{\Gamma}^{(N+1)}_{i i_1 i_2 \dots i_N}(0, \dots, 0) \Phi_{i_1} \dots \Phi_{i_N} \qquad (5\text{-}51)$$

which is the *equation of state*, giving the relation between the magnetic field and the magnetization, or the pressure and the density.

Thus any systematic approximation to the vertex functions gives us a corresponding approximation to the free energy and to the equation of state.

The procedure is now reversed. One first of all calculates, as best one can, the effective potential (5-49), with the symmetric vertex functions. Then the vacuum, or ground state, or the broken symmetry state is identified by minimizing $U(\Phi)$.

Next one computes the full vertex functions, in either the symmetric or in the non-symmetric state, by (5-41), i.e., by identifying in $\Gamma\{\bar{\phi}\}$ the coefficient of $(\bar{\phi}_{i_1}(x_1) - v_{i_1})(\bar{\phi}_{i_2}(x_2) - v_{i_2}) \dots$, where v is the value of the classical field obtained by minimizing U. In other words, one computes:

$$\Gamma^{(N)}(1, \dots, N; v) = \frac{\delta^N \Gamma\{\bar{\phi}\}}{\delta\bar{\phi}(1) \dots \delta\bar{\phi}(N)} \bigg|_{\bar{\phi}=v} \qquad (5\text{-}52)$$

We will consider some explicit examples in the next chapter. Here we will conclude with a few comments.

The functional Γ is the free energy for some prescribed distribution of the average values of the magnetization, to use the language of magnetism. In contrast, $F\{J\}$ is the free energy corresponding to a given distribution of the external magnetic fields. Clearly, $F\{J\}$ can be calculated for any distribution

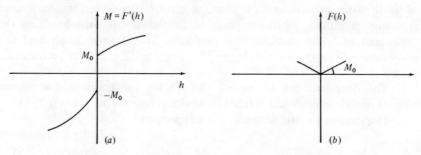

FIGURE 5-11
The inaccessible coexistence region.

$J(x)$. But the situation may, and usually does, arise, that some distributions $\bar{\phi}(x)$ are not produced for any $J(x)$. This manifests itself in Γ by the fact that for some distributions, $\bar{\phi}(x)$, Γ develops an *imaginary* part. One obtains *metastable states* for these values of the magnetization. An analogous phenomenon occurs also in field theory, where one finds that certain vacua are intrinsically unstable. We will see this phenomenon in the examples which will be considered below.[8]

In magnetism one is quite familiar with such situations.[9] If one is in the magnetic state, the magnetization, or the derivative of F with respect to h has the form shown in Fig. 5-11a and F has the form shown in Fig. 5-11b. For no value of h can values of M in the interval $(-M_0, M_0)$ be obtained. In the gas–liquid system the corresponding states are obtained by supercooling or superheating, and are, in fact, metastable.

In applications of the above formalism to field theory one searches for the vacuum among the uniform classical fields. This is consistent with the rather restricted form which the free propagator can take in a relativistically invariant theory. In statistical physics the situation is richer, in that one can obtain a whole host of ground states depending on the momentum at which the instability of the symmetric phase appears. Such cases as antiferromagnetism, spiral orderings, or crystals are common (see, e.g., the discussion of the Ising model in Sec. 2-4-3). Once the suspected location, in momentum space, of the instability is determined the theory can be expanded in low momenta about that value, and the formulation in terms of $U(\Phi)$ can be used.

5-6 WARD–TAKAHASHI IDENTITIES AND GOLDSTONE'S THEOREM

The effort invested in introducing the Legendre transform $\Gamma\{\bar{\phi}\}$ bears another important fruit. In the case in which the Lagrangian possesses a continuous *global symmetry* (independent of position) in the space of the field components, one can derive identities connecting vertex functions with different numbers of external points. These, in turn, lead to many important results, the most popular of which is the appearance of infinite range correlations when the continuous symmetry is broken. In the language of field theory it corresponds to the appearence of boson particles with zero mass. The identities imply that this phenomenon, named after Goldstone,[10] occurs to all orders in perturbation theory.

The discussion can be carried through for any continuous symmetry group. For simplicity we will indicate its workings here for the group $0(2)$.[11]

One considers a field with two real components

$$\phi(x) = \begin{pmatrix} \pi(x) \\ \sigma(x) \end{pmatrix}$$

The Lagrangian is symmetric under rotations in the two-dimensional space of π and σ:

$$\mathscr{L}(\phi) = \tfrac{1}{2}[(\nabla\phi)^2 + \mu^2\phi^2] + \mathscr{L}_1(\phi^2) \qquad (5\text{-}53)$$

In other words, if

$$\phi' = \begin{pmatrix} \cos\theta & -\sin\theta \\ \sin\theta & \cos\theta \end{pmatrix} \phi = T\phi \qquad (5\text{-}54)$$

then

$$\mathscr{L}(\phi') = \mathscr{L}(\phi) \qquad (5\text{-}55)$$

Adding a source J, which breaks the symmetry (5-55), is equivalent to adding a term of the form $J \cdot \phi$ to $\mathscr{L}$. Therefore, the generating functionals $Z\{J\}$ and $F\{J\}$ are invariant under the transformation:

$$J \to J' = TJ \qquad (5\text{-}56)$$

This is true because in the calculation of Z, or F, ϕ is a dummy integration variable which we can rotate by T without affecting anything. But if both ϕ and J are rotated, $J\phi$ does not change and neither does $\mathscr{L}$, as has been assumed.

Since T is a continuous group of transformations we can consider its infinitesimal action, which is given by

$$T = 1 + \epsilon \begin{pmatrix} 0 & -1 \\ 1 & 0 \end{pmatrix} \qquad (5\text{-}57)$$

or

$$\begin{aligned} J'_\pi &= J_\pi - \epsilon J_\sigma \\ J'_\sigma &= J_\sigma + \epsilon J_\pi \end{aligned} \qquad (5\text{-}58)$$

Since F is invariant under this transformation we have

$$\delta F = \int dx \left\{ \frac{\delta F\{J\}}{\delta J_\sigma(x)} J_\pi(x) - \frac{\delta F\{J\}}{\delta J_\pi(x)} J_\sigma(x) \right\} = 0 \qquad (5\text{-}59)$$

This equation implies an invariance of $\Gamma\{\phi\}$, since by using (5-18) and (5-20) one finds that it is equivalent to:

$$\int dx \left\{ \bar\phi_\sigma(x) \frac{\delta\Gamma\{\bar\phi\}}{\delta\bar\phi_\pi(x)} - \bar\phi_\pi(x) \frac{\delta\Gamma\{\bar\phi\}}{\delta\bar\phi_\sigma(x)} \right\} = 0 \qquad (5\text{-}60)$$

Which is a statement that Γ is invariant when $\bar\phi$ undergoes the transformation (5-54), i.e.,

$$\bar\phi \to \bar\phi' = T\bar\phi \qquad (5\text{-}61)$$

Irrespective of whether we are in the symmetric state, or in the state with broken symmetry, $\Gamma\{\bar{\Phi}\}$ satisfies the identity (5-60) — *the Ward–Takahashi identity* for the generating functional.

From this identity one can derive an unlimited number of other identities by taking derivatives with respect to $\bar{\phi}$, and then setting $\bar{\phi} = v$. It provides for a unified treatment of the symmetric (disordered) and the broken symmetry (ordered) states.

Taking a derivative of (5-60) with respect to $\bar{\phi}_\pi(y)$ one finds:

$$\int dx \left[\bar{\phi}_\sigma(x) \frac{\delta^2 \Gamma}{\delta \bar{\phi}_\pi(x) \delta \bar{\phi}_\pi(y)} - \delta(x - y) \frac{\delta \Gamma}{\delta \bar{\phi}_\sigma(x)} - \bar{\phi}_\pi(x) \frac{\delta^2 \Gamma}{\delta \bar{\phi}_\sigma(x) \delta \bar{\phi}_\pi(y)} \right] = 0 \tag{5-62}$$

In the state in which the symmetry is broken in the σ-direction, keeping the uniform external field in the direction of σ, we have

$$\Phi = \begin{pmatrix} 0 \\ u \end{pmatrix}$$

Equation (5-62) becomes:

$$u \int dx \frac{\delta^2 \Gamma}{\delta \bar{\phi}_\pi(x) \delta \bar{\phi}_\pi(y)} = \frac{\delta \Gamma}{\delta \bar{\phi}_\sigma(y)} = J_\sigma \tag{5-63}$$

If now $J_\sigma \to 0$, the integrand on the left-hand side becomes $\Gamma^{(2)}_{\pi\pi}(x - y)$. Furthermore, if there is a spontaneously broken symmetry u does not vanish. Consequently,

$$\lim_{p \to 0} \Gamma^{(2)}_{\pi\pi}(p) = 0 \tag{5-64}$$

which implies that $G^{(2)}$ has a pole at $p = 0$. In the language of field theory one says that the π particle has a zero mass. This is the famous *Goldstone boson.* Another example is provided by Exercise 5-11.

In the language of statistical physics one expresses this result by saying that in a situation of broken continuous symmetry the correlations transverse to the magnetization have infinite range. We will encounter Goldstone bosons in the examples which will be discussed in the next chapter.

5-7   VERTEX PARTS FOR GREEN FUNCTIONS WITH COMPOSITE OPERATORS

Of the graphs of $G^{(2,1)}$ represented in Figure 4-18, (h) and (i) contain vacuum parts — they may be discarded. Then one notices connected graphs — those which do not separate into two parts each depending on a different set of coordinates — and disconnected graphs. To the first kind belong (b), (c), (e) and (f), and to the second (a), (d) and (g).

The properties of disconnected graphs can be deduced from those of products of lower order Green functions. In this way the disconnected graphs in Fig. 4-18 appear in the product $G^{(2)}G^{(0,1)}$ (see Exercise 5-12). Furthermore, usually we are interested in Green functions containing ϕ^2 fields as derivatives with respect to temperature, or mass, of Green functions (see, e.g., Eq. (2-92)). But derivatives of connected functions remain connected. Thus, we proceed to study the way connected Green functions, which include the composite operator ϕ^2, are generated.

Returning to (2-90), with Z, a functional of both J and t, we have, as usual, that

$$F\{J, t\} = \ln Z\{J, t\} \qquad (5\text{-}65)$$

will give rise to the cumulants of ϕ and ϕ^2. For example,

$$\frac{\delta F\{J, t\}}{\delta J(1)} = Z^{-1}\{J, t\}\frac{\delta Z}{\delta J(1)} \xrightarrow[J \to 0]{} G^{(1)}(1, \{t\}) \xrightarrow[t \to 0]{} G^{(1)}(1) \qquad (5\text{-}66)$$

$$\frac{\delta^2 F\{J, t\}}{\delta J(1)\delta J(2)} = Z^{-1}\{J, t\}\frac{\delta^2 Z}{\delta J(1)\delta J(2)} - Z^{-2}\{J, t\}\frac{\delta Z}{\delta J(1)}\frac{\delta Z}{\delta J(2)} \xrightarrow[J \to 0]{} G^{(2)}(1, 2, \{t\})$$

$$- G^{(1)}(1, \{t\})G^{(1)}(2, \{t\}) \xrightarrow[t \to 0]{} G^{(2)}(1, 2) - G^{(1)}(1)G^{(1)}(2)$$

$$\qquad (5\text{-}67)$$

$$\frac{\delta^3 F\{J, t\}}{\delta J(1)\delta J(2)\delta t(3)} \xrightarrow[J \to 0]{} G^{(2, 1)}(1, 2, 3, \{t\}) - G^{(2)}(1, 2, \{t\})G^{(0, 1)}(3, \{t\})$$

$$- G^{(1, 1)}(1, 3, \{t\})G^{(1)}(2, \{t\}) - G^{(1, 1)}(2, 3, \{t\})G^{(1)}(1, \{t\})$$

$$+ 2G^{(1)}(1, \{t\})G^{(1)}(2, \{t\})G^{(0, 1)}(3, \{t\}) \xrightarrow[t \to 0]{} G^{(2, 1)}(1, 2, 3)$$

$$- G^{(2)}(1, 2)G^{(0, 1)}(3) - G^{(1, 1)}(1, 3)G^{(1)}(2) - G^{(1, 1)}(1, 3)G^{(1)}(2)$$

$$+ 2G^{(1)}(1)G^{(1)}(2)G^{(0, 1)}(3) \qquad (5\text{-}68)$$

where we have introduced the notation:

$$G^{(N, L)}(x_i, y_i, \{t\}) = \lim_{J \to 0} Z^{-1}\{J, t\}\frac{\delta^N Z}{\delta J(x_1) \ldots \delta J(x_N)\delta t(y_1) \ldots \delta t(y_L)} \qquad (5\text{-}69)$$

which is nothing but $G^{(N, L)}$ calculated in the presence of the *interaction*

$$\mathscr{L}_{\text{Int}} = -\int \frac{t(y)}{2!}\phi^2(y)\, dy \qquad (5\text{-}70)$$

It is clear that the general derivative of $F\{J, t\}$ with respect to J and t will give the Green function from which all possible factorizations have been subtracted. We can write

$$\frac{\delta^{N + L} F\{J, t\}}{\delta J(x_1) \ldots \delta J(x_N)\delta t(y_1) \ldots \delta t(y_L)}\bigg|_{J = 0} \equiv G_c^{(N, L)}(x_1, \ldots, x_N, y_1, \ldots, y_L, \{t\})$$

$$\qquad (5\text{-}71)$$

from which it follows that

$$G_c^{(N,L+1)}(x_1,\ldots,x_N,y_1,\ldots,y_L,y_{L+1},\{t\}) = \frac{\delta G_c^{(N,L)}(x_1,\ldots,x_N,y_1,\ldots y_L,\{t\})}{\delta t(y_{L+1})}$$

(5-72)

The limit of $G_c^{(N,L+1)}(\{t\})$ as $t \to 0$ is the connected $G_c^{(N,L+1)}$.

From (5.69) we deduce that

$$G_c^{(N,L)}(x_i,y_j,\{t\}) = \sum_{K=0}^{\infty} \frac{1}{K!} \int dy_{L+1}\cdots dy_{L+K} t(y_{L+1})\cdots t(y_{L+K})$$

$$\times G_c^{(N,L+K)}(x_i,y_1,\ldots,y_L,y_{L+1},\ldots,y_{L+K})$$

(5-73)

for any values of N and L.

In terms of graphs the above statements mean the following: The presence of an interaction such as (5-70) gives rise to two-point interaction vertices in the graphs of $G^{(N)}(x_i,\{t\})$, for example. The only difference concerning the rules for the computation of graphs, as given in Sec. 4-4, is that for these interactions we introduce $t(y_i)$ for λ_2.

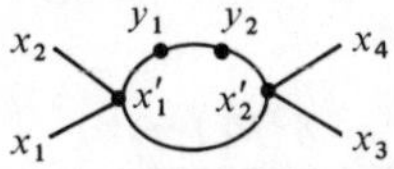

FIGURE 5-12
A graph of $G_c^{(4)}(\{t\})$.

A typical case will be a graph of $G_c^{(4)}$ depicted in Fig. 5-12, which is second order in t. Its contribution is:

$$I\{t\} = \lambda^2 \int dx_1' \, dx_2' \, dy_1' \, dy_2' \, G_0(x_1-x_1')G_0(x_2-x_1')G_0(x_3-x_2')G_0(x_4-x_2')$$

$$G_0(x_1'-x_2')G_0(x_1'-y_1')G_0(y_1'-y_2')G_0(y_2'-x_2')t(y_1')t(y_2')$$

(5-74)

Differentiating $I\{t\}$ with respect to $t(y)$ will give two terms of $G^{(4,1)}$. They will be different, and both connected (see Fig. 5-13). The only case, in which there may be some doubt as to whether the derivative of a connected function will be connected, is in graphs which are one-particle reducible. Namely, such as graph (a)

FIGURE 5-13
Graphs of $\delta G_c^{(4)}/\delta t(y)$.

in Fig. 5-14. It leads to graph (b). The contribution of (b) is a product but the coordinate y appears in both terms (see Exercises 5-13—5-14). This will lead to a convolution in momentum space.

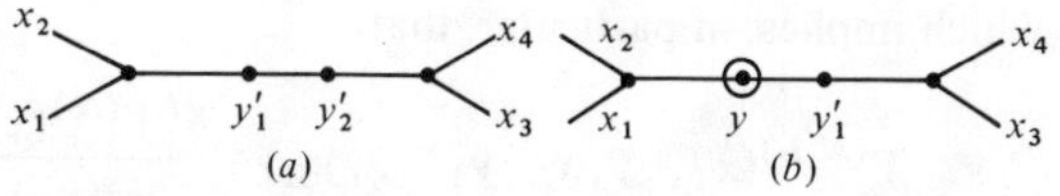

FIGURE 5-14
Graphs of $G_c^{(4)}(\{t\})$ and $G_c^{(4,1)}$.

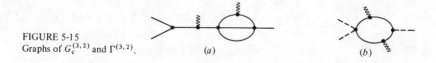

(a)

(b)

Finally, one can easily convince oneself that the symmetry factors calculated via Eq. (5-72) are the same as those obtained by the rules discussed in Sec. 4-7.

Next we move to vertex parts, or 1PI parts of the Green functions.[12] These can again be viewed in two ways. Either by studying the Legendre transform of $F\{J, t\}$ with respect to J, in analogy with what was done in Sec. 5-4, or by discussing the topological properties of the graphs. We start with the latter way.

The 1PI part of $G_c^{(N)}$ was defined as the sum of all graphs of $G_c^{(N)}$, which cannot be separated into two parts by cutting a single line, without their external legs. The 1PI part of $G_c^{(N,L)}$ can be defined as the sum of all graphs of $G_c^{(N,L)}$, which cannot be separated into two parts by cutting a single line, without the external legs *corresponding to the N ϕ-fields*. In Fig. 5-15 graph (a) is reducible, graph (b) is not.

FIGURE 5-15
Graphs of $G_c^{(3,2)}$ and $\Gamma^{(3,2)}$.

(a)

(b)

Consider the graphs of $G^{(N,L)}(\{t\})$ – those which have a quadratic interaction of the type (5-70) – among those focus on the 1PI ones. Taking a derivative of any of these graphs with respect to $t(y)$ will result in a 1PI graph of $G^{(N,L+1)}(\{t\})$. This is obvious. But what is also true is:

(a) The numerical coefficient – the combinatorial one – is equal to that of the corresponding graph of $G_c^{(N,L+1)}$.

(b) All graphs of $G_c^{(N,L+1)}\{t\}$, which are 1PI, are obtained by taking a derivative of the 1PI-graphs of $G_c^{(N,L)}$ with respect to $t(y)$.

The proof of the above statements is left as Exercise 5-15. Defining the 1PI part of $G_c^{(N,L)}(\{t\})$ as $\Gamma^{(N,L)}(\{t\})$ we have

$$\frac{\delta}{\delta t(y_{L+1})} \Gamma^{(N,L)}(x_1, \ldots, x_N, y_1, \ldots, y_L, \{t\})$$

$$= \Gamma^{(N,L+1)}(x_1, \ldots, x_N, y_1, \ldots, y_{L+1}, \{t\}) \qquad (5\text{-}75)$$

which implies, in particular, that

$$\Gamma^{(N,L)}(x_1,\ldots,x_N,y_1,\ldots,y_L) = \frac{\delta^L \Gamma^{(N)}(x_1,\ldots,x_N,\{t\})}{\delta t(y_1)\ldots\delta t(y_L)}\bigg|_{t=0} \qquad (5.76)$$

and hence

$$\Gamma^{(N)}(x_1,\ldots,x_N;t) = \sum_{L=0}^{\infty} \frac{1}{L!} \int dy_1 \ldots dy_L \, \Gamma^{(N,L)}(x_1,\ldots,x_N,y_1,\ldots,y_L)$$

$$\times\, t(y_1)\ldots t(y_L) \qquad (5\text{-}77)$$

When t is independent of y it can be considered as a shift of the temperature, and Eq. (5-77) will provide an expansion of $\Gamma^{(N)}$ about any given temperature. It reads, by analogy with Eq. (2-92),

$$\Gamma^{(N)}(x_1,\ldots,x_N;\delta t) = \int \sum_{L=0}^{\infty} \frac{1}{L!}(\delta t)^L \, dy_1\ldots dy_L \, \Gamma^{(N,L)}(x_1,\ldots,x_N,y_1,\ldots,y_L)$$

$$(5\text{-}78)$$

in which the left-hand side is calculated at $\mu^2 + \delta t$ and the right-hand side at μ^2. When written in momentum space one has to exercise some care about the order of the limits $p_i \to 0$ and the summation of the series.

Finally, one can follow the alternative course and consider the functional

$$\Gamma\{\bar{\phi},t\} = \Sigma\bar{\phi}(i)\,J(i) - F\{J,t\} \qquad (5\text{-}79)$$

where

$$\bar{\phi} = \bar{\phi}(i,\{J,t\}) = \frac{\delta F\{J,t\}}{\delta J(i)} \qquad (5\text{-}80)$$

In other words the Legendre transform is performed with respect to J only.

Clearly Eq. (5-23), with all quantities now functionals of t, holds just as before, namely,

$$\sum_k \frac{\delta^2 F\{J,t\}}{\delta J(i)\,\delta J(k)} \frac{\delta^2 \Gamma}{\delta\bar{\phi}(k,\{t\})\,\delta\bar{\phi}(j,\{t\})} = \delta(i,j) \qquad (5\text{-}81)$$

$J(i)$ becomes $J(i,\{t\})$ when $\bar{\phi}(k)$ is fixed. Taking now a derivative of (5-81) with respect to $t(l)$ leads, by analogy with (5-27), to

$$G_c^{(2,1)}(i_1,i_2,i_3) = -G_c^{(2)}(i_1,j_1)\,G_c^{(2)}(i_2,j_2)\,\Gamma^{(2,1)}(j_1,j_2,i_3) \qquad (5\text{-}82)$$

where

$$\Gamma^{(2,1)}(i,j,k) = \frac{\delta^3 \Gamma\{\bar{\phi},t\}}{\delta\bar{\phi}(i)\,\delta\bar{\phi}(j)\,\delta t(k)}\bigg|_{J=t=0} \qquad (5\text{-}83)$$

The main difference is that on the right-hand side of Eq. (5-82) there are only two $G_c^{(2)}$'s, for three in (5-27). They are the external legs associated with the ϕ-fields. This difference is related to the fact that the Legendre transform was performed with respect to J only.

One can now proceed to show that

$$\Gamma^{(N,L)} \equiv \frac{\delta^{N+L}\Gamma\{\bar{\phi}, t\}}{\delta\bar{\phi}(x_1)\ldots\delta\bar{\phi}(x_N)\delta t(y_1)\ldots\delta t(y_L)}\bigg|_{J=t=0} \qquad (5\text{-}84)$$

are the irreducible vertex parts defined diagrammatically above.

EXERCISES

5-1 What are the restrictions imposed on the momenta of two lines of a graph, if the graph can be separated into two parts by cutting these two lines?

5-2 Exhibit an eighth order graph of $G^{(4)}$ which is not "one-particle-reducible".

5-3 Show that all the terms of $G^{(N)}(k_1,\ldots,k_N)$ which are disconnected

(a) into two groups, one with $k_1,\ldots,k_r$ the other with $k_{r+1}\ldots k_N$, are given with the correct numerical factors by

$$G^{(r)}(k_1,\ldots,k_r)\,G^{(N-r)}(k_{r+1},\ldots,k_N)$$

(b) Consider the case in which they are disconnected into a general number of groups.

5-4 Show that if $G^{(N)}(k_1,\ldots,k_N)$ is written as a sum of products of connected $G^{(M)}$'s, with $M \leqslant N$, then every product, in which the momenta have been distributed in a given way, enters exactly once. Derive the fact that $F = \ln Z$.

5-5 Write $G^{(4)}$ and $G^{(6)}$ in terms of connected functions for a ϕ^3 theory.

5-6 Show that if one has an interaction which is a general polynomial in ϕ, the argument about the factorization of a one-particle-reducible graph of $G_c^{(2)}$ goes through.

5-7 What graphs enter $\Sigma(k)$ to 4th order in a ϕ^3 interaction if $\langle\phi\rangle = 0$?[13]

5-8 Same as Exercise 5-7 above to 3rd order in a ϕ^6 theory.

5-9 What are the 1PI graphs in $G^{(3)}$ and $G^{(4)}$, to 5th order in a ϕ^3 theory?

5-10 Prove that $\bar{\Gamma}^{(N)}$ as defined by Eq. (5-30) is 1PI. One can proceed by induction. Assuming a separation of the type (5-31) for all $G^{(K)}$ $K \leqslant N$, one has to classify all terms of $G^{(N+1)}$ obtained by taking one more derivative of (5-31).

5-11 Using the Ward–Takahashi identity for the generating functional show that

$$\Gamma_\pi^{(2)}(p) - \Gamma_\sigma^{(2)}(p) = -u\Gamma_{\sigma\pi\pi}^{(3)}(p;0,-p)^{14}$$

5-12 Calculate the terms of $G^{(2,1)}$ without vacuum parts up to second order in λ. Show that the terms which are disconnected are exactly equal to the terms appearing in $G^{(2)}G^{(0,1)}$.

5-13 Calculate the contribution of graphs (a) and (b) in Fig. 5-14. Show that the result for (b), calculated as a derivative, is the same as that calculated by the rules of Sec. 4-7.

5-14 The same for the graphs in Fig. 5-13.

5-15 Prove that

$$\frac{\delta}{\delta t(y_{L+1})}\Gamma^{(N,L)}(x_1,\ldots,x_N,y_1,\ldots,y_L,\{t\})$$
$$= \Gamma^{(N,L+1)}(x_1,\ldots,x_N,y_1,\ldots,y_{L+1},\{t\})$$

by considering the graphs.

REFERENCES

1. J. Schwinger, *Proceedings of the National Academy of Sciences,* **37**, 452 and 455 (1951) and **44**, 956 (1958). See also P. Nozieres and J. M. Luttinger, *Physical Review,* **127**, 1423 and 1431 (1962).
2. C. De Dominicis, *Journal of Mathematical Physics,* **4**, 255 (1962); C. De Dominicis and P. C. Martin, *Journal of Mathematical Physics,* **5**, 14 (1964).
3. G. Jona-Lasinio, *Nuovo Cimento,* **34**, 1790 (1964).
4. J. C. Ward, *Physical Review,* **78**, 182 (1950); Y. Takahashi, *Nuovo Cimento,* **6**, 370 (1957).
5. B. W. Lee, *Chiral Dynamics* (Gordon and Breach, N.Y., 1972). See also S. Coleman and E. Weinberg, *Physical Review,* **D7**, 1888 (1973) and K. Symanzik "Renormalization of Theories with Broken Symmetries", in Cargése Lectures (1970), D. Bessis, ed. (Gordon and Breach, N.Y., 1972).
6. H. B. Callen, *Thermodynamics* (John Wiley, N.Y., 1960), Chap. 5.
7. H. Goldstein, *Classical Mechanics* (Addison-Wesley, Reading, Mass., 1950) Chap. 7.
8. For the appearance of this phenomenon in particle physics see, e.g., S. Coleman and E. Weinberg, *Physical Reveiw,* **D7**, 1888 (1973), and S. Coleman, R. Jackiw and H. D. Politzer, *Physical Review,* **D10**, 2491 (1974).
9. See, e.g., Chap. 9 of H. Callen, Ref. 6 above.
10. J. Goldstone, *Nuovo Cimento,* **19**, 154 (1961). In the context of statistical physics see, e.g., R. V. Lange, *Physical Review,* **146**, 301 (1966) and H. Wagner, *Zeitschrift für Physik,* **195**, 273 (1966).
11. B. W. Lee, Ref. 5 above, and E. S. Abers and B. W. Lee, *Physics Reports,* **9C**, 1 (1973).
12. J. Zinn-Justin, Ref. 4-7, K. Symanzik in Ref. 4-7 and KS.
13. D. J. Amit, *Journal of Physics,* **A9**, 1441 (1976).
14. Abers and Lee, Ref. 11.

EXPANSIONS IN THE NUMBER OF LOOPS
AND IN THE NUMBER OF COMPONENTS

6-1 INTRODUCTION

In the present chapter we will study two types of approximations in which the various quantities in the theory can be calculated explicitly. Both approximations belong to a systematic expansion in a parameter – other than the coupling constants. The first is an expansion in which the terms are classified by the number of loops (or internal integrations) they contain. As we shall show in the next section, if $\mathscr{L} \to a^{-1} \mathscr{L}$, then the above is an expansion in powers of a. In quantum field theory it is an expansion in powers of $\hbar$ – an expansion about the classical theory.

In this chain of approximations the first one is the tree approximation or the Landau–Ginzburg theory.[1] Within this theory one can see broken symmetry and Goldstone bosons. At this level no divergences occur and one has a self-contained theory. To see that at some values of the parameters the fluctuations become large and that one cannot expect a good approximation to the exact theory, one has to go beyond trees.

The generating functional can be calculated in the one-loop approximation. This exhibits the instability in the ordered – broken symmetry – phase, as well as the resurgence of divergences. It provides a first taste of mass and coupling constant renormalization. On the same level we find that the scale of the composite operator ϕ^2 must also be renormalized. The scale of the operator ϕ has to be renormalized only at the two-loop level — which shows that the renormalization of ϕ and ϕ^2 are independent.

Finally, we study briefly an expansion which classifies the graphs in a ϕ^4 theory with O(M) symmetry by their dependence on M. The lowest order term in this expansion in powers of M^{-1}, is the well-known spherical model of Berlin and Kac,[2] which is currently being rediscovered by field theorists.[3] Again, to lowest order, in M^{-1}, Γ can be calculated in closed form, and another self-contained theory — rather different from either the Gaussian theory, or from the loop expansion — can be fully calculated and studied.

6-2 THE EXPANSION IN THE NUMBER OF LOOPS AS A POWER SERIES[4]

Consider a field theory with a Lagrangian $a^{-1} \mathcal{L}$. The generating functional will be:

$$Z\{J\} = \mathcal{N}_1 \exp\left\{-\int a^{-1} \mathcal{L}_I\left(\frac{\delta}{\delta J}\right)\right\} \int \mathcal{D}\phi \exp\left\{-\frac{1}{2}\int \phi a^{-1} G_0^{-1}\phi + \int J\phi\right\}$$

in which the variables are not written explicitly, since they are immaterial to the argument. When the free part is integrated over ϕ one obtains an exponential of a quadratic form in the J's, with the inverse of $a^{-1} G_0^{-1}$, i.e., aG_0. The result is:

$$Z\{J\} = \mathcal{N}\exp\left\{-\int a^{-1} \mathcal{L}_I\left(\frac{\delta}{\delta J}\right)\right\} \exp\left\{\frac{1}{2}\int JaG_0 J\right\} \qquad (6\text{-}1)$$

If we use this generating functional to obtain the graphical expansion, the only change from our previous procedure is that (i) every interaction vertex has to be multiplied by a^{-1}, (ii) every internal line (propagator) has to be multiplied by a.

Consider a general graph of nth order in perturbation theory, belonging to a vertex function with E external points, and having I internal lines, it will be multiplied by a^{I-n}. On the other hand, in momentum space we have an integration for every internal line, but a momentum conserving δ function for every vertex. Remembering that only $n - 1$ of the δ functions will be effective in suppressing integrations — since one δ function survives to provide overall momentum conservation — we conclude that the number of momentum integrations, is

$$L = I - (n - 1) \qquad (6\text{-}2)$$

This graph will therefore be multiplied by a^{L-1}. Thus, an approximation which keeps only terms up to a certain number of momentum integrations — also called *loops* — is an approximation up to a given power of a.

In quantum field theory $\hbar$ plays the role of a, and thus an expansion in the number of loops, is an expansion in powers of $\hbar$ around the classical theory.

In a theory with a pure monomial interaction, and in the symmetric state, the expansion of every vertex function in the number of loops is also an expansion in the coupling constant. However, even in this case, *an expansion of different functions to the same order in the number of loops, is not of the same order in the interaction.* Compare, for example, Eqs. (6-3) and (6-4) below.

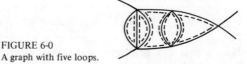

FIGURE 6-0
A graph with five loops.

Example:
In the graph of Fig. 6-1 we have

$$E = 4; \quad n = 5; \quad I = 9, \quad L = 5$$

which satisfy Eq. (6-2).

6-3 THE TREE (LANDAU–GINZBURG) APPROXIMATION

The first approximation to be considered is the one in which there are no loops. In order to construct the generating functional Γ, or the effective potential, we have to determine what is the contribution to each vertex function. Another technique for calculating Γ will be discussed in App. 6-1.

For simplicity we will discuss a ϕ^4 theory, but the number of components will be kept free, requiring only $0(M)$ symmetry. The two-point vertex $\Gamma_{ij}^{(2)}(k_1, k_2)$ consists simply of:

$$\Gamma_{ij}^{(2)}(k_1, k_2) = (2\pi)^d \delta(k_1 + k_2) \delta_{ij}(k_1^2 + \mu^2) \qquad (6\text{-}3)$$

This is its free part. Clearly, any term involving the ϕ^4 coupling constant λ will involve an integration, since in order to leave only two external legs the other two have to be contracted.

As we are calculating in the symmetric state, $\Gamma^{(2N+1)} \equiv 0$, and next comes $\Gamma_{i_1 \ldots i_4}^{(4)}(k_1 \ldots k_4)$. It consists of:

$$\Gamma_{i_1 \ldots i_4}^{(4)}(k_1 \ldots k_4) = (2\pi)^d \delta(\Sigma k_i) \lambda S_{i_1 \ldots i_4} \qquad (6\text{-}4)$$

where the tensor S is the $0(M)$ symmetric tensor defined in Eq. (4-36). One can easily convince oneself that any higher order term in $\Gamma^{(4)}$ has to have loops, and that any vertex part with more than four external points, in a ϕ^4 theory, will include at least one loop.

Rewriting $\Gamma\{\bar{\phi}\}$ in momentum space, as

$$\Gamma\{\bar{\phi}\} = \sum_{N=1}^{\infty} \frac{1}{N!} \sum_{i_1 \dots i_N} \int \prod_{i=1}^{N} \frac{dq_i}{(2\pi)^d} \Gamma_{i_1 \dots i_N}^{(N)}(q_1, \dots, q_N) \bar{\phi}_{i_1}(-q_1) \dots \bar{\phi}_{i_N}(-q_N)$$

$$(6\text{-}5)$$

the zero-loop approximation takes on the form†:

$$\Gamma_0\{\bar{\phi}\} = \frac{1}{2!} \int dq_1 \, dq_2 \, \delta(q_1 + q_2)(q_1^2 + \mu^2) \sum_{i_1} \bar{\phi}_{i_1}(-q_1)\bar{\phi}_{i_1}(-q_2)$$

$$+ \frac{\lambda}{4!} \int dq_1 \dots dq_4 \, \delta(\Sigma q_i) S_{i_1 \dots i_4} \bar{\phi}_{i_1}(-q_1) \dots \bar{\phi}_{i_4}(-q_4) \qquad (6\text{-}6)$$

Notice that this is exactly the action, $\int \mathcal{L} dx$, in which the fluctuating quantum field has been replaced by the classical average field. The corresponding expression in coordinate space is:

$$\Gamma_0\{\bar{\phi}\} = \frac{1}{2} \int dx \, [(\nabla \bar{\Phi})^2 + \mu^2 \bar{\Phi}^2] + \frac{\lambda}{4!} \int dx \, [\bar{\phi}^2(x)]^2 \qquad (6\text{-}7)$$

which is just the Landau–Ginzburg free energy functional, as well as the classical action of the Lagrangian. The case of more general Lagrangians is left as Exercise 6-1. Compare also with App. 6-1.

In the presence of an external field $J(x)$ we will have

$$J_i(x) = \frac{\delta\Gamma\{\bar{\phi}\}}{\delta\bar{\phi}_i(x)} = (-\nabla^2 + \mu^2) \, \bar{\phi}_i(x) + \frac{\lambda}{3!} S_{ijkl} \bar{\phi}_j(x)\bar{\phi}_k(x)\bar{\phi}_l(x) \qquad (6\text{-}8)$$

which, as $J \to 0$, is the Landau–Ginzburg equation, or the classical field equation, obtained by a variation of the action with respect to the field.

To determine the symmetry of the state we should take a uniform $\bar{\phi}$, and compute U. The result is the Landau free energy given by:

$$U(\Phi) = \frac{1}{2}\mu^2(\Phi)^2 + \frac{\lambda}{4!}(\Phi^2)^2 \qquad (6\text{-}9)$$

Note that since we have approximated the free part by k^2, any non-uniformity in space will increase Γ_0, in Eq. (6-7). Thus the uniform distribution $\bar{\phi} = \Phi$ which minimizes (6-9) will also minimize (6-7).

In (6-9) we must assume $\lambda > 0$, otherwise U is unbounded from below. If also $\mu^2 \geqslant 0$, i.e., $T > T_0$ (see Eq. (2-62)), then $U(\Phi)$ is monotonically increasing with Φ. The only minimum is at $\Phi = 0$ — no symmetry breaking. This implies that the transition temperature of the Landau theory is the same as that for the Gaussian approximation.

---

† From now on we omit the $(2\pi)^d$ which is implied by every momentum integral, and every momentum δ function.

If $\mu^2 < 0$, $U(\Phi)$ develops side minima as a function of $(\Phi)^2$. These minima are at

$$(\Phi)^2 = -6\frac{\mu^2}{\lambda} > 0 \qquad (6\text{-}10)$$

All directions in the space of the components of Φ are equivalent. We choose the direction in which the symmetry is broken as the Mth component, and write:

$$v_i = 0 \qquad (i = 1, \ldots, M-1)$$
$$v_M = \left(-6\frac{\mu^2}{\lambda}\right)^{1/2} \qquad (6\text{-}11)$$

and define new classical fields, shifting by the spontaneous average,

$$\pi_i(x) = \bar{\phi}_i(x)$$
$$\sigma(x) = \bar{\phi}_M(x) - v_M \qquad (6\text{-}12)$$

(see Exercises 6-4–6-5).

The gradient term in $\Gamma_0\{\bar{\phi}\}$, Eq. (6-7), is unaffected by the constant shift. The local part becomes:

$$\frac{1}{2}\mu^2 \sum_{i=1}^{M} \bar{\phi}_i^2 + \frac{\lambda}{4!}\left(\sum_{i=1}^{M} \bar{\phi}_i^2\right)^2 = \frac{1}{2}\mu^2 \left(\sum_{i=1}^{M-1} \pi_i^2 + \sigma^2 + 2v_M\sigma + v_M^2\right)$$

$$+ \frac{\lambda}{4!}(\Sigma\pi_i^2 + \sigma^2 + 2v_M\sigma + v_M^2)^2 = \frac{\lambda}{3!}v_M^2\sigma^2 + \frac{\lambda}{3!}v_M\sigma(\Sigma\pi_i^2 + \sigma^2) + \frac{\lambda}{4!}(\Sigma\pi_i^2 + \sigma^2)^2$$

where use has been made of Eq. (6-11) and a term independent of π_i and σ has been dropped. The first term on the right-hand side can be further modified, using (6-11), to read

$$\frac{\lambda}{3!}v_M^2\sigma^2 = -\mu^2\sigma^2 = \frac{1}{2}(-2\mu^2)\sigma^2 \qquad (6\text{-}13)$$

Recall that we are in the region where $\mu^2 < 0$, and hence $-2\mu^2 > 0$.

In terms of the π and σ fields, Γ_0 in Eq. (6-7) becomes:

$$\Gamma_0\{\pi, \sigma\} = \frac{1}{2}\int dx\,[(\nabla\pi)^2 + (\nabla\sigma)^2 + (-2\mu^2)\sigma^2] + \frac{\lambda v_M}{3!}\int dx\,\sigma(\pi^2 + \sigma^2)$$

$$+ \frac{\lambda}{4!}\int dx\,(\pi^2 + \sigma^2)^2 \qquad (6\text{-}14)$$

In order to read off the vertex functions it is more convenient to go again into momentum space, where:

$$\Gamma_0\{\pi, \sigma\} = \frac{1}{2}\int dq_1 \ dq_2 \delta(q_1 + q_2)$$

$$\left[q_1^2 \sum_{i=1}^{M-1} \pi_i(q_1)\pi_i(q_2) + (q_1^2 + |\ 2\mu^2\ |)\sigma(q_1)\sigma(q_2) \right]$$

$$+ \frac{\lambda v_M}{3!}\int dq_1 \ dq_2 \ dq_3 \delta(\Sigma q_i)\sigma(q_1)[\Sigma \pi_i(q_2)\pi_i(q_3) + \sigma(q_2)\sigma(q_3)]$$

$$+ \frac{\lambda}{4!}\int dq_1 \ldots dq_4 \delta(\Sigma q_i)[(\pi^2 + \sigma^2)^2](q_1 \ldots, q_4) \qquad (6\text{-}15)$$

Above the transition, in the symmetric state, we can read the vertex functions directly from (6-6) and we find (6-3) and (6-4), of course. Below, we can use (6-15), which is already an expansion in $\boldsymbol{\phi} - v = (\pi, \sigma)$. Thus:

$$\Gamma_{\pi\pi}^{(2)}(q) = q^2 \qquad (6\text{-}16)$$

which are the $M - 1$ Goldstone bosons. $\Gamma_{\pi\pi}^{(2)} \to 0$ as $q \to 0$. The σ propagator is:

$$\Gamma_{\sigma\sigma}^{(2)}(q) = q^2 + 2\ |\mu\ |^2 \qquad (6\text{-}17)$$

It has a finite mass whose square is twice that of the propagator above, for the same absolute value of μ^2 in the Lagrangian.

Below the transition we find also that three-point vertices appear, they are:

$$\Gamma_{\sigma\pi\pi}(q_1, q_2, q_3) = \frac{1}{3}\lambda v_M \delta(\Sigma q_i) \qquad (6\text{-}18)$$

$$\Gamma_{\sigma\sigma\sigma}(q_1, q_2, q_3) = \lambda v_M \delta(\Sigma q_i) \qquad (6\text{-}19)$$

These should be compared with Exercise 6-6.

Notice that the generating functional in the ordered state still has an $0(M - 1)$ symmetry between the $M - 1$ Goldstone bosons. Furthermore, since the approximation treats the whole Lagrangian on the same footing, all the conclusions following from the spontaneous breaking of a continuous symmetry are preserved, though the proof was carried through for the exact theory. (See, e.g., Exercises 6-3 and 6-4.)

From the results listed above we can conclude that

$$\eta = 0; \beta = \tfrac{1}{2}\ ; \gamma = 1; \nu = \tfrac{1}{2}$$

The dominant term in the specific heat will come from the term in the free energy which is independent of the order parameter. It is the term which was calculated in Sec. 2-5-4. There we found (Eq. (2-85)), that

$$\alpha = \tfrac{1}{2} (4 - d)$$

which implies a divergent specific heat for $d < 4$. The additional contribution due to the ordering introduces the familiar discontinuity of the Landau theory. The analysis of the scaling laws satisfied by this theory is left as Exercise 6-7. See also Exercises 6-8–6-9.

6-4 THE ONE-LOOP APPROXIMATION AND THE GINZBURG CRITERION

As was mentioned above, the Landau theory is a self-contained theory. The only way of detecting the limits of its validity is to consider it as one rung in a ladder of approximations to the full theory. The loop expansion provides the natural framework for this discussion. In fact, Ginzburg[5] who introduced the criterion to detect the breakdown of the Landau theory, was implicitly assuming such a wider framework. Within the tree approximation there simply are no fluctuations. These appear first on the one-loop level.

To calculate the effective potential we need the vertex parts, including one loop, in the symmetric state. Using the relation connecting the number of loops to the number of internal lines and to the order in perturbation theory, Eq. (6-2), we find for $L = 1$

$$I = n \qquad (6\text{-}20)$$

In a ϕ^4 theory the number of internal lines I, of external lines E, and of the order in perturbation theory n are related via the equation

$$4n - E = 2I \qquad (6\text{-}21)$$

Thus, together with (6-20), we have

$$n = \tfrac{1}{2} E \qquad (6\text{-}22)$$

E must, of course, be even, and thus one finds the graphs shown in Fig. 6-1.

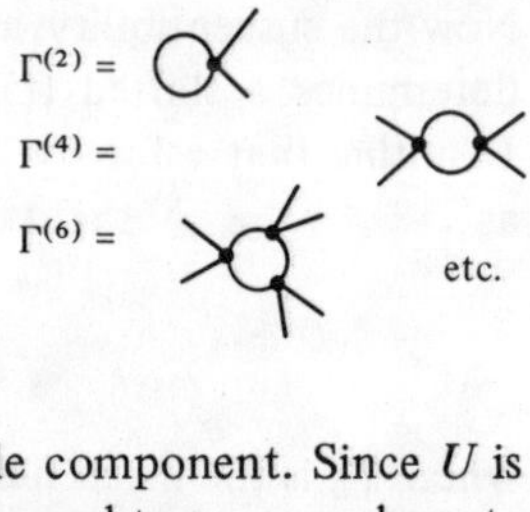

FIGURE 6-1
One-loop graphs of $\Gamma^{(E)}$.

Next we restrict ourselves to a field with a single component. Since U is calculated with all momenta in the vertex functions set equal to zero, we have to calculate the symmetry factor of a graph with a given distribution of p_i and then

$$4n \times 3 \times 4(n-1) \times 3 \cdots = 12^n\, n!$$

$$2(n-1) \times 2(n-2) \cdots = 2^{n-1}(n-1)!$$

$$\frac{(2n)!}{2^n\, n!}$$

$$\left\{ 12^n n!\, 2^{n-1}(n-1)! \right\} \left\{ \frac{(2n)!}{2^n n!} \right\} \left\{ \frac{1}{(2n)!} \right\} \left\{ \left(\frac{\lambda}{4!}\right)^n \frac{1}{n!} \right\}$$

$$= \frac{1}{2n}\left(-\frac{\lambda}{2}\right)^n$$

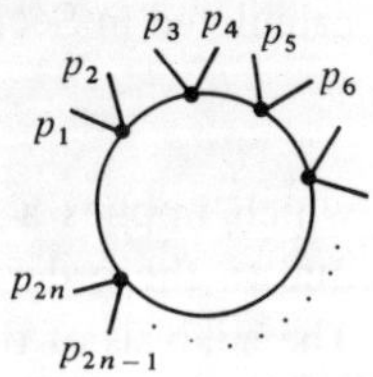

FIGURE 6-2

multiply by the number of distinct ways of distributing the p_i's (see Fig. 6-2). Finally, we have to multiply by an additional $(E!)^{-1} = (2n!)^{-1}$.

The result for $U_1(\Phi)$ is:

$$U_1(\Phi) = -\sum_{n=1}^{\infty} \frac{1}{2n} \left(-\tfrac{1}{2}\lambda\Phi^2\right)^n \int dq\, \frac{1}{(q^2+\mu^2)^n} \qquad (6\text{-}23)$$

the derivation is left as Exercises 6-10 to 6-11. This series can be summed to give:

$$U_1(\Phi) = \frac{1}{2}\int dq \ln\left(1 + \frac{\lambda\Phi^2/2}{q^2+\mu^2}\right) \qquad (6\text{-}24)$$

Adding to it the zero-loop contribution we arrive at the effective potential calculated up to the order of one loop:

$$U(\Phi) = \frac{1}{2}\mu^2\Phi^2 + \frac{\lambda}{4!}\Phi^4 + \frac{1}{2}\int dq \ln\left(q^2+\mu^2+\frac{\lambda\Phi^2}{2}\right) \qquad (6\text{-}25)$$

where we have reintroduced the free part of the free energy, Eq. (2.83).

The first use to which one can put (6-25) is to determine the limit of validity of the Landau theory. The susceptibility of the system to a uniform external field, to use the language of magnetism, is the inverse of the coefficient of $\frac{1}{2}\Phi^2$, namely,

$$\chi^{-1} = \mu^2 + \frac{\lambda}{2}\int dq\, \frac{1}{q^2+\mu^2} \qquad (6\text{-}26)$$

Now the susceptibility no longer diverges at $\mu^2 = 0$. Instead the vanishing of χ^{-1} determines a shifted transition temperature — lower than the mean field one. Denoting that value by μ_c^2 we can rewrite the condition for a transition to occur as

$$\mu_c^2 = T_c - T_0 = -\frac{\lambda}{2}\int dq\, \frac{1}{q^2+\mu_c^2} \qquad (6\text{-}27)$$

where T_0 is the mean field transition temperature.

Notice that all the manipulations carried out above are meaningful only if the integral is cut off at high momenta. This is indeed the case in statistical physics. In quantum field theory the relation between μ_c^2 and μ^2 involves infinite terms about which the theory has nothing to say.

If the loop expansion is an expansion in a small parameter, then we can set $\mu_c^2 = 0$ in the integrand on the right-hand side of (6-27), since the expansion in μ_c^2 will generate terms with an increasing number of loops. Thus we find, to the order of one loop,

$$T_c = T_0 - \frac{\lambda}{2} \int dq \, \frac{1}{q^2} \qquad (6\text{-}28)$$

The transition temperature has been depressed.

Coming back to (6-26) we can now express things in terms of the temperature difference from the "true" transition temperature T_c. For μ^2 we have:

$$\mu^2 = \mu_c^2 + T - T_c = \mu_c^2 + \delta T \qquad (6\text{-}29)$$

Keeping terms consistently to the order of one loop, (6-26) can be written as:

$$\chi^{-1} = \delta T + \frac{\lambda}{2} \int dq \, \frac{1}{q^2 + \chi^{-1}} + \mu_c^2 = \delta T + \frac{\lambda}{2} \int dq \left(\frac{1}{q^2 + \chi^{-1}} - \frac{1}{q^2} \right)$$

$$= \delta T - \frac{\lambda}{2} \chi^{-1} \int dq \, \frac{1}{q^2(q^2 + \chi^{-1})} \qquad (6\text{-}30)$$

The Landau theory predicts χ^{-1} to be linear in the temperature difference from the transition temperature. Thus, the systematic way of stating the Ginzburg criterion[6] — or of finding the limit of applicability of the Landau theory — is to say that the Landau theory breaks down where

$$\frac{\lambda}{2} \int dq \, \frac{1}{q^2(q^2 + \delta T)} \approx 1 \qquad (6\text{-}31)$$

Above four dimensions the integral is finite for all values of δT. If λ is small enough, the left-hand side can stay small relative to 1, and the Gaussian theory remains valid all the way to the transition temperature. On the other hand, below four dimensions the integral on the left-hand side has an infrared divergence as $\delta T \to 0$. Consequently for any value of λ, the Landau theory will break down as the transition is approached. It turns out[6] that this same condition, Eq. (6-31), indicates the breakdown of the Landau theory for all thermodynamic quantities, both above and below the transition (see, e.g., Exercise 6-12).

If one were to take Eq. (6-30) as a description of a theory, in which the second term on the right-hand side becomes important, but the higher order terms still negligible, the result would be (see Exercise 6-13) that

$$\chi \sim (T - T_c)^{-2/(d-2)}$$

However, when the one-loop correction becomes important one faces a real catastrophe, since the contributions of diagrams with any number of loops become equally important. There is though one case in which (6-30) becomes exact. That is the limit of a field theory with an infinite number of components, which we shall discuss later.

Before turning our attention to the divergences which appear in the one-loop approximation, we note that $U(\Phi)$ in Eq. (6-25) will develop an imaginary part in the ordered state $-\mu^2$ or δT negative $-$ if U is evaluated for Φ such that

$$\Phi^2 \leqslant \frac{2|\mu^2|}{\lambda} \qquad (6\text{-}32)$$

In this range the argument of the logarithm in Eq. (6-25) will be negative, expressing the instability in the two-phase region, which was mentioned in the previous chapter. It should be pointed out that the instability appears too late. After all, the spontaneous value of Φ^2 according to Eq. (6-11) is $6|\mu^2|/\lambda$. Hence the argument of the previous section leads us to expect that it is there that instabilities should manifest themselves, rather than at the much smaller value of $2|\mu^2|/\lambda$. The problem is that the loop expansion is not rich enough to provide a Maxwell construction, insuring the convexity of the effective potential. Our formula for U allows us to penetrate into the coexistence region until a real instability $-$ negative susceptibility $-$ appears. This situation is portrayed in Fig. 6-3.

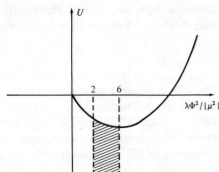

FIGURE 6-3
The form of the effective potential below the transition.

6-5   MASS AND COUPLING CONSTANT RENORMALIZATION IN THE ONE-LOOP APPROXIMATION

Consider again $U(\Phi)$, Eq. (6-25), or χ^{-1}, Eq. (6-26). Both will diverge in the ultraviolet $-$ when $\Lambda \to \infty$ $-$ if the number of dimensions will be greater than two. In both quantities we can absorb this divergence into a newly defined parameter. One such possibility was exhibited in the previous section: it was χ^{-1}, which played the role of a mass squared. If we denote χ^{-1} by m_1^2 we can write (6-30) as:

$$m_1^2 = \delta T - \frac{\lambda m_1^2}{2} \int \frac{1}{q^2(q^2 + m_1^2)} \tag{6-33}$$

$$U(\Phi) = \frac{1}{2} m_1^2 \Phi^2 + \frac{\lambda}{4!} \Phi^4 + \frac{1}{2} \int \ln \left(q^2 + m_1^2 + \frac{\lambda \Phi^2}{2} \right) - \frac{\lambda \Phi^2}{4} \int \frac{1}{q^2 + m_1^2} \tag{6-34}$$

where we have further economized the notation by dropping the dq. What have we gained?

In the case of quantum field theory, where there is no a priori cutoff, we obtain χ^{-1}, $U(\Phi)$ (apart from a Φ independent constant $-\int \ln q^2$) and all vertex parts finite, as long as $d < 4$. We paid a price of course. Our new parameter m_1^2, which we take to be finite, is an arbitrary parameter. The original parameter μ^2 is related to m_1^2 via

$$\mu^2 = m_1^2 - \frac{\lambda}{2} \int \frac{1}{q^2 + m_1^2} \tag{6-35}$$

and is thus infinite and meaningless. Nevertheless this appears to be a worthwhile price to pay for a finite theory. Especially if we realize that we did not know μ^2 any better than m_1^2.

At the one-loop level the two-point vertex in the symmetric phase is given by

$$\Gamma^{(2)}(k) = k^2 + \chi^{-1} = k^2 + m_1^2 \tag{6-36}$$

which is also finite.

As far as critical phenomena are concerned, there is no intrinsic need to redefine the parameter μ^2. However, nothing could be more natural. First, it is clear that χ^{-1} $(= m_1^2)$ is the parameter which becomes small as we approach the transition. This selects it, rather than μ^2, as a measure of the distance to the transition. Second, the critical behavior is dominated by low-momentum (large-scale) fluctuations. Thus, the presence of a microscopic cutoff should be unimportant. In fact, since the integrals in (6-33) or (6-34) converge in the ultraviolet the upper limit in these integrals can be extended to infinity as long

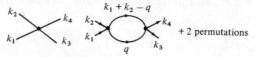

FIGURE 6-4
The graphs of $\Gamma^{(4)}(k_1, \ldots, k_4)$ to one-loop order.

as $d < 4$, the difference being very small. The only quantity which depends on the cutoff in an important way is the shift in the transition temperature – Eq. (6-27).

Anticipating the future we name m_1^2 *the renormalized mass*. Next we consider the four-point vertex in the symmetric state. The graphs, to one-loop order, are given in Fig. 6-4, where $\Sigma k_i = 0$. The corresponding algebraic expressions are:

$$\Gamma^{(4)}(k_i) = \lambda - \frac{\lambda^2}{2} \int \frac{1}{(q^2 + \mu^2)[(k_1 + k_2 - q)^2 + \mu^2]} + 2 \text{ permutations} \qquad (6\text{-}37)$$

If μ^2 is replaced by m_1^2 the difference is again of higher order in the number of loops. $\Gamma^{(4)}$ is finite as long as $d < 4$, when the cutoff is set to infinity. It behaves in a similar way to the relation between m_1^2 and δT, Eq. (6-33), in that it has an infrared divergence as $m_1^2 \to 0$ for $d < 4$, and as $d \to 4$ an ultraviolet logarithmic divergence develops in both. No other vertex function has an ultraviolet divergence at $d = 4$.

But, of course, it is at $d = 4$ that quantum field theory operates. Furthermore, as we have seen above, $d = 4$ is just the dimension which divides a well-defended classical theory $(d > 4)$ from a necessarily non-classical critical behavior $(d < 4)$. Thus, if we want to be able to expand the theory as a continuous deviation from a classical theory, we should include $d = 4$ in its range of allowed dimensions. Moreover, as we have argued at the beginning of this section, there is a definite advantage in formulating the theory in terms of integrals which converge as $\Lambda \to \infty$, since in this way the microscopic details are isolated. As a result, the same means as would be applied to the treatment of the intrinsic divergence at four dimensions in quantum field theory will be very useful for the discussion of critical phenomena.

Again, $U(\Phi)$, Eq. (6-34), will also diverge if $\Lambda \to \infty$, at $d = 4$, reflecting the divergence of $\Gamma^{(4)}$. This gives us a clue about what has to be done. The only divergent term is the one proportional to Φ^4. Hence, one can absorb the divergence by a redefinition of the coupling constant by analogy with the absorption of the divergence of the coefficient of Φ^2 in a redefined mass. We write:

$$\frac{\lambda}{4!} - \frac{\lambda^2}{16} \int \frac{1}{(q^2 + m_1^2)^2} = \frac{g_1}{4!} \qquad (6\text{-}38)$$

The new parameter g_1 is called the *renormalized coupling constant*. Clearly the λ^2 in front of the integral can be replaced by g_1^2. The difference is of higher order in the loop expansion. $U(\Phi)$ will now read:

$$U(\Phi) = \frac{1}{2}m_1^2\Phi^2 + \frac{g_1}{4!}\Phi^4 + \frac{1}{2}\int \ln(q^2 + m_1^2 + \tfrac{1}{2}g_1\Phi^2) - \frac{g_1\Phi^2}{4}\int \frac{1}{q^2 + m_1^2}$$

$$+ \frac{1}{16}g_1^2\Phi^4 \int \frac{1}{(q^2 + m_1^2)^2} \qquad (6\text{-}39)$$

If in (6-39) m_1^2 and g_1 are finite, then $U(\Phi)$ is finite when $\Lambda \to \infty$ as long as $d < 6$ and $m_1^2 \neq 0$. For finite cutoff Λ the new parameters are connected to the original ones by well-defined relations, namely,

$$\mu^2 = m_1^2 - \frac{g_1}{2} \int \frac{1}{q^2 + m_1^2} \tag{6-40}$$

$$\lambda = g_1 + \tfrac{3}{2} g_1^2 \int \frac{1}{(q^2 + m_1^2)^2} \tag{6-41}$$

where λ in (6-35) and in (6-38) has been replaced by g_1. The difference is of higher order in the loop expansion. In a theory without a cutoff, finite m_1^2 and g_1 imply infinite *bare* parameters μ^2 and λ in four dimensions.

In a relation like (6-33), which gives the susceptibility — equal to m_1^{-2} at this stage — in terms of the bare parameter δT, we can also replace λ by g_1. But without a cutoff the relation will be meaningful only if $d < 4$. On the other hand, we can now set $\Lambda \to \infty$ in $U(\Phi)$, even in the application to statistical physics, the differences at $d = 4$ will be very small. As far as the four-point function is concerned we consider (6-37) with λ-replaced by (6-41), and keep terms consistently to the order of one loop. Then:

$$\Gamma^{(4)}(k_i) = g_1 - \frac{g_1^2}{2} \int \left[\frac{1}{(q^2 + m_1^2)[(k_1 + k_2 - q)^2 + m_1^2]} - \frac{1}{(q^2 + m_1^2)^2} \right]$$

$$+ 2 \text{ permutations} \tag{6-42}$$

In terms of the new parameters, $\Gamma^{(4)}(k_i)$ is finite below $d = 6$. It is easy to see that all higher vertices will be finite as well (see, e.g., Exercise 6-14).

Notice that the choice of m_1^2 and g_1 we have made is rather special. It happens to be the values of $\Gamma^{(2)}$ and $\Gamma^{(4)}$, respectively, in the symmetric state at zero external momenta. Equation (6-36) implies that

$$m_1^2 = \Gamma^{(2)}(k = 0) = \left. \frac{\partial^2 U}{\partial \Phi^2} \right|_{\Phi = 0} \tag{6-43}$$

and Eq. (6-42) implies that

$$g_1 = \Gamma^{(4)}(k_i = 0) = \left. \frac{\partial^4 U}{\partial \Phi^4} \right|_{\Phi = 0} \tag{6-44}$$

If the objective is to render the theory finite, a large amount of freedom is available in the choice of the renormalized mass and coupling constant. We could have just as well chosen the relations (6-37) and (6-38) at some non-zero momenta, or at a value of $\Phi \neq 0$. In fact, if the theory is studied at its critical point — in its zero-mass limit — one is forced into one of the above alternatives. Otherwise infrared divergences will plague the theory, making such equations as (6-39) meaningless. This extra freedom, which leaves all physical quantities invariant, is just what underlies the renormalization group, which we shall study in the following chapters.

For the moment we turn to consider some other quantities which need to be renormalized.

6-6   COMPOSITE FIELD RENORMALIZATION

A special feature of the one-loop approximation in a ϕ^4 theory is that the two-point function has the same momentum dependence as on the zero-loop level. This conceals the fact that one more quantity, apart from the mass and coupling constant, has to be renormalized before all functions with fields at different points are finite. This last quantity is the *scale of the field*.

Before discussing situations in which this additional renormalization is required, we will show that even on the one-loop level there exist operators which give rise to infinite vertex functions, while all the single field products are finite.

Consider, for example, the operator $\phi^2(k)$ defined by

$$\phi^2(k) \equiv \frac{1}{2} \int dx \, \exp(ikx)\phi^2(x) = \frac{1}{2} \int \frac{dp_1}{(2\pi)^d} \, \phi(p_1)\phi(k - p_1) \qquad (6\text{-}45)$$

The vertex function $\Gamma^{(2,1)}(k_1, k_2; k_3)$, corresponding to the Green function $\langle \phi(k_1)\phi(k_2)\phi^2(k_3) \rangle$, contains, up to the one-loop level, the graphs shown in

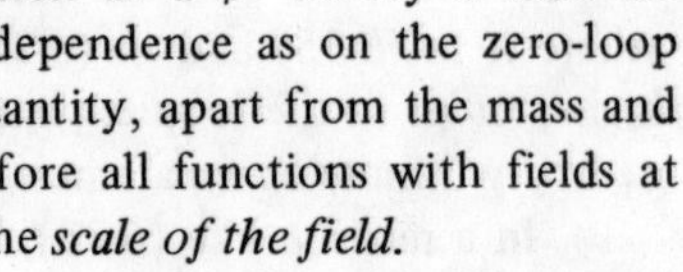

FIGURE 6-5
Graphs of $\Gamma^{(2,1)}$ to one-loop level.

Fig. 6-5 (see Secs. 4-7 and 5-7) which are calculated without their external legs, and the factor $(2\pi)^d \, \delta(k_1 + k_2 + k_3)$ omitted. The result is:

$$\Gamma^{(2,1)}(k_1, k_2; k_3) = 1 - \frac{\lambda}{2} \int \frac{1}{(q^2 + \mu^2)[(k_3 + q)^2 + \mu^2]} \qquad (6\text{-}46a)$$

in which $k_3 = -(k_1 + k_2)$. This expression is rather similar to the four-point function discussed in the previous section, Eq. (6-37). Yet there is an important difference. Both terms in $\Gamma^{(4)}$ depend on λ, while in $\Gamma^{(2,1)}$ only the second one does. But it was just the interplay between these two terms which allowed us, by a redefinition of the coupling constant, to absorb the divergence which appears in the second term at four dimensions. Here this cannot be done.

Of course, $\Gamma^{(2,1)}$ can be reexpressed in terms of the renormalized quantities, m_1^2 and g_1:

$$\Gamma^{(2,1)}(k_1, k_2; k_3) = 1 - \frac{g_1}{2} \int \frac{1}{(q^2 + m_1^2)[(q + k_3)^2 + m_1^2]} \qquad (6\text{-}46b)$$

the difference being of higher order in the number of loops. But even after the substitution of m_1^2 and g_1, $\Gamma^{(2,1)}$ diverges at $d = 4$ as $\Lambda \to \infty$.

This divergence can be removed by multiplying $\Gamma^{(2,1)}$ by a number independent of the momenta. This number, which will depend on m_1^2 on g_1 and on Λ, can be chosen for example as the inverse of $\Gamma^{(2,1)}(k_i = 0)$. Thus, defining $\Gamma_R^{(2,1)}$ via

$$\Gamma_R^{(2,1)}(k_1, k_2; k_3) = Z_{\phi^2}^1 \Gamma^{(2,1)}(k_1, k_2; k_3)$$

$$\equiv \left[1 - \frac{g_1}{2} \int \frac{1}{(q^2 + m_1^2)^2} \right]^{-1} \Gamma^{(2,1)}(k_i) \qquad (6\text{-}47)$$

where the subscript R stands for renormalized, we find by keeping terms to one-loop order:

$$\Gamma_R^{(2,1)}(k_i) = 1 - \frac{g_1}{2} \int \left[\frac{1}{(q^2 + m_1^2)[(q + k_3)^2 + m_1^2]} - \frac{1}{(q^2 + m_1^2)^2} \right] \qquad (6\text{-}48)$$

This expression is finite for $d < 6$. As long as the cutoff is finite $Z_{\phi^2}^1$ is well defined and is given by

$$Z_{\phi^2}^1(g_1, m_1^2, \Lambda) = 1 + \frac{g_1}{2} \int^{\Lambda} \frac{1}{(q^2 + m_1^2)^2} \qquad (6\text{-}49)$$

Its introduction in problems of statistical physics is unnecessary. But, since in $\Gamma_R^{(2,1)}$ we can set $\Lambda \to \infty$, $Z_{\phi^2}^1$ allows us to lump the dependence on the microscopic cutoff into a multiplicative factor. In the remainder, the dependence on the cutoff becomes a tiny correction which can be neglected, or treated as a perturbation (see, e.g., Sec. 10-2).

In quantum field theory $Z_{\phi^2}^1$ is infinite, but its introduction makes all vertex functions, with any number of ϕ^2 operators, finite at $d = 4$ (see Exercises 6-15 and 6-16). All except the vertex corresponding to $\langle \phi^2(k)\phi^2(-k) \rangle$ (see Exercise 6-17).

6-7 RENORMALIZATION OF THE FIELD AT THE TWO-LOOP LEVEL

The last concept that is needed for the general discussion of renormalization appears in the calculation to the order of two loops. While a general expression for $U(\Phi)$ is rather difficult to obtain, the two-point and the four-point functions in the symmetric state can be explicitly discussed, as can be any single vertex function.[7]

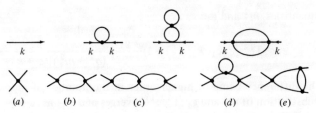

FIGURE 6-6
The two- and four-point functions to order two loops.

In terms of graphs these two functions are given in Fig. 6-6. The main difference is that now the last term in $\Gamma^{(2)}$ depends on k. If we choose to eliminate the quadratic ultraviolet divergence in $\Gamma^{(2)}$, which is present in the last three terms on the right-hand side, the result will not be as simple as (6-36). For setting

$$m_1^2 = \Gamma^{(2)}(k = 0) \qquad (6\text{-}50)$$

as in (6-43), leads to

$$m_1^2 = \mu^2 + \frac{\lambda}{2}D_1(\mu^2, \Lambda) - \frac{\lambda^2}{4}D_2(\mu^2, \Lambda)D_1(\mu^2, \Lambda) - \frac{\lambda^2}{6}D_3(0, \mu^2, \Lambda) \qquad (6\text{-}51)$$

where

$$D_1(\mu^2, \Lambda) = \int^\Lambda \frac{1}{q^2 + \mu^2} \qquad (6\text{-}52)$$

$$D_2(\mu^2, \Lambda) = \int^\Lambda \frac{1}{(q^2 + \mu^2)^2} \qquad (6\text{-}53)$$

$$D_3(k, \mu^2, \Lambda) = \int^\Lambda \frac{1}{(q_1^2 + \mu^2)(q_2^2 + \mu^2)[(k - q_1 - q_2)^2 + \mu^2]} \qquad (6\text{-}54)$$

The last two terms in (6-51) are already of the order of two loops. Hence μ^2 can be replaced by m_1^2 in these terms. The first term is of the order of one loop. Hence, to be consistent in our expansion, we must write

$$D_1(\mu^2, \Lambda) = \int \frac{1}{q^2 + m_1^2 - \frac{\lambda}{2}D_1(m_1^2, \Lambda)} = D_1(m_1^2, \Lambda) + \frac{\lambda}{2}D_2(m_1^2, \Lambda)D_1(m_1^2, \Lambda) \qquad (6\text{-}55)$$

with corrections of three loops. Hence (6-51) can be rewritten as

$$\mu^2 = m_1^2 - \frac{\lambda}{2}D_1(m_1^2, \Lambda) + \frac{\lambda^2}{6}D_3(0, m_1^2, \Lambda) \qquad (6\text{-}56)$$

which, in the presence of a finite cutoff, is a well-defined expression for μ^2 in terms of the susceptibility.

$\Gamma^{(2)}(k)$ can now be written as:

$$\Gamma^{(2)}(k) = k^2 + m_1^2 - \frac{\lambda^2}{6} [D_3(k, m_1^2, \Lambda) - D_3(0, m_1^2, \Lambda)] \qquad (6\text{-}57)$$

The subtraction in the square brackets reduces the degree of ultraviolet divergence of D_3 by *two* powers of Λ (Exercise 6-18). Consequently, below four dimensions $\Gamma^{(2)}(k)$ of (6-57) is finite. As $d \to 4$ a logarithmic divergence appears in $\Gamma^{(2)}$ — it diverges like $\ln \Lambda$.

Before turning our attention to the removal of this divergence, let us make sure that the renormalization of the coupling constant does not dispose of it. First we notice that as $d \to 4$ a quadratic divergence appears in graph (d) of $\Gamma^{(4)}$ in Fig. 6-6. But this divergence is easily taken care of by the renormalization of the mass. Writing

$$\Gamma^{(4)}(k_i) = \lambda - \frac{\lambda^2}{2} [I(k_1 + k_2, \mu^2, \Lambda) + 2 \text{ permutations}]$$

$$+ \frac{\lambda^3}{4} [I^2(k_1 + k_2, \mu^2, \Lambda) + 2 \text{ permutations}]$$

$$+ \frac{\lambda^3}{2} [I_3(k_1 + k_2, \mu^2, \Lambda) D_1(\mu^2, \Lambda) + 2 \text{ permutations}]$$

$$+ \frac{\lambda^3}{2} [I_4(k_i, \mu^2, \Lambda) + 5 \text{ permutations}] \qquad (6\text{-}58)$$

where

$$I(k, \mu^2, \Lambda) = \int \frac{1}{(q^2 + \mu^2)[(k - q)^2 + \mu^2]} \qquad (6\text{-}59)$$

$$I_3(k, \mu^2, \Lambda) = \int \frac{1}{(q^2 + \mu^2)^2[(k - q)^2 + \mu^2]} \qquad (6\text{-}60)$$

$$I_4(k_i, \mu^2, \Lambda) =$$

$$\int \frac{1}{(q_1^2 + \mu^2)[(k_1 + k_2 - q_1)^2 + \mu^2](q_2^2 + \mu^2)[(k_3 + q_1 + q_2)^2 + \mu^2]} \qquad (6\text{-}61)$$

We note that in the last three terms in (6-58) μ^2 can be simply replaced by m_1^2. The second term in (6-58) is of order one loop, and so it has to be expanded by analogy with (6-55). The result is that the fourth term cancels. This is a typical cancellation due to mass renormalization.

The result after this mass renormalization is:

$$\Gamma^{(4)}(k_i) = \lambda - \frac{\lambda^2}{2}\left[I(k_1 + k_2, m_1^2, \Lambda) + 2 \text{ permutations}\right]$$

$$+ \frac{\lambda^3}{4}\left[I^2(k_1 + k_2, m_1^2, \Lambda) + 2 \text{ permutations}\right]$$

$$+ \frac{\lambda^3}{2}\left[I_4(k_i, m_1^2, \Lambda) + 5 \text{ permutations}\right] \qquad (6\text{-}62)$$

We are left with no divergences for $d < 4$. At $d = 4$ we have logarithmic divergences – *squared ones in the last two terms*. A glance at diagrams (c) and (e) in Fig. 6-6 reveals that each of them includes a subgraph of type (b) which is itself logarithmically divergent (see also Exercise 6-19).

To deal with the logarithmic divergences of $\Gamma^{(4)}$ we define again a new parameter g_1, which is the value of $\Gamma^{(4)}$ with all external momenta set equal to zero (or some other value). Then,

$$g_1 = \lambda - \tfrac{3}{2}\lambda^2 D_2(m_1^2, \Lambda) + \tfrac{3}{4}\lambda^3\left[D_2(m_1^2,\Lambda)\right]^2 + 3\lambda^3 I_4(k_i = 0, m_1^2, \Lambda) \qquad (6\text{-}63)$$

in which we have used D_2 as defined by Eq. (6-53), as well as the fact that all the permutations become equal when $k_i = 0$. The relation (6-63) can be inverted replacing λ by g_1 to order two loops. The result, the proof of which is left as Exercise 6-20, is:

$$\lambda = g_1 + \tfrac{3}{2}g_1^2 D_2(m_1^2, \Lambda) + \tfrac{15}{4}g_1^3[D_2(m_1^2, \Lambda)]^2 - 3g_1^3 I_4(k_i = 0, m_1^2, \Lambda) \qquad (6\text{-}64)$$

Substituting λ in Eq. (6-62), and keeping again terms to order two loops, gives

$$\Gamma^{(4)}(k_i) = g_1 - \tfrac{1}{2}g_1^2\{[I(k_1 + k_2, m_1^2, \Lambda) - D_2(m_1^2, \Lambda)] + 2 \text{ permutations}\}$$

$$+ \tfrac{1}{4}g_1^3\{[I(k_1 + k_2, m_1^2, \Lambda) - D_2(m_1^2, \Lambda)]^2 + 2 \text{ permutations}\}$$

$$+ \tfrac{1}{2}g_1^3\{[I_4(k_i, m_1^2, \Lambda) - I_4(0, m_1^2, \Lambda)]$$

$$- D_2(m_1^2, \Lambda)[I(k_1 + k_2, m_1^2, \Lambda) - D_2(m_1^2, \Lambda)] + 5 \text{ permutations}\}$$

$$(6\text{-}65)$$

It is now clear that in order to express $\Gamma^{(2)}(k)$, Eq. (6-57), in terms of g_1, one simply replaces λ by g_1. The other terms in (6-64) are at least of the order of one loop, and will contribute to order three loops in $\Gamma^{(2)}$. We therefore rewrite $\Gamma^{(2)}$ as:

$$\Gamma^{(2)}(k, m_1^2, g_1) = k^2 + m_1^2 - \frac{g_1^2}{6}[D_3(k, m_1^2, \Lambda) - D_3(0, m_1^2, \Lambda)] \qquad (6\text{-}66)$$

Also μ^2 has to be rewritten in terms of g_1. To the order to which we are calculating, only the second term on the right-hand side of (6-56) is modified by the substitution of (6-64). The result is:

$$\mu^2 = m_1^2 - \tfrac{1}{2}g_1 D_1(m_1^2, \Lambda) - \tfrac{3}{4}g_1^2 D_2(m_1^2, \Lambda)D_1(m_1^2, \Lambda) + \tfrac{1}{6}g_1^2 D_3(0, m_1^2, \Lambda)$$

$$(6\text{-}67)$$

At this stage $\Gamma^{(2)}(k)$ and $\Gamma^{(4)}(k_i)$, as functions of m_1^2 and of g_1, are finite below four dimensions as $\Lambda \to \infty$. On approaching $d = 4$, $\Gamma^{(4)}(k_i, m_1^2, g_1)$ will remain finite. $\Gamma^{(2)}$, on the other hand, will diverge as $\ln \Lambda$. It is the third term in (6-66) in which the divergence resides. The fact that $\Gamma^{(4)}$ remains finite is again an unfortunate peculiarity of a ϕ^4 theory at the two-loop level, where the only self-energy insertion is momentum independent (Fig. 6-6d). On the three-loop level, as well as in a ϕ^3 theory at six dimensions, for example, logarithmic divergences survive in $\Gamma^{(4)}$ as well (see Exercises 6-21 and 6-22).

To deal with the remaining logarithmic dependence in $\Gamma^{(2)}$ we proceed as in Sec. 6-6 above. In other words we try to remove the strong Λ dependence by absorbing it in a multiplicative factor. The new two-point vertex is written as:

$$\Gamma_R^{(2)} = Z_\phi(g_1, m_1, \Lambda)\Gamma^{(2)}(k, m_1^2, \Lambda) \qquad (6\text{-}68)$$

in which $Z_\phi^{1/2}$ is called the *field renormalization constant*. The new function Z_ϕ is expanded in the number of loops and the various terms are determined so as to make $\Gamma_R^{(2)}$ finite when $\Lambda \to \infty$ at four dimensions. We write

$$Z_\phi = 1 + g_1 z_1 + g_1^2 z_2 + \dots \qquad (6\text{-}69)$$

Recall that in the symmetric ϕ^4 theory the loop expansion of a given vertex function is also an expansion in the coupling constant. This is not the case for interactions which are not pure monomials, or in a state of broken symmetry.

Inserting (6-66) into (6-68) gives

$$\Gamma_R^{(2)}(k, m_1^2, \Lambda) = k^2 + m_1^2(1 + g_1^2 z_2)$$
$$- \tfrac{1}{6}g_1^2 [D_3(k, m_1^2, \Lambda) - D_3(0, m_1^2, \Lambda) - 6z_2 k^2] \qquad (6\text{-}70)$$

where z_1 was set equal to zero, since on the one-loop level $\Gamma^{(2)}$ is finite. The term proportional to Λ^2 in $D_3(k, m^2, \Lambda)$ is independent of k. It is cancelled. The difference of the D_3's then starts with k^2 which is the term proportional to $\ln \Lambda$. One easily convinces oneself that if D_3 is expanded beyond its k^2 term, all terms are convergent in the ultraviolet. Thus, if we choose

$$z_2 = \frac{1}{6}\frac{\partial}{\partial k^2} D_3(k, m_1^2, \Lambda)\bigg|_{k=0} \qquad (6\text{-}71)$$

the logarithmic divergence will be cancelled too.

The above choice is an arbitrary one. Any finite k-independent function added to z_2 will not hurt. We might have also subtracted the Taylor expansion around a momentum which differs from zero, etc.

For a theory with a cutoff z_2 is finite and the redefinition of $\Gamma^{(2)}$ is a matter of convenience. In field theory z_2 is infinite and only $\Gamma^{(2)}_R$, the renormalized vertex, is finite and meaningful.

But if z_2 diverges then (6-70) indicates that the mass is no longer finite. We have to reconsider all the quantities we have been generating along the way. The mass will be redefined so that

$$m^2 = Z_\phi m_1^2 \approx m_1^2(1 + g_1^2 z_2) \qquad (6\text{-}72)$$

is finite. The replacement of m_1^2 by m^2 in (6-65) and in (6-70) gives corrections of higher order in the expansion. The problem is that before writing the final expression for the renormalized theory we must reconsider $\Gamma^{(4)}$ again.

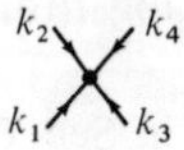

FIGURE 6-7

Let us regress for a moment and consider $G_c^{(4)}(k_i, m_1^2, g_1)$. The simplest term of $G_c^{(4)}$ which appears in $\Gamma^{(4)}$ is the first order graph given in Fig. 6-7 which in $G_c^{(4)}$ corresponds to

$$-g_1 G^{(2)}(k_1) \dots G^{(2)}(k_4) \qquad (6\text{-}73)$$

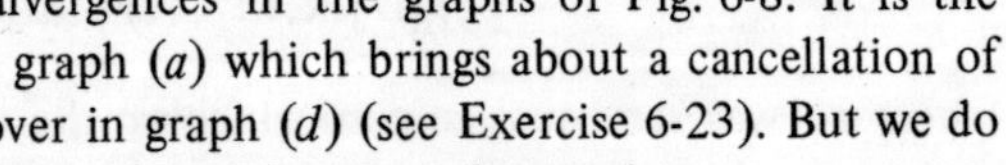

FIGURE 6-8   (a)   (b)   (c)   (d)

The partial renormalization of the mass and the coupling constant performed so far takes care of the leading divergences in the graphs of Fig. 6-8. It is the replacement of $G^{(2)}$ by $G^{(2)}_R$ in graph (a) which brings about a cancellation of the logarithmic divergence left over in graph (d) (see Exercise 6-23). But we do not have $G^{(2)}_R$'s, we have $G^{(2)}$'s. The relation between the two is:

$$G^{(2)} = Z_\phi G^{(2)}_R \qquad (6\text{-}74)$$

since $G^{(2)}$ is the inverse of $\Gamma^{(2)}$.

All graphs which have at least one loop are not affected by this replacement. The zero loop graph (Fig. 6-8a), however, is

$$\text{Eq. (6-73)} = -g_1 Z_\phi^4 G^{(2)}_R(k_1) \dots G^{(2)}_R(k_4) \qquad (6\text{-}75)$$

Let us redefine the renormalized coupling constant

$$g = Z_\phi^2 g_1 \qquad (6\text{-}76)$$

and a new $G_c^{(4)}$ by:

$$G_{cR}^{(4)} = Z_\phi^{-2} G_c^{(4)} \qquad (6\text{-}77)$$

If g is finite then, clearly, $G_{cR}^{(4)}$ will be finite to order two loops. The replacement of g_1 by g in the terms containing loops changes nothing. Thus $G_{cR}^{(4)}$ is a function of g and m^2. The same is true for $\Gamma_R^{(2)}$, in which a replacement of g_1 by g generates terms with four loops.

But how did we know to split the Z_ϕ^4 in (6-75) in just this way? The point is that one would like to be able to absorb the strong cutoff dependence, in all correlation functions and to all orders in the expansion in the mass, in the coupling constant and, if there is no choice, also in the overall scale of the correlation function. If we take for example the pair of graphs in Fig. 6-9 then replacing the $G^{(2)}$ by $G_R^{(2)}$'s will again make the insertion in the window in

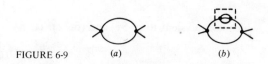

FIGURE 6-9   (a)   (b)

Fig. 6-9b cancel against the one-loop graph. This time there are six $G^{(2)}$'s in (a), and the replacement means that (a) has a factor Z_ϕ^6. Using (6-76), four of these factors are absorbed in the interaction vertices, and the remaining two in the definition of $G_{cR}^{(4)}$, Eq. (6-77). This generalizes to all orders. Thus, if we take any graph of $G_{cR}^{(4)}$ multiply it by Z_ϕ^{-2} and replace each g_1 by $Z_\phi^{-2}g$ the graph will provide the cancellation terms for higher order graphs, which are generated by insertions of self-energies into this graph.

As far as $\Gamma^{(4)}$ is concerned, we define it as a finite quantity via:

$$\begin{aligned}
\Gamma_R^{(4)}(k_i, m^2, g) &= -[G_R^{(2)}(k_1)]^{-1} \ldots [G_R^{(2)}(k_4)]^{-1} G_{cR}^{(4)}(k_i, m_1^2, g) \\
&= Z_\phi^2 \Gamma^{(4)}(k_i, m^2, g)
\end{aligned} \qquad (6.78)$$

We can now consider any vertex function, or connected Green function, and render it finite by the following recipe:

1. Calculate the bare function.
2. Replace μ^2 by m^2 using (6-56) and (6-72).
3. Replace λ by g using (6-64) and (6-76).
4. Multiply $\Gamma^{(E)}(p_i, m^2, g)$ by $Z_\phi^{E/2}$ ($G^{(E)}$ has to be multiplied by $Z_\phi^{-E/2}$), where Z_ϕ is given by (6-69) and (6-71).

The resulting functions, denoted by $\Gamma_R^{(E)}$ and $G_R^{(E)}$, are finite up to two-loop order. The subscript R stands for renormalized. The proof that this procedure does in fact make all single-field vertex functions finite up to the indicated order is left as Exercise 6-24.

To repeat: as long as Λ is finite, all the vertex functions are finite, as is the case for statistical physics. To produce the renormalized functions is to express the theory in terms of a perturbation expansion, in which all the integrals converge when $\Lambda \to \infty$. That is, the dependence on Λ becomes very weak, except in the parameters μ^2, λ and Z_ϕ.

The procedure described above can now be formulated in reverse order. We know that the bare vertex functions can be made finite by replacing (μ^2, λ) by (m^2, g) and multiplying each by a factor $Z_\phi^{E/2}$. This relation can be written as

$$\Gamma_R^{(E)}(k_i, m^2, g) = Z_\phi^{E/2} \Gamma^{(E)}(k_i, \mu^2, \lambda, \Lambda) \qquad (6\text{-}79)$$

The equations determining one set of parameters in terms of the other, as they were used above, are

$$\Gamma_R^{(2)}(0, m^2, g) = m^2, \qquad (6\text{-}80)$$

which is equivalent to (6-51) and (6-72). Then

$$\left. \frac{\partial}{\partial k^2} \Gamma_R^{(2)}(k, m^2, g) \right|_{k^2 = 0} = 1 \qquad (6\text{-}81)$$

which is equivalent to (6-70) and (6-71). And finally

$$\Gamma_R^{(4)}(k_i, m^2, g)|_{k_i=0} = g \qquad (6\text{-}82)$$

which is equivalent to (6-78) with (6-76) with (6-63).

These three equations, called *the normalization conditions*, can be used to compute μ^2, λ and Z_ϕ as functions of m^2, g and Λ (see Exercise 6-25).

To close this section we comment on the fate of the correlation functions which include the composite operator ϕ^2. In Sec. 6-6 we saw that one needed a special factor $Z_{\phi^2}^1$ to multiply $\Gamma^{(2,1)}$ in order to make it finite on the one-loop level. The question is: what changes are induced by the renormalization of the field?

Since $\Gamma^{(2,1)}$ is closely related to $\Gamma^{(4)}$, field renormalization does not appear at the two-loop level. The graphs to this order are shown in Fig. 6-10. In four dimensions graph (b) has $\ln \Lambda$ divergence, (c) has Λ^2 divergence, (d) has

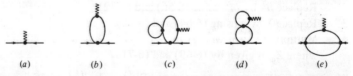

(a)   (b)   (c)   (d)   (e)

FIGURE 6-10
Graphs of $\Gamma^{(2,1)}$ to order two loops.

FIGURE 6-11
Field renormalization in $G^{(2,1)}$.

$(\ln \Lambda)^2$ divergence and (e) has internal $\ln \Lambda$ divergence. Clearly, the Λ^2 term in (c) is cancelled by mass renormalization in (b). The $\ln \Lambda$ term in (e) is cancelled by coupling constant renormalization in (b). The $\ln \Lambda$ in (b) is cancelled by $Z_{\phi^2}^{\frac{1}{2}}$, which multiplies (a). But $Z_{\phi^2}^{\frac{1}{2}}$ itself contains a log Λ term, which multiplies (b), producing a term which together with the coupling constant renormalization in (b) cancels the $(\ln \Lambda)^2$ in (d). The proof that all the combinatoric factors conspire just so as to make the above statements true, is left as Exercise 6.26.

$G_c^{(2,1)}$, like $G_c^{(4)}$ before, is affected by the renormalization of the field, already on the two-loop level. Together with graph (a), of Fig. 6-10, which now includes its external legs, there is also the graph Fig. 6-11. The difference between the original, *bare*, Green functions and the renormalized ones starts at the order of two loops. So no graph of Fig. 6-10 is changed. But it is the change in graph (a), which has only two external legs, that will compensate for the logarithmic divergence of the term in Fig. 6-11, after the quadratic divergence will have been removed by mass renormalization.

If the lowest order term in $G_c^{(2,1)}$ – the one corresponding to (a) – is multiplied by a factor Z_ϕ^{-2} the two external $G^{(2)}$'s will change into $G_R^{(2)}$'s. The difference will cancel the divergence of the graph in Fig. 6-11. The other terms will not be changed by the replacement of $G^{(2)}$ by $G_R^{(2)}$ in their lines. But we have to consider higher order terms to check that Z_ϕ^{-2} is an overall factor.

Consider, for example, the graph of $G^{(2,1)}$, which corresponds to Fig. 6-10e. Its lines will have to be renormalized to cope with graphs such as those of Fig. 6-12. There are six $G^{(2)}$'s in (e), and when they are converted to $G_R^{(2)}$ there is a factor Z_ϕ^6. The two interaction vertices, when converted from g_1 to g using (6-76), give a factor Z_ϕ^{-4}. Hence an overall Z_ϕ^2 which is cancelled by the Z_ϕ^{-2} mentioned above.

This is true at all orders (see Exercise 6-27). Consequently the renormalized $G_c^{(2,1)}$ is obtained via†

$$G_{cR}^{(2,1)}(k_i; m^2, g) = \overline{Z}_{\phi^2} Z_\phi^{-2} G_c^{(2,1)}$$

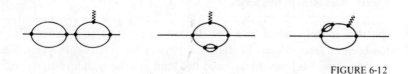

FIGURE 6-12

† This definition of Z_{ϕ^2} differs from that of (BLZ) by a factor of Z_ϕ. It does allow for a standard definition of the renormalization of a composite operator (see Sec. II-2-3).

Since $G_c^{(2,1)}$ has only two external lines, we can define the corresponding vertex function via

$$\Gamma_R^{(2,1)}(k_i; m^2, g) = \frac{G_{cR}^{(2,1)}(k_i; m^2, g)}{G_{cR}^{(2)}(k_1) G_{cR}^{(2)}(k_2)} = Z_{\phi^2} Z_\phi \Gamma^{(2,1)} \qquad (6\text{-}83)$$

$$Z_{\phi^2} = \overline{Z}_{\phi^2} Z_\phi^{-1} \qquad (6\text{-}84)$$

The condition which we used in Sec. 6-6 to renormalize ϕ^2 is equivalent (see Exercise 6-28) to the normalization:

$$\Gamma_R^{(2,1)}(k_i; m^2, g)\,|_{k_i=0} = 1 \qquad (6\text{-}85)$$

Using similar arguments one can convince oneself of the following generalizations (see Exercise 6-29):

$$G_R^{(E,1)} = Z_{\phi^2} Z_\phi^{-E/2} G^{(E,1)} \qquad (6\text{-}86)$$

Thus,

$$\Gamma_R^{(E,1)} = Z_{\phi^2} Z_\phi^{E/2} \Gamma^{(E,1)} \qquad (6\text{-}87)$$

And finally,

$$\Gamma_R^{(E,L)} = Z_{\phi^2}^L Z_\phi^{E/2} \Gamma^{(E,L)} \qquad (6\text{-}88)$$

6-8 THE 0(M)-SYMMETRIC THEORY IN THE LIMIT OF LARGE M

6-8-1 General Remarks

The expansion in the number of loops is a general technique applicable to any type of interacting Lagrangian. We now turn to another approximation scheme, which is systematic, but is restricted to cases in which the theory possesses a certain type of global symmetry. Here we will discuss a special case, that of a ϕ^4 theory with an 0(M) symmetry, in the limit when M becomes very large. The systematic expansion is an expansion in powers of M^{-1}. We will study only the lowest order term in this series.[8]

The result one obtains is a non-trivial theory. It is the exact solution of the spherical model,[9] which is a well-defined spin system on a lattice. This model has been of great interest in statistical physics for over twenty years. Recently, particle physicists have rediscovered this limit in a flurry of investigations.[3]

We will not discuss the general question of the type of symmetry group which gives rise to this type of approximation, though the general impression is that the group has to be a continuous group. We will discuss the case in which fields form the basis of the fundamental representation of the 0(M) symmetry.

Therefore the Lagrangian must be a function of ϕ^2 only. In fact one can treat, at the lowest order in M^{-1}, a general Lagrangian of this type.[10] One can then describe multicritical phenomena and the crossover between them.[11] Furthermore, one can construct a ϕ^3 interaction in which the set of fields $\{\phi\}$ are the basis for a high angular momentum representation, of $0(3)$, for example.[12] In this case one obtains again closed expressions for the physical quantities, and much insight into the technique of the renormalization group. Probably many other interesting cases can be constructed.

In the present context the interest of the infinite M approximation is in the fact that it provides for closed expressions for $\Gamma^{(2)}$, $\Gamma^{(4)}$ $\Gamma^{(2,1)}$ etc. One can then observe the renormalization process at work. The process is somewhat amputated in that there is no field (wave-function) renormalization at this order. The coupling constant and the composite field ϕ^2 do get renormalized. It is interesting to mention that in the infinite angular momentum limit of the ϕ^3 theory, it is the coupling constant which stays unrenormalized, while the field and the square of the field do require renormalization. Moreover, the closed expressions allow for the calculation of critical exponents without recourse to the ϵ-expansion of Chap. 9.

6-8-2 The Origin of the M-Dependence of the Coupling Constant

The Lagrangian of the theory is the same as the one given in Eq. (4-35), with the slight difference that the coupling constant is made to depend on M explicitly, i.e.,

$$\mathscr{L} = \tfrac{1}{2}\left[(\nabla\phi)^2 + \mu^2\phi^2\right] + \frac{1}{4!}\frac{\lambda}{M}(\phi^2)^2 \qquad (6\text{-}89)$$

Perhaps the simplest way to rationalize the appearance of the factor M^{-1} is to carry out Exercise (2-3). The theory on the lattice is $0(M)$ invariant, and if in addition one imposes the condition that the size of the spins at every site be unity, one finds, on transforming to continuous fields, that the coefficient of $(\phi^2)^2$ is proportional to $(M+2)^{-1}$. To leading order in M, this factor can be replaced by M^{-1}.

In the light of the preliminary discussion in Sec. 2-3, together with the result of Chap. 8, the values of the bare parameters are not very important as far as the final behaviour of the theory is concerned. As we shall see, the explicit M^{-1} term in Eq. (6-89) is there to stay.

Considering perturbation theory one finds that, due to the factors of M generated by the internal summations over field indices in a graph, M^{-1} in the coupling constant is just the borderline between the case in which

(a) The coupling constant vanishes faster than M^{-1}, which, in the limit $M \to \infty$, leads to a free theory and that in which

(b) The coupling constant vanishes more slowly than M^{-1}, which leads to infinite quantities in the limit $M \to \infty$.

When the coupling constant is proportional to M^{-1} some graphs, at every order in the perturbation series, will vanish when M becomes large. The remaining series can be summed. (cf. Exercises 6-30 and 6-31.)

Let us consider as an example the four-point function. Its lowest order term is the coupling constant

$$\Gamma_0^{(4)} = \frac{\lambda}{3M} = \text{(Fig. 6-13}a\text{)}$$

The one- and two-loop contributions are

$$\Gamma_1^{(4)}(0) = -\frac{\lambda^2}{M^2}\frac{(M+8)}{18}I = \text{(Fig. 6-13}b\text{)} \qquad (6\text{-}90)$$

$$\Gamma_2^{(4)}(0) = \frac{\lambda^3}{3M^3}\left(\frac{M^2+6M+20}{36}I^2 + \frac{5M+22}{9}I_4\right) = \text{(Fig. 6-13}c\text{)} \qquad (6\text{-}91)$$

FIGURE 6-13   (a)   (b)   (c)

The derivation of Eq. (6-91) was the purpose of Exercise 4-11. Notice that the lowest order term (the Born term) is $O(M^{-1})$, as is the one-loop term. Among the two two-loop terms the second one is $O(M^{-2})$, and hence becomes vanishingly small as $M \to \infty$. In fact, for large M, $\Gamma^{(4)}$ to the order of two loops will be

$$\Gamma^{(4)}(0) = \frac{\lambda}{3M}\left[1 - \frac{\lambda I}{6} + \left(\frac{\lambda I}{6}\right)^2 + \ldots\right]$$

which is the beginning of a geometric series.

6-8-3 Faithful Representation of Graphs and the Dominant Terms in $\Gamma^{(4)}$

In order to discuss systematically, for large M, the form of the leading terms we will adopt temporarily a more faithful graphical representation of the interaction. After all, the spin indices (the different mesons) always enter in pairs. Thus, instead of denoting the interaction by a point, we will represent it by a dashed line, such that the two indices at each end are equal (see Fig. 6-14). In this representation a graph like the one in Fig. 6-13a appears as three different

FIGURE 6-14
Graphical representation of the $O(M)$-symmetric interaction vertex.

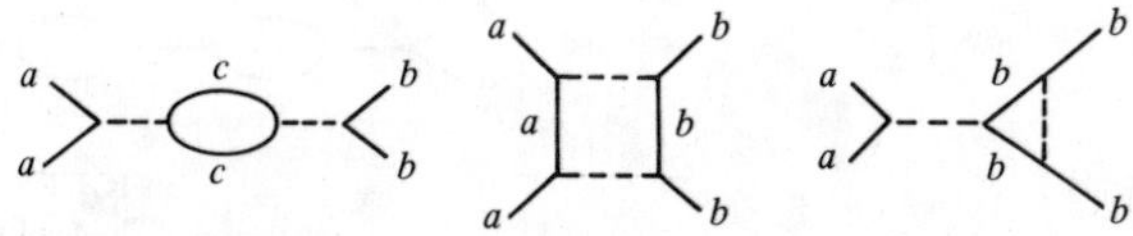

FIGURE 6-15
The second order graphs of $\Gamma^{(4)}$ in the faithful representation.

graphs. They are drawn in Fig. 6-15. The momentum dependence of these three graphs is, of course, the same as that of the original one, as expressed in Eq. (6-90).

Each of the two third-order graphs in Eq. (6-91) gives rise to six topologically distinct graphs in the faithful representation. These are depicted in Figs. 6-16 and 6-17.

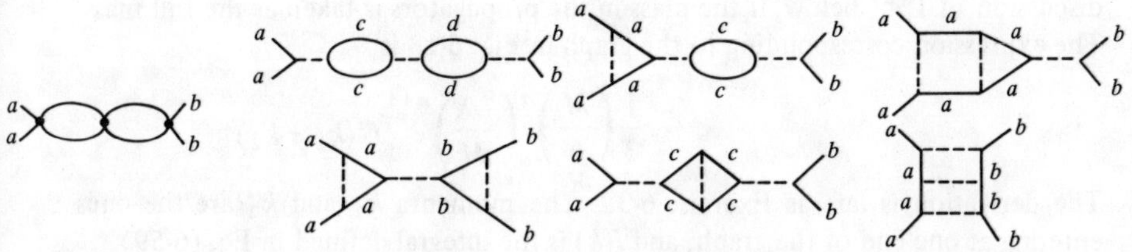

FIGURE 6-16
Faithful representation of the first third order of $\Gamma^{(4)}$.

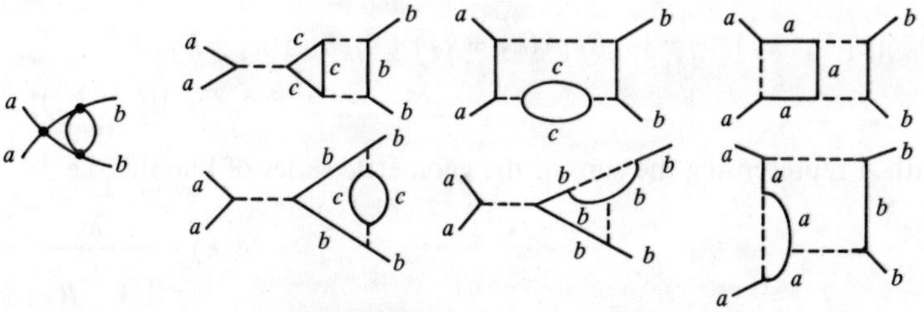

FIGURE 6-17
Faithful representation of the second third order graph of $\Gamma^{(4)}$.

In each of these graphs there is still the question of the distribution of momenta over the external legs. We return to this question below. For the moment notice that of the three graphs in Fig. 6-15 only the first one has a free internal spin index. For large M, since the masses are all equal, this makes this graph greater than the other two by a factor of M. Of the 12 third-order graphs in Figs. 6-16 and 6-17 the first graph in Fig. 6-16 is the only one to have two free internal indices. Thus it is greater than the others by at least a factor M.

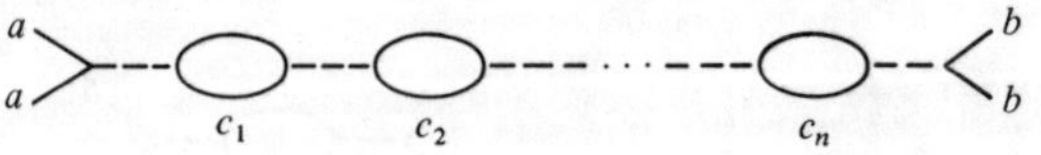

FIGURE 6-18
The leading graph of order $n + 1$ in $\Gamma^{(4)}_{aabb}$.

The conclusion is that in general we can read off the power of M accompanying a graph simply from its topological structure. For each propagator loop – full line – there is one power of M. Thus, the leading contribution as $M \rightarrow \infty$ at every order in perturbation theory comes from the graph with the highest number of such loops. One can then easily convince oneself that for $\Gamma^{(4)}_{aabb}$ these are the graphs of the type presented in Fig. 6-18.

Note that we are ignoring self-energy corrections. This is justified by the discussion of $\Gamma^{(2)}$ below, if the mass in the propagators is taken as the full mass. The expression corresponding to the graph in Fig. 6-18 is

$$ -\frac{1}{3}\left(\frac{M}{6}\right)^n \left(\frac{-\lambda}{M}\right)^{n+1} I^n(k_1 + k_2) $$

The derivation is left as Exercise 6-32. The momenta k_1 and k_2 are the ones entering at one end of the graph, and $I(k)$ is the integral defined in Eq. (6-59).

In order to obtain the full expression for $\Gamma^{(4)}$ in the large M limit one observes that, apart from terms with all four external indices equal, there are two other possible distributions of external momenta. The result is:

$$ \Gamma^{(4)}_{ijkl}(k_1 \ldots k_4) = \frac{1}{3M}\left[\delta_{ij}\delta_{kl}A(k_1 + k_2) + \delta_{ik}\delta_{jl}A(k_1 + k_3)\right. $$
$$ \left. + \delta_{il}\delta_{jk}A(k_1 + k_4)\right] \qquad (6\text{-}92) $$

with A representing the sum of the geometric series of bubbles, i.e.,

$$ A(k) = \frac{\lambda}{1 + \frac{\lambda}{6}I(k)} \qquad (6\text{-}93) $$

6-8-4 $\Gamma^{(2)}$ in the Infinite M Limit

Next we discuss $\Gamma^{(2)}$ and $\Gamma^{(2,1)}$. In both these functions there are terms of zeroth order in perturbation theory, which are therefore of order unity as $M \rightarrow \infty$. In $\Gamma^{(2)}(k)$ this is $k^2 + \mu^2$. In $\Gamma^{(2,1)}$ it is 1.

The graphs of $\Gamma^{(2)}$ up to second order are presented in Fig. 6-19. Clearly, only the first and third graphs are of $0(1)$ as $M \rightarrow \infty$. The others are at least of $0(M^{-1})$. In fact, one can easily convince oneself that the only way to

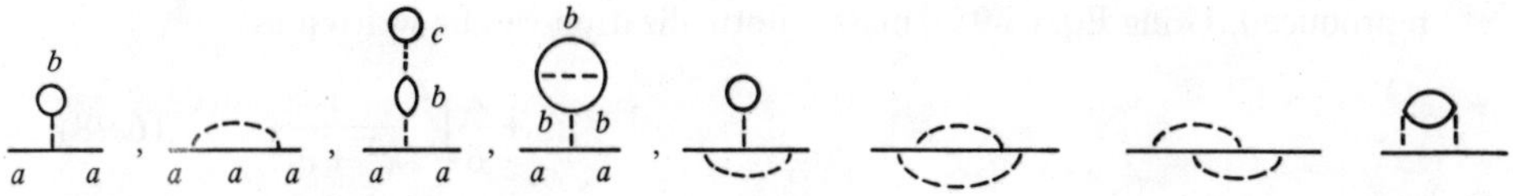

FIGURE 6-19
Faithful graphs of $\Gamma_{aa}^{(2)}$.

compensate in $\Gamma^{(2)}$ for the powers of M^{-1} coming from the interactions is to draw graphs with the greatest number of "tadpoles" (the first graph in Fig. 6-19). At third order, for example, there will be two such graphs (see Fig. 6-20 and Exercise 6-33).

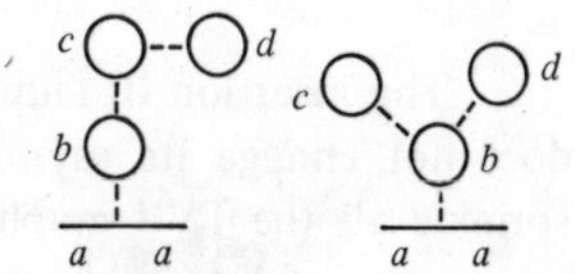

FIGURE 6-20
Dominant third order graphs in $\Gamma^{(2)}$.

The first point to notice is that all momentum-dependent graphs are at least of $0(M^{-1})$. The proof is left as Exercise 6-33. $\Gamma^{(2)}(k)$ can therefore be written as:

$$\Gamma^{(2)}(k, \mu^2) = k^2 + \mu^2 - \Sigma(\mu^2) \qquad (6\text{-}94)$$

Denoting the inverse susceptibility by m^2 we have

$$\Gamma^{(2)}(k = 0, \mu^2) \equiv m^2 = \mu^2 - \Sigma \qquad (6\text{-}95)$$

and hence

$$\Gamma^{(2)}(k, \mu^2) = k^2 + m^2 \qquad (6\text{-}96)$$

Since the coefficient of k^2 is finite in any number of dimensions, as $\Lambda \rightarrow \infty$, it follows that $Z_\phi = 1$ (cf. Sec. 6-7). In the relation between m^2 and μ^2, Eq. (6-95), as well as in $\Gamma^{(4)}$ there are, of course, divergences.

Equation (6-95) is the expression of mass renormalization. It gives us μ^2 as a function of m^2, λ and Λ. It can be put in a more explicit form by noting that the sum of all graphs of the type appearing in Fig. 6-20, which was called Σ, satisfies the equation

$$\Sigma = -\frac{\lambda}{6} \int \frac{1}{k^2 + \mu^2 - \Sigma} \qquad (6\text{-}97)$$

This is simply the statement that if the sum of all these graphs, including the free part, is inserted as the propagator of the single tadpole, the same set of graphs is reproduced. Using Eq. (6-95), mass renormalization can be written as

$$m^2 = \mu^2 + \frac{\lambda}{6} \int^\Lambda \frac{1}{k^2 + m^2} \qquad (6\text{-}98)$$

which is quite similar to the result for the one-loop approximation, Eq. (6-26), given in Sec. 6-4. It can be analyzed in the same way, leading to a critical temperature

$$\mu_c^2 = T_c - T_0 = -\frac{\lambda}{6} \int^\Lambda \frac{1}{k^2} \qquad (6\text{-}99)$$

and, to a susceptibility index

$$\gamma = \frac{2}{d-2} \qquad (6\text{-}100)$$

The insertion of tadpoles into the graphs of $\Gamma^{(4)}$, or into any other vertex, does not change its asymptotic dependence on M. Thus, one would have to sprinkle all the $\Gamma^{(4)}$ graphs considered above with tadpoles. But this is easily taken care of by replacing μ^2 by m^2, using an argument analogous to the one which justified Eq. (6-97).

As far as $\Gamma_{aa}^{(2,1)}(k;p)$ is concerned, the ϕ^2 insertion, which corresponds to a derivative with respect to μ^2 (temperature), is

$$\frac{1}{2} \sum_{i=1}^{M} \int \phi_i^2(x) \, dx$$

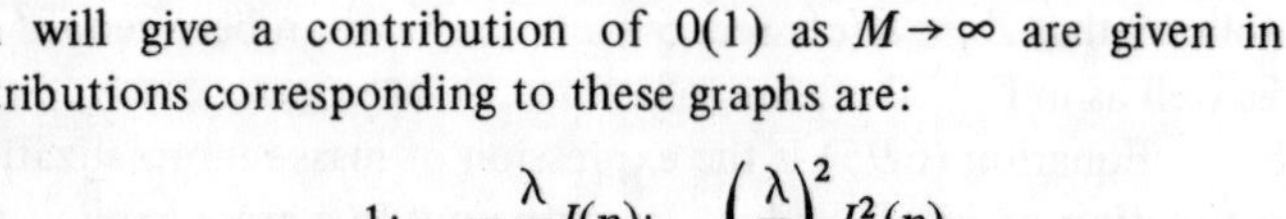

FIGURE 6-21
Graphs of $\Gamma^{(2,1)}$ which are $0(1)$ as $M \to \infty$.

The graphs which will give a contribution of $0(1)$ as $M \to \infty$ are given in Fig. 6-21. The contributions corresponding to these graphs are:

$$1; \quad -\frac{\lambda}{6} I(p); \quad \left(\frac{\lambda}{6}\right)^2 I^2(p) \dots$$

where the propagators contain the full mass.

The result is that $\Gamma^{(2,1)}$ is also a geometric series when $M \to \infty$. Its sum is:

$$\Gamma^{(2,1)}(k;p) = \frac{1}{1 + \frac{1}{6}\lambda I(p)} \qquad (6\text{-}101)$$

6-8-5 Renormalization

In both $\Gamma^{(4)}$ and $\Gamma^{(2,1)}$ each term in the series diverges logarithmically as $d \to 4$ and $\Lambda \to \infty$. The reflection of these divergences in the sum is the vanishing of (6-93) and (6-101). One has to follow the program of Sec. 6-7 to show that it is possible to find two functions $\lambda(g, m, \Lambda)$ and $Z_{\phi^2}(g, m, \Lambda)$ so as to make $\Gamma^{(4)}$ and $\Gamma^{(2,1)}$ finite as $\Lambda \to \infty$.

Note first that if $k_i = 0$, then $\Gamma^{(4)}$ of Eq. (6-92) can be written as:

$$\Gamma_{ijkl}^{(4)}(k_i = 0) = M^{-1} A(k = 0) S_{ijkl} \qquad (6\text{-}102)$$

where S is the tensor defined in Eq. (4-36). Generalizing the normalization condition Eq. (6-82) to read

$$\Gamma_{ijklR}^{(4)}(k_i = 0) = \frac{g}{M} S_{ijkl} \qquad (6\text{-}103)$$

one finds:

$$g = \frac{\lambda}{1 + \tfrac{1}{6} \lambda I(0)} \qquad (6\text{-}104)$$

where

$$I(0) = \int^{\Lambda} \frac{1}{(k^2 + m^2)^2} \qquad (6\text{-}105)$$

The function $\lambda(g, m, \Lambda)$ is therefore:

$$\lambda^{-1} = g^{-1} - \tfrac{1}{6} I(0) \qquad (6\text{-}106)$$

and $\Gamma^{(4)}$ becomes:

$$\Gamma_{ijklR}^{(4)}(k_i) = \frac{1}{3M} \left\{ \delta_{ij}\delta_{kl} \frac{1}{g^{-1} + \tfrac{1}{6}[I(k_1 + k_2) - I(0)]} + 2 \text{ permutations} \right\} \qquad (6\text{-}107)$$

For finite g, m and k_i this function is finite up to six dimensions as $\Lambda \to \infty$. This is true also for every term in the expansion of $\Gamma^{(4)}$ in powers of g.

Similarly, using Eq. (6-106), $\Gamma^{(2,1)}$ can be written as

$$\Gamma^{(2,1)}(k; p) = \frac{g\lambda^{-1}}{1 + \tfrac{1}{6} g [I(p) - I(0)]} \qquad (6\text{-}108)$$

To make $\Gamma^{(2,1)}$ finite Z_{ϕ^2} can be chosen as

$$Z_{\phi^2}(g, m, \Lambda) = \lambda g^{-1} = \frac{1}{1 - \tfrac{1}{6} g I(0)} \qquad (6\text{-}109)$$

which satisfies Eq. (6-85). The renormalized $\Gamma^{(2,1)}$ is then:

$$\Gamma_R^{(2,1)}(k;p) = \frac{1}{1 + \frac{1}{6}g[I(p) - I(0)]} \qquad (6\text{-}110)$$

The renormalization process in the infinite M limit is reconsidered in Sec. 8-13.

6-8-6 Broken Symmetry

So far the model has been discussed in its symmetric state. We now consider the possibility that the $0(M)$ symmetry may be broken, either explicitly by a field or spontaneously.

First one notes that the classical field (average magnetization) is of order $M^{\frac{1}{2}}$, and the same is true for the source (external field). To see this, consider the tree approximation with a uniform classical field. The potential is simply the Lagrangian calculated with the classical field replacing the fluctuating field. From Eq. (6-9) we read:

$$U(\mathbf{\Phi}) = \frac{1}{2}\mu^2(\mathbf{\Phi})^2 + \frac{\lambda}{4!M}(\mathbf{\Phi}^2)^2 \qquad (6\text{-}111)$$

The minimum of U is at

$$\mathbf{\Phi}^2 = -\frac{6M}{\lambda}\mu^2 \equiv v^2 \qquad (6\text{-}112)$$

Thus, near the minimum of U, U itself is of order, M, which gives a finite free energy per degree of freedom as $M \to \infty$. For a meaningful minimum to exist in the infinite M limit, the two terms in Eq. (6-111) must be of the same order of magnitude, which implies that $\mathbf{\Phi}^2$ is of order M. Furthermore, if the symmetry is explicitly broken, the source (external field) is given as the derivative of the potential with respect to the classical field. Hence:

$$h = \mu^2 v + \frac{\lambda}{6M}v^3 = 0(M^{\frac{1}{2}}) \qquad (6\text{-}113)$$

The direction in which the symmetry is broken is chosen, as in Sec. 6-3, as the Mth direction, and is also referred to as longitudinal. The other $M - 1$ directions are called transverse.

First we consider the two-point functions. There are two of them, $\Gamma_T^{(2)}$ and $\Gamma_L^{(2)}$, denoted in Sec. 6-3 by $\Gamma_{\pi\pi}^{(2)}$ and $\Gamma_{\sigma\sigma}^{(2)}$, respectively. The perturbation expansion of these functions can be performed by using Eqs. (5.44) and (5.52), which express them in terms of symmetric vertices only.

As far as $\Gamma_T^{(2)}$ is concerned there is one new type of graph which is of order 1 in the state of broken symmetry. If the classical field is represented by a

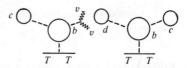

FIGURE 6-22
Two third order graphs of $\Gamma_T^{(2)}$ in the ordered state.

wiggly line, then the two graphs in Fig. 6-22 are both O(1). Equations (6-96) and (6-98), therefore, are replaced by

$$\Gamma_T^{(2)}(k) = k^2 + t \qquad (6\text{-}114)$$

and

$$t = \mu^2 + \frac{\lambda}{6M}(v^2 + N) \qquad (6\text{-}115)$$

with

$$N = M \int \frac{1}{k^2 + t} \qquad (6\text{-}116)$$

The longitudinal function has another contribution, which is momentum dependent. It comes from graphs such as those in Fig. 6-23. Notice that since v is the classical value of the longitudinal component of the field, no such graphs can enter $\Gamma_T^{(2)}$. These graphs can also be summed using the results of Sec. 6-8-3. The result is:

$$\Gamma_L^{(2)}(k) = k^2 + t + 2v^2 \Pi(k) \qquad (6\text{-}117)$$

where

$$\Pi(k) = \frac{\dfrac{\lambda}{6M}}{1 + \tfrac{1}{6}\lambda I(k)} \qquad (6\text{-}118)$$

and

$$I(k) = \int dq\, G_T(q) G_T(q + k) \qquad (6\text{-}119)$$

The derivations of (6-114) and (6-117) are left as Exercise (6-34). An important observation that can be made at this point is that the renormalization — (6-106) and (6-109) — suffice to remove the divergences in the phase with broken symmetry.

The critical point is the point at which v and t vanish. Both $\Gamma_L^{(2)}$ and $\Gamma_T^{(2)}$ behave there as k^2. The value of μ^2, or of the temperature, which defines this point is identical with the one obtained by coming from the high temperature side, Eq. (6-99).

FIGURE 6-23
Special graphs of $\Gamma_L^{(2)}$.

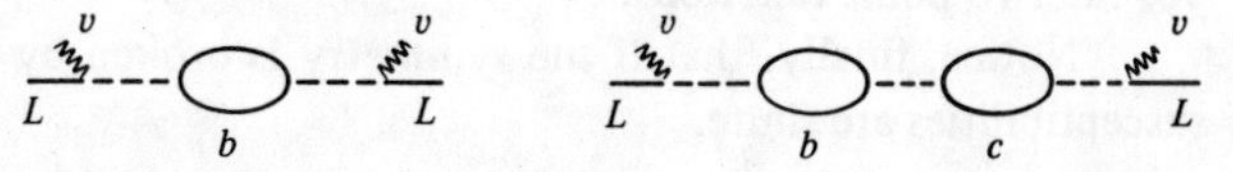

Considering graphs again one can write down the free energy, or $U(v)$. The result is:

$$U(v) = \tfrac{1}{2}\mu^2(v^2 + N) + \frac{\lambda}{4!M}(v^2 + N)^2 - N\left[\tfrac{1}{2}\mu^2 + \frac{\lambda}{12M}(v^2 + N)\right] + \frac{M}{2}\int \ln(k^2 + t)$$

$$= \tfrac{1}{2}\mu^2 v^2 + \frac{\lambda}{24M}(v^4 - N^2) + \frac{M}{2}\int \ln(k^2 + t) \qquad (6\text{-}120)$$

The derivation is left as Exercise (6-35). The first line is written in a form which hints at the result for $U(v)$ for a Lagrangian which is a general polynomial in Φ^2.

The external field is given by

$$h = \frac{\partial U}{\partial v} = tv \qquad (6\text{-}121)$$

Hence, if the symmetry is broken spontaneously, i.e. $h = 0$, $v \neq 0$, we have

$$t = 0$$

everywhere below the transition. The transverse $\Gamma^{(2)}$ is consequently

$$\Gamma_T^{(2)} = k^2$$

which are our familiar $M - 1$ Goldstone modes.

But here a new feature appears, which is more realistic than what the tree approximation was able to produce, namely, below the transition[13]

$$\Gamma_L^{(2)}(k) \xrightarrow[k \to 0]{} 0 \qquad (6\text{-}122)$$

This follows from the fact that when $t = 0$, $I(k)$ diverges as $k \to 0$ for $d < 4$. Hence $\Pi(k) \to 0$ when $k \to 0$.

The inverse longitudinal susceptibility can be expressed in two different forms:

$$\chi_L^{-1} = \Gamma_L^{(2)}(k = 0)$$

or

$$\chi_L^{-1} = \frac{\partial h}{\partial M}$$

Using (6-117) and (6-121) one can verify this relation, which serves as a check on the consistency of the expression for the free energy with the expressions for the two-point functions.

Notice, finally, that if the symmetry is broken by a field, $t \neq 0$, and both susceptibilities are finite.

Appendix 6-1

THE METHOD OF STEEPEST DESCENT AND
THE LOOP EXPANSION

It was shown in Sec. 6-2 that an expansion in the number of loops is an expansion in powers of a, where a^{-1} is a large parameter multiplying the action, $\int (\mathscr{L} - J\phi)$. In particular, to obtain the generating functional for the 1PI vertex functions, or the free energy, to a given number of loops, all vertex functions with the specified number of loops are calculated and an expression like Eq. (6-5) is used.

Normally, however, one would approach a problem such as the calculation of an integral of the type:

$$Z\{J\} = \int \mathscr{D}\phi \exp\{-a^{-1} \int [\mathscr{L}(\phi) - J\phi] \, dx\} \equiv \exp\{a^{-1} F\{J\}\} \qquad (A6\text{-}1)$$

in which a is small number, using the method of steepest descent. In other contexts this method is called the method of stationary phase, or the expansion about the saddle-point.[14]

The method consists of an expansion of the integrand about the value of the dummy variable $\phi(x)$ for which the exponent is stationary. The large negative value of $-a^{-1}$ is supposed to supress the contributions of configurations which deviate much from the stationary one. This is, of course, a valid argument only if the stationary point is a real minimum. Usually, it is a saddle-point. Nevertheless, the method does generate an expansion in powers of a. It provides a useful technique for effectively summing infinite series such as (6-5) with a given number of loops.

The method can be developed for a general Lagrangian. Here a scalar ϕ^4 theory will be considered. The generalization should be straightforward. Consider

$$\mathscr{L} = \tfrac{1}{2}[(\nabla\phi)^2 + \mu^2\phi^2] + \frac{\lambda}{4!}\phi^4 \qquad \text{(A6-2)}$$

$$I[\phi] \equiv \int dx\{\mathscr{L}[\phi(x)] - J\phi(x)\} \qquad \text{(A6-3)}$$

The saddle-point is at $\phi = \phi_0(x)$, which satisfies:

$$\left.\frac{\delta}{\delta\phi(x)} I[\phi(x)]\right|_{\phi=\phi_0} = (-\nabla^2 + \mu^2)\phi_0(x) + \frac{\lambda}{3!}\phi_0^3(x) - J(x) = 0 \qquad \text{(A6-4)}$$

This is the familiar Landau–Ginzburg equation (cf. Sec. 6-3). $J(x)$ is chosen to vanish at infinity and then, if one requires that $\phi_0(x)$ vanish at infinity, the solution of (A6-4) is unique and it satisfies the condition:

$$\phi_0[J] \to 0 \quad \text{as} \quad J(x) \to 0 \qquad \text{(A6-5)}$$

Expansion of the action I about ϕ_0 is performed by writing

$$\phi(x) = \phi_0(x) + \psi(x) \qquad \text{(A6-6)}$$

Then:

$$I[\phi] = I[\phi_0] + \int \left[\tfrac{1}{2}(\nabla\psi)^2 + \tfrac{1}{2}(\mu^2 + \tfrac{1}{2}\phi_0^2)\psi^2 + \frac{\lambda}{3!}\phi_0\psi^3 + \frac{\lambda}{4!}\psi^4 \right] dx \qquad \text{(A6-7)}$$

The generalization of the last equation to the case of arbitrary Lagrangians is left as Exercise (6-36).

Inserting (A6-7) in (A6-1) enables the following conclusion to be immediately drawn: the function $F\{J\}$ to zeroth order in a is:

$$F_0\{J\} = -I\{\phi_0\{J\}, J\} \qquad \text{(A6-8)}$$

The proof is as follows:

$$\exp\{a^{-1}(F\{J\} + I\{\phi_0\})\} = \mathscr{N}\int \mathscr{D}\psi \, \exp\{-a^{-1}[I\{\phi\} - I\{\phi_0\}]\}$$

$$= \mathscr{N}'\int \mathscr{D}\psi \, \exp\left\{-\int\left[\tfrac{1}{2}(\nabla\psi)^2 + \tfrac{1}{2}(\mu^2 + \tfrac{1}{2}\phi_0^2)\psi^2\right.\right.$$

$$\left.\left. + a^{1/2}\frac{\lambda\phi_0}{3!}\psi^3 + a\frac{\lambda}{4!}\psi^4\right]dx\right\} \qquad \text{(A6-9)}$$

in which the integration variable ψ was scaled by the factor a. Recall that $\mathcal{N}$ (or $\mathcal{N}$) is there simply to insure that $Z\{J=0\} = 1$.

Now, as $a \to 0$ the right-hand side of Eq. (A6-9) remains finite. This implies on the left-hand side that Eq. (A6-8) is true.

From Eqs. (A6-8) and (A6-4) one has that:

$$\phi_0(x) = -\frac{\delta I\{J\}}{\delta J(x)} = \frac{\delta F_0\{J\}}{\delta J(x)} \qquad \text{(A6-10)}$$

since the only contribution to the derivative comes from the explicit J.

To obtain the free energy Γ to this order, we have to perform a Legendre transform on F_0. Using Eqs. (5-19) and (A6-10) we can write:

$$\Gamma_0\{\bar\phi\} = \int \bar\phi J \, dx - F_0\{\bar\phi\} = \int \mathcal{L}(\bar\phi) \, dx \qquad \text{(A6-11)}$$

which is exactly the zero loop approximation for Γ derived in Sec. 6-3.

Next, one proceeds to obtain a power series expansion for F, writing:

$$F\{J\} = F_0\{J\} + aF_1\{J\} + a^2 F_2\{J\} + \ldots \qquad \text{(A6-12)}$$

To this expansion there corresponds a power series for the classical field, namely:

$$\bar\phi(x) = \frac{\delta F\{J\}}{\delta J(x)} = \phi_0(x) + a\phi_1(x) + a^2 \phi_2(x) + \ldots \qquad \text{(A6-13)}$$

which will allow us to perform the Legendre transform to a given order in a.

Let us carry the next step explicitly. In order to calculate F_1 all we need is the limit of the right-hand side of Eq. (A6-9) as $a \to 0$, namely:

$$\exp[F_1\{J\}] = \frac{\int \mathscr{D}\psi \, \exp\{-\int [\frac{1}{2}(\nabla\psi)^2 + \frac{1}{2}(\mu^2 + \frac{1}{2}\phi_0)\psi^2]\}}{\int \mathscr{D}\psi \, \exp\{-\int [\frac{1}{2}(\nabla\psi)^2 + \frac{1}{2}\mu^2 \psi^2]\}} \qquad \text{(A6-14)}$$

Both numerator and denominator are Gaussian integrals which, given $\phi_0(x)$, can be computed. The symbolic result is

$$F_1\{J\} = -\frac{1}{2}\ln \det \frac{K_{xy}(\phi_0\{J\})}{K_{xy}(0)} = -\frac{1}{2}\operatorname{Tr} \ln \frac{K_{xy}(\phi_0)}{K_{xy}(0)} \qquad \text{(A6-15)}$$

where K_{xy} is the matrix of coefficients in the quadratic form in Eq. (A6-14), namely,

$$K_{xy}(\phi_0) = \left[\frac{\partial^2}{\partial x \partial y} + \mu^2 + \frac{1}{2}\lambda\phi_0^2(x)\right]\delta(x - y) \qquad \text{(A6-16)}$$

In general K_{xy} will not be diagonal in momentum space since ϕ_0 depends on x. Things simplify if ϕ_0 is uniform. This is the only case that was treated in

Sec. 6-4 (see Exercise 6-37). In the present method a much more general result is obtained.

In order to perform the Legendre transform to order a we calculate the classical field.

$$\bar{\phi}(x) = \phi_0(x) + a \frac{\delta F_1 \{J\}}{\delta J(x)} + O(a^2)$$

$$= \phi_0(x) + a \int \frac{\delta F_1}{\delta \phi_0(y)} \frac{\delta \phi_0(y)}{J(x)} \, dy + O(a^2)$$

Differentiating Eq. (A6-4) with respect to $J(y)$ and using (A6-16) one arrives at:

$$\bar{\phi}(x) = \phi_0(x) + a \int \frac{\delta F_1 \{\phi_0\}}{\delta \phi_0(y)} K_{xy}^{-1}\{\phi_0\} \, dy + O(a^2)$$

$$= \phi_0(x) + a \int \frac{\delta F_1 \{\bar{\phi}\}}{\delta \bar{\phi}(y)} K_{xy}^{-1}\{\bar{\phi}\} \, dy + O(a^2) \qquad \text{(A6-17)}$$

Next the Legendre transform is also expanded in a. We write:

$$\Gamma\{\bar{\phi}\} = \Gamma_0\{\bar{\phi}\} + a\Gamma_1\{\bar{\phi}\} + a^2 \Gamma_2\{\bar{\phi}\} + O(a^3) \qquad \text{(A6-18)}$$

with Γ_0 given by Eq. (A6-11). On the other hand, Γ is given by

$$\Gamma\{\bar{\phi}\} = \int \bar{\phi} J - F\{J\}$$

$$= \int \bar{\phi} J - F_0\{\phi_0, J\} - aF_1\{\phi_0\} - a^2 F_2\{\phi_0\} + O(a^3)$$

where the notation implies that the F_i's, for $i > 0$, depend on J only through ϕ_0. This follows from Eq. (A6-9).

One now uses the fact that $\bar{\phi} - \phi_0$ vanishes when $a \to 0$, and that F_0 is stationary at $\phi = \phi_0$, to write:

$$\Gamma\{\bar{\phi}\} = \int J\bar{\phi} - F_0\{\phi\} + [F_0\{\bar{\phi}\} - F_0\{\phi\}] - aF_1 - a^2 F_2 + O(a^3)$$

$$= \Gamma_0\{\bar{\phi}\} - [I\{\bar{\phi}\} - I\{\phi_0\}] - aF_1 - a^2 F_2 + O(a^3)$$

which together with Eqs. (A6-7) and (A6-13) gives:

$$\Gamma\{\bar{\phi}\} = \Gamma_0\{\bar{\phi}\} - a^2 \int \left[\frac{1}{2}(\nabla\phi_1)^2 + \frac{1}{2}\left(\mu^2 + \frac{\lambda}{2}\bar{\phi}^2 \right) \phi_1^2 \right] dx - aF_1 - a^2 F_2 + O(a^3)$$

$$= \Gamma_0\{\bar{\phi}\} - \frac{a^2}{2} \int \phi_1(x) K_{xy}(\bar{\phi})\phi_1(y) \, dx \, dy - aF_1 - a^2 F_2 + O(a^3) \qquad \text{(A6-19)}$$

Comparing Eqs. (A6-19) and (A6-18) one reads directly:

$$\Gamma_1\{\bar{\phi}\} = -F_1\{\bar{\phi}\} = \tfrac{1}{2}\,\mathrm{Tr}\ln\frac{K_{xy}(\bar{\phi})}{K_{xy}(0)} \qquad (A6\text{-}20)$$

$$\Gamma_2\{\bar{\phi}\} = -F_2\{\bar{\phi}\} - \frac{1}{2}\int \phi_1(x)K_{xy}(\bar{\phi})\phi_1(y)\,dx\,dy + \int \frac{\delta F_1\{\bar{\phi}\}}{\delta\bar{\phi}(x)}\phi_1(x)\,dx \qquad (A6\text{-}21)$$

The last term originates from the difference between $F_1\{\phi_0\}$ which appears in (A6-19) and $F_1\{\bar{\phi}\}$ which was included in (A6-20).

The expression for Γ_2 can be further simplified using Eq. (A6-17). It can be written as:

$$\Gamma_2\{\bar{\phi}\} = -F_2\{\bar{\phi}\} + \frac{1}{2}\int \frac{\delta F_1}{\delta\bar{\phi}(x)}\,K_{xy}^{-1}(\bar{\phi})\,\frac{\delta F_1}{\delta\bar{\phi}(y)}\,dx\,dy \qquad (A6\text{-}22)$$

Equations (A6-11), provide explicit expression for the coefficients in the expansion of the free energy in powers of a. These coefficients are functions of the classical field — the average of the order parameter. According to the discussion in Sec. 6-2 $\Gamma_0, \Gamma_1, \Gamma_2$ are the sums of all graphs in Γ with zero, one or two loops, respectively, i.e., these are the sums of all 1PI graphs with the corresponding number of loops.

Finally, these results can be interpreted in terms of the perturbation theory implied by Eq. (A6-9). As we shall see, the result is that the sum of all graphs with a given number of loops in the original theory, of which there is an infinite number already at the single-loop level (Sec. 6-4), reduces to a sum of a finite number of terms in the new perturbation theory. In this new perturbation theory one has to calculate all 1PI graphs of a theory in which

(a) the free propagator is $K_{xy}^{-1}(\bar{\phi})$;

(b) there are two interactions ψ^3 and ψ^4;

(c) the only graphs to be considered are vacuum to vacuum graphs, since J is absent.

For example, consider the contribution to Γ_2 calculated directly from (A6-9). First we need F_2, the sum of connected vacuum graphs with two loops. There are three such graphs, which are depicted in Fig. 6-24. Clearly, these three graphs will be of order a, and thus will contribute a term proportional to a^2 in F.

Care should be exercised due to the fact that, when $\bar{\phi}$ depends on position, $D_{xy}^{-1}(\bar{\phi})$ is not translationally invariant, and one should use the rules of Sec. 4-4 in the computation of graphs.

In Γ_2 there should be only 1PI graphs. Thus the third graph in Fig. 6-24

FIGURE 6-24
Connected vacuum graphs with two loops.

should be eliminated. This is exactly the role of the second term on the right-hand side of Eq. (A6-22) (see also Exercise 6-38).

In perturbation theory this last graph corresponds to the expression:

$$\tfrac{1}{8}a\lambda^2 \phi_0^2 \int G_0(x,x)G_0(x,y)G_0(y,y)\,dx\,dy$$

in which

$$G_0(x,y) = K_{xy}^{-1}(\phi_0)$$

Since the full power of a is already explicitly present, ϕ_0 can be replaced by $\bar\phi$. Thus, the contribution of this graph to F_2 is

$$J = \tfrac{1}{8}\lambda^2 \bar\phi^2 \int K_{xx}^{-1}(\bar\phi)K_{xy}^{-1}(\bar\phi)K_{yy}^{-1}(\bar\phi) \qquad (A6\text{-}23)$$

Next we transform the second term in (A6-22). Since in the expression for F_1, e.g., (A6-20), we have the trace of the logarithm of the matrix K, the derivative with respect to $\bar\phi$ is easily obtained, namely:

$$\frac{\delta F_1\{\bar\phi\}}{\delta\bar\phi(z)} = \tfrac{1}{2}\,\mathrm{Tr}\,\frac{\delta}{\delta\bar\phi(z)}\ln K_{xy}(\bar\phi) = \tfrac{1}{2}\,\mathrm{Tr}\int K_{xt}^{-1}\frac{\delta K_{ty}}{\delta\bar\phi(z)}\,dt$$

Using (A6-16) this reduces to:

$$\frac{\delta F_1\{\bar\phi\}}{\delta\bar\phi(z)} = \tfrac{1}{2}\lambda\bar\phi K_{zz}^{-1} \qquad (A6\text{-}24)$$

Inserting in (A6-22) we find that the second term exactly cancels the contribution (A6-23) in F_2.

The proof that this is a general feature will not be pursued here. After Exercise 6-38 has been performed a proof will not be necessary. Otherwise, the reader is referred to the literature.[15]

EXERCISES

6-1 Show that in the zero-loop approximation, for a Lagrangian which is a general polynomial in ϕ, $\Gamma\{\bar\phi\}$ is simply the action with the classical field substituted for the field.

6-2 Derive Eq. (6-7).

6-3 Prove that Ward–Takahashi identities hold in every order of the loop expansion.

6-4 How does symmetry breaking occur in the tree approximation? Compare with the discussion of broken symmetry at the end of Sec. 2-4.

6-5 Can long-range order take place in the tree approximation if the gradient term is absent?

6-6 Verify the Ward identity (Exercise 5-11) in the tree approximation.

6-7 Show that in the tree approximation the terms in the free energy which depend on the order parameter lead to a finite specific heat, discontinuous at $\mu^2 = 0$.

6-8 Calculate δ in the tree approximation with $M = 1$.

6-9 Discuss scaling laws in the framework of the tree approximation.

6-10 Derive the combinational factors for the expansion of $U_1(\phi)$ for a single component ϕ^4 theory.

6-11 As previous Exercise for a ϕ^3 theory.

6-12 Show that the rationalized Ginzburg criterion, Eq. (6-31), is also the condition which would indicate the breakdown of the calculation of the spontaneous magnetization in the Landau theory.

6-13 Show that the one-loop calculation for $d < 4$, Eq. (6-30), implies that $\gamma = 2/(2 - \epsilon)$.

6-14 Calculate the two- and four-point functions, in the broken symmetry phase, as expressed in terms of the renormalized parameters.

6-15(*a*) What are the diagrams which contribute to $\Gamma^{(N,1)}$ on the one-loop level in the symmetric state?
  (*b*) What is their symmetry factor?

6-16 Show that the introduction of a factor of $Z_{\phi^2}^1$ with every operator ϕ^2 in $\Gamma^{(E,L)}$, makes all these functions finite at the one-loop level when $d \to 4$.

6-17(*a*) Show that $\Gamma^{(0,2)}(k)$ does not become finite by the introduction of m_1^2, g_1 and $Z_{\phi^2}^1$, at the one-loop level.
  (*b*) Prove that no multiplicative factor will remedy $\Gamma^{(0,2)}$.

6-18 Prove that the subtraction in Eq. (6-57) reduces the divergence by two powers of Λ.

6-19 Exhibit a graph of $\Gamma^{(4)}$ beyond two loops which does not include as a subgraph a divergent graph. What is the ultraviolet divergence of this graph?

6-20 Show that λ is given in terms of g_1 and m_1^2 to order two loops by Eq. (6-64), and $\Gamma^{(4)}(k_i)$ by Eq. (6-65).

6-21 Consider the graph in Fig. 6-8*d*. Show that mass and coupling constant renormalization leave it logarithmically divergent.

6-22 Carry the renormalization of a ϕ^3 theory to the two-loop level. Consider the case in which $\langle \phi \rangle = 0$, and require the theory to be finite at six dimensions.[16]

6-23(a) Show that to order two loops the partial renormalization $\mu^2 \rightarrow m_1^2$, $\lambda \rightarrow g_1$, leaves only logarithmic divergences in $G_c^{(4)}$ at four dimensions.

(b) Show that to the same order the replacement of $G^{(2)}$ by $G_R^{(2)}$ removes this divergence.

6-24 Show that the procedure which made $\Gamma^{(2)}$ and $\Gamma^{(4)}$ finite up to two-loop order, would also make $\Gamma^{(E)}$ finite for arbitrary E.

6-25 Using Eqs. (6-79)–(6-82) calculate μ^2, λ and Z_ϕ to order two loops. Then obtain the form of $\Gamma^{(2)}$, $\Gamma^{(4)}$ and $\Gamma^{(6)}$.

6-26 Show in detail that mass, coupling constant and ϕ^2 renormalization make $\Gamma^{(2,1)}$ finite.

6-27 Show that renormalizing the internal lines and the interactions in any graph of $G_c^{(2,1)}$ gives an overall factor Z_ϕ^2.

6-28 Using the normalization condition, Eq. (6-86), calculate Z_{ϕ^2} to order two loops.

6-29 Show that the overall factor of a general graph of $G_c^{(E,1)}$ is $Z_\phi^{E/2+1}$.

6-30 Show that if the interacting part of the Lagrangian has "cubic" symmetry

$$\mathscr{L}_{\text{Int}} = \lambda \sum_{i=1}^{M} \phi_i^4$$

one cannot devise a dependence of λ on M, such that perturbation theory is significantly simplified.

6-31(a) What is the dependence on M of the coupling constant of ϕ^6 in the field theory obtained in Exercise 2-3?

(b) What graphs will be selected in perturbation theory in the limit of large M?

6-32(a) Show that the coefficient of the integral in the graph in Fig. 6-12 is, to leading order in M,

$$\frac{1}{3}\left(\frac{M}{6}\right)^n \left(\frac{-\lambda}{M}\right)^{n+1}$$

for $a \neq b$. What is the dependence of this term on momentum?

(b) What is the leading term in M if $a = b$?

6-33 Show that the only graphs of $O(1)$ in $\Gamma^{(2)}$ are those obtained by planting tadpoles into tadpoles. In particular prove that any momentum-dependent graph is at least of $O(M^{-1})$.

6-34 Consider the graphs entering $\Gamma_T^{(2)}$ and $\Gamma_L^{(2)}$, which remain finite as $M \to \infty$, with their weights. Derive from them Eqs. (6-114) and (6-117).

6-35(a) Considering the graphs of U which are $O(M)$ as $M \to \infty$, derive the result Eq. (6-120).

   (b) If the Lagrangian is

$$\mathcal{L} = \tfrac{1}{2}(\nabla\phi)^2 + \tfrac{1}{2}U_1(\phi^2)$$

   show that

$$U(v) = \tfrac{1}{2}U_1(v^2 + N) - \tfrac{1}{2}N\dot{U}_1(v^2 + N) + \frac{M}{2}\int \ln(k^2 + \dot{U}_1)$$

   where $\dot{U}_1(x) = \dfrac{d}{dx}U_1$

   (c) What are $\Gamma_L^{(2)}$ and $\Gamma_T^{(2)}$?

6-36 Derive an expansion of the action, corresponding to a general Lagrangian, about the saddle-point.[17]

6-37 Calculate F_1 of Eq. (A6-15) for uniform ϕ_0. Perform the Legendre transform, and derive Eq. (6-25).

6-38 Obtain an expression for Γ_3 by using the loop-expansion of the explicit Legendre transform. Show, by considering the perturbation theory generated by Eq. (A6-9), that the result is just the 1PI vacuum graphs.

REFERENCES

1. V. L. Ginzburg and L. D. Landau, *Soviet Physics-J. Exptl. Theoret. Phys.* (USSR), **20**, 1064 (1950). The same approximation is discussed in a more general context in L. P. Kadanoff et al. *Reviews of Modern Physics*, **39**, 395 (1967).
2. T. H. Berlin and M. Kac, *Physical Review*, **86**, 821 (1952).
3. K. G. Wilson, *Physical Review*, **D7**, 2911 (1973); L. Dolan and R. Jackiw, *Physical Review*, **D9**, 3320 (1974); H. J. Schnitzer, *Physical Review*, **D10**, 1800 and 2042 (1974); S. Coleman, R. Jackiw and H. D. Politzer, *Physical Review*, **D8**, 2491 (1974); D. J. Gross and A. Neveu, *Physical Review*, **D10**, 3235 (1974).
4. S. Coleman and E. Weinberg, *Physical Review*, **D7**, 1888 (1973), and references cited therein.
5. V. L. Ginzburg, *Soviet Physics-Solid State*, **2**, 1824 (1960). The criterion was proposed earlier by A. P. Levanyuk, *Soviet Physics-J. Exptl. Theoret. Phys.*, **36**, 571 (1959).
6. D. J. Amit, *Journal of Physics C: Solid State*, **7**, 3369 (1974).

7. An explicit calculation of the renormalization of a ϕ^4 theory, regularized by a cutoff, at four dimensions is given in IIM. One should, however, beware of abundant misprints.

8. In the context of statistical physics the study of this approximation scheme was initiated by S. K. Ma, *Physical Review Letters*, **29**, 1311 (1972) and *Physical Review*, **A7**, 2172 (1973), where the calculation is carried to order M^{-1}, and by R. Abe, *Progress in Theoretical Physics* (Kyoto), **48**, 1414 (1972) and **49**, 113 (1973). Below the transition the approximation has been applied by E. Brézin and D. J. Wallace, *Physical Review*, **B7**, 1967 (1973). R. Abe, *Progress in Theoretical Physics*, **49**, 1877 (1973) calculated η to order M^{-2} in three dimensions.

9. E. H. Stanley, *Introduction to Phase Transitions and Critical Phenomena* (Clarendon Press, Oxford, 1971). The proof of the equivalence is given in M. Kac and C. J. Thompson, *Proceedings of the Norwegian Academy of Sciences*, **5**, 163 (1971). The solution of the spherical model is given in T. H. Berlin and M. Kac, *Physical Review*, **86**, 821 (1952).

10. S. K. Ma, *Reviews of Modern Physics*, **45**, 589 (1973).

11. D. J. Amit and C. De Dominicis, *Physics Letters*, **45A**, 193 (1973); D. J. Amit and M. Zannetti, *Journal of Statistical Physics*, **11**, 331 (1974), and M. Zannetti, *Journal of Physics*, **A10**, 1175 (1977).

12. D. J. Amit and D. Roginsky, to be published.

13. See Brézin and Wallace, Ref. 8 above. A particularly beautiful exploitation of the presence of Goldstone modes has led A. M. Polyakov *Physics Letters*, **59B**, 79 (1975) and E. Brézin, J. C. Le Guillou and J. Zinn-Justin *Physical Review Letters*, **36**, 691 (1976) and *Physical Review*, **B14**, 3110 (1976) to an expansion of the critical exponents in the vicinity of two dimensions.

14. Here we follow the exposition of IIM. See also BLZ. Ch. II, Sec. 3.

15. R. Jackiw, *Physical Review*, **D9**, 1686 (1974).

16. See, e.g., D. J. Amit, *Journal of Physics*, **A9**, 1441 (1976).

17. See, e.g., BLZ, Sec. II.3.

RENORMALIZATION

7-1 INTRODUCTION

In the previous chapter we described a procedure by which all the important dependence on the cutoff was absorbed into a few parameters, leaving us with correlation functions which depend very weakly on the cutoff. We have done this for a ϕ^4 theory up to the order of two loops. Now we can proceed to introduce the general concepts and theorems which allow us to perform renormalization for a wide class of interactions, to all orders in perturbation theory. In doing this we will refrain from providing lengthy proofs for the central theorems, which involve the combinatorics of general graphs in the perturbation series. For these the reader is referred to the bibliography.

We studied the ϕ^4 theory at four dimensions. This was no accident. Below we will try to elucidate the connection between the various types of interactions and the number of space-dimensions in which they are *renormalizable*. In other words, we shall identify that number of dimensions at which, for a given interaction, the important cutoff dependence can again be absorbed in a *finite* number of parameters.

For a theory without an intrinsic cutoff the introduction of a momentum cutoff is one out of a variety of possible ways of *regularization*, that is, of defining finite expressions corresponding to infinite Feynman integrals, such that there is a well-defined limiting procedure which restores these expressions to the original values of the Feynman integrals, wherever these are defined. For example, the momentum cutoff can be made infinite, and the finite cutoff integral will equal the original one if the dimension of space is low enough.

Another possibility is to continue analytically in the number of space dimensions, and in this way provide finite expressions. When the dimensionality is made equal to an integer number, at which the original integral converged, the limit will give that same finite result. Otherwise the limit will be infinite. This is the *dimensional regularization* of 't Hooft and Veltman.[1] It is a very useful technique even in problems of critical phenomena where an intrinsic cutoff exists.

In fact, using partial integrations in the cutoff theory, which is the procedure by which the graphs are analytically continued in the number of dimensions, we will see that the critical number of dimensions, the relevant operators, renormalization, etc. can all be discussed by focusing attention on the infrared behavior alone. This is a more natural approach to critical phenomena than the discussion in terms of the large momentum behavior (cf. Sec. 9-9). The work of 't Hooft and Veltman implies, of course, that the two approaches are equivalent.

After regularizing a theory it has to be *renormalized*. In the context of field theory this means that a procedure has to be devised to allow a passage to the physical limit $- \Lambda \to \infty$, or dimensionality $\to 4 -$ such that the resulting theory be finite. For critical phenomena that same procedure will insure that the microscopic cutoff has been made unimportant.

7-2 SOME CONSIDERATIONS CONCERNING ENGINEERING DIMENSIONS

In the theory, as we have defined it in Chaps. 2 and 3, the only quantity with a dimension is the length (h and c have been set equal to one, as was k_B). Thus, we can assign a length, or momentum, dimension to every variable. As we shall see below, the naive dimensional analysis is a quite helpful tool, a fact which leads us to a short discussion of the dimensions of the various quantities.

As was indicated in Sec. 2-5-3, the dimension of the field can be determined from the free part of the Lagrangian. For the boson field we are considering one can write†:

$$[\phi] = L^{1-\frac{1}{2}d} \quad \text{or} \quad \Lambda^{\frac{1}{2}d-1} \tag{7-1}$$

---

† L and Λ serve only to denote units of length and inverse length, respectively.

This follows from the fact that $\mathscr{L}$ must have a dimension of inverse volume, namely,

$$[\mathscr{L}] = L^{-d} \quad \text{or} \quad \Lambda^d \qquad (7\text{-}2)$$

From (7-1) and (7-2) we can immediately find the dimensions of all the coupling constants — the coefficients of the various powers of ϕ. Using the fact that

$$[\lambda_r \phi^r] = \Lambda^d \qquad (7\text{-}3)$$

we have:

$$[\lambda_r] = \Lambda^{r+d-\frac{1}{2}rd} \equiv \Lambda^{\delta_r} \qquad (7\text{-}4)$$

For example,

$$[\mu^2] = \Lambda^2 \qquad (7\text{-}5)$$

$$[\lambda_3] = \Lambda^{\frac{1}{2}(6-d)} \qquad (7\text{-}6)$$

$$[\lambda_4] = \Lambda^{4-d} \qquad (7\text{-}7)$$

etc.

It is interesting to note that to each coupling constant there corresponds a number of space dimensions at which it will be dimensionless. As we shall see below, this is just the number of dimensions at which the theory is renormalizable. It happens also to be the number of dimensions which separates Gaussian from critical behavior in the context of statistical physics.

As far as the Green functions are concerned, their dimensions are:

$$[G^{(N)}(x_1, \ldots, x_N)] = [\phi]^N = \Lambda^{N(\frac{1}{2}d-1)} \qquad (7\text{-}8)$$

where we used (7-1). Its Fourier transform has the dimension

$$[G^{(N)}(k_i)] = \Lambda^{-Nd}[G^{(N)}(x_i)] = \Lambda^{-N(\frac{1}{2}d+1)} \qquad (7\text{-}9)$$

and after the overall momentum conserving δ function is removed, as in Eq. (4-62), we have

$$[\bar{G}^{(N)}(k_i)] = \Lambda^{d-N(\frac{1}{2}d+1)} \qquad (7\text{-}10)$$

Using Eq. (5-31) one computes the dimension of the vertex function to be:

$$[\Gamma^{(N)}(x_i)] = [G^{(N)}(x_i)] \, [V]^{-N} \, [G^{(2)}(x_i)]^{-N} = \Lambda^{N(\frac{1}{2}d+1)} \qquad (7.11)$$

where V is a volume. The Fourier transforms have the dimensions:

$$[\Gamma^{(N)}(k_i)] = \Lambda^{-N(\frac{1}{2}d-1)} \qquad (7.12)$$

$$[\bar{\Gamma}^{(N)}(k_i)] = \Lambda^{N+d-\frac{1}{2}Nd} \qquad (7\text{-}13) \cdot$$

The exponent of Λ in the above equations is sometimes called the *canonical dimension* of the quantity, or its *engineering dimension*.

Since the word "dimension" enters in the theory in more than one sense it seems reasonable to reemphasize the special meaning of engineering dimension.[2]

Consider a theory with parameters a_i having dimensions

$$[a_i] = \Lambda^{\Delta_i}$$

If the physical quantity G calculated within this theory has dimension

$$[G] = \Lambda^g$$

then the transformation of the length scale, corresponding to

$$\Lambda \to \alpha\Lambda \qquad (7\text{-}14)$$

will lead to

$$G \to \alpha^g G \qquad (7\text{-}15)$$

The two important points to remember are:

1. All parameters having non-zero dimensions are transformed.
2. Equation (7-15) is *always satisfied exactly*.

For example, if all momenta are scaled according to (7-14) along with all dimensional parameters, then the two-point Green function will change according to

$$G^{(2)}(k) \to \alpha^{-2} G^{(2)}(k) \qquad (7\text{-}16)$$

This seems quite natural as far as the free $G_0^{(2)}$ is concerned. If $k \to \alpha k$ and $\mu^2 \to \alpha^2 \mu^2$, then

$$G_0^{(2)}(k) = \frac{1}{k^2 + \mu^2} \to \frac{1}{\alpha^2(k^2 + \mu^2)} = \alpha^{-2} G_0^{(2)}(k) \qquad (7\text{-}17)$$

It becomes less trivial when one considers $G^{(2)}$ at T_c in the interacting theory. There

$$G^{(2)} \sim k^{-2+\eta} \qquad (7\text{-}18)$$

and the above transformation would imply that

$$G^{(2)} \to \alpha^{-2+\eta} G^{(2)}$$

rather than (7-16). But this is wrong! Equation (7-16) stays true and in (7-18) there must be another dimensional quantity, say $\Lambda^{-\eta}$, multiplying the right-hand side. How it comes about is for the theory to explain. But what becomes clear is that dimensional analysis alone is not sufficient to give the same factor as does the change of scale of the momenta. It gives an independent power, even when the function is scale invariant. This is a question we shall return to below.

7-3 POWER COUNTING AND PRIMITIVE DIVERGENCES

In order to determine whether a certain graph, in a theory with a cutoff, depends strongly or weakly on the cutoff the asymptotic behavior of the integrand has to be determined.[3] If the graph contains a single momentum integration — one loop — the situation is very simple. The integral will behave asymptotically as a power of Λ equal to the number of powers of momentum in the numerator of the integrand, minus the number of powers in the denominator. For example, to the one-loop graph of $\bar{\Gamma}^{(3)}$ in a ϕ^3 theory —

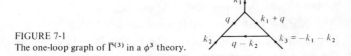

FIGURE 7-1
The one-loop graph of $\bar{\Gamma}^{(3)}$ in a ϕ^3 theory.

Fig. 7-1, there corresponds the integral

$$\int \frac{dq}{(q^2 + \mu^2)[(q + k_1)^2 + \mu^2][(q - k_2)^2 + \mu^2]} \qquad (7\text{-}19)$$

The integration volume is d-dimensional. Hence, this integral will behave as Λ^{d-6} when $\Lambda \to \infty$.

If there is more than one loop the situation is more complex. The graphs of a certain vertex part may be treated *as if* every factor in the denominator depended on every one of the integration momenta. In this way one obtains again a power of Λ, which is equal to the total number of momentum powers in the numerator — originating either from the momentum integration volumes, or from momentum dependence of the interactions†— minus twice the number of internal lines.

For example, consider the two-loop graphs shown in Fig. 7-2.

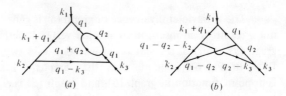

FIGURE 7-2
Two-loop graphs of $\bar{\Gamma}^{(3)}$ in a ϕ^3 theory.

---

† If one considers fields with higher spin, momentum powers will also enter the numerator through the internal lines. See Sec. 4-5.

$$\text{Fig. 7-2}a = \int dq_1 \, dq_2 \frac{1}{(q_1^2 + \mu^2)^2(q_2^2 + \mu^2)[(q_2 + q_1)^2 + \mu^2][(q_1 - k_3)^2 + \mu^2][k_1 + q_1)^2 + \mu^2]}$$

(7-20)

$$\text{Fig. 7-2}b = \int dq_1 \, dq_2$$

$$\frac{1}{(q_1^2 + \mu^2)(q_2^2 + \mu^2)[(k_1 + q_1)^2 + \mu^2][(q_1 - q_2)^2 + \mu^2][(q_2 - k_3)^2 + \mu^2][(q_1 - q_2 - k_2)^2 + \mu^2]}$$

(7-21)

If we calculate the power of Λ in the naive way indicated above we will find Λ^{2d-12} for both graphs Figs. 7-2a and 7-2b.

Notice that we could have obtained this from dimensional analysis (engineering dimensions) alone: The power $2d - 12$ is simply the dimension of the integrals in momentum units. Since both terms are proportional to $(\lambda_3)^5$, and both have to have the same dimension – that of $\bar{\Gamma}^{(3)}$ – it follows that the dimension of each integral must be that of $\bar{\Gamma}^{(3)}$ divided by that of $(\lambda_3)^5$. But the dimension of λ_3 can be determined from the Lagrangian, as in the previous section.

Using (7-6) and (7-13) we find

$$\left[\frac{\bar{\Gamma}^{(3)}}{(\lambda_3)^5} \right] = \Lambda^{2(d-6)}$$

(7-21)

Notice also that if the dimension of an integral, in powers of Λ, is negative it does not imply that the integral vanishes as $\Lambda \to \infty$. It means that the integral converges in the ultraviolet.

Looking closer at (7-20) we see that there is an internal integration which complicates matters. It is the integration over q_2. It has only two denominators and thus behaves as Λ^{d-4}. Or like Λ^2 when $d = 6$. The integral over q_1 has four extra denominators, and is convergent at $d = 6$. Thus the insertion of the bubble makes the graph of Fig. 7-2a behave like Λ^2 rather than like Λ^0 – logarithmically – as is implied by power counting. No such difficulty appears in the graph of Fig. 7-2b.

The ultraviolet divergence of graph (b) is called a *primitive divergence*. It is not a result of an insertion of another vertex function, such as the divergence in graph (a), which is a result of an insertion of a two-point function. Considering $\Gamma^{(4)}$, in Fig. 6-6, one discerns that graphs (c) and (e) are insertions of a four-point function in graph (b), and graph (d) is equivalent to graph (b) with a two-point function insertion. Graph (b) is primitively divergent, while there are no two-loop graphs without internal divergences.

Recall the discussion in Chap. 6. There it was seen that, on the one-loop level, only $\Gamma^{(2)}$ and $\Gamma^{(4)}$ have primitive divergences. All higher vertex functions did not. The same is true at the two-loop level, as can easily be checked.

Furthermore, when $\Gamma^{(2)}$ and $\Gamma^{(4)}$ were made finite, they took care of the divergences which appeared in higher vertices due to the insertion of the lower ones. Once $\Gamma^{(2)}$ and $\Gamma^{(4)}$ were properly renormalized, the cancellation of divergences due to insertions was simply a question of combinatorics, which is on our side.

Consequently, in any theory we have to focus on the primitive divergences. These will depend, in general, on the type of interaction, on the number of space dimensions, on the vertex function in question, and on the order in perturbation theory.

Consider a theory with a pure ϕ^r interaction in d dimensions. A graph of nth order of a vertex function with E external legs, having no divergences as $\Lambda \to \infty$ due to subintegrations, will behave asymptotically as $\Lambda^{\delta(r,d,E,n)}$ with

$$\delta(r, d, E, n) = Ld - 2I \qquad (7\text{-}22)$$

where L is the number of loops, and I the number of internal lines. Notice that we have assumed the propagators to behave as k^{-2} for large k. This changes as the spin increases.

The number of internal integrations L is equal to the number of internal lines I less the number of momentum conservation conditions. Each interaction introduces a momentum conserving δ-function, but one is ineffective since we have overall momentum conservation for the graph. Hence:

$$L = I - (n - 1) \qquad (7\text{-}23)$$

The number of internal lines is given by the total number of lines emitted by the vertices, nr, less the number connected to external points, E. But each two lines form a propagator, hence

$$I = \tfrac{1}{2}(nr - E) \qquad (7\text{-}24)$$

Substituting (7-23) and (7-24) in (7-22) leads to:

$$\delta = n(\tfrac{1}{2}rd - d - r) + (d + E - \tfrac{1}{2}Ed) = -n\delta_r + (d + E - \tfrac{1}{2}Ed) \qquad (7\text{-}25)$$

where δ_r is defined in Eq. (7-4). We could easily have obtained this result by dimensional analysis.

To see this one uses the fact that all terms in $\bar{\Gamma}^{(E)}$ have, necessarily, the same dimension as $\bar{\Gamma}^{(E)}$ itself. But Eq. (7-13) implies that this is just the second term on the right-hand side of (7-25). Thus, the rest must simply compensate for the dimensions introduced by $(\lambda_r)^n$ as given by Eq. (7-4). This leads directly to the first term in (7-25).

We find that the primitive divergence of a graph is composed of a term which is determined by the canonical dimension of the corresponding vertex — and thus independent of the order in pertubation theory, and a part which is linear in the order and in the dimension of the coupling constant. The conclusion is that *dimensionless coupling constants are a necessary and sufficient condition for the primitive divergences of all vertex parts to be independent of the order in perturbation theory.*

Using (7-25), or equivalently (7-4), we find that for every monomial interaction there is a unique number of space dimensions at which the primitive divergences are independent of n. It is

$$d_c = \frac{2r}{r - 2} \qquad (7\text{-}26)$$

$d_c = 4$ for a ϕ^4 theory, 6 for a ϕ^3, 3 for a ϕ^6, etc.

The importance of this special *critical dimension* is the following. If the primitive divergences of the graphs of a vertex function increase with the order of perturbation theory, there is no way in which the strong Λ-dependence can be absorbed in a finite number of constants. Clearly, one primitively divergent graph cannot bring about cancellations in another, and thus every time the degree of divergence increases by two powers we need another subtraction, another parameter.

In a theory without a cutoff one introduces in this way an infinite number of arbitrary constants, which renders the theory useless. Unless, of course, a totally different approach is found. This is the situation for $d > d_c$. The theory is then *non-renormalizable*. If we are at $d = d_c$, the theory is said to be *renormalizable*. Finally, for $d < d_c$ the degree of primitive divergence decreases as we go to higher orders in perturbation theory, and the theory is called *super-renormalizable*.

Notice that this nomenclature is somewhat at odds with the conceptions of a statistical mechanic. In critical phenomena it is when $d > d_c$ that all is simple, and the theory is Gaussian, and it is there that it is called non-renormalizable. While for $d < d_c$, where the theory of critical phenomena suffers most, the field theory is called super-renormalizable. The reason for this difference is that in field theory it is the ultraviolet behavior which is treated by the renormalization techniques, while in critical phenomena it is the infrared behavior which concerns us.

As far as critical phenomena are concerned the following logic for arriving at the same conclusions may be better motivated. We focus exclusively on the infrared divergences by giving the external momenta and the masses a scale α which will tend to zero. Any graph of any vertex function can be made ultraviolet convergent in the following way. If it is such to begin with, nothing has to be done. If it is not we can perform an integration by parts. The surface term will be analytic for small α since all integration momenta are large. The

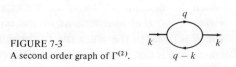

FIGURE 7-3
A second order graph of $\Gamma^{(2)}$.

remaining term can be recast in a way which increases the number of powers of momentum in the denominator, relative to that in the numerator, by one. An example should make this process clear.

Consider the graph in Fig. 7-3, which is a graph of $\Gamma^{(2)}$ in a ϕ^3 theory. The expression corresponding to it is

$$I(k) = \int \frac{1}{(q^2 + m^2)[(k-q)^2 + m^2]} \qquad (7\text{-}27)$$

This integral is ultraviolet divergent when $d > 4$. Inserting in the integral the identity

$$\frac{1}{d} \sum_{i=1}^{d} \frac{\partial q_i}{\partial q_i} = 1 \qquad (7\text{-}28)$$

called "partial-q" by 't Hooft and Veltman. $I(k)$ can be rewritten as

$$I(k) = \frac{1}{d} \int_S \frac{\mathbf{q} \cdot d\mathbf{s}}{(q^2 + m^2)[(k-q)^2 + m^2]}$$
$$+ \frac{1}{d} \int \left[\frac{2q^2}{(q^2 + m^2)^2[(k-q)^2 + m^2]} - \frac{2\mathbf{q} \cdot (\mathbf{k}-\mathbf{q})}{(q^2 + m^2)[(k-q)^2 + m^2]^2} \right]$$

The first term is calculated on the surface, where $|q| \sim \Lambda$, and is analytic at small k and m. Thus it can be neglected when one is concerned with singularities introduced by infrared divergences.

The remaining terms can now be written as

$$I(k) = \frac{1}{d} \left[4I(k) - 2 \int \frac{m^2}{(q^2 + m^2)^2[(k-q)^2 + m^2]} \right.$$
$$\left. - 2 \int \frac{k(k-q) + m^2}{(q^2 + m^2)[(k-q)^2 + m^2]^2} \right]$$

which leads to

$$I(k) = \frac{2}{4-d} \left[\int \frac{m^2}{(q^2 + m^2)^2[(k-q)^2 + m^2]} + \int \frac{k(k-q) + m^2}{(q^2 + m^2)[(k-q)^2 + m^2]^2} \right]$$

$$(7\text{-}29)$$

Now the right-hand side converges for $d < 5$. The procedure can be continued until one arrives at convergent integrals, dropping along the way terms which are harmless in the infrared regime. The proof that the procedure is general is left as Exercise 7-5.

Once the integrals are convergent we can set $\Lambda \to \infty$. Again the difference is a harmless function of α as $\alpha \to 0$. The new integrals are *homogeneous functions* of α, since along with the external momenta and the masses we can scale the integration variables without any effect on the limits. The degree of homogeneity of a graph is given by its dimension, and is therefore equal to δ [Eq. (7-25)] . But now we ask an "infrared" question.

Since the second term in (7-25) gives the small α behavior of the free theory (see Exercise 7-6): given r, for what values of d can one expect lower powers of α? Such lower powers are due to infrared singularities. The answer is clear: If the first term in (7-25) is positive, i.e. when $d > d_c$, the leading infrared behavior will be given by the free theory. If $d < d_c$, the theory is non-classical. The value of d_c is given by Eq. (7-26).

As was already mentioned in the discussion of the one-loop approximation, our attempt to obtain an expansion about the classical theory leads to the attempt to renormalize the theory around the critical dimensionality. In fact, as we shall see below, one is strongly bound to the neighborhood of d_c by the method itself. Since we renormalize in the sense of removing ultraviolet divergences, renormalizing at d_c insures that the theory will become finite for $d < d_c$. For these lower dimensions one has performed some unnecessary work, like renormalizing the coupling constant in a ϕ^4 theory on the one-loop level for $d < 4$. No harm is done, of course, and a continuous limit as $d \to d_c$ is insured.

The last step is to identify which vertex functions are primitively divergent at $d = d_c$. This is obtained from (7-25) by setting $d = d_c$. Then

$$\delta_c(E) = \delta(r, d_c, E, n) = d_c(1 - \tfrac{1}{2}E) + E \qquad (7\text{-}30)$$

independent of r. The condition for $G^{(E)}$ to be primitively divergent at d_c, is:

$$\delta_c(E) > 0 \qquad (7\text{-}31)$$

which together with (7-26) implies:

$$E \leqslant \frac{2d_c}{d_c - 2} = r \qquad (7\text{-}32)$$

For example, in a ϕ^4 theory, $\Gamma^{(2)}$ and $\Gamma^{(4)}$ are primitively divergent at $d = d_c = 4$. The fact that $\delta_c(2) = 2$ implies that $G^{(2)}$ is quadratically divergent, thus requiring two subtractions. Further,

$$\delta_c(4) = 0$$

which indicates a logarithmic divergence of $\Gamma^{(4)}$, calling for just one subtraction. This was the situation which we incurred in Chap. 6, calculating to the order of two loops in a ϕ^4 theory.

On the other hand, in a ϕ^3 theory, in a symmetric state, $\Gamma^{(2)}$ and $\Gamma^{(3)}$ are primitively divergent at $d = d_c = 6$. $\Gamma^{(2)}$ is, as always, quadratically divergent, while $\Gamma^{(3)}$ is logarithmically divergent (see Exercise 7-7).

The above considerations identify all the primitively divergent functions of single fields. But, as we have seen in Chap. 6, functions which include composite operators may give rise to new primitive divergences, and new renormalizations.

Considering vertices with ϕ^2's in addition to ϕ's, one notes the following:

Every insertion of a ϕ^2 in a graph which is primitively divergent leaves the graph primitively divergent, and reduces its degree of divergence by 2, since it adds one more internal line. The degree of divergence of $\Gamma^{(E,L)}$ is

$$\delta' = \delta - 2L = n(\tfrac{1}{2}rd - d - r) + (d + E - \tfrac{1}{2}Ed) - 2L \qquad (7\text{-}33)$$

Therefore, the critical dimensionality is the same as for the $\Gamma^{(N)}$'s. For a ϕ^4 theory, at d_c, $\Gamma^{(0,2)}$ and $\Gamma^{(2,1)}$ are divergent. In a ϕ^3 theory $\Gamma^{(0,2)}$, $\Gamma^{(1,2)}$ and $\Gamma^{(2,1)}$ are divergent — the first quadratically, and the last two logarithmically.

7-4 RENORMALIZATION OF A CUTOFF ϕ^4 THEORY[4]

In the previous section we have seen that a ϕ^4 theory is renormalizable at four dimensions, and that the primitively divergent vertex parts, containing only ϕ's and ϕ^2's, are

$$\Gamma^{(2)}, \Gamma^{(4)}, \Gamma^{(0,2)} \quad \text{and} \quad \Gamma^{(2,1)}$$

As was already hinted in Exercise 6-17, $\Gamma^{(0,2)}$ is a class by itself. So first we focus on the other three. The degree of divergence of these functions, as a functions of the cutoff, is Λ^2 for $\Gamma^{(2)}$, $\ln \Lambda$ for $\Gamma^{(4)}$ and for $\Gamma^{(2,1)}$. Thus, four subtractions are needed to make all of them finite as $\Lambda \to \infty$, two for $\Gamma^{(2)}$ and one each for $\Gamma^{(4)}$ and $\Gamma^{(2,1)}$, just like in the loop-expansion in Chap. 6.

These functions depend on μ^2, λ and Λ, apart from their dependence on the external momenta. The generalization of the results of Chap. 6 would be:

There exist four functions μ^2, λ, Z_ϕ and Z_{ϕ^2} which depend on new parameters m^2 and g, as well as on Λ, such that

$$\Gamma_R^{(E,L)}(k_1, \ldots, k_E, p_1, \ldots, p_L; m^2, g, \Lambda) = Z_\phi^{E/2} Z_{\phi^2}^L \Gamma^{(E,L)}(k_i, p_i; \mu^2, \lambda, \Lambda)$$

$$(7\text{-}34)$$

and, for $d \leqslant 4$, $\Gamma_R^{(E,L)}$ are finite as $\Lambda \to \infty$ for all E and L, at every order in a perturbation expansion in g.†

The content of this statement is that one calculates the bare $\Gamma^{(E,L)}$ by the usual rules. Then one writes μ^2, λ, Z_ϕ and Z_{ϕ^2} as power series in g, in which the coefficients are functions of m^2 and Λ. One then finds that there is a way of choosing these coefficients so as to make the resulting expression on the right-hand side of (7-34), which has become a power series in g, convergent at every order in g. Chapter 6 provides one specific example of the way this process can be carried out — one out of an infinity of possible ways.

---

†All $\Gamma^{(E,L)}$ except $\Gamma^{(0,0)}$ and $\Gamma^{(0,2)}$ (see Sec. 7-5).

Let us note that from dimensional analysis it follows that:

$$\mu^2(m^2, g, \Lambda) = \Lambda^2 \hat{\mu} \left(\frac{m}{\Lambda}, m^{-\epsilon}g \right) \qquad (7\text{-}35)$$

The reason is that $[\mu^2] = \Lambda^2$, and thus $\hat{\mu}^2$ is a dimensionless function, which can depend only on dimensionless variables (cf. Sec. 7-2). In the same way

$$\lambda(m^2, g, \Lambda) = \Lambda^\epsilon \hat{\lambda} \left(\frac{m}{\Lambda}, m^{-\epsilon}g \right) \qquad (7\text{-}36)$$

$$Z_\phi(m^2, g, \Lambda) = \hat{Z}_\phi \left(\frac{m}{\Lambda}, m^{-\epsilon}g \right) \qquad (7\text{-}37)$$

$$Z_{\phi^2}(m^2, g, \Lambda) = \hat{Z}_{\phi^2} \left(\frac{m}{\Lambda}, m^{-\epsilon}g \right) \qquad (7\text{-}38)$$

The canonical meaning of ϵ has become

$$\epsilon = d_c - d \qquad (7\text{-}39)$$

which in the present case is $\epsilon = 4 - d$. The power series in which the functions $\hat{\mu}^2$, $\hat{\lambda}$, $\hat{Z}_\phi$ and $\hat{Z}_{\phi^2}$ are expanded will therefore be series in $m^{-\epsilon}g$ with coefficients which depend on m/Λ only.

Another general conclusion one can draw is that the lowest order term – the zero-loop approximation – in each of these functions should be finite as $\Lambda \to \infty$, since the lowest order terms in $\Gamma^{(2)}$, $\Gamma^{(4)}$ and $\Gamma^{(2,1)}$ are finite. Consequently one can easily show that apart from a trivial constant

$$\mu_0^2 = m^2 \Rightarrow \hat{\mu}^2 = (m/\Lambda)^2 + 0(g) \qquad (7\text{-}40)$$

$$\lambda_0 = g \Rightarrow \hat{\lambda} = (m/\Lambda)^\epsilon (m^{-\epsilon}g) + 0(g^2) \qquad (7\text{-}41)$$

$$Z_\phi = \hat{Z}_\phi = 1 + 0(g) \qquad (7\text{-}42)$$

$$Z_{\phi^2} = \hat{Z}_{\phi^2} = 1 + 0(g) \qquad (7\text{-}43)$$

Finally, turning to $\Gamma^{(0,2)}$, which we avoided so far, it is easily seen that there is no further parameter to renormalize so as to make it finite, nor will a multiplicative factor remove its divergence. The difficulty can be traced to the fact that this function has an ultraviolet divergence already in zeroth order in perturbation theory.

One therefore resorts to additive renormalization,[5] namely, defining

$$\Gamma_R^{(0,2)}(p_1, p_2; m^2, g, \Lambda) = Z_{\phi^2}^2 \left[\Gamma^{(0,2)}(p_1, p_2; \mu^2, \lambda, \Lambda) - \overline{\Gamma}^{(0,2)} \right] \qquad (7\text{-}44)$$

where $\overline{\Gamma}^{(0,2)}$ on the right-hand side is the bare function calculated at some arbitrary, but fixed, value of the external momenta. Since $\Gamma^{(0,2)}$ cannot enter as an insertion, having no external legs, it is easy to see that $\Gamma_R^{(0,2)}$ is finite as $\Lambda \to \infty$.

This procedure obscures some of the infrared behavior of $\Gamma^{(0,2)}$ if the subtraction is carried out at zero momentum, since one is subtracting much more than one has to. If the subtraction is done at non-zero momentum, the singularity of the specific heat $\Gamma^{(0,2)}(,p_i = 0)$ is obtained relative to a finite constant.

7-5 NORMALIZATION CONDITIONS FOR MASSIVE AND MASSLESS THEORIES

The prescriptions of the previous section leave the renormalization functions undetermined to a large extent. One way of fixing these functions is by normalizing the finite vertex functions. We saw one example of this normalization in Sec. 6-7 above. There we found that fixing:

$$\Gamma_R^{(2)}(0; m^2, g) = m^2 \qquad (7\text{-}45)$$

$$\frac{\partial}{\partial k^2} \Gamma_R^{(2)}(0; m^2, g) = 1 \qquad (7\text{-}46)$$

$$\Gamma_R^{(4)}(k_i = 0; m^2, g) = g \qquad (7\text{-}47)$$

$$\Gamma_R^{(2,1)}(k_i = 0; m^2, g) = 1 \qquad (7\text{-}48)$$

was sufficient to fix μ^2, λ, Z_ϕ and Z_{ϕ^2}. The renormalization of $\Gamma^{(0,2)}$ as suggested in the previous section can be added to this list by demanding that

$$\Gamma_R^{(0,2)}(,p_i = 0; m^2, g) = 0 \qquad (7\text{-}49)$$

This normalization is fine, and it suggests itself quite naturally, since most computations are simpler when the external momenta vanish. However, one cannot go strictly to the limit $m \to 0$, i.e., it cannot be used at the critical point itself. The reason is that the renormalization constant, such as λ, Z_ϕ, etc., which should be finite in the regularized theory, will develop infrared divergences. This will happen even when the Green functions are calculated at finite external momenta, where they are finite (see, e.g., Eqs. (6-64) and (6-71)).

The behavior of correlation functions at the critical point, as functions of the scale of the external momenta, is of central interest. It defines the exponent η, for example. Despite the difficulty of reaching the limit $m = 0$, this can be achieved by identifying the leading term of $\Gamma_R^{(2)}(k; m^2, g)$ at high values of k/m. The point is that if scaling holds (see Chap. 1), then by dimensional considerations

$$\Gamma_R^{(2)}(k) \sim k^2 f\left(\frac{k}{m}\right) \qquad (7\text{-}50)$$

If the behavior of $f(x)$ for large x is known to be

$$f(x) \sim x^{-\eta}$$

then this identifies η. In fact,

$$m = \xi^{-1} \qquad (7\text{-}51)$$

in the above normalization (see Exercise 7-9) and the meaning of (7-50) is

$$\Gamma_R^{(2)}(k) \sim k^2 f(k\xi) \qquad (7\text{-}52)$$

Thus, large k/m means small x/ξ, which defines the critical region. In other words, the logic of the argument is that the behavior well inside the correlation length, $x \ll \xi$, is the same as that for arbitrary x and infinite ξ.

   This was the approach originally used by some authors.[6] It was then rather satisfying to discover that a calculation carried out directly at T_c, $m = 0$, leads to the same results at the critical point.

   When the mass vanishes we can impose the following normalization conditions, for example,

$$\Gamma_R^{(2)}(0; g) = 0 \qquad (7\text{-}53)$$

$$\frac{\partial}{\partial k^2} \Gamma_R^{(2)}(k; g)\bigg|_{k^2 = \kappa^2} = 1 \qquad (7\text{-}54)$$

$$\Gamma_R^{(4)}(k_i; g)\big|_{\text{SP}} = g \qquad (7\text{-}55)$$

$$\Gamma_R^{(2,1)}(k_1, k_2, p; g)\big|_{\overline{\text{SP}}} = 1 \qquad (7\text{-}56)$$

$$\Gamma_R^{(0,2)}(p; g)\big|_{p^2 = \kappa^2} = 0 \qquad (7\text{-}57)$$

κ is a mass, which gives the scale of the momentum at which the normalization is fixed. In order to make the calculation more symmetric (see below), wherever more than one momentum remains finite, the momenta are chosen at a symmetry point (SP). In (7-55) this implies in addition to $k_i^2 = \frac{3}{4}\kappa^2$, also

$$\text{SP}: k_i \cdot k_j = \frac{\kappa^2}{4}(4\delta_{ij} - 1) \qquad (7\text{-}58a)$$

which leads to $(k_i + k_j)^2 = \kappa^2$ for $i \neq j$. In (7-56)

$$\overline{SP} : k_i^2 = \frac{3}{4}\kappa^2 \qquad k_1 \cdot k_2 = -\frac{1}{4}\kappa^2 \qquad (7\text{-}58b)$$

implying $p^2 = (k_1 + k_2)^2 = \kappa^2$.

Clearly $\Gamma_R^{(2)}$ could have also been normalized at $k^2 = \kappa^2$, with κ^2 on the right-hand side of Eq. (7-53). But since it does not develop infrared singularities at $d = 4$, (7-53) is usually chosen for convenience.

The result of this operation is that

$$\Gamma_R^{(N,L)}(k_i, p_i; g, \kappa) = Z_\phi^{N/2} Z_{\phi^2}^L \Gamma^{(N,L)}(k_i, p_i; \lambda, \Lambda) \qquad (7\text{-}59)$$

has a finite limit as $\Lambda \to \infty$ for $d \leqslant 4$. The variables appearing on both sides of the last equation will be discussed in the next section.

In both sets of normalization equations the right-hand side was chosen as the lowest order term, in the perturbation expansion in g, of the function in question. This is a rather natural choice since at lowest order all functions, except $\Gamma^{(0,2)}$, are finite, and there is no reason to have the renormalized functions differ from the bare ones. But this limit would not have been affected by the presence of higher order terms in g on the right-hand sides of the normalization equations. The first time that this freedom found a beautiful use was in the approach of 't Hooft and Veltman,[1] which will be described in Secs. 9-9—9-11.

In hindsight one can say that the normalization equations were completely unnecessary since we could have determined the renormalization functions by the simple requirement that from graphs of $\Gamma^{(2)}$, for example, the terms proportional to Λ^2 and to $\ln \Lambda$ be subtracted, etc. This procedure, which we will follow in the framework of dimensional regularization, can fix the renormalized vertices. Then one can check, for curiosity's sake alone, what would have been the corresponding normalization conditions, by calculating the finite Γ_R's at the points indicated in (7-53)—(7-56). The right-hand side will include an infinite number of terms, starting with those that were kept in the normalization equations.

Since most of the literature still uses normalization conditions, most of the following development will be carried on in this way. All quantities so far calculated in the two procedures show no difference. This independence of universal quantities from the renormalization procedure has been explained by Gross.[23]

7-6 RENORMALIZATION CONSTANTS FOR A MASSLESS THEORY TO ORDER TWO LOOPS

Chapter 6 can be used as an example of the utilization of the normalization conditions (7-45)—(7-48). Here we will briefly indicate some of the steps by which (7-53)–(7-56) are used to determine the renormalization functions. Three special features are new:

(1)   The renormalized functions, in the limit as $\Lambda \to \infty$, depend on the mass scale κ. Thus we start with a bare theory with two free parameters λ and Λ. The term μ^2 is determined by these two to give a critical theory. The resulting theory also has two parameters, g and κ. This should be contrasted with the case of finite mass, in which we start with μ^2, λ and Λ, and end with m^2 and g only.

(2)   The renormalization functions become dependent on the particular normalization point. The role of the symmetric point (SP) is technically quite important.

(3)   In $\Gamma^{(2)}$ there are infrared divergent graphs (see below) but they are cancelled by the mass renormalization. This is an interesting feature. At four dimensions the integrals which have a pure Λ^2 ultraviolet behavior do not have an infrared divergence. Only those which have $\ln\Lambda$ will be problematic in the infrared. Those get cancelled, a fact that makes Eq. (7-53) possible.

The considerations mentioned in point (3) above allow us to make a shortcut – Eq. (7-53) can be used, by itself, to determine the critical temperature in the form,

$$\mu_c^2 = \mu_c^2(\lambda,\Lambda) \qquad (7\text{-}60)$$

To second order, in the cutoff theory, we can write

$$\mu_c^2 + \frac{\lambda}{2} D_1(\mu_c^2, \Lambda) - \frac{\lambda^2}{4} D_1(\mu_c^2, \Lambda) D_2(\mu_c^2, \Lambda) - \frac{\lambda^2}{6} D_3(0, \mu_c^2, \Lambda) = 0 \qquad (7\text{-}61)$$

in which Z_ϕ was divided out. (Compare Sec. 6-7). Expanding μ_c^2 in powers of λ,

$$\mu_c^2 = \sum_{i=1}^{\infty} \mu_i(\Lambda)\lambda^i \qquad (7\text{-}62)$$

where we have used the fact that $\mu_c^2 = 0$ in the free theory, we can determine μ_1 and μ_2 by expanding the integrals in (7-61) in powers of λ. The result is:

$$\mu_1 = -\frac{1}{2} \int^{\Lambda} \frac{1}{q^2} \qquad (7\text{-}63)$$

$$\mu_2 = \frac{1}{6} \int^{\Lambda} \frac{1}{q_1^2 q_2^2 (q_1 + q_2)^2} \qquad (7\text{-}64)$$

The calculation of μ_3 is left as Exercise 7-10. Notice that the infrared divergence appearing in D_2, in the third term, at $\mu_c^2 = 0$ is cancelled by mass renormalization of the second term, i.e., by the expansion of D_1.

Equations (7-54) and (7-55) have to be used in order to determine λ and Z_ϕ. These are expanded in powers of g:

$$\lambda = \sum_{i=1}^{\infty} \lambda_i g^i = g + \lambda_2 g^2 + \lambda_3 g^3 \qquad (7\text{-}65)$$

$$Z_\phi = \sum_{i=0}^{\infty} z_i g^i = 1 + z_2 g^2 + \ldots \qquad (7\text{-}66)$$

Considering the graphs shown in Fig. 6-6, we can write (7-54) and (7-55) as:

$$Z_\phi \left[1 - \frac{\lambda^2}{6} \frac{\partial}{\partial k^2} \;\; \text{⬭} \;\; \bigg|_{k^2 = \kappa^2} \right] = 1 \qquad (7\text{-}67)$$

$$Z_\phi^2 \left[\lambda - \frac{3}{2} \lambda^2 \;\; \text{⬭} \;\; \bigg|_{SP} + \frac{3}{4} \lambda^3 \;\; \text{⬭⬭} \;\; \bigg|_{SP} + 3\lambda^3 \;\; \text{⬭} \;\; \bigg|_{SP} \right] = g$$

$$(7\text{-}68)$$

One graph in $\Gamma^{(4)}$ is cancelled when the renormalization of the mass is taken into account. Here we come across the significance of the symmetric choice of the normalization point. In (7-68) the first graph will contribute

$$I(k_1 + k_2, \Lambda) = \int^{\Lambda} dq \, \frac{1}{(q + k_1 + k_2)^2 q^2} \qquad (7\text{-}69)$$

together with its two permutations. But the integral can depend only on $(k_1 + k_2)^2$, which at SP equals κ^2, and is independent of the permutation. This is the origin of the factor in the first and second graphs in (7-68). The proof that all six permutations of the last graph are equal is left as Exercise 7-11.

Since λ starts at first order in g,

$$z_2 = \frac{1}{6} \frac{\partial}{\partial k^2} D_3(k, \Lambda) \bigg|_{k^2 = \kappa^2} \qquad (7\text{-}70)$$

Inserting (7-65) and (7-66) in (7-68) we have:

$$(1 + 2z_2 g^2)[g + \lambda_2 g^2 + \lambda_3 g^3 - \tfrac{3}{2}(g + \lambda_2 g^2)^2 I_{SP} + \tfrac{3}{4}g^3 I_{SP}^2 + 3g^3 I_{4SP}] = g$$

Comparing powers of g one finds:

$$\lambda_2 = \tfrac{3}{2} I_{SP} \qquad (7\text{-}71)$$

and

$$\lambda_3 = \tfrac{15}{4} I_{SP}^2 - 3 I_{4SP} - 2z_2 \qquad (7\text{-}72)$$

Notice that the quadratic divergence in z_2 is not removed by subtraction but by a derivative. Thus, z_2 would have had a logarithmic infrared singularity as $k \to 0$ for $d \leqslant 4$, which μ_c^2 does not have (see also Exercise 7-12).

Finally, we have to compute Z_{ϕ^2} to the same order. Writing

$$\overline{Z}_{\phi^2} \equiv Z_\phi Z_{\phi^2} = \sum_0^\infty c_i g^i = 1 + c_1 g + c_2 g^2 + \dots \qquad (7\text{-}73)$$

and Eq. (7-56) as

$$\overline{Z}_{\phi^2} \left[1 - \tfrac{1}{2} \lambda I_{\overline{SP}} + \tfrac{1}{4} \lambda^2 I_{\overline{SP}}^2 + \tfrac{1}{2} \lambda^2 I_{4\overline{SP}} \right] = 1 \qquad (7\text{-}74)$$

we can solve for c_1 and c_2. In writing the last equation we have taken the contributions of the graphs appearing in Fig. 6-10. Graph (c) was omitted after mass renormalization. The choice of the normalization momenta for this function — Eq. (7-58b) — is such as to make

$$I_{\overline{SP}} = I_{SP}; I_{4\overline{SP}} = I_{4SP} \qquad (7\text{-}75)$$

(see Exercise 7-13). Thus, for the calculation of all the renormalization constants up to two-loop order we need to calculate only three integrals, I_{SP}, I_{4SP} and $\partial D_3 / \partial k^2$. They will be calculated in Chap. 9.

7-7 RENORMALIZATION AWAY FROM THE CRITICAL POINT

The renormalization at the critical point is particularly convenient from the technical point of view. The integrals are much easier to compute, and as one goes to higher orders this becomes a crucial consideration. But most of the time one is interested in situations which are away from the critical point. In fact, one would like to obtain a description of the thermodynamic quantities in a whole region about this point. This region is spanned by the external — symmetry breaking — field, h, and by the deviation of the temperature from the critical temperature, and possibly additional relevant parameters. This region can be divided as follows:

(a) $T > T_c$, $h = 0$ and therefore a symmetric theory, $\overline{\phi} = 0$ [see Eq. (5-45)].

(b) $T > T_c$ and $h \neq 0$ $\Big\}$ $\overline{\phi} \neq 0$
 $T < T_c$ and any h

We start by discussing how the renormalization of the massless theory is extended to temperatures above T_c. The technique was introduced by Weinberg[7] and applied to critical phenomena by Zinn-Justin.[8] Its full power is revealed when it is combined with the renormalization group equation. This is the subject of the next chapter.

We start with a theory having a bare parameter $\mu^2 \propto T - T_0$, also called r_0 in some circles. In the Lagrangian we write

$$\mu^2 \phi^2 = \mu_c^2 \phi^2 + (\mu^2 - \mu_c^2)\phi^2 = \mu_c^2 \phi^2 + \delta\mu^2 \phi^2 \qquad (7\text{-}76)$$

The difference $\delta\mu^2$ we consider as a limit of a spatially varying quadratic interaction, as it tends towards a constant. Alternatively, we can consider $\delta\mu^2(q)$ in the limit $\delta\mu^2(q) \to \delta\mu^2\delta(q)$.

Using the results of Sec. 5-7 we can write any vertex function in the cutoff theory as

$$\Gamma^{(N,L)}(k_i, p_i; \mu^2, \lambda, \Lambda) = \sum_{M=0}^{\infty} \frac{1}{M!} \int dq_1 \dots dq_M r(q_1) \dots r(q_M)$$

$$\Gamma^{(N, L+M)}(k_i, p_i, q_i; \mu_c^2, \lambda, \Lambda) \qquad (7\text{-}77)$$

[See Eq. (5-73) in which t was replaced by r.] On the right-hand side of the last equation we have vertex functions, with ϕ and ϕ^2 operators, all calculated at the critical point. On the left-hand side we obtain $\Gamma^{(N,L)}$ at an arbitrary temperature above T_c.

As we take the limit in which r becomes constant in coordinate space, $r \to \delta\mu^2$, and (7-77) tends towards:

$$\Gamma^{(N,L)}(k_i, p_i; \mu^2, \lambda, \Lambda) = \sum_{M=0}^{\infty} \frac{1}{M!} (\delta\mu^2)^M \Gamma^{(N, L+M)}(k_i, p_i, q_i = 0; \mu_c^2, \lambda, \Lambda)$$

$$(7\text{-}78)$$

If $\Lambda \to \infty$ there will be plenty of divergences on each side of (7-78). However, the functions on the right-hand side can be renormalized by writing

$$\Gamma_R^{(N,M)}(k_i, p_i; g, \kappa) = Z_\phi^{N/2} Z_{\phi^2}^M \Gamma^{(N,M)}(k_i, p_i; \mu_c^2, \lambda, \Lambda) \qquad (7\text{-}79)$$

except for $\Gamma^{(0,2)}$, which cannot be renormalized multiplicatively. Equation (7-78) can be therefore rewritten as

$$Z_\phi^{N/2} Z_{\phi^2}^L \Gamma^{(N,L)}(k_i, p_i; \mu^2, \lambda, \Lambda) = \sum_{M=0}^{\infty} \frac{1}{M!} (\delta t)^M \Gamma_R^{(N, L+M)}(k_i, p_i, q_i = 0; g, \kappa)$$

$$(7\text{-}80)$$

for $N \neq 0$, in which

$$\delta\mu^2 = T - T_c = Z_{\phi^2} \delta t \qquad (7\text{-}81)$$

Thus, if δt — the renormalized temperature difference — is finite then the right-hand side of (7-80) is finite as $\Lambda \to \infty$, order by order in perturbation theory. So must also be the left-hand side, despite the fact that the Z_ϕ and Z_{ϕ^2} *are the renormalization constants of the critical theory*, i.e., those which are obtained from Eqs. (7-53)–(7-56). The result is

$$\Gamma_R^{(N,L)}(k_i, p_i; \delta t, g, \kappa) = \sum_{M=0}^{\infty} \frac{1}{M!} (\delta t)^M \Gamma_R^{(N,L+M)}(k_i, p_i, q_i = 0; g, \kappa) \qquad (7\text{-}82)$$

(see also Exercises 7-14–7-15).

A final remark: The insertion of many ϕ^2's at zero momentum leads to infrared singularities. This implies that the limit $q_i \to 0$ is not interchangeable with the sum over M.

Case (b), that of broken symmetry, is studied in an analogous way. If $\bar{\phi}(x)$ is the conjugate to $h(x)$, which was called $J(x)$ in Chap. 4, then in the cutoff theory, we have the expansion:

$$\Gamma^{(N,L)}(k_i, p_i; \mu^2, \bar{\phi}, \lambda, \Lambda) = \sum_{I,J=0}^{\infty} \frac{1}{I!J!} \int dl_1 \dots dl_I \, dq_1 \dots dq_J$$

$$\times \bar{\phi}(l_1) \dots \bar{\phi}(l_I) \, r(q_1) \dots r(q_J) \, \Gamma^{(N+I,L+J)}(k_i, l_i, p_i, q_i; \mu_c^2, \lambda, \Lambda) \qquad (7\text{-}83)$$

in which we expand each vertex function about the *symmetric massless state* by using (5-44) and (5-30), and then use the expansion about T_c, as above. On the right-hand side we have *symmetric vertices at the critical point only*! They, again, can be multiplicatively renormalized using the renormalization constants of the critical theory determined from (7-53)–(7-56).

The result is that multiplying $\Gamma^{(N,L)}$, which is the vertex calculated in a state of broken symmetry at $T \neq T_c$, by $Z_\phi^{N/2} Z_{\phi^2}^L$ we manage to renormalize it:

$$\lim_{\Lambda \to \infty} Z_\phi^{N/2} Z_{\phi^2}^L \, \Gamma^{(N,L)}(k_i, p_i, \mu^2, \bar{\phi}, \lambda, \Lambda) = \Gamma_R^{(N,L)}(k_i, p_i; \delta t, M, g, \kappa)$$

$$= \sum_{I,J} \frac{1}{I!J!} M^I (\delta t)^J \, \Gamma_R^{(N+I,L+J)}(k_i, l_i = 0, p_i, q_i = 0; g, \kappa) \qquad (7\text{-}84)$$

in which δt is given by (7-81), and

$$\bar{\phi} = Z_\phi^{1/2} M \qquad (7\text{-}85)$$

In particular one obtains a renormalized equation of state which reads

$$H(\delta t, M, g, \kappa) = \Gamma_R^{(1)}(\delta t, M, g, \kappa)$$

$$= \sum_{N=1}^{\infty} \frac{1}{N!} M^N \Gamma_R^{(1+N)}(k_i = 0; \delta t, g, \kappa) \qquad (7\text{-}86)$$

$$= \sum_{N,L} \frac{1}{N!L!} M^N (\delta t)^L \, \Gamma_R^{(1+N,L)}(k_i = 0, p_i = 0; g, \kappa)$$

Here we see the great advantage of the representation in terms of vertex functions. Nowhere does one have to state whether the symmetry is broken, explicitly or spontaneously, and all vertex functions can be renormalized by treating the symmetric theory alone[9] – all vertex functions but $\Gamma^{(0,L)}$ for $L \leqslant 2$. Even these are amenable to rational treatment[10] as will be discussed in the next section.

7-8 COUNTERTERMS

The statement of the renormalizability of a ϕ^4 theory (Sec. 7-4), as well as the renormalizability of any other theory, can be formulated on the level of the Lagrangian.[11] This formulation has certain advantages which are complementary to those of the renormalization procedure described in the four preceding sections. In particular, the systematic structure, which includes both multiplicative and additive renormalizations, is clearly discerned. The two formulations are, of course, completely equivalent.

In order to effect the transition to the Lagrangian it is convenient to state the renormalization theorem in terms of the connected Green functions, since in the generation of these functions the ϕ's and the ϕ^2's enter in a similar way — as derivatives with respect to sources. The statement which corresponds to (7-34) is:

$$G_{cR}^{(N,L)}(k_i, p_i; m^2, g, \Lambda) = Z_\phi^{-N/2} Z_{\phi^2}^L G_c^{(N,L)}(k_i, p_i; \mu^2, \lambda, \Lambda) \qquad (7\text{-}87)$$

in which the left-hand side has a finite limit as $\Lambda \to \infty$. Using Eq. (5-65) and the discussion following it, the right-hand side can be written as:

$$Z_\phi^{-N/2} Z_{\phi^2}^L \frac{\delta^{(N+L)} F\{J, t\}}{\delta J(k_1) \ldots \delta J(k_N) \, \delta t(p_1) \ldots \delta t(p_L)} \Bigg|_{J=t=0}$$

$$= \frac{\delta^{N+L} F\{Z_\phi^{-1/2} J, Z_{\phi^2} t\}}{\delta J(k_1) \ldots \delta J(k_N) \, \delta t(p_1) \ldots \delta t(p_L)} \Bigg|_{J=t=0} \qquad (7\text{-}88)$$

The generating functional F on the right-hand side of the last equation is simply the one which follows from the Lagrangian

$$\mathscr{L}' = \tfrac{1}{2}(\nabla \phi)^2 + \tfrac{1}{2}\mu^2 \phi^2 + \frac{\lambda}{4!} \phi^4 - J'\phi - \tfrac{1}{2}t'\phi^2 \qquad (7\text{-}89)$$

in which the source terms have been included. The functions J' and t' are defined by

$$J' = Z_\phi^{-1/2} J \qquad (7\text{-}90)$$

$$t' = Z_{\phi^2} t \qquad (7\text{-}91)$$

respectively. But, since ϕ is an integration variable, we can define a field ϕ_R, the renormalized field, via

$$\phi_R = Z_\phi^{-1/2} \phi \qquad (7\text{-}92)$$

and F will be produced in terms of ϕ_R in the same way as it was in terms of ϕ. The Lagrangian $\mathscr{L}'$ can be rewritten as

$$\mathscr{L}' = \tfrac{1}{2} Z_\phi (\nabla \phi_R)^2 + \tfrac{1}{2} Z_\phi \mu^2 \phi_R^2 + \frac{\lambda Z_\phi^2}{4!} \phi_R^4 - J\phi_R - \tfrac{1}{2} Z_{\phi^2} Z_\phi t \phi_R^2 \qquad (7\text{-}93)$$

Defining

$$\mathcal{L}_R = \tfrac{1}{2} (\nabla\phi_R)^2 + \tfrac{1}{2} m^2 \phi_R^2 + \frac{g}{4!} \phi_R^4 \qquad (7\text{-}94)$$

Eq. (7-93) can be put into the form:

$$\mathcal{L}' = \mathcal{L}_R - J\phi_R - \tfrac{1}{2} t\phi_R^2 + CT$$

where CT stands for *counterterms*, and is given by

$$CT = \tfrac{1}{2} (Z_\phi - 1)(\nabla\phi_R)^2 + \tfrac{1}{2} (Z_\phi\mu^2 - m^2)\phi_R^2 + \frac{1}{4!} (\lambda Z_\phi^2 - g)\phi_R^4 - \tfrac{1}{2} (Z_{\phi^2} Z_\phi - 1)t\phi_R^2 \qquad (7\text{-}95)$$

So far all the manipulations have been carried out in the presence of a cutoff. The statement of the renormalizability now becomes:

given the Lagrangian,

$$\mathcal{L} = \tfrac{1}{2} (\nabla\phi)^2 + \tfrac{1}{2} \mu^2 \phi^2 + \frac{\lambda}{4!} \phi^4 \qquad (7\text{-}96)$$

one can replace it by

$$\mathcal{L} = \tfrac{1}{2} (\nabla\phi)^2 + \tfrac{1}{2} m^2 \phi^2 + \frac{g}{4!} \phi^4 \qquad (7\text{-}97)$$

and add the counterterms

$$CT = \tfrac{1}{2} a(\nabla\phi)^2 + \tfrac{1}{2} b\phi^2 + \frac{1}{4!} c\phi^4 + \tfrac{1}{2} ft\phi^2 \qquad (7\text{-}98)$$

Then the connected Green functions $G_c^{(N,L)}$ generated by the source term

$$\mathcal{L}_S = -J\phi - \tfrac{1}{2} t\phi^2 \qquad (7\text{-}99)$$

as derivatives with respect to J and to t, can be made to have a limit as $\Lambda \to \infty$ by choosing the four constants a, b, c and f as appropriate functions of m, g and Λ (see Exercise 7-16).

The proof of this statement consists of nothing more than retracing the steps (7-89) through (7-95) so as to be able to use Eq. (7-34). Notice that the subscript R was omitted since ϕ is just a running variable.

Looking back at Eq. (7-89) we notice an easy way of taking care of the divergence of $G_c^{(0,2)}$. Adding to $\mathcal{L}'$ a term of the form

$$\mathcal{L}_t = - \tfrac{1}{2} A(t')^2 \qquad (7\text{-}100)$$

which is independent of the field ϕ, changes F by an additive constant:

$$F\{J',t'\} \to F\{J',t'\} + \tfrac{1}{2} A (t')^2 \qquad (7\text{-}101)$$

the only Green function which is affected by this addition is $G_c^{(0,2)}$. Since the divergence of $\Gamma^{(0;2)}$ is logarithmic in four dimensions, it suffices to choose A as the value of $G_c^{(0,2)}$ at some momentum, so as to provide for one subtraction. In a cutoff theory this shift in F is well defined and it is non-singular in the infrared region.

Similarly, $G_c^{(0,1)}$ has a quadratic divergence which can be eliminated by adding to $\mathscr{L}'$ a term proportional to t'. The proof that a single subtraction, in addition to the one implied by $G_c^{(0,2)}$, will do is left as Exercise 7-17.

We can include all of these among the counterterms by introducing two new constants d and e, such that

$$CT \to CT + dt + \tfrac{1}{2}et^2 \qquad (7\text{-}102)$$

Then the statement is that six functions, a through f, of m, g and Λ can be found, so as to make *all* Green functions including ϕ's and ϕ^2's in the symmetric state finite as $\Lambda \to \infty$. The Green functions are generated by derivatives with respect to J and t in $\mathscr{L}_S$ – Eq. (7-99). The proof, which consists of exhibiting d and e in terms of the previously defined renormalization constants, is left as Exercise 7-18.

The six counterterms in (7-98) and (7-102) are *all the operators which can be constructed from the field and the sources whose canonical dimension† is not greater than* d_c *at* $d = d_c$, *and which preserve the symmetry of the Lagrangian* (see also Sec. 7-12).

This is a general rule which was discussed in detail by Symanzik and by Zinn-Justin.[12] In the case discussed above, $d_c = 4$. There, the dimension of ϕ is 1, of J is 3, and of t is 2. Thus, besides the six terms which were considered explicitly above one could have also added J. But the presence of J modifies only $G^{(1)}$, which vanished in the symmetric theory (see also Exercises 7-19 and 7-20). Furthermore, one can easily construct a correspondence between each counterterm and a primitively divergent vertex function. The correspondence is one to one.

Finally, following the same steps, one can renormalize the theory using counterterms defined relative to the massless critical theory (see Exercise 7-21).

7-9 RELEVANT AND IRRELEVANT OPERATORS

The question of relevant operators arose at an early stage in the discussion. When in Chap. 2 the discrete Ising model was transformed into a continuous field theory an infinite series of powers of the field appeared in the Lagrangian, Eq. (2-45). A similar infinity of powers appears if the Lagrangian is constructed by appealing to symmetry arguments alone, as was suggested in Sec. 2-2. We argued there that in a theory with a symmetry $\phi \to -\phi$, no terms beyond ϕ^4 are

† In units of momentum.

needed to describe the critical behavior. The higher powers were said to be *irrelevant*.

Similarly, the momentum dependence in the Lagrangian was severely restricted by appealing to irrelevance. For example, in the free part only quadratic terms in the momentum were kept (see, e.g., the discussion leading to Eq. (2-53)). Then in the quartic part no momentum dependence at all was preserved. Though, a priori, Eq. (2-45) indicated that such momentum dependence does in fact exist.

In the present section the concept of relevance will be discussed by an analysis of the effect of the various operators on the infrared singularities in the theory.

Consider the generalization of the power-counting argument leading to Eq. (7-25), which gives the difference between the number of powers of momentum in the numerator and the denominator of a graph, to the case in which there are many momentum-independent interactions. A graph with n_r interactions of type ϕ^r will have

$$L = I - \sum_r n_r + 1 \qquad (7\text{-}103)$$

loops, as each interaction reduces the number of momentum integrations by one, and

$$I = \frac{1}{2} \left(\sum_r n_r r - E \right) \qquad (7\text{-}104)$$

internal lines. E is the number of external lines. The generalization of Eq. (7-25) is:

$$\delta = Ld - 2I = \sum_r n_r (\tfrac{1}{2} rd - r - d) + (d + E - \tfrac{1}{2} Ed) = -\sum_r n_r \delta_r + (d + E - \tfrac{1}{2} Ed)$$

$$= L(d - 2) - 2 \sum_r n_r + 2 \qquad (7\text{-}105)$$

Hence, for a given number of loops, δ will be highest if all vertices are of the type with highest r available. This makes $\sum n_r$ smallest. On the other hand, δ is smallest if all vertices are of the lowest r available. Thus, for a given number of loops, the interaction with the smallest number of legs will lead to the strongest infrared divergences, as is suggested by the arguments following Eq. (7-29).

What this interaction is for any given theory is determined either by a symmetry argument, such as the one which eliminates ϕ^3 for a magnetic system, or for a superfluid. Or there may be an accidental vanishing of one of the couplings, such as may be the case at a tricritical point which sits at the end of a critical line. The thermodynamic phase space available for such accidental vanishing is, of course, very constrained.

At the critical dimension of the most *relevant* operator — the interaction leading to the strongest infrared divergences — the dimension δ_r of the corresponding coupling constant vanishes. Any other interaction will have a higher r and consequently a lower d_c (see, e.g., Eq. (7-26)). Thus, near the critical number of space dimensions for the most relevant operator, interactions with higher r have no infrared singularities, and are *irrelevant*. Equivalently, we can say that near the critical number of dimensions for the most relevant operator the operators with higher r have coupling constants with negative dimension. This is a convenient way to identify irrelevant operators. They can lead, at most, to some small corrections in the critical region. Such corrections are discussed in Secs. II-(2-3) — (2-4).

On the other hand, if a theory is perturbed, be it ever so slightly, by an operator which is more relevant than the one kept, its behavior will change drastically. Such will be the effect of the introduction of a magnetic field, or shifting the temperature from its critical value.

As far as the momentum dependence of the interactions is concerned, the considerations are rather similar, namely, if any monomial in the field ϕ is multiplied by a power of momentum to produce a term

$$O = k^s \phi^r$$

the dimension of O is

$$[O] = [\phi^r] \Lambda^s$$

Hence the dimension of the corresponding coupling constant becomes smaller than that of the coupling constant of ϕ^r. This is a reflection of the fact that the extra powers of k soften the infrared behavior of the graph.

For example, if ϕ^4 is the interaction of lowest r, $d_c = 4$, and the relevant operators are those whose dimension is not greater than 4. This ensures that the corresponding coupling constants have positive dimensions. The dimension of ϕ is 1 and of k is 1, thus the only *relevant* operators are

$$\phi^2 \; ; k^2 \phi^2 \; ; \phi^4$$

ϕ and ϕ^3 are eliminated by symmetry (see also Exercises 7-22—7-24).

7-10 RENORMALIZATION OF A ϕ^4 THEORY WITH AN 0(M) SYMMETRY

A ϕ^4 theory with an order parameter having M components can be renormalized in a way which is very similar to the one used for the single component theory, provided that the following two conditions are satisfied in all orders of perturbation theory.

Given that the interaction Lagrangian is

$$\mathscr{L}_{\text{Int}} = \lambda T_{ijkl} \phi_i \phi_j \phi_k \phi_l \qquad (7\text{-}106)$$

with T, a tensor, symmetric in all four indices:

(a) The two-point function is diagonal in the space of the components

$$\Gamma_{ij}^{(2)}(k) = \Gamma^{(2)}(k)\, \delta_{ij} \qquad (7\text{-}107)$$

(b) At a point $k_1 \ldots k_4$ at which $\Gamma^{(4)}$ is symmetric in the momenta

$$\Gamma_{ijkl}^{(4)}(k_i) = \Gamma^{(4)}(k_i)T_{ijkl} \qquad (7\text{-}108)$$

If these conditions are not satisfied, the renormalization constants will, in general, be matrices, rather than numbers (see Exercise 7-27).

The general conditions which have to be imposed on T_{ijkl}, so as to satisfy conditions (a) and (b), are rather complex, and are not fully known.[13] Here we discuss the case of an $0(M)$-symmetric theory in which it is easy to show that (a) and (b) hold. The interaction Lagrangian is

$$\mathscr{L}_{\text{Int}} = \frac{\lambda}{4!} S_{ijkl}\phi_i\phi_j\phi_k\phi_l = \frac{\lambda}{4!}\left(\sum_1^M \phi_i^2\right)^2 \qquad (7\text{-}109)$$

With S_{ijkl} given by Eq. (4-36), one can show that in all orders in perturbation theory $\Gamma_{ij}^{(2)}(k)$ is proportional to δ_{ij}. Furthermore, $\Gamma_{ijkl}^{(4)}(k_1, \ldots, k_4)$, at a point at which it is symmetric in the momenta, is proportional to S_{ijkl} at every order in perturbation theory (see Sec. 4-5 and Exercises 4-10 and 4-11).

The general statement of renormalizability, (7-59), can be rewritten with very slight modification, namely[14]

$$\Gamma_{i_1 \ldots i_N R}^{(N)}(k_i; g, \kappa) = Z_\phi^{N/2}\, \Gamma_{i_1 \ldots i_N}^{(N)}(k_i; \lambda, \Lambda) \qquad (7\text{-}110)$$

The renormalization constants can be determined by first writing:

$$\Gamma_{ij}^{(2)}(k) = \Gamma^{(2)}(k)\delta_{ij} \qquad (7\text{-}111)$$

$$\Gamma_{ijkl}^{(4)}\Big|_{\text{SP}} = \Gamma^{(4)}\Big|_{\text{SP}} S_{ijkl} \qquad (7\text{-}112)$$

which will hold for both the bare and the renormalized vertex functions, and then imposing normalization conditions in a zero mass theory:

$$\Gamma_R^{(2)}(0) = 0 \qquad (7\text{-}113)$$

$$\frac{\partial}{\partial k^2}\, \Gamma_R^{(2)}(k)\Big|_{k^2 = \kappa^2} = 1 \qquad (7\text{-}114)$$

$$\Gamma_R^{(4)}\Big|_{\text{SP}} = g \qquad (7\text{-}115)$$

The insertion of ϕ^2 operators is taken care of by defining the insertion as the operator

$$\phi^2 \rightarrow \tfrac{1}{2}\Sigma\phi_i^2 \qquad (7\text{-}116)$$

which is the only quadratic $0(M)$-invariant.

Consider, for example, the four-point function to order one loop. Using Eq. (4-38) we can write:

$$\Gamma^{(4)}_{i_1 \ldots i_4}(k_1 \ldots k_4) = \lambda S_{i_1 \ldots i_4} - \frac{\lambda^2}{2} \left\{ \tfrac{1}{9} \left[(M+4)\delta_{i_1 i_2}\delta_{i_3 i_4} + 2\delta_{i_1 i_3}\delta_{i_2 i_4} \right.\right.$$

$$\left.\left. + 2\delta_{i_1 i_4}\delta_{i_2 i_3} \right] I(k_1 + k_2) + (i_2 k_2 \leftrightarrow i_3 k_3) + (i_2 k_2 \leftrightarrow i_4 k_4) \right\} \qquad (7\text{-}117)$$

At the symmetry point, SP,

$$\Gamma^{(4)}_{i_1 \ldots i_4} |_{\text{SP}} = \left(\lambda - \frac{\lambda^2}{2} \frac{M+8}{3} I_{\text{SP}} \right) S_{i_1 \ldots i_4} \qquad (7\text{-}118)$$

Comparison of this result with Eqs. (7-68) and (7-71) gives

$$\lambda = g + g^2 \frac{3}{2} \left(\frac{M+8}{9} \right) I_{\text{SP}} \qquad (7\text{-}119)$$

Thus, the only difference with the case of a single component is the appearance of the factor $(M+8)/9$. Clearly, the subtraction generated by (7-119) will cancel the divergences in all three terms proportional to λ^2 in Eq. (7-117), even though for general momenta this term is not proportional to S_{ijkl}.

Similarly, we can compute the first momentum-dependent term in $\Gamma^{(2)}_{ij}(k)$, so as to be able to calculate Z_ϕ using Eq. (7-67). The expression corresponding to this graph is:

$$\frac{\lambda^2}{6} S_{iklm}S_{klmj}D_3(k) = \frac{M+2}{18} \lambda^2 D_3(k)\delta_{ij} \qquad (7\text{-}120)$$

Inserting in Eq. (7-67) one finds for Z_ϕ:

$$Z_\phi = 1 + g^2 \frac{M+2}{18} \frac{\partial}{\partial k^2} D_3(k) \bigg|_{k^2 = \kappa^2} \qquad (7\text{-}121)$$

Using the results of Exercise 4-11 one has for $\Gamma^{(4)}$ at the symmetry point:

$$\Gamma^{(4)} \big|_{\text{SP}} = \lambda - \lambda^2 \frac{M+8}{6} I_{\text{SP}} + \lambda^3 \left[\frac{M^2 + 6M + 20}{36} I^2_{\text{SP}} + \frac{5M+22}{9} I_{4\text{SP}} \right] \qquad (7\text{-}122)$$

From this one obtains, instead of Eqs. (7-71) and (7-72), the following coefficients in the renormalization constants:

$$z_2 = \frac{M+2}{18} \frac{\partial}{\partial k^2} D_3(k) \bigg|_{k^2 = \kappa^2} \qquad (7\text{-}123)$$

$$\lambda_2 = \frac{M+8}{6} I_{\text{SP}} \qquad (7\text{-}124)$$

$$\lambda_3 = \frac{M^2 + 26M + 108}{36} I_{SP}^2 - \frac{5M + 22}{9} I_{4SP} - 2z_2 \qquad (7\text{-}125)$$

(See also Exercises 7-25—7-27.)

Finally, the calculation of Z_{ϕ^2} necessitates no new computations since the integrals are the same as those of $\Gamma^{(4)}$; the symmetry factors are those of the single component theory, and the tensorial contraction of a graph is the same as that of the corresponding graph of $\Gamma^{(2)}$ — the one into which the ϕ^2 insertion has been made. This follows simply from the fact that the ϕ^2 operator is proportional to δ_{ij}.

We therefore use the graphs in Fig. 6-10, including the tensor S_{ijkl}, to replace Eq. (7-74) by:

$$\bar{Z}_{\phi^2} \left\{ 1 - \lambda \frac{M+2}{6} I_{SP} + \lambda^2 \left[\left(\frac{M+2}{6} \right)^2 I_{SP}^2 + \frac{M+2}{6} I_{4SP} \right] \right\} = 1 \qquad (7\text{-}126)$$

(See Exercise 7-28.)

Inserting $\lambda(g)$ via

$$\lambda = g + g^2 \frac{M+8}{6} I_{SP} \qquad (7\text{-}127)$$

we obtain:

$$\bar{Z}_{\phi^2}^{-1} = 1 - g \frac{M+2}{6} I_{SP} + g^2 \frac{M+2}{6} (I_{4SP} - I_{SP}^2) \qquad (7\text{-}128)$$

7 -11 WARD IDENTITIES AND RENORMALIZATION

In the present section we are going to see the utility of the identities derived in Sec. 5-6 for the special case of an $0(2)$-symmetry. These identities, of which one can generate an infinite number, make very strong statements on the process of renormalization. They make two types of statements:

(a) Relating infinite parts of different correlation functions. Statements of this type reduce the number of renormalization constants, or counterterms.

(b) Relating different physical (renormalized) quantities, such as the longitudinal and transverse correlation lengths in the state of broken symmetry (the masses of the π and σ).

We consider two examples of the first type. Both are related to the σ-model discussed in Sec. 5-6. The first leads to a result which was taken for granted in the previous section. It is the tensorial structure of the bare regularized four-point vertex function in the symmetric state at a symmetry point in the momenta, Eq. (7-112), which reads:

$$\Gamma^{(4)}_{ijkl}\Big|_{SP} = \Gamma^{(4)}\Big|_{SP} S_{ijkl} \qquad (7\text{-}129)$$

The tensor S, given by (4-36), is

$$S_{ijkl} = \tfrac{1}{3}(\delta_{ij}\delta_{kl} + \delta_{ik}\delta_{jl} + \delta_{il}\delta_{jk}) \qquad (7\text{-}130)$$

This is the same tensor as the one which renders the original Lagrangian rotationally invariant.

Now one can very easily convince oneself that unless the indices of $\Gamma^{(4)}$ are equal in pairs the element vanishes in every order in perturbation theory. The question as to whether $\Gamma^{(4)}$ satisfies Eq. (7-129) reduces to finding the relation between $\Gamma^{(4)}_{\sigma\sigma\sigma\sigma}|_{SP}(= \Gamma^{(4)}_{\pi\pi\pi\pi}|_{SP})$ and $\Gamma^{(4)}_{\sigma\sigma\pi\pi}|_{SP}(= \Gamma^{(4)}_{\pi\pi\sigma\sigma}|_{SP}$ etc.). It is just this relation which is provided by a Ward–Takahashi identity.

Starting from Eq. (5-62), which we rewrite in a self-explanatory abbreviated notation as:

$$\int dx\,[\sigma(x)\Gamma_{\pi\pi}(x,y) - \delta(x-y)\Gamma_\sigma(x) - \pi(x)\Gamma_{\sigma\pi}(x,y)] = 0 \qquad (7\text{-}131)$$

we take three consecutive functional derivatives with respect to $\sigma(z)$, $\sigma(t)$, $\sigma(w)$, and then set $\sigma(x) = \pi(x) = 0$. The first derivative is written explicitly since it will be of use below. It reads:

$$\int dx\,[\sigma(x)\Gamma_{\pi\pi\sigma}(x,y,z) + \delta(x-z)\Gamma_{\pi\pi}(x,y) - \delta(x-y)\Gamma_{\sigma\sigma}(x,z)$$

$$- \pi(x)\Gamma_{\sigma\pi\sigma}(x,y,z)] = 0 \qquad (7\text{-}132)$$

Two more derivatives and one arrives at:

$$\Gamma_{\pi\pi\sigma\sigma}(z,y,t,w) + \Gamma_{\pi\pi\sigma\sigma}(w,y,z,t) + \Gamma_{\pi\pi\sigma\sigma}(t,y,z,w) = \Gamma_{\sigma\sigma\sigma\sigma}(y,z,t,w)$$

Taking the Fourier transform at a symmetry point gives:

$$3\Gamma_{\pi\pi\sigma\sigma}|_{SP} = \Gamma_{\sigma\sigma\sigma\sigma}|_{SP} \qquad (7\text{-}133)$$

which directly implies Eq. (7-129). The generalization to a rotational symmetry $O(M)$, with $M > 2$, is straightforward.

The result of the identity (7-133), or (7-129), is that only one constant is needed in order to renormalize $\Gamma^{(4)}$.

A somewhat more interesting result is the outcome of the Ward identity (7-132).[16] Considering the state of broken symmetry with ordering in the σ-direction, generated either spontaneously or by a uniform external field, then, in the spatially uniform case, one has:

$$\Gamma_{\sigma\sigma}(p) - \Gamma_{\pi\pi}(p) = v\Gamma_{\pi\pi\sigma}(0, p, -p). \qquad (7\text{-}134)$$

with $v = \langle \sigma \rangle$ (see Exercise 5-11). The vertex functions are considered to be the bare ones regularized in a way which respects the 0(2)-symmetry. But they are all calculated with a non-vanishing expectation value for the σ-field.

The main consequences of (7-134) are:

(i) The field renormalization for the σ and π propagators are equal..

(ii) The difference between the momentum-independent parts of these two propagators, both of which are quadratically divergent at four dimensions, is only logarithmically divergent. This allows, as will be shown below, a determination of the difference of the renormalized masses.

One way of proving the above statements is to use an expansion of $\Gamma_{\pi\pi\sigma}$ around the symmetric theory† — an expansion of the type given by Eq. (7-83). Since the three-point function vanishes in the symmetric state the lowest vertex function appearing in the expansion is a four-point function, which has only logarithmic *primitive* divergences at four dimensions. Thus, a derivative of $\Gamma_{\pi\pi\sigma}$ with respect to p^2 has no *primitive* divergences. Taking a derivative of both sides of Eq. (7-134) with respect to p^2 reveals that the difference

$$\frac{\partial}{\partial p^2} \Gamma_{\sigma\sigma}(p) - \frac{\partial}{\partial p^2} \Gamma_{\pi\pi}(p) = v \frac{\partial}{\partial p^2} \Gamma_{\pi\pi\sigma} \qquad (7\text{-}135)$$

also has no primitive divergences. Consequently, the same subtractions which remove the logarithmic divergences of $(\partial/\partial p^2)\Gamma_{\sigma\sigma}$ will remove those of $(\partial/\partial p^2)\Gamma_{\pi\pi}$.

It should be pointed out that the above does not imply that the finite parts of the two derivatives on the left-hand side of Eq. (7-135) are equal. Their difference can be computed (see, e.g., Ref. 16 and Exercise 7-29).

The same considerations lead also to statement (ii). Both vertices $\Gamma_{\sigma\sigma}$ and $\Gamma_{\pi\pi}$ have a part which survives as $v \rightarrow 0$. This part diverges primitively like Λ^2. On the other hand, the right-hand side of Eq. (7-134) has logarithmic primitive divergences only. Thus the Λ^2 parts of both vertices must be exactly equal.

One can also obtain this result by expanding the two vertices about the symmetric state, using Eqs. (5-44) or (7-83). The zeroth order term is just the symmetric two-point vertex, which has a momentum-independent part, diverging like Λ^2 The higher order terms start with $\Gamma^{(4)}$. They are at most logarithmically divergent.

To conclude this part, we draw in Figs. 7-4 and 7-5 a few graphs of $\Gamma_{\pi\pi\sigma}$, $\Gamma_{\pi\pi}$ and $\Gamma_{\sigma\sigma}$, to illustrate the above considerations. The wiggly lines in the

---

† Another way is to consider the graphs of $\Gamma_{\pi\pi\sigma}$ in the ordered state, where in addition to the four-point interaction there are three- and two-point interactions proportional to v and v^2, correspondingly. See, e.g., Ref. 17.

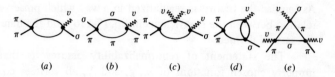

$$(a) \qquad (b) \qquad (c) \qquad (d) \qquad (e)$$

FIGURE 7-4
Graphs of $\Gamma_{\pi\pi\sigma}$ in the ordered state.

graphs represent $v = \langle \sigma \rangle$. From Fig. 7-4 it should become clear that the most divergent graphs of $\Gamma_{\pi\pi\sigma}$ are those of $\Gamma_{\pi\pi\sigma\sigma}$ in which one external σ-leg is replaced by a v. They diverge logarithmically. Graphs with higher powers of v, such as (c) and (e) in Fig. 7-4, are related to higher vertex functions. They are primitively finite.

Similarly, a glance at Fig. 7-5 suggests that the lowest order terms in the difference between $\Gamma_{\sigma\sigma}$ and $\Gamma_{\pi\pi}$ are proportional to v^2. These behave, as a function of momentum, like $\Gamma^{(4)}$.

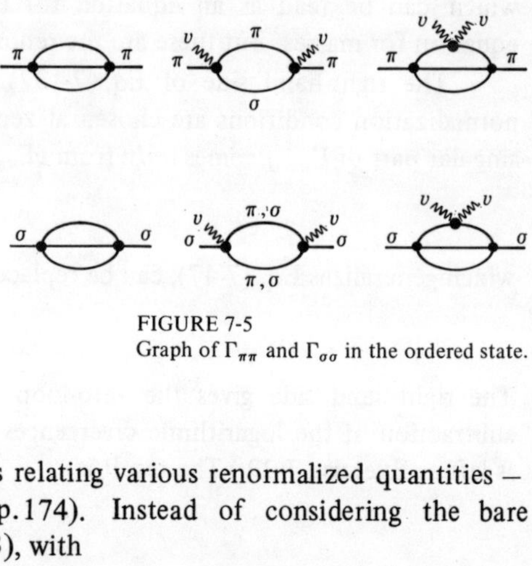

FIGURE 7-5
Graph of $\Gamma_{\pi\pi}$ and $\Gamma_{\sigma\sigma}$ in the ordered state.

Next we come to conclusions relating various renormalized quantities — conclusions of type (b) above (p.174). Instead of considering the bare Lagrangian of the σ-model, Eq. (5-53), with

$$\mathscr{L}_1(\phi) = (\phi^2)^2$$

we consider that same Lagrangian with its counterterms. According to the rule enunciated at the end of Sec. 7-8, the counterterms are all the operators of dimension less than or equal to four which respect the symmetry of the bare Lagrangian. We restrict ourselves for simplicity to the case in which only vertices without composite operators are treated. Then, we can write:

$$\mathscr{L} = \tfrac{1}{2}(\nabla\phi)^2 + \tfrac{1}{2}m^2\phi^2 + \frac{g}{4!}(\phi^2)^2 + \tfrac{1}{2}a(\nabla\phi)^2 + \tfrac{1}{2}b\phi^2 + \frac{c}{4!}(\phi^2)^2 \qquad (7\text{-}136)$$

As long as the theory is regularized in a way which preserves the symmetry, the relation between the coefficients in Eq. (7-136) and the bare parameters $-\mu^2$, λ, $\Lambda-$ is well defined.

The statement of renormalizability assures us that if a, b and c are properly chosen functions of m, g, and Λ, all vertices computed with will be finite as $\Lambda \to \infty$. Furthermore, a, b and c can be chosen so as to give the functions $\Gamma^{(2)}$, $(\partial/\partial p^2)\Gamma^{(2)}$ and $\Gamma^{(4)}$ the values m^2, 1 and g at some symmetric momentum point.

So far we have discussed the symmetric state. Once the symmetry is broken, spontaneously or explicitly, there are two two-point vertices etc. But the Lagrangian with the counterterms is symmetric under O(2). Hence, the vertices generated by $\mathscr{L}$ satisfy all the Ward identities, including (5-62) and (7-134). The difference is that now on both sides of the equation stand renormalized functions. An immediate conclusion is that the appearance of Goldstone bosons persists in the renormalized theory.

Taking the limit $p \to 0$, Eq. (7-134) gives:

$$m_\sigma^2 - m_\pi^2 = v\Gamma_{\pi\pi\sigma}(0,0,0) \qquad (7\text{-}137)$$

which can be read as an equation for inverse correlation lengths, or as an equation for masses. But these are the renormalized quantities.

The right-hand side of Eq. (7-137) takes on a very simple form if the normalization conditions are chosen at zero momentum. Remembering that the singular part of $\Gamma_{\pi\pi\sigma}$ comes *only* from $v\Gamma_{\pi\pi\sigma\sigma}$, the normalization

$$\Gamma^{(4)}_{ijklR}(p_i = 0) = gS_{ijkl} \qquad (7\text{-}138)$$

which generalizes Eq. (7-47), can be replaced by

$$\Gamma^{(3)}_{\pi\pi\sigma R}(p_i = 0) = vg \qquad (7\text{-}139)$$

The right-hand side gives the zero-loop term of $\Gamma_{\pi\pi\sigma}$, and provides for the subtraction of the logarithmic divergences of $\Gamma^{(4)}$. (The proof of this statement is left as Exercise 7-29.) The result is

$$m_\sigma^2 - m_\pi^2 = v^2 g \qquad (7\text{-}140)$$

A word of caution should be added. Normalization at zero momentum can be used in a massive theory only. Since, as we saw in Sec. 5.6, if the symmetry is spontaneously broken a Goldstone mode appears, $m_\pi^2 = 0$, and (7-137) is meaningless. On the other hand, Eq. (7-140) remains useful if the symmetry is broken by an external field.

Finally, gauge invariance leads to Ward identities as well. These Ward identities imply that in quantum electrodynamics the renormalization constant of the particle field is equal to that of the particle's charge. For further details on this subject the reader is referred to the literature.[18]

7-12 ITERATIVE CONSTRUCTION OF COUNTERTERMS

In Sec. 7-8 it was shown that renormalization by redefinition of scales of operators and of coupling constants can be reexpressed as an addition of counterterms to the Lagrangian. The rule by which the counterterms for a given theory are selected was stated, without justification, at the end of that section. When the symmetry of the Lagrangian is simple the origin of the counterterms as well as their complete list can be realized very easily. But often this is not the case and a systematic way of constructing counterterms and of proving that the list is complete is needed.

Such a procedure was invented by Bogoliubov.[19] It is an iterative method which can be used to justify the rule of Sec. 7-8 and to identify the counterterms constructively. Since it is iterative, the method allows one to prove theorems about the counterterms by induction. We will now proceed to discuss this technique and to illustrate it with a case in which the counterterms are not quite obvious. The example will be that of the bi-critical point induced by quadratic symmetry breaking of an $O(M)$ symmetric theory.[20]

Given a bare Lagrangian the procedure involves the following steps:

(a) Determine the vertex functions with *primitive* divergences.

(b) Identify the fields, masses and coupling constants which appear in $\mathscr{L}$ as the renormalized ones.

(c) Calculate the divergent vertices in a loop-expansion until the lowest order in which a divergence appears. Expand divergent integrals in powers of the external momenta. (In a massive theory the expansion can be performed about zero momentum, otherwise about κ.)

(d) To each *divergent* term in the Taylor series associate a monomial which consists of the combination of momenta in the divergent term acting on a product of fields corresponding to the external legs of the vertex. This is a counterterm at the given order in the loop-expansion. It should be added with an opposite sign to the Lagrangian. The powers of momenta can, of course, be replaced by derivatives.

(e) Using the Lagrangian with the counterterms calculate the divergent vertices to the next order and repeat (c).

The central theorem then asserts that in this way all divergences are eliminated order by order in the expansion. In every cycle the divergences originating from divergent sub-graphs of lower order are cancelled by the counterterms. This is a complex combinatorial theorem which will not be reproduced here (see Ref. 19).

Let us first of all observe that a graph calculated with a Lagrangian possessing a certain symmetry will produce only counterterms which respect that symmetry. It concerns internal symmetry as well as space-time symmetry, namely, the tensorial structure of the counterterms is covariant under the internal symmetry group, which follows from the fact that every counterterm has the structure of a Green function calculated with the given Lagrangian [step (d)]. The space–time symmetry follows from the fact that the integrals are calculated with propagators which possess the symmetry.

Consider next the number of counterterms that can be produced by a given graph. Since we are dealing with primitive divergences only, dimensional analysis provides the answer.

The degree of divergence of a graph, as given by Eq. (7-105), is:

$$\delta = D - \sum_r n_r \delta_r \qquad (7\text{-}141)$$

where D is the engineering dimension of the vertex in question, n_r is the number of r interactions, in the graph†, each having a coupling constant of dimension δ_r [Eq. (7-4)].

In the expansion of a graph [step (c)] terms with increasing momentum powers behave asymptotically as a lower power of the cutoff Λ, when $\Lambda \to \infty$. This is a direct consequence of dimensional analysis. Thus, a graph with a primitive divergence of degree δ will produce a finite number of counterterms as the divergences are reduced in integer steps from δ to zero.

Let us denote by δ_{CT} the dimension of the coupling constant associated with a counterterm which was generated by a primitively divergent vertex with E external legs. Since such a counterterm must have E fields and at most δ derivatives.

$$\delta_{CT} \geq d - E\left(\frac{d}{2} - 1\right) - \delta \qquad (7\text{-}142)$$

with d, the number of space dimensions. Using Eq. (7-141), together with Eq. (7-12), the inequality reads:

$$\delta_{CT} \geq \Sigma n_r \delta_r \qquad (7\text{-}143)$$

which is independent of the number of external legs. Hence, the *coupling constants of the counterterms have dimensions which are greater or equal to the sum of the dimensions of the coupling constants in the graph which generated them.* Since, on the other hand, $\delta_{CT} < d$ one finds that if all coupling constants in the original lagrangian had $\delta_r \geq 0$, the total number of counterterms is finite. The theory is renormalizable. Non-renormalizability manifests itself by the presence of coupling constants with negative δ_r. Those give rise to an infinite number of counterterms.

To derive the rule at the end of Sec. 7-8 one has only to combine the

---

†We are assuming interactions without derivatives. The generalization is straightforward.

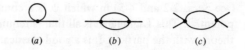

FIGURE 7-6

First graphs contributing to counter-terms in a ϕ^4-theory.

considerations about the symmetry of the counterterms with the obvious fact that the dimension of any operator they contain is simply $d - \delta_{CT}$.

As illustration we consider the Lagrangian

$$\mathcal{L} = \tfrac{1}{2}(\nabla\phi)^2 + \tfrac{1}{2}m^2\phi^2 + \frac{g}{4!}(\phi^2)^2 \qquad (7\text{-}144)$$

at four dimensions. The only primitively divergent vertices, without composite operators, are $\Gamma^{(2)}$ and $\Gamma^{(4)}$. The first divergent terms correspond to the graphs shown in Fig. 7-6. Graphs (a) and (b) are proportional to δ_{ij}, with i and j indices of field components. Graph (a) is momentum-independent and has a Λ^2 divergence. It gives a one-loop contribution to the mass counterterm $\delta\mu^2\phi^2$. Graph (b) is a momentum-dependent, two-loop graph. It again has a Λ^2 divergence which can be expressed as

$$\text{Fig. 7-6}b = A\Lambda^2 + Bp^2\ln\Lambda + \text{finite terms}$$

(See the discussion preceding Eq. (6-71).) The two-loop constant A will contribute to $\delta\mu^2$ again. But now there is the extra counterterm, $(Z_\phi - 1)p^2\phi^2$, or $(Z_\phi - 1)(\nabla\phi)^2$, to which B gives the first contribution. Symmetry dictates the rotational symmetry in p and in ϕ.

Graph 7-6c has a logarithmic divergence only. Hence it has to be calculated at some fixed momentum point. In a massive theory this can be $p_i = 0$. It then gives a counterterm proportional to S_{ijkl}. If one would like to treat a critical (massless) theory, one can choose a symmetric finite momentum point (see Exercises 7-30 and 7-19—7-21).

When all these are added as counterterms one ends up with a Lagrangian which has the same symmetry properties as the original one. This is a first step in an inductive process in which the nature of the counterterms can be established to all orders. The fact that the counterterms are identical with the terms in $\mathcal{L}$ is a special feature of the example. If, for example, we start from a massless theory, a mass counterterm will be generated (see Exercise 7-30).

A more interesting case, which will be barely mentioned, is that of the renormalization of electrodynamics. Scalar electrodynamics, for example, can be described by a Lagrangian of the form:

$$\mathcal{L} = \tfrac{1}{2}\,|\,(\nabla - ieA)\psi\,|^2 + \tfrac{1}{2}m^2\,|\,\psi\,|^2 - \tfrac{1}{4}(\partial_\mu A_\nu - \partial_\nu A_\mu)(\partial^\mu A^\nu - \partial^\nu A^\mu) \qquad (7\text{-}145)$$

(see Secs. 2-2 and 4-5) in which ψ is a complex scalar field, and A is the vector potential. This Lagrangian is all that is required to embed gauge invariance in the theory with the particle. It is a good classical theory in the symmetric state.

On computing vertex functions one soon realizes that the presence of interactions of the form:

$$ie(A\psi^* \cdot \nabla\psi - \nabla\psi^* \cdot A\psi), \quad e^2 A^2 \mid \psi \mid^2$$

generates divergent terms of $\Gamma^{(4)}$ – four ψ's – already at the one-loop level. Thus, one finds that a $\mid \psi \mid^4$ interaction is essential for the renormalization of the model. For further details the reader is referred to the literature (see, e.g., Ref. 21).

Next we turn to the construction of counterterms in situations of explicitly broken symmetry. If the symmetry-breaking terms are *soft* (i.e., they have coupling constants with positive dimensions), such as an external field, or a mass anisotropy, renormalization can generate at most non-symmetric terms with

$$0 \leqslant \delta_{CT} \leqslant d$$

This is a consequence of the general theorem stated above.[22] So that, if all the soft symmetry-breaking terms, which may still respect some lower symmetry, are included in $\mathscr{L}$, the counterterms will introduce no new interactions. In particular, *they will not hurt the symmetry of interactions with* $\delta_r = 0$ (see below).

Before turning to some examples of the effects of *soft* symmetry-breaking terms we make a short digression to discuss the role of soft interactions which do not break the symmetry. The simplest case is the introduction of a ϕ^2 interaction into a ϕ^4 theory near four dimensions.

Let

$$\mathscr{L} = \tfrac{1}{2}(\nabla\phi)^2 + \tfrac{1}{2}m^2\phi^2 + \frac{g}{4!}(\phi^2)^2 + \tfrac{1}{2}t\phi^2 \qquad (7\text{-}146)$$

An expansion in g and t will lead to new divergences in $\Gamma^{(2)}$ only. All these divergences will be linear in t. This follows simply from the fact that the presence of a ϕ^2 interaction in a graph reduces its *primitive* degree of divergence by two units. It is also clear that the divergent graphs obey the $O(M)$ symmetry. Hence, the form of the counterterm induced by the presence of the soft term is:

$$CT = \tfrac{1}{2}ft\phi^2 \qquad (7\text{-}147)$$

as in Eq. (7-98), where

$$f = Z_{\phi^2}Z_\phi - 1 \qquad (7\text{-}148)$$

After the fields are scaled by $Z_\phi^{1/2}$, Z_{ϕ^2} becomes the proportionality constant between bare and renormalized temperature, Eq. (7-81). The introduction of this counterterm, Eq. (7-147), insures that $\Gamma^{(2)}(p; g, m, t)$ is finite as $\Lambda \to \infty$. It therefore makes

$$\Gamma^{(2,1)} = \frac{\partial}{\partial t} \Gamma^{(2)} \bigg|_{t=0} \qquad (7\text{-}149)$$

finite as well. The point is that this counterterm is not the same as would have been produced by a BPHZ procedure applied to $\Gamma^{(2,1)}$, but rather to $t\Gamma^{(2,1)}$. This situation is somewhat analogous to the fact that $p^2(Z_\phi - 1)\phi^2$ is not the subtraction of $\partial\Gamma^{(2)}/\partial p^2$, but of $p^2 \partial\Gamma^{(2)}/\partial p^2$. Passing through Eq. (7-149) is equivalent to setting $t = 1$ in the counterterm, which then becomes a proper counterterm for $\Gamma^{(2,1)}$. On the other hand, Z_{ϕ^2} of Eq. (7-148) still allows for a multiplicative renormalization $\Gamma^{(2,1)}$, as is evident from the discussion in Sec. 7-8.

Coming back to soft symmetry breaking we consider the example of the anisotropic mass in the Heisenberg model—quadratic symmetry breaking. To the Lagrangian (7-144) we add the quadratic interaction of the form

$$\mathscr{L}_m = \tfrac{1}{2}(\delta m_1^2 \phi_1^2 + \delta m_2^2 \phi_2^2) \qquad (7\text{-}150)$$

where

$$\phi_1^2 = \sum_{i=1}^{K} \phi_i^2 \qquad \phi_2^2 = \sum_{i=K+1}^{M} \phi_i^2 \qquad (7\text{-}151)$$

The $0(M)$ symmetry is broken, but an $0(K)$ symmetry and $0(M - K)$ symmetry are preserved. Therefore, no linear or cubic counterterms will appear. Equation (7-150) is the most general way of introducing two lengths, one associated with K components and one with $M - K$ components. But the same interaction can be represented as

$$\mathscr{L}_m = \tfrac{1}{2} t\phi^2 + \tfrac{1}{2} yB \qquad (7\text{-}152)$$

with

$$B = a\phi_1^2 + b\phi_2^2 \qquad (7\text{-}153)$$

This form, though completely equivalent to the former, is more useful since, as we show below, it allows the separation of the quadratic interaction into two parts each generating its own counterterms.

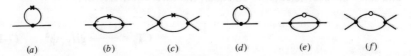

(a)   (b)   (c)   (d)   (e)   (f)

FIGURE 7-7
Graphs of $\Gamma^{(2)}$ and $\Gamma^{(4)}$ with quadratic symmetry breaking.

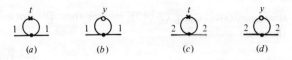

FIGURE 7-8
New divergences of $\Gamma^{(2)}$ due to quadratic interactions.

Due to the additional interaction new graphs will be generated in addition to those of Fig. 7-6. They are represented in Fig. 7-7. In the graphs, an x and a ○ represent a $\boldsymbol{\phi}^2$ and a B interaction vertex, respectively. As was discussed above, graphs with more than one quadratic interaction have no primitive divergences.

Furthermore, the two graphs of $\Gamma^{(4)}$, i.e. (c) and (f), are finite. Hence the counterterms with four ϕ's are $0(M)$ symmetric. Similarly, graphs (b) and (d) are only logarithmically divergent. Their derivative with respect to p^2 has, therefore, no primitive divergence, from which it follows that the field renormalization counterterms are unaffected by the symmetry breaking. This is a generalization of the result (i) in Sec. 7-11 (see Exercises 7-31 and 7-32). In conclusion, one finds that the only counterterms which are generated the symmetry breaking interaction (7-150) are quadratic in the fields and can therefore be written in the form (7-152).

Finally, we turn to the question: Can one choose a and b in (7-152) so that the operator B will generate counterterms with an operator structure of B only? Clearly, $\boldsymbol{\phi}^2$ has this property, and since the possibility of separating the most general $\mathscr{L}_m$ in the form (7-152) is independent of the values of a and b, the existence of such a B implies the possibility of renormalizing the temperature and the anisotropy parameter separately. We return to the application of this result in Part II.

To answer the question, note that the only new divergences appear in $\Gamma^{(2)}$. On the one-loop level the pertinent graphs are those shown in Fig. 7-8. The label 1 on the external legs indicates that it belongs to ϕ_i ($i \leqslant K$). The label 2 stands for $K < i \leqslant M$. Graphs (a) and (c) generate counterterms of the form

$$\frac{M+2}{6} gtI_{SP} \phi_i^2$$

and since the coefficients are all equal, the total counterterm is

$$CT_t = \frac{M+2}{6} gtI_{SP}\boldsymbol{\phi}^2 \qquad (7\text{-}154)$$

On the other hand, graphs (b) and (d) lead to the following total counterterm:

$$CT_y = \tfrac{1}{6}\,[a(K+2)+b(M-K)]\,gyI_{SP}\phi_2^2 + \tfrac{1}{6}[aK+b(M-K+2)]\,gyI_{SP}\phi_2^2$$
$$(7\text{-}155)$$

This still contains a ϕ^2 contribution which is eliminated by the choice

$$a = \frac{1}{M}\,; \qquad b = -\frac{1}{M-K} \qquad (7\text{-}156)$$

leading to

$$CT_y = \tfrac{2}{3}\,gyI_{SP}B$$

With the choice (7-156) the counterterms will have the form

$$CT_m = \tfrac{1}{2}f_1\,t\vec{\phi}^2 + \tfrac{1}{2}f_2 yB \qquad (7\text{-}157)$$

Since at higher orders one is concerned with primitive divergences only, the above considerations can be easily generalized to all orders. We leave the details as Exercise 7-33.

EXERCISES

7-1(a) Determine the dimension of the source $J(x)$ and $J(k)$.

   (b) Using the result derive the dimensions of $\Gamma^{(N)}(x_i)$ and $\Gamma^{(N)}(k_i)$ from their definition as functional derivatives.

7-2(a) Calculate the primitive divergence of a general graph in a theory with a polynomial interaction, by counting loops and lines.

   (b) Compute the same using dimensional analysis.

7-3(a) What is the dimension of general coupling constant of a monomial composed of spin-$\tfrac{1}{2}$ fermions?

   (b) The same for a product of spin-0 bosons and spin-$\tfrac{1}{2}$ fermions.

7-4 Consider the primitive divergences of graphs with monomial many-fermion interactions. Ignore the spinorial structure.

7-5 Prove that the degree of ultraviolet divergence of any graph can be reduced by "partial-q". ('t Hooft and Veltman[1])

7-6(a) Prove that the canonical dimension of a Green function is equal to the power in the asymptotic behavior of its free part, when all momenta are uniformly large.

   (b) Prove also that it equals the power of α — the small momentum and mass scale — of the free theory.

7-7(a) What functions are primitively divergent in a ϕ^r theory?

   (b) What is the degree of divergence of each at $d = d_c$?

   (c) Which $\Gamma^{(E,L)}$, with L ϕ^2-insertions diverge at $d = d_c$?

7-8 Show that the renormalization parameters calculated in Chap. 6 satisfy Eqs. (7-35)–(7-38).

7-9 Using definition (2-81) for the correlation length and the normalization conditions (7-45)–(7-46), prove that $m \propto \xi^{-1}$

7-10 Calculate the critical bare mass in a ϕ^4 theory in third order in the bare coupling constant. Show that the result is finite, for finite cutoff.

7-11 Show that all six permutations of $I_4(k_i)$, Eq. (6-61), are equal at the symmetric point SP.

7-12 The expression z_2 in Eq. (7-70) diverges as $\kappa \to 0$ if $d \leqslant 3$. Show that for any $d < 4$ there are terms in the sequence z_n, Eq. (7-66), which diverge as $\kappa \to 0$.

7-13 Show that the integrals entering $\Gamma_{SP}^{(2,1)}$, with the choice of momenta (7-58b), are equal to the ones entering $\Gamma_{SP}^{(4)}$.

7-14 Calculate $\Gamma_R^{(2)}(k)$, $\Gamma_R^{(4)}(k_i)$, $\Gamma^{(2,1)}(k_1 k_2, p)$ in the massless theory to order two loops.

7-15 Show that with Z_ϕ, determined from the massless theory, one can make $\Gamma^{(2)}$ finite for all μ^2, up to two-loop level. What is m^2?

7-16 From the statement of the renormalization of a ϕ^4 theory by counter-terms, Eqs. (7-96)–(7-99), calculate a, b, c, and f using the finite mass normalization conditions, Eqs. (7-45)–(7-48).

7-17 Prove that the Green function $G_c^{(0,1)}$ can be made finite by a single subtraction of the form $A + Bt$.

7-18 Prove that $d(m, g, \Lambda)$ and $e(m, g, \Lambda)$ can be found so that the counterterms in (7-102) will make $G_c^{(0,1)}$ and $G_c^{(0,2)}$ finite.

7-19 In a theory with a Lagrangian

$$\mathscr{L} = \tfrac{1}{2}(\nabla \phi)^2 + \frac{\mu^2}{2}\,\phi^2 + \frac{\lambda}{6!}\,\phi^6$$

what are the counterterms?[15]

7-20 What are the counterterms for

$$\mathscr{L} = \tfrac{1}{2}(\nabla \phi)^2 + \frac{\mu^2}{2}\,\phi^2 + \frac{\lambda}{3!}\,\phi^3$$

7-21 Choosing

$$\mathscr{L} = \tfrac{1}{2}(\nabla\phi)^2 + \frac{g}{4!}\,\phi^4$$

show that six functions of g, κ and Λ can be found so as to construct counterterms, which make all ϕ and ϕ^2 vertex functions finite.

7-22 Consider the two loop graphs of $\Gamma^{(4)}$ with any mixture of ϕ^3, ϕ^4, ϕ^6. Show that those with ϕ^3 only have strongest infrared divergence.

7-23 Discuss the relevance of $k^s \phi^r$ by using direct power counting arguments.

7-24 In a ϕ^6 theory, what momentum-dependent terms, are relevant?

7-25 Show that the renormalization constants Eqs. (7-123)–(7-125) make the correlation functions finite in the $0(M)$ symmetric theory.

7-26 Calculate the renormalization constants if the interaction is purely cubic

$$\mathcal{L}_{\text{Int}} = \lambda \sum_{i=1}^{N} \phi_i^4$$

7-27 Consider the interaction Lagrangian

$$\mathcal{L}_S = \lambda \left[\left(\sum_1^N \phi_i^2 \right)^2 + \sum_1^N \phi_i^4 \right]$$

(a) Is $\Gamma_{ij}^{(2)}$ diagonal to two-loop order?
(b) Can the divergences in $\Gamma^{(4)}$ be removed by a single renormalization constant $\lambda(g)$?

7-28 Calculate the tensorial contractions of the graphs in Fig. 6-10, in an $0(M)$ symmetric theory, and in a theory with a cubic symmetry. Compare with the results of the corresponding graphs of $\Gamma^{(2)}$.

7-29 Use the normalization condition (7-139) to the order of two loops to calculate the counterterms. Show that $\Gamma^{(4)}(p_i = 0)$ is finite as $\Lambda \to \infty$, or $\epsilon \to 0$.

Having fixed $\partial/\partial p^2 \Gamma_{\pi\pi} \mid_{p^2=0} = 1$, calculate $\partial/\partial p^2 \Gamma_{\sigma\sigma} \mid_{p^2=0}$ to the same order.

7-30 Calculate the counterterms to a massless $0(M)$ symmetric theory to order two loops. Show that the terms calculated to order one loop leave only primitive divergences at the two-loop level.

7-31 Given a Lagrangian

$$\mathcal{L} = \tfrac{1}{2}(\nabla \phi)^2 + \frac{1}{4!} g(\phi^2)^2 + \tfrac{1}{2}(m_1^2 \phi_1^2 + m_2^2 \phi_2^2)$$

Show that if the counterterms calculated to n loops have that form, this will also be their form to $n + 1$ loops.

7-32 What types of counterterms will be needed if the symmetry of a ϕ^4 theory is broken by a ϕ^3 operator?

7-33 Show that if on the n-loop level CT_m the form (7-157), with a and b given by Eq. (7-156), the counterterms on the $n + 1$ level will have the same form.

REFERENCES

1. G. 't Hooft and M. Veltman, *Nuclear Physics*, **B44**, 189 (1972); G. 't Hooft, *Nuclear Physics*, **B61**, 465 (1973); in the context of critical phenomena see J. D. Lawrie, *Journal of Physics*, **A9**, 961 (1975) and D. J. Amit, *Journal of Physics*, **A9**, 1441 (1976).
2. S. Coleman, "Scaling Anomalies" in International Summer School "Etore Majorana (1971)" (Academic Press, N.Y. 1972).
3. An extensive study of the asymptotic behavior of Feynman graphs can be found in S. Weinberg, *Physical Review*, **118**, 838 (1960).
4. This process is discussed in detail for a theory in four dimensions by IIM.
5. S. Coleman and R. Jackiw, *Annals of Physics* (N.Y.), **67**, 552 (1971) and K. Symanzik (KS).
6. E. Brézin, J. C. Le Guillou and J. Zinn-Justin, Ref. 4, Chap. 2. See also P. K. Mitter, *Physical Review*, **D7**, 2927 (1973).
7. S. Weinberg, *Physical Review*, **D8**, 3497 (1973).
8. J. Zinn-Justin "Wilson Theory of Critical Phenomena and Renormalized Theory". Lectures delivered at the Cargése Summer School 1973. K. Symanzik, op. cit. and KS.
9. See e.g. AL.
10. K. Symanzik, "Wilson Theory of Critical Phenomena and Renormalized Theory". Lectures delivered at the Cargése Summer School 1973. See also Chap. VI of BLZ.
11. This approach goes back to Bogoliubov. See, e.g., BS Sec. 26. K. Symanzik, Ref. 10 above; G. 't Hooft, Ref. 1 above. This is also the approach adopted in BLZ.
12. K. Symanzik in *Renormalization of Theories with Broken Symmetries* D. Bessis, ed., Cargése Lectures (Gordon and Breach, N.Y., 1970); J. Zinn-Justin in *Trends in Elementary Particle Theory*, H. Rollnik and K. Dietz, eds. (Springer-Verlag, Berlin, 1975).
13. See, e.g., R. K. P. Zia and D. J. Wallace, *Journal of Physics*, **A8**, 1089 (1975).
14. E. Brézin, J. C. Le Guillou and J. Zinn-Justin, *Physical Review*, **B10**, 892 (1974).
    This model has been studied extensively using the Feynman graph expansion technique by D. J. Wallace, *Journal of Physics*, **C6**, 1390 (1973), and by A. Aharony, in Vol. VI of DG. See also references cited therein.
15. See, e.g., Chap. VIII of BLZ.
16. AL Secs. 17 and 18.
17. Brézin, Wallace and Wilson Ref. (4-1); D. J. Amit, *Journal of Physics C: Solid State*, **7**, 3369 (1974).
18. See, e.g., BS, and C. Itzykson and J. B. Zuber, IZ.
19. The procedure is called BPHZ after Bogoliubov, Parasyuk, Hepp and Zimmerman. See, e.g., BS, Zimmerman, and K. Hepp, *Théorie de la Renormalization* (Springer-Verlag, Berlin, 1969).
    A particularly gentle exposition of the subject can be found in S. Coleman, "Renormalization and Symmetry: a Review for Non-Specialists" in *International School "Etore Majorana (1971)"* (Editrice Compositori, Bologna, 1973).
20. D. J. Amit and Y. Goldschmidt, *Annals of Physics*, (In press). This is the same physical system as was treated by D. R. Nelson, E. Domany, *Physical Review*, **B13**, 236 (1976) and H. Horner, *Zeitschrift für Physik*, **B23**, 183 (1976).
21. S. Coleman, Ref. 19 above, and BS. Sec. 33.
22. K. Symanzik, in *Fundamental Interactions at High-Energies*, A. Perlmutter et al., eds. (Gordon and Breach, N. Y., 1970).
23. D. J. Gross, in *Methods in Field Theory* (Proceedings of the Les Houches Summer School XXVIII 1975), Elsevier North-Holland, 1976.

THE RENORMALIZATION GROUP AND SCALING IN THE CRITICAL REGION

8.1 INTRODUCTION

The effort invested in the renormalization program, apart from assuring us that there is a systematic way of eliminating the strong cutoff dependence of a theory which is regularized with a cutoff, leads to partial differential equations for the Green's functions. These differential equations, whether they are the *renormalization group equations* or the *Callan-Symanzik equations* (see below) lead to extremely useful results which lie beyond perturbation theory.

Apart from actual computational success, these equations lead to a very beautiful formulation of the flows in coupling constant space, of universality, of stability, of scaling, etc. All of these concepts have been introduced by Wilson as the new and very fruitful language for the description of critical phenomena, as well as of high energy physics.

All the equations to be derived below follow from the fact that, behind all the different versions in which a given theory can be renormalized, lies one single physical theory, i.e. that theory which the original Lagrangian tried to represent.

The underlying physical theory, invariant under different renormalization procedures, gives rise to the *renormalization group.*[1] This is a group of transformations between different versions of the renormalized theory corresponding to one given bare theory. Here we will restrict ourselves to the freedom left in the choice of the renormalization momentum κ, Eqs. (7-53)–(7-58), in a critical theory. In this we will follow the exposition of Illiopoulos, Itzykson and Martin (IIM). The differential expression of the underlying invariance leads to the renormalization group equations.

Given an equation for the Green function of the critical theory one can proceed to derive equations in the whole critical region by using the expansions described in Sec. 7-7.

In a theory which is renormalized at $\kappa = 0$, but finite mass, one can show that the variation of the bare theory under changes of the mass – correlation length – is very simple. Thus a comparison of theories, renormalized at zero momentum, but with different renormalized masses, leads to the Callan-Symanzik equations.[2]

Finally, inverting the logic, one can derive relations between bare theories with different cutoff, by appealing to the fact that a single renormalized theory can be constructed for all of them. This approach, introduced by Zinn-Justin,[3] is closest in spirit to the original approach of Wilson.[4]

The differential equations obtained in any of these ways are linear partial differential equations. They can be solved quite generally, as we shall show below. The analysis of the solutions in particular physical instances is left for the following chapters.

8-2   THE RENORMALIZATION GROUP FOR THE CRITICAL (MASSLESS) THEORY

Consider for simplicity Eq. (7-59) with $L = 0$. This does not limit the generality of the argument – (see Exercise 8-1). We have

$$\Gamma_R^{(N)}(k_i; g(\kappa_1), \kappa_1) = Z_\phi^{N/2} \Gamma^{(N)}(k_i; \lambda, \Lambda) \qquad (8\text{-}1)$$

in which we have explicitly indicated on the left-hand side the fact that g, the renormalized coupling constant, is determined from Eqs. (7-53)–(7-55) at momentum κ_1, for a given bare theory. Of course, we also have

$$Z_\phi = Z_\phi(g(\kappa_1), \kappa_1, \Lambda) \qquad (8\text{-}2)$$

These general statements should be compared with the explicit expressions obtained in Sec. 7-6.

Recall that the left-hand side of Eq. (8-1) is the limit as $\Lambda \to \infty$, which is finite, of the right-hand side, and that Z_ϕ diverges logarithmically at four dimensions as $\Lambda \to \infty$, with finite g.

Assume now that κ_2 were used in the normalization conditions instead of

κ_1. From Eq. (8-1), with the same bare theory, it follows that

$$\Gamma_R^{(N)}\,(k_i;g(\kappa_1),\kappa_1) = [Z(\kappa_2,g_2,\kappa_1,g_1)]^{N/2}\,\Gamma_R^{(N)}(k_i;g(\kappa_2),\kappa_2) \qquad (8\text{-}3)$$

where we have denoted $g(\kappa_i)$ by g_i. Z is given by

$$Z(\kappa_2,g_2,\kappa_1,g_1) = Z_\phi(g_1,\kappa_1,\Lambda)/Z_\phi(g_2,\kappa_2,\Lambda) \qquad (8\text{-}4)$$

in the limit $\Lambda \to \infty$, and since it is a ratio of two renormalized vertex functions, it is finite.

Thus, a change in the momentum scale, at which the theory is normalized, is equivalent to a *finite* rescaling of the fields $-Z^{1/2}-$ and a *transformed* coupling constant.

Applying to Eq. (8-3) the three normalization conditions (7-53)–(7-55) at κ_2, one finds that the first one is satisfied trivially, as both sides of the equation vanish at $k = 0$. The normalization of $\partial/\partial k^2\,\Gamma_R^{(2)}$ gives a relation between the four parameters κ_1, κ_2, g_1 and g_2. Namely, setting $N = 2$ in Eq. (8-3), taking a derivative with respect to k^2, at $k^2 = \kappa_2^2$ gives:

$$Z(\kappa_2,g_2,\kappa_1,g_1) = \frac{\partial}{\partial k^2}\,\Gamma_R^{(2)}(k;g_1,\kappa_1)\,\bigg|_{k^2=\kappa_2^2} \qquad (8\text{-}5)$$

This relation proves that Z is a function of three variables, $Z(\kappa_2,\kappa_1,g_1)$, given by the right-hand side.

The last normalization, that of $\Gamma_R^{(4)}$, applied to Eq. (8-3) describes the way in which a renormalized coupling constant, calculated to be g_1 at normalization momentum κ_1, develops when the normalization momentum reaches κ_2. Setting $N = 4$ and $k_i = \mathrm{SP}(\kappa_2)$ in Eq. (8-3) one finds:

$$g_2 = [Z(\kappa_2,\kappa_1,g_1)]^{-2}\,\Gamma_R^{(4)}(k_i;g_1,\kappa_1)\,\big|_{k_i=\,\mathrm{SP}(\kappa_2)} \equiv R(\kappa_2,\kappa_1,g_1) \qquad (8\text{-}6)$$

In the last equation we used the notation $\mathrm{SP}(\kappa_2)$ to stand for a symmetry point as defined by (7-58), but with magnitude κ_2^2. The function R satisfies:

$$R(\kappa,\kappa,g) = g \qquad (8\text{-}7)$$

We are now in a position to define the renormalization group. This is a group of transformations τ_i under which the normalization momentum is multiplied by a real positive number t_i. Under $\tau_1 * \tau_2$ the normalization momentum scales by $t_1 t_2$. The realization of this multiplicative group is given by:

$$\Gamma_R^{(N)}(k_i;g_1,\kappa_1) = Z^{N/2}\,\Gamma_R^{(N)}(k_i;R(\kappa_2,\kappa_1,g_1),\kappa_2) \qquad (8\text{-}8)$$

in which Z and R are given by (8-5) and (8-6). Eq. (8-8) is called the *functional equation of the group*.

One can write the functional equation in terms of the generating functional of the 1PI functions, Γ, or in terms of the potential. It reads:

$$\Gamma\{\bar{\phi}, g_1, \kappa_1\} = \Gamma\{Z^{1/2}\bar{\phi}, R(\kappa_2, \kappa_1, g_1), \kappa_2\} \qquad (8\text{-}9)$$

The proof is left as Exercise 8-2 (see also Exercise 8-3).

To the functional equation there corresponds a differential equation which is obtained by making the change in κ infinitesimal. The differential equation can be derived from Eq. (8-8) (see Exercise 8-7). Here we prefer to derive it directly from (8-1).

Since the bare theory is independent of κ we can write

$$\left(\kappa\,\frac{\partial}{\partial\kappa}\right)_{\lambda,\Lambda}\,[Z_\phi^{-N/2}\Gamma_R^{(N)}(k_i; g, \kappa)] = 0 \qquad (8\text{-}10)$$

in the limit $\Lambda \to \infty$. This equation can be rewritten as

$$\left[\kappa\,\frac{\partial}{\partial\kappa} + \bar{\beta}(g,\kappa)\,\frac{\partial}{\partial g} - \tfrac{1}{2}N\gamma_\phi(g,\kappa)\right]\Gamma_R^{(N)}(k_i; g, \kappa) = 0 \qquad (8\text{-}11)$$

In which

$$\bar{\beta}(g,\kappa) = \left(\kappa\,\frac{\partial}{\partial\kappa}g\right)_{\lambda,\Lambda} \qquad (8\text{-}12)$$

and

$$\gamma_\phi(g,\kappa) = \left(\kappa\,\frac{\partial\ln Z_\phi}{\partial\kappa}\right)_{\lambda,\Lambda} \qquad (8\text{-}13)$$

The functions $\bar{\beta}$ and γ_ϕ have been written as functions of g and κ only — though, ab initio, they are functions of Λ also. The point here is that while λ and Z_ϕ diverge when $\Lambda \to \infty$ at $d = 4$, $\bar{\beta}$ and γ_ϕ are finite. The functions appearing in (8-11)–(8-13) are their limits as $\Lambda \to \infty$. The fact that these functions are finite can be deduced either by noticing that $\bar{\beta}$ can be obtained from Eqs. (8-6), together with the initial condition (8-7), and γ_ϕ can be obtained from Eqs. (8-5) and (8-4) (see Exercises 8-4 and 8-5). Or, by applying the normalization conditions directly to the renormalization group equation, (8-11), to obtain expressions for $\bar{\beta}$ and γ_ϕ in terms of renormalized vertex functions[5] (see Exercise 8-6).

The reason for the bar on top of β is the following. Both λ and g have dimensions Λ^{4-d}. Hence one can define two dimensionless quantities u_0 and u via

$$\lambda = u_0\kappa^\epsilon, \qquad g = u\kappa^\epsilon \qquad (8\text{-}14)$$

The renormalized vertex functions can be considered as functions of k_i, κ and u, and the renormalization group equation can be rewritten as

$$\left[\kappa \frac{\partial}{\partial \kappa} + \beta(u) \frac{\partial}{\partial u} - \tfrac{1}{2} N \gamma_\phi(u) \right] \Gamma_R^{(N)}(k_i; u, \kappa) = 0 \qquad (8\text{-}15)$$

The difference between this equation and (8-11) is that here $\kappa \partial/\partial \kappa$ is evaluated at constant u, while there it was evaluated at constant g. The functions β and γ_ϕ, are given by

$$\beta(u) = \left(\kappa \frac{\partial u}{\partial \kappa} \right)_\lambda \qquad (8\text{-}16)$$

$$\gamma_\phi(u) = \kappa \left(\frac{\partial \ln Z_\phi}{\partial \kappa} \right)_\lambda \qquad (8\text{-}17)$$

They are dimensionless, and hence they are functions of u only. At four dimensions $\epsilon = 0$, and this maneuver is unnecessary.

The functions β and γ_ϕ can be put into a somewhat more useful form. First we note that

$$\kappa \left(\frac{\partial u}{\partial \kappa} \right)_\lambda = - \frac{\kappa (\partial \lambda / \partial \kappa)_u}{(\partial \lambda / \partial u)_\kappa} \qquad (8\text{-}18)$$

and from dimensional analysis it follows that

$$\lambda = \kappa^\epsilon u_0 (u, \kappa/\Lambda) \qquad (8\text{-}19)$$

since u_0 is a dimensionless function. Furthermore, as we have seen above, u_0 is finite as $d \to 4$ ($\epsilon \to 0$) if the cutoff is held fixed. But it is also finite if $d < 4$ and $\Lambda \to \infty$. On the other hand β, Eq. (8-16), is finite even in the double limit $\epsilon \to 0$ $\Lambda \to \infty$.

It is therefore most convenient to proceed to calculate the right-hand side of (8-18) by calculating u_0 for $d < 4$ ($\epsilon > 0$) in the limit of infinite cutoff. The fact that at four dimensions u_0 diverges as $\Lambda \to \infty$ will reflect itself as singularities in ϵ, as we shall see below. The function β will nevertheless have a finite limit as $\epsilon \to 0$. Calculating u_0 in this limit leaves it a function of u only. Consequently,

$$\left(\kappa \frac{\partial \lambda}{\partial \kappa} \right)_u = \epsilon \lambda \qquad (8\text{-}20)$$

and β is given by:

$$\beta(u) = -\epsilon \left(\frac{\partial \ln u_0}{\partial u} \right)^{-1} \qquad (8\text{-}21)$$

which is a power series in u, with coefficients which depend on ϵ.

Similarly, using Eq. (8-21) we can recast γ_ϕ in the form

$$\gamma_\phi(u) = \left(\kappa \, \frac{\partial u}{\partial \kappa} \right) \frac{\partial \ln Z_\phi}{\partial u} = \beta(u) \frac{\partial \ln Z_\phi}{\partial u} \qquad (8\text{-}22)$$

To arrive at Eq. (8-22) one uses again the logic employed in the derivation of (8-21). Namely, γ_ϕ is finite in the double limit $\Lambda \to \infty$ and $\epsilon \to 0$. Hence Z_ϕ is calculated at $\epsilon > 0$ in the limit $\Lambda \to \infty$. It is then a function of u and ϵ only, and not of κ/Λ.

A renormalization group equation can also be derived for $\Gamma^{(N,L)}$. Instead of using Eq. (8-1) one uses Eq. (7-79). The result, the proof of which is left as Exercise 8-9, is

$$\left[\kappa \, \frac{\partial}{\partial \kappa} + \beta(u) \frac{\partial}{\partial u} - \tfrac{1}{2} N \gamma_\phi(u) + L \gamma_{\phi^2}(u) \right] \Gamma_R^{(N,L)}(k_i, p_i; u, \kappa) = 0 \qquad (8\text{-}23)$$

where

$$\gamma_{\phi^2}(u) = - \left(\kappa \, \frac{\partial \ln(Z_{\phi^2})}{\partial \kappa} \right)_\lambda = -\beta(u) \frac{\partial \ln(Z_{\phi^2})}{\partial u} \qquad (8\text{-}24)$$

All the above considerations, including the derivation of the renormalization group equations, do not depend on any particular set of normalization conditions. They depend only on statements like Eq. (8-1). Thus, the differential equations apply also to the case in which functions were renormalized by minimal subtraction of dimensional singularities (See Sec. 9-10, below).

The functions β, γ_ϕ and γ_{ϕ^2} obtained in this way are the same as those which would have been obtained from (8-16) or (8-18) calculated at finite Λ, in the limit $\Lambda \to \infty$, including the four-dimensional case. One can compare, for example, the results for β and γ_ϕ calculated in Chap. 9 after taking the limit $\epsilon \to 0$, with the two-loop calculation of these functions directly in four dimensions in the limit $\Lambda \to \infty$. (see Iliopoulos et al.). What should be kept in mind is that at four dimensions β and γ_ϕ have finite limits as $\Lambda \to \infty$ only in the sense that *the coefficients of any given power of* g *or* u *in their expansion will be finite.* Thus, in an expression such as (8-18) the quotient should be developed as a power series in u, and only then the limit taken, giving a finite power series for β. Correspondingly, the limit $\epsilon \to 0$ in (8-21), or in (8-22), should be considered after an expansion in powers of u has been affected.

One implication of the above comments is the following: in (8-21) there is an explicit ϵ. If the limit as $\epsilon \to 0$ of the right-hand side is to exist, $(\partial \ln u_0/\partial u)^{-1}$ can have at most simple poles in ϵ. In fact, as we shall see in the following chapter, $u_0(u, \epsilon)$ has poles of arbitrary order, as do $\ln u_0$ and its derivative with respect to u. Only the inverse of the derivative, expanded as a power series in u, will have simple poles in its coefficients. Thus, extensive cancellations have to occur.

Considering γ_ϕ in Eq. (8-22) we know that it has a finite limit as $\epsilon \to 0$, as does β. But *it does not follow* that $\partial \ln Z_\phi / \partial u$ is finite as $\epsilon \to 0$. There are in $Z_\phi(u, \epsilon)$, as well as in its logarithmic derivative, poles of all orders. On the other hand, the coefficients in the expantion of β in powers of u are polynomials in ϵ. The product of the two can again be regrouped as a power series in u. Enough cancellations then take place, to insure that the coefficient of every power of u in the expansion of γ_ϕ, is a polynomial in ϵ.

The above remarks will become more meaningful when specific examples are considered in detail. This will be done in Chap. 9 in the course of the actual calculation of critical exponents. It should however be realized at this stage that the "magic" cancellations, which have to take place in all orders, follow directly from the statement that the theory is renormalizable at four dimensions, together with the fact that β and γ_ϕ can be expressed in terms of renormalized Green functions (Exercise 8-6).

8-3   REGULARIZATION BY CONTINUATION IN THE NUMBER OF DIMENSIONS

The way to systematize the remarks of Sec. 8-2 which led from the dependence of the renormalization constants on κ/Λ to a dependence on ϵ, is via a new type of regularization of integrals. So far the only regularization we have considered is the introduction of a momentum cutoff. Another approach is the following: Every term in the perturbation series converges when $\Lambda \to \infty$ for $d < d_0$, if d_0 is small enough. It will then converge in a circle in the complex plane of d, if $|d| < d_0$. The functional form of the integrals, in terms of d, inside the circle where the function is analytic, can be used to perform an analytic continuation of the integrals to the entire d-plane. The fact that at some integer d_0 the integral diverges, implies that the function obtained by this analytic continuation is meromorphic. It will have poles on a set of real rational values of the dimensionality.[6]

As an example consider the integral (7-27) when $m = 0$. The computation of the integral, using App. 8-1, is straightforward. It is left as Exercise 8-10. In the domain in which it converges it is equal to

$$I(k) = [\tfrac{1}{2}\Gamma(\tfrac{1}{2}d)\Gamma(2 - \tfrac{1}{2}d)] \left[\frac{\Gamma^2(\tfrac{1}{2}d - 1)}{\Gamma(d - 2)} (k^2)^{(d-4)/2} \right] \qquad (8\text{-}25)$$

For $2 < d < 4$ the right-hand side is equal to the integral. The restriction $d > 2$ follows from the fact that for $m = 0$, $I(k)$ has an infrared divergence when $d < 2$. This singularity is reflected in the expression in the second square brackets in Eq. (8-25). We ignore it for the moment (see also Exercise 8-10).

The Γ-functions are analytic functions, and thus $I(k)$ is an analytic function in the whole d-plane. It coincides with the integral inside a ring, and is therefore an analytic continuation of the integral. The fact that the integral diverges at $d = 4$ is reflected in the pole of $\Gamma(2 - \tfrac{1}{2}d)$ at this value of d. The function $I(k)$ turns out to have poles at all even values of d for $d \geqslant 4$ (for some examples, see Exercise 8-11).

The above procedure gives a prescription for the regularization of any graph. The role of renormalization is to remove the singularities in d, so as to render the theory finite at the number of dimensions at which it is renormalizable. If the particular example of Eq. (8-25) stands for the graph in Fig. 7-3, it is a contribution to the two-point function in a ϕ^3 theory. Then, it is the pole near $d = 6$ which has to be treated. The same integral enters $\Gamma^{(4)}$ in a ϕ^4 theory where the pole near $d = 4$ is relevant.

8-4 MASSLESS THEORY BELOW FOUR DIMENSIONS – THE EMERGENCE OF ϵ

The existence of a critical theory below four dimensions is far from trivial. While the normalization conditions of what we called the massless theory insure that

$$\Gamma_R^{(2)}(k = 0) = 0$$

they do not guarantee that

$$\Gamma_R^{(2)}(k) \xrightarrow[k \to 0]{} 0 \qquad (8\text{-}26)$$

In fact, if we write

$$\Gamma_R^{(2)}(k, g, \kappa) = k^2 F(k, g, \kappa) \qquad (8\text{-}27)$$

then in the expansion of F in powers of g, there will be, at order n,

$$F_n = g^n (k^{-\epsilon n} + \dots) \qquad (8\text{-}28)$$

This follows simply from dimensional analysis. The dots stand for terms of the form $k^{-\epsilon n + i} \kappa^{-i}$, which are less singular.

The result is that, as one proceeds in the perturbation series, when ϵn becomes greater than 2 these terms contribute either a finite or an infinite amount, in the limit $k \to 0$. In other words, if the theory that was constructed is really a massless theory in the sense of (8-26), it is a property of the sum, not of the individual orders in the *renormalized* perturbation expansion.

At four dimensions g is dimensionless. To the extent that there are divergences, as in (8-28), dimensional analysis limits them to the form

$[\ln(k/\kappa)]^n$. These can never overpower the k^2 which was factored out in (8-27). Thus at four dimensions one has a renormalized massless theory in every order in g.

The closest we know how to approach this four-dimensional situation is to make a double expansion in g and in ϵ. On doing this, and using the expansion

$$x^\epsilon = e^{\epsilon \ln x} = \sum_0^\infty \frac{1}{n!} \epsilon^n (\ln x)^n \qquad (8-29)$$

we arrive at a situation in which every term $g^n \epsilon^n$ has at most a logarithmic divergence. And in this double expansion we have a massless limit in every order.[6]

At this stage the ϵ expansion, which is an essential tool in actual computations of properties in the critical region, enters as a necessity. It gives a sense to a critical theory below four dimensions, as long as we can only handle perturbation expansions. The other side of the ϵ expansion, to be discussed in the next chapter, provides a small parameter by which the results can be controlled. A small parameter for which the theory was waiting for a long time.

It should be pointed out that the intrinsic difficulty, which made us introduce the ϵ expansion, is not a peculiarity of the massless theory, or of the fashion in which it was renormalized. As we shall see, this same problem enters also when the renormalization is carried out at a finite mass.

8-5 THE SOLUTION OF THE RENORMALIZATION GROUP EQUATION

Let us turn back to Eq. (8-15), forgetting for the moment that it was derived in perturbation theory, or that below four dimensions it was well defined only in an ϵ expansion. In fact this equation itself can be used to leap beyond perturbation theory, its solutions defining the sum of the perturbation series. We will first limit ourselves to the simplest case, that of Eq. (8-15), leaving the extensions to $\Gamma^{(N, L)}$ and to non-critical theories to be done later. Most of the essential features of the technique, and of the analysis of the solution, appear already here.

The equation (8-15) is a linear first-order partial differential equation. This will turn out to be the case for the renormalization group equations for functions away from the critical temperature as well. The solution of such equations is standard practice in the theory of differential equations, and the technique associated with it is the method of *characteristics*.

The solution of Eq. (8-15) is basically a re-expression of the fact that there is a one-parameter group of invariance, as discussed in Sec. 8-2. The solution can be written as:

$$\Gamma_R^{(N)} (k_i; u, \kappa) = \exp\left[-\frac{N}{2} \int_1^\rho \gamma_\phi (u(\rho)) \frac{dx}{x} \right] \cdot \Gamma_R^{(N)} (k_i; u(\rho), \kappa\rho)$$

$$(8-30)$$

where the characteristic equation is:

$$\rho \, \frac{du(\rho)}{d\rho} = \beta(u(\rho)) \qquad (8\text{-}31)$$

with the initial condition

$$u(\rho = 1) = u. \qquad (8\text{-}32)$$

In order to verify that (8-30) is indeed the solution of Eq. (8-15), note first that, with the initial condition (8-32), for $\rho = 1$ the right-hand-side of (8-30) is identical to the left-hand-side. The function $\Gamma_R^{(N)}(k_i; u(\rho), \kappa\rho)$ satisfies the same renormalization group equation as $\Gamma_R^{(N)}(k_i; u, \kappa)$, if κ is replaced by $\kappa\rho$ and u by $u(\rho)$. Hence one can show that the right-hand-side of (8-30) is independent of ρ. Yet ρ is arbitrary.

Using dimensional analysis one can further extract the dependence of the solution on $\kappa\rho$. Eq. (8-30) can be rewritten as:

$$\Gamma_R^{(N)}(k_i; u, \kappa) = (\kappa\rho)^{(N + d - \frac{1}{2}Nd)} \exp\left[-\frac{N}{2} \int \gamma_\phi(u(x)) \, \frac{dx}{x} \right]$$

$$\Gamma_R^{(N)}\left(\frac{k_i}{\kappa\rho} \,;\, u(\rho), 1 \right) \qquad (8\text{-}33)$$

Before drawing some conclusions from Eq. (8-33) we remark that Eq. (8-31) can be used to change variables from x to u. Namely, any integral of the type:

$$\int_1^\rho f(u(x)) \, \frac{dx}{x} = \int_u^{u(\rho)} \frac{f(u)}{\beta(u)} \, du. \qquad (8\text{-}34)$$

The sensitive behavior for small x on the left-hand-side becomes that of the neighborhood of the zero's of β on the right-hand-side.

One way of reading Eq. (8-33) is to replace k_i by ρk_i. Then one has:

$$\Gamma_R^{(N)}(\rho k_i; u, \kappa) = \rho^{N + d - \frac{1}{2}Nd} \exp\left[-\frac{N}{2} \int_1^\rho \gamma_\phi(u(x)) \, \frac{dx}{x} \right]$$

$$\cdot \, \Gamma_R^{(N)}(k_i; u(\rho), \kappa) \qquad (8\text{-}35)$$

In words: a change in the scale of the momenta is equivalent to

1. Multiplication by that scale to the power of the canonical dimension of the function.
2. A modified coupling constant, which flows with Eq. (8-31), with β as a velocity function.
3. An additional complicated factor.

An amusing pictorial interpretation of Eq. (8-11) was suggested by Coleman[7]. The equation can be viewed as a flow of bacteria in a fluid streaming in a one-dimensional channel. The time is $x = \ln \kappa$, the velocity of the fluid at the point u is $\beta(u)$ and $\frac{1}{2} N \gamma_\phi$ is a source or a sink term — depending on its sign — describing the spontaneous changes in the density of bacteria.

An immediate consequence of Eq. (8-33) is the following: suppose the function under consideration depends on just one momentum variable. This will, in particular, be the case of $\Gamma^{(2)}$. When (8-33) is written for $\Gamma^{(2)}$ it reads:

$$\Gamma_R^{(2)}(k; u, \kappa) = (\kappa \rho)^2 \exp\left[-\int_1^\rho \gamma_\phi \frac{dx}{x}\right] \Gamma_R^{(2)}\left(\frac{k}{\kappa \rho}; u(\rho), 1\right). \qquad (8\text{-}36)$$

Since $\kappa \rho$ is still arbitrary it can be chosen as:

$$\kappa \rho = k. \qquad (8\text{-}37)$$

Eq. (8-36) now becomes:

$$\Gamma_R^{(2)}(k; u, \kappa) = k^2 \exp\left[-\int_1^{k/\kappa} \gamma_\phi \frac{dx}{x}\right] \Phi(u(k/\kappa)) \qquad (8\text{-}38)$$

where

$$\Phi(u) = \Gamma_R^{(2)}(1; u, 1) \qquad (8\text{-}39)$$

is an arbitrary function of u.

8-6 FIXED POINTS, SCALING, AND ANOMALOUS DIMENSIONS

As we have seen in the previous section, the change of the vertex functions, and hence also of the correlation functions, under a change in the scale of the momenta is rather complex — nothing like the type of simple scaling behavior one expects in a critical theory. But there are special circumstances in which the simple behavior is recovered. This happens if the coupling constant reaches a value such that any further change in the scale of the momenta does not affect it. Using Eq. (8-37), we can identify those points as those for which

$$\beta(u) = 0 \qquad (8\text{-}40)$$

The values of u which satisfy Eq. (8-40) are called *fixed points*. In the language of the flowing bacteria, these are places at which the fluid is stationary. Considering Eq. (8-15) at a fixed point $u = u^*$, we have

$$\left[\kappa \frac{\partial}{\partial \kappa} - \tfrac{1}{2} N \gamma_\phi(u^*)\right] \Gamma_R^{(N)}(k_i; u^*, \kappa) = 0 \qquad (8\text{-}41)$$

whose solution is:

$$\Gamma_R^{(N)}(k_i; u^*, \kappa) = \kappa^{\frac{1}{2}N\gamma_\phi(u^*)}\Phi(k_i) \qquad (8\text{-}42)$$

Scaling the momenta according to (8-34) leads to

$$\Gamma_R^{(N)}(\rho k_i; u^*, \kappa) = \rho^{(N+d-\frac{1}{2}Nd)-\frac{1}{2}N\gamma_\phi(u^*)}\Gamma_R^{(N)}(k_i; u^*, \kappa) \qquad (8\text{-}43)$$

Thus, a simple *scaling* property.

In particular $\Gamma_R^{(2)}$ behaves as

$$\Gamma_R^{(2)}(\rho k) = \rho^{2-\gamma_\phi(u^*)}\Gamma(k) \qquad (8\text{-}44)$$

which identifies the exponent η as

$$\eta = \gamma_\phi(u^*) \qquad (8\text{-}45)$$

which is also called twice the *anomalous dimension* of the field ϕ.[8]

The origin of this name is related to the discussion in Sec. 7-2. There we saw that the canonical dimension of $\bar{\Gamma}$ is $\Lambda^{N+d-\frac{1}{2}Nd}$. Hence the free vertex would scale under a dilation of the momenta, according to †

$$\Gamma^{(N)0}(\rho k_i) = \rho^{d-N[(d/2)-1]}\Gamma^{(N)0}(k_i)$$

In analogy one defines the dimension of ϕ by

$$\Gamma^{(N)}(\rho k_i) = \rho^{d-Nd_\phi}\Gamma^{(N)}(k_i) \qquad (8\text{-}46)$$

whenever $\Gamma^{(N)}$ scales, which in the free case gives

$$d_\phi^0 = \frac{d}{2} - 1$$

the naive dimension of the field.

At a fixed point $\Gamma_R^{(N)}$ indeed scales, and a comparison with Eq. (8-43) gives:

$$d_\phi = \frac{d}{2} - 1 + \frac{\eta}{2} \qquad (8\text{-}47)$$

Now, in the absence of a length scale $-m = 0$, one expects that a scaling of the momenta will bring out a factor to multiply $\Gamma^{(N)}$, i.e., one expects $\Gamma^{(N)}$ to be a homogeneous function. Since, naively speaking, in the massless theory there is no length except the scale of the momenta, one expects the factor multiplying $\Gamma^{(N)}$ to be ρ to the power of the canonical (engineering) dimension of $\Gamma^{(N)}$. What we find from (8-43) and from (8-44) is that this is not the case.

First of all even the massless theory does not automatically scale. And then, when it does, the resulting factor differs from the canonical dimension by $\rho^{-\eta/2}$ for every field ϕ in $\Gamma_R^{(N)}$. These two facts are of course related to the appearance of the length κ^{-1}, without which the infinities cannot be removed

†Here we write Γ for $\bar{\Gamma}$ of Sec. 7-2.

from the theory. The difference between the naive expectation and the correct result, $d_\phi - d_\phi^0$, is the anomalous dimension.

Since in $\Gamma_R^{(2)}$ only a single momentum appears, it follows from Eq. (8-44) that at the fixed point $\Gamma_R^{(2)}$ has the form:

$$\Gamma_R^{(2)}(k) = C\kappa^\eta k^{2-\eta} \qquad (8\text{-}48)$$

where C is a constant. Dimensional analysis, together with the fact that the bare functions know no κ, leads to

$$\Gamma^{(2)}(k) = C'\Lambda^\eta k^{2-\eta} \qquad (8\text{-}48')$$

Namely, at the fixed point, the field renormalization constant, which is dimensionless, behaves as

$$Z_\phi(u^*,\kappa/\Lambda) = C''(\kappa/\Lambda)^\eta$$

At the fixed point one can solve Eq. (8-23) as well, and obtain $\Gamma_R^{(N,L)}$. The result will be a homogeneous function of the momenta, which will give for the anomalous dimension of the composite operator ϕ^2:

$$d_{\phi^2} = -2 + \gamma_{\phi^2}(u^*) \qquad (8\text{-}49)$$

(see Exercise 8-13.) As we shall see later on γ_{ϕ^2} is related to our critical exponents through the relation:

$$\nu^{-1} - 2 = -\gamma_{\phi^2}(u^*) \qquad (8\text{-}50)$$

Thus, given $\gamma_\phi(u^*)$ and $\gamma_{\phi^2}(u^*)$, we can compute η and ν, and using the scaling relations, Eqs. (1-12), all the other static exponents.

8-7 THE APPROACH TO THE FIXED POINT – ASYMPTOTIC FREEDOM

In the previous section we have studied the behavior of the vertex functions when the renormalized coupling constant was exactly at the fixed point. However, given any arbitrary value of the bare coupling constant, it is rather unlikely that the renormalized one will be precisely u^*. Consequently, we have to return to Eq. (8-35) in order to investigate the question as to whether, and under what conditions, will the renormalized coupling constant flow into the fixed point, given that it has some arbitrary value at some prescribed set of momenta. The variable which induces this flow is, of course, the scale of the momenta itself. The answer depends strongly on the form of the function β, as we shall now see.

Let us start by assuming that β has a simple zero at u^*. Then, in the vicinity of u^*

$$\beta(u) = a(u^* - u) \qquad (8\text{-}51)$$

Inserting in Eq. (8-31) we find,

$$\frac{\partial u(s)}{\partial s} = a(u^* - u) \qquad (8\text{-}52)$$

whose solution, with the initial condition Eq. (8-32), is:

$$u^* - u(s) = ce^{-as} = (u^* - u)e^{-as} \qquad (8\text{-}53)$$

where $s = \ln\rho$.

Two different limits are of interest. The first is $s \to -\infty$, namely $\rho \to 0$. In this limit the low-momentum or infrared behavior of the vertex functions is studied. It is this limit which is of interest in statistical physics.

The other limit is $s \to +\infty$, or $\rho \to \infty$. In this limit the vertex functions are probed at high Euclidean momenta. This limit is of interest in the study of deep inelastic scattering.

It is easy to see from Eq. (8-53) that if $a > 0$ then

$$u(s) \xrightarrow[s \to \infty]{} u^* \qquad (8\text{-}54)$$

and if $a < 0$

$$u(s) \xrightarrow[s \to -\infty]{} u^* \qquad (8\text{-}54')$$

Namely, depending on the slope of the function β at its zero, a renormalized coupling constant, starting in the neighborhood of this point, will flow to the fixed point either in the high-momentum limit, or in the low-momentum limit – never in both. In the first case we say that the fixed point is *ultraviolet-stable*, and in the second that it is *infrared stable*. These two situations are depicted in Fig. 8-1, in which $\beta(u)$ is schematically drawn. The point u_1^* is an infrared-stable fixed point, and u_2^* is ultraviolet-stable. (Notice that $a = -\beta'(u^*)$.)

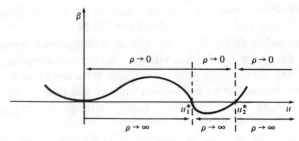

FIGURE 8-1
A function β with an ultraviolet- and an infrared-fixed point.

If our initial renormalized coupling constant is near an ultraviolet fixed point and $\rho \to 0$, u will move away from that point and towards the nearest infrared-stable fixed point. In fact all coupling constants between two ultraviolet fixed points will be *attracted* to the infrared fixed point, which must be situated between them. This range of coupling constants is called the *domain of attraction* of the infrared fixed point. Similarly, we can define a domain of attraction of an ultraviolet fixed point.

The whole argument presented above does not depend on the linear form of β, Eq. (8-51), but only on the fact that β has a simple zero, and a given sign between two consecutive roots. One can easily generalize the above considerations to show that if β is negative to the left of a zero and positive to its right, then the zero is an infrared-stable fixed point.

Returning to Eq. (8-35) we see that, even for $u \neq u^*$, if u is in the infrared domain of attraction of u^*, as $\rho \to 0$, $u(s) \to u^*$. What happens to the prefactor in (8-35) as the fixed point is approached?

Assuming that γ_ϕ behaves as

$$\gamma_\phi(u) = \gamma_\phi^* + \gamma_\phi'(u - u^*) \qquad (8\text{-}55)$$

near the fixed point, the integral in the exponent will read:

$$\int_1^\rho \gamma_\phi(u(x)) \, \frac{dx}{x} = \int_u^{u(s)} \frac{\gamma_\phi(u')}{\beta(u')} \, du'$$

$$= \gamma_\phi^* \int_u^{u(s)} \frac{du'}{a(u^* - u')} - \frac{\gamma_\phi'}{a} \int_u^{u(s)} du' = \gamma_\phi^* s - \frac{\gamma_\phi'}{a} [u(s) - u] \qquad (8\text{-}56)$$

where use has been made of Eq. (8-34).

The prefactor (8-35) now becomes, as $u \to u^*$

$$\exp\left[-\frac{N}{2} \int_1^\rho \gamma_\phi \, \frac{dx}{x} \right] \to C \rho^{-N\gamma_\phi^*/2}$$

where

$$C = \exp\left[-\frac{N}{2} \frac{\gamma_\phi'}{a} (u^* - u) \right] \qquad (8\text{-}57)$$

This is just the result obtained in the previous section, except that here it appears as a consequence of the asymptotic behavior of the vertex functions, as functions of the scale of the momenta, rather than a special behavior at $u = u^*$.

Before discussing a somewhat more complicated case for β and γ, it is interesting to notice that, logically, the following situation may arise: we can start with an interacting theory, $u_0 \neq 0$. The function β always vanishes as $u \to 0$. Hence, in one of the asymptotic limits, either the ultraviolet or the infrared, u will tend to zero. In other words, in that limit the theory will be *asymptotically free.* Which of the two limits will be free depends on the form of the function β, i.e., on whether the origin is an ultraviolet or infrared fixed point. The function γ_ϕ vanishes faster than β, as $\eta \to 0$ (see Exercise 8-12). Thus, the anomalous dimension will vanish.

This particular question of asymptotic freedom has been at the center of the very exciting developments in high energy physics in the last few years. Deep inelastic electron scattering indicated that not only did the scattering amplitudes scale – a phenomenon called Bjorken scaling – but the anomalous dimensions appeared to be essentially zero. Attention was then focused on this curious vanishing of the anomalous dimensions, which was emphasized by K. G. Wilson. Since the stability of the origin can be studied in perturbation theory the available theories were checked in order to find out which one of them could possibly be asymptotically free. First it was noticed[9] that theories with non-Abelian gauge fields could give rise to asymptotic ultraviolet freedom. It was then proven[10] that no other theory could. This discovery ushered in the great interest in formulating elementary particle physics in terms of these gauge fields, which in turn has given rise to such new ideas as quark confinement, and the unification of the theories of weak and electromagnetic interactions. But these are topics beyond the scope of this book.

Asymptotic freedom is not complete freedom. The remnants of the interaction can be detected by the fact that the vertex functions, or scattering amplitudes, have logarithmic corrections. These can be experimentally seen both in situations of high-energy scattering, as well as in phase transitions. To understand the origin of these corrections consider the case in which β has a double zero:

$$\beta(u) = a(u - u^*)^2 \qquad (8\text{-}58)$$

In this case, with $s = \ln \rho$

$$u^* - u(s) = \frac{u^* - u}{(u^* - u)as + 1} \qquad (8\text{-}59)$$

which is a solution of Eq. (8-31) with the initial condition (8-32). For any sign of a, the second derivative of β at the fixed point, u^* will be attractive in the ultraviolet on one side and in the infrared on the other. For example, if β has the form as in Fig. 8-2, $a > 0$, then if the initial value of u is less than u^*, as $s \to \infty$

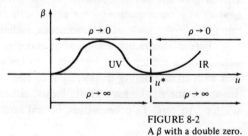

FIGURE 8-2
A β with a double zero.

$u(s) \to u^*$. This means that to the left of u^* the fixed point is ultraviolet attractive. It is ultraviolet repulsive to the right of u^*, but it attracts in the infrared.

Even when this point attracts it does so much less strongly than in the case of a single zero. There the approach was exponential, while here it is a power. This has a strong effect on the prefactor in (8-35). Taking γ_ϕ as in Eq. (8-55), we have:

$$\int_1^\rho \gamma_\phi \frac{dx}{x} = \int_u^{u(s)} \frac{\gamma_\phi(u')}{\beta(u')} \, du' = \gamma_\phi^* s + \frac{\gamma_\phi'}{a}\left\{ \ln[u(s) - u^*] - \ln(u - u^*) \right\}$$

(8-60)

On the other hand, from (8-31) we have:

$$\ln \rho = s = -\frac{1}{a}\left[\frac{1}{u(s) - u^*} - \frac{1}{u - u^*} \right]$$ (8-61)

The second term is independent of s, and as $u(s) \to u^*$ the first one will dominate. Inserting it in (8-60) gives for the prefactor:

$$\exp\left[-\frac{N}{2} \int_1^\rho \gamma_\phi \frac{dx}{x} \right] \to C \exp\left[-\frac{N}{2} \gamma_\phi^* s + \frac{N}{2} \frac{\gamma_\phi'}{a} \ln s \right] = C \rho^{-N\gamma_\phi^*/2} (\ln \rho)^{N\gamma_\phi'/2a}$$

(8-62)

The result is that, apart from the anomalous dimension, there is an additional factor produced by the change of the length scale near the fixed point. It is a power of $\ln\rho$. If the theory is asymptotically free, $\gamma_\phi^* = 0$, but $\gamma_\phi' \neq 0$. It turns out that at four dimensions $\beta(u)$ starts always with u^2, i.e., the origin is a double zero. For theories without non-Abelian gauge fields, β increases at the origin, and thus the origin is an infrared-stable fixed point, but unstable in the ultraviolet (see Exercise 8-14).

8-8 RENORMALIZATION GROUP EQUATION ABOVE T_c – IDENTIFICATION OF ν

Moving away from the critical point, but staying still in the symmetric theory, i.e., $T > T_c$, one can obtain a renormalization group equation for the vertex functions by using the expansion (7-82) for $N \neq 0$. Applying the differential operator

$$O = \kappa \frac{\partial}{\partial \kappa} + \beta(u) \frac{\partial}{\partial u} - \tfrac{1}{2} N \gamma_\phi(u) + \gamma_{\phi^2} t \frac{\partial}{\partial t}$$ (8-63)

to $\Gamma_R^{(N)}(k_i)$, after replacing δt by t, we obtain:

$$O\Gamma_R^{(N)}(k_1 \ldots k_N; t, u, \kappa)$$

$$= \lim_{p_i \to 0} O \sum_{L=0}^{\infty} \frac{1}{L!} t^L \Gamma_R^{(N,L)}(k_i, p_i; u, \kappa)$$

$$= \lim_{p_i \to 0} \sum_{L=0}^{\infty} \frac{t^L}{L!} \left[\kappa \frac{\partial}{\partial \kappa} + \beta \frac{\partial}{\partial u} - \tfrac{1}{2} N \gamma_\phi + L \gamma_{\phi^2} \right] \Gamma_R^{(N,L)}(k_i, p_i; u, \kappa)$$

$$(8\text{-}64)$$

Each term in the sum vanishes since $\Gamma_R^{(N,L)}$ satisfies a renormalization group equation, (8-23), in the massless theory. Thus we have

$$\left[\kappa \frac{\partial}{\partial \kappa} + \beta(u) \frac{\partial}{\partial u} - \tfrac{1}{2} N \gamma_\phi(u) + \gamma_{\phi^2}(u) t \frac{\partial}{\partial t} \right] \Gamma_R^{(N)}(k_i; t, u, \kappa) = 0 \qquad (8\text{-}65)$$

(See also Exercise 8-15.)

This equation can be solved in a general form along lines similar to those by which we reached Eq. (8-30). It can then be shown that $\Gamma_R^{(N)}$ will be a *homogeneous function of the k_i's and t, jointly,* only at the fixed point u^*, at which β vanishes (see Exercise 8-16). Here we will study the consequences of Eq. (8-65) at the fixed point. It will be shown that $\Gamma_R^{(N)}$ obeys scaling, and that the relation (8-50),

$$\nu^{-1} - 2 = -\gamma_{\phi^2}(u^*) \equiv \theta \qquad (8\text{-}66)$$

holds, where ν is the exponent giving the dependence of the correlation length on the temperature difference $T - T_c$, Eq. (1-2).

The equation to be solved is:

$$\left[\kappa \frac{\partial}{\partial \kappa} - \tfrac{1}{2} N \eta - \theta t \frac{\partial}{\partial t} \right] \Gamma_R^{(N)}(k_i; t, u^*, \kappa) = 0 \qquad (8\text{-}67)$$

Since the value of u is fixed at u^* we omit it from our notation. The solution of the equation is:

$$\Gamma_R^{(N)}(k_i; t, \kappa) = \kappa^{\frac{1}{2}N\eta} F^{(N)}(k_i; \kappa t^{1/\theta}) \qquad (8\text{-}68)$$

In other words, $\Gamma_R^{(N)}$ depends on a special combination of κ and t.

The implications of this solution are found by scaling the lengths as we did in Sec. 8-6. Using dimensional analysis again, one can write

$$\Gamma_R^{(N)}(k_i; t, \kappa) = \rho^{N+d-\frac{1}{2}Nd} \Gamma_R^{(N)}(\rho^{-1} k_i; \rho^{-2} t, \rho^{-1} \kappa)$$

where use was made of the fact that the dimension of t is that of μ^2, namely Λ^2. Substitution in Eq. (8-68) gives

$$\Gamma_R^{(N)}(k_i; t, \kappa) = \rho^{d + \frac{N}{2}(2-d-\eta)} \kappa^{\frac{1}{2}N\eta} F^{(N)}(\rho^{-1}k_i; (\rho^{-1}\kappa) \cdot (\rho^{-2}t)^{1/\theta}) \qquad (8\text{-}69)$$

But so far ρ has been arbitrary. We now choose it to satisfy:

$$(\rho^{-1}\kappa)(\rho^{-2}t)^{1/\theta} = 1$$

or

$$\rho = \kappa(t/\kappa^2)^{\frac{1}{\theta+2}} \qquad (8\text{-}70)$$

The vertex function becomes:

$$\Gamma_R^{(N)}(k_i; t, \kappa) = \kappa^{d + \frac{N}{2}(2-d)} (\kappa^{-2}t)^{\frac{d+N(2-d-\eta)/2}{\theta+2}} F^{(N)}\left(\kappa^{-1}k_i (\kappa^{-2}t)^{-\frac{1}{\theta+2}}\right) \qquad (8\text{-}71)$$

This is a remarkable result. The vertex function depends only on the combinations $k_i\xi$ with

$$\xi \propto t^{-1/(\theta+2)} \qquad (8\text{-}72)$$

apart from a power of t. Thus, it is a homogeneous function of the k_i's and of ξ together.

Comparison with Eq. (1-2) gives

$$\nu^{-1} = 2 + \theta = 2 - \gamma_{\phi^2}^* \qquad (8\text{-}73)$$

with γ_{ϕ^2} given by Eq. (8-24). If we define, using Eq. (7-73),

$$\bar{\gamma}_{\phi^2} = -\beta(u)\frac{\partial \ln(Z_{\phi^2} Z_{\phi})}{\partial u} = -\beta(u)\frac{\partial \ln \bar{Z}_{\phi^2}}{\partial u} \qquad (8\text{-}74)$$

in analogy with γ_ϕ, then from (8-24) and (8-45) it follows that

$$\nu^{-1} = 2 - \bar{\gamma}_{\phi^2}^* - \eta \qquad (8\text{-}75)$$

And it is usually the case that one first computes η by calculating Z_ϕ from Eq. (7-54). Then Eq. (7-57), or (7-74), gives $\bar{Z}_{\phi^2}$, and not Z_{ϕ^2}. Therefore Eq. (8-75) is the natural expression for the calculation of ν.

To summarize, we have shown in this section that at the fixed point all correlation functions scale at $T > T_c$, in the sense that they are functions of $k_i\xi$ only. Namely, the temperature dependence enters only through $\xi \propto (T - T_c)^{-\nu}$.

Furthermore, the exponent ν can be expressed in terms of the renormalization constants which are computed at T_c. This result can be obtained directly by deriving a renormalization group equation for ξ^2 itself, and by solving for $\xi^2(t)$ (see Exercise 8-17).

In particular for $N = 2$, if we choose $\rho = k$, we find for the inverse of the two-point correlation function

$$\Gamma_R^{(2)}(k; t, \kappa) = \kappa^\eta k^{2-\eta} f(k\xi) \qquad (8\text{-}76)$$

The proof of this relation is left as Exercise 8-18. As the critical point is approached $\xi \to \infty$, and our previous result, Eq. (8-48), implies that

$$f(x) \xrightarrow[x \to \infty]{} C \qquad (8\text{-}77)$$

Away from T_c, $\Gamma_R^{(2)}$ is not a pure power since the length ξ is still relevant even at the fixed point. Nevertheless, $\Gamma_R^{(2)}$ satisfies scaling. This form can be used to prove the third scaling relation in (1-12). Clearly, Eq. (8-76) can be rewritten as

$$\Gamma_R^{(2)}(k; t, \kappa) = \kappa^\eta \xi^{-2+\eta} f_1(k\xi) \qquad (8\text{-}78)$$

As $k \to 0$, $\Gamma_R^{(2)}$ tends to the inverse susceptibility. Here $f_1(x)$ must have a finite limit as $x \to 0$, and we find that

$$\chi \propto \xi^{2-\eta}$$

from which it follows that

$$\gamma = \nu(2 - \eta)$$

$\Gamma_R^{(N)}$, Eq. (8-71), can now be expressed in terms of ν and γ as:

$$\Gamma_R^{(N)}(k_i; t, \kappa) = \kappa^{d-N[(d/2)-1]}(\kappa^{-2}t)^{d\nu[1-(N/2)]+\frac{1}{2}N\gamma}F^{(N)}(k_i\xi) \qquad (8\text{-}79)$$

8-9 BELOW THE CRITICAL TEMPERATURE – THE SCALING FORM OF THE EQUATION OF STATE

If one is willing to accept the scaling relations of Chap. 1, the discussion can stop here, except for the numerical evaluation of Z_ϕ and Z_{ϕ^2}. However, we will now proceed to show that the rest of the scaling relations hold within the framework presented here. We will also demonstrate the fact that the equation of state has a homogeneous form, which gives rise to the rest of the scaling relations except the last one. In fact, it can be shown that the equation of state has a universal form which depends only on the properties of the fixed point, and can be calculated in an ϵ expansion. We deal with this aspect in Sec. II-3-2.

In Eq. (7-86) we have a renormalized equation of state. Replacing again δt by t, we rewrite it

$$H(t, M, u, \kappa) = \sum_{N=1}^{\infty} \frac{1}{N!} M^N \Gamma_R^{(1+N)}(k_i = 0; t, u, \kappa) \qquad (8\text{-}80)$$

Recall that t is proportional to $T - T_c$, and that the zero momentum limit is taken after the summation.

Each term in the sum satisfies a renormalization group equation, Eq. (8-65). Hence one finds immediately that H satisfies the equation:

$$\left\{ \kappa \frac{\partial}{\partial \kappa} + \beta(u) \frac{\partial}{\partial u} - \tfrac{1}{2} \eta(u) \left(1 + M \frac{\partial}{\partial M} \right) - [v^{-1}(u) - 2] t \frac{\partial}{\partial t} \right\} H(t, M, u, \kappa) = 0$$

(8-81)

where we have used the notation $\gamma_\phi(u) = \eta(u)$ and $\gamma_{\phi^2}(u) = v^{-1}(u) - 2$. This is the renormalization group equation for the equation of state.

Again, the general solution can be written down, and its behavior, when the coupling constant flows, can be studied. We leave these derivations as Exercises 8-19—8-21. Here we will discuss the equation at the fixed point. First we notice that at this point

$$H(t, M, \kappa) = \kappa^{\frac{1}{2}\eta} h_1 \left(\kappa M^{2/\eta}, \kappa t^{1/(v^{-1} - 2)} \right)$$

(8-82)

where u is omitted since its value is fixed at u^*.

All the variables in H have dimensions, as does H. From the discussion in Sec. 7-2 we deduce that

$$[M] = \Lambda^{d/2 - 1}$$

$$[H] = [\lambda_1] = \Lambda^{d/2 + 1}$$

and that

$$H(t, M, \kappa) = \rho^{(d+2)/2} H \left(\frac{t}{\rho^2}, \frac{M}{\rho^{(d-2)/2}}, \frac{\kappa}{\rho} \right)$$

(8-83)

Using (8-82), we have:

$$H(t, M, \kappa) = \rho^{(d+2-\eta)/2} \kappa^{\eta/2} h_1 \left[\frac{\kappa}{\rho} \left(\frac{M}{\rho^{(d-2)/2}} \right)^{2/\eta}, \frac{\kappa}{\rho} \left(\frac{t}{\rho^2} \right)^{\frac{1}{v^{-1} - 2}} \right]$$

(8-84)

Next we choose ρ to be a power of M such that

$$\frac{\kappa}{\rho} \left(\frac{M}{\rho^{(d-2)/2}} \right)^{2/\eta} = 1$$

(8-85)

The corresponding ρ is:

$$\rho = \kappa \left(\frac{M}{\kappa^{(d-2)/2}} \right)^{\frac{1}{d - 2 + \eta}}$$

(8-86)

Inserting in Eq. (8-84), one obtains directly the scaled equation of state, namely,

$$H(t, M, \kappa) = \kappa^{(d+2)/2} \left(\frac{M}{\kappa^{(d-2)/2}} \right)^{\frac{d+2-\eta}{d-2+\eta}} h \left[\frac{t}{\kappa^2} \left(\frac{M}{\kappa^{(d-2)/2}} \right)^{-\frac{2}{\nu(d-2+\eta)}} \right] \quad (8\text{-}87)$$

This is just the type of equation of state considered in Exercise 1-1. It allows us to identify the exponents:

$$\delta = \frac{d+2-\eta}{d-2+\eta} \quad (8\text{-}88)$$

and

$$\beta = \tfrac{1}{2}\nu(d-2+\eta) \quad (8\text{-}89)$$

Using these in conjuction with the scaling relation $\gamma = \nu(2-\eta)$ one immediately derives the scaling relations

$$2\beta + \gamma = d\nu \quad (8\text{-}90)$$

and

$$2\beta\delta - \gamma = d\nu \quad (8\text{-}91)$$

In addition (8-87) implies that

$$\gamma = \gamma' \quad (8\text{-}92)$$

(See Exercise 1-1.) That is, the exponents for the susceptibility above and below the transition are equal. One can now proceed to show that $\nu = \nu'$ by considering the correlation function below T_c. This is left as Exercise 8-22.

But what is no less remarkable is that from Eq. (8-87) it follows that, apart from fixing a scale for H, M and t, the homogeneous function relating these three variables is completely determined by the fixed point. To the extent that a range of bare theories leads to the same fixed point, the equation of state for all these theories is the same. And whenever the properties of the system at the fixed point can be computed one can obtain the equation of state, as well as the exponents. The demonstration of these statements will be deferred to II-3.

8-10 THE SPECIFIC HEAT – RENORMALIZATION GROUP EQUATION FOR AN ADDITIVELY RENORMALIZED VERTEX

In Secs. 2-5 and 2-6 we have seen that the specific heat C is related directly to $G_c^{(0,2)}(p, -p; \mu^2, \lambda, \Lambda)$ as $p \to 0$. In the symmetric state, in a ϕ^4 theory, all connected graphs of $G^{(0,2)}$ are also 1PI (Exercise 8-23). Hence

$$G_c^{(0,2)} = -\Gamma^{(0,2)} \quad (8\text{-}93)$$

This vertex function was found, in Sec. 7-4, to be problematic, in the sense that it could not be multiplicatively renormalized. We then proceeded to renormalize it by an additive constant, Eq. (7-44). But there the renormalization was performed at a finite mass. To show how things work in the present scheme, which uses only functions computed at T_c ($m = 0$), we rewrite Eq. (7-44) in the form:

$$\Gamma_R^{(0,2)}(,p,-p;u,\kappa) = Z_{\phi^2}^2 \left[\Gamma^{(0,2)}(,p,-p;\lambda,\Lambda) - \Gamma^{(0,2)}(,p,-p;\lambda,\Lambda)\Big|_{p^2=\kappa^2} \right]$$

(8-94)

where $T = T_c$, $m = 0$. This insures that $\Gamma_R^{(0,2)}$ will be finite as $\Lambda \to \infty$ for all $p \neq 0$, and that the normalization condition, Eq. (7-57), be satisfied. In fact, since all the parameters of the theory are fixed by Eqs. (7-53) through (7-56), (8-94) is an explicit solution for the additive constant, needed to satisfy (7-57). Z_ϕ and Z_{ϕ^2} are the same constants as the ones used throughout our discussion (see Exercise 8-24).

From Eq. (8-94) one can deduce a renormalization group ·equation for $\Gamma_R^{(0,2)}$ by applying to both sides $\kappa\partial/\partial\kappa \mid_{\lambda,\Lambda}$. The new feature is that the additive constant leads to an inhomogeneous term in the equation. One finds:

$$\left[\kappa \frac{\partial}{\partial\kappa} + \beta(u)\frac{\partial}{\partial u} - 2\left(\frac{1}{\nu(u)} - 2\right) \right] \Gamma_R^{(0,2)}(,p,-p;u,\kappa) = \kappa^{-\epsilon}\bar{B}\left(u_0, \frac{\kappa}{\Lambda}\right)$$

(8-95)

where

$$\kappa^{-\epsilon}\bar{B}\left(u_0, \frac{\kappa}{\Lambda}\right) = -Z_{\phi^2}^2 \kappa \frac{\partial}{\partial\kappa} \Gamma^{(0,2)}(,p,-p;\lambda,\Lambda)\Big|_{p^2=\kappa^2}$$

$$= -\left[\kappa \frac{\partial}{\partial\kappa} - 2\left(\frac{1}{\nu} - 2\right) \right] Z_{\phi^2}^2 \Gamma^{(0,2)}(,p,-p;\lambda,\Lambda)\Big|_{p^2=\kappa^2}$$

(8-96)

$\nu(u)$ is defined as in Eq. (8-81), and the explicit $\kappa^{-\epsilon}$ on the right-hand side of Eq. (8-95) follows from dimensional analysis. Since $\kappa^{-\epsilon}\bar{B}$ equals the left-hand side of Eq. (8-95), which is renormalized, it has a finite limit as $\Lambda \to \infty$ at $d = 4$, *order by order in u*, and the right-hand side of (8-95) can be written as $\kappa^{-\epsilon}B(u)$.

So far we have an equation for $\Gamma_R^{(0,2)}$ at T_c, but with $p \neq 0$. If both m and p vanish $\Gamma_R^{(0,2)}$ will be infinite. This is the real divergence of the specific heat. To obtain an equation away from T_c one expands $\Gamma_R^{(0,2)}$ in a power series in t, whose coefficients are $\Gamma_R^{(0,2+L)}$. The important point to keep in mind is that only $\Gamma^{(0,2)}$ needs the subtraction, as in Eq. (8-94). Thus, using arguments similar to those used in Sec. 7-7, we conclude that

$$\Gamma_R^{(0,2)}(,p,-p;t,u,\kappa) = Z_{\phi^2}^2 \left[\Gamma^{(0,2)}(,p,-p;\mu^2,\lambda,\Lambda) - \Gamma^{(0,2)}(,p,-p;\lambda,\Lambda)\Big|_{p^2=\kappa^2} \right]$$

(8-97)

in which the subtraction is exactly the same as at T_c. The details of the proof are left as Exercise 8-25.

If $t \neq 0$ we can set $p = 0$ in $\Gamma^{(0,2)}$ (see Exercise 8-26), and this function satisfies the renormalization group equation

$$\left[\kappa \frac{\partial}{\partial \kappa} + \beta(u) \frac{\partial}{\partial u} - \left(\nu^{-1}(u) - 2 \right) \left(2 + t \frac{\partial}{\partial t} \right) \right] \Gamma_R^{(0,2)}(,0,0;t,u,\kappa) = \kappa^{-\epsilon} B(u)$$

(8-98)

The solution of this equation at the fixed point is:

$$\Gamma_R^{(0,2)} = C(t) = C_1 \kappa^{-\epsilon} (t/\kappa^2)^{-(2-d\nu)} - \frac{\nu}{2-d\nu} B(u^*) \kappa^{-\epsilon}$$

(8-99)

Comparing with Eq. (1-5), we find:

$$\alpha = 2 - d\nu$$

which is the last missing scaling relation.

8-11 THE CALLAN–SYMANZIK EQUATIONS

An alternative method for the derivation of scale invariance of interacting field theories uses the renormalization of the vertex functions at zero external momenta and non-zero mass.[1][2] In this procedure the renormalization constants are determined from Eqs. (7-45)–(7-48), and instead of depending on the ratio κ/Λ they depend on m/Λ. In other words, the renormalization constants will be temperature dependent. This, as well as the fact that the $m \to 0$ limit is problematic (see discussion in Sec. 7-5), have slowly displaced this technique in favor of the expansion around the critical theory. We therefore give a brief description of this method.

The idea underlying the Callan–Symanzik equations is a comparison of different renormalized theories which originate from a set of bare theories with a fixed bare coupling constant and a fixed cutoff, i.e., the bare theories have different bare masses.

Renormalizability of the theory is summarized by Eq. (7-34), which for simplicity, we reproduce here for the case $L = 0$. In this case we have:

$$\Gamma_R^{(N)}(k_i; m^2, g) = Z_\phi^{N/2} \Gamma^{(N)}(k_i; \mu^2, \lambda, \Lambda)$$

(8-100)

Dimensional analysis implies:

$$\mu^2 = m^2 \bar{\mu}^2(u, m/\Lambda)$$

(8-101)

$$\lambda = m^{\epsilon} u_0(u, m/\Lambda) \quad (8\text{-}102)$$

$$Z_{\phi} = Z_{\phi}(u, m/\Lambda) \quad (8\text{-}103)$$

in which u is defined via

$$g = m^{\epsilon} u \quad (8\text{-}104)$$

$\Gamma_R^{(N)}$ can also be considered as a function of k_i, m^2 and u.

Taking a derivative of Eq. (8-100) with respect to ln$m$, at fixed λ and Λ, one finds:

$$\left[m \frac{\partial}{\partial m} + \beta(u) \frac{\partial}{\partial u} - \frac{N}{2} \gamma_{\phi}(u) \right] \Gamma_R^{(N)}(k_i; m^2, u) = Z_{\phi}^{N/2} m \left(\frac{\partial \mu^2}{\partial m} \right)_{\lambda, \Lambda} \frac{\partial}{\partial \mu^2} \Gamma^{(N)}(p_i; \mu^2, \lambda, \Lambda)$$

$$(8\text{-}105)$$

The same logic which led us from Eqs. (8-16) and (8-17) to Eqs. (8-21) and (8-22), respectively, leads to very similar results for β and γ_{ϕ}, namely,

$$\beta(u) = \left(m \frac{\partial u}{\partial m} \right)_{\lambda, \Lambda} = -\epsilon \left(\frac{\partial \ln u_0}{\partial u} \right)^{-1} \quad (8\text{-}106)$$

and

$$\gamma_{\phi}(u) = m \left(\frac{\partial \ln Z_{\phi}}{\partial m} \right)_{\lambda, \Lambda} = \beta(u) \frac{\partial \ln Z_{\phi}}{\partial u} \quad (8\text{-}107)$$

To investigate the right-hand side of Eq. (8-105), we use Eq. (5-75) in the form:

$$\left(\frac{\partial}{\partial \mu^2} \Gamma^{(N)} \right) = \Gamma^{(N, 1)}$$

and then, using Eq. (7-34), Eq. (8-105) can be rewritten as:

$$O\Gamma_R^{(N)} = \left(m \frac{\partial \mu^2}{\partial m} \right)_{\lambda, \Lambda} Z_{\phi^2} \Gamma_R^{(N, 1)} \quad (8\text{-}108)$$

The factor in front of $\Gamma_R^{(N,1)}$ can be determined by considering this last equation for $N = 2$ at $k_i = 0$. Both $\Gamma_R^{(2)}$ and $\Gamma_R^{(2,1)}$ are then given by the normalization conditions, which leads to the Callan–Symanzik equations written in terms of renormalized quantities only:

$$\left[m \frac{\partial}{\partial m} + \beta(u) \frac{\partial}{\partial u} - \frac{N}{2} \gamma_{\phi}(u) \right] \Gamma_R^{(N)}(k_i; m, u) = [2 - \gamma_{\phi}(u)]m^2 \Gamma_R^{(N, 1)}(k_i, 0; m, u)$$

$$(8\text{-}109)$$

This equation becomes useful when one notices that, for $k_i/m \to \infty$, the right-hand side can be neglected with respect to the left-hand side. At four dimensions this statement is true order by order in the expansion in u. It is a consequence of Weinberg's theorem, which states[13] that when all external momenta of a graph increase uniformly in the Euclidean region a graph with an additional propagator will be smaller than one without it by two powers of the scale of the momenta. But it is exactly the region $k_i/m \to \infty$ which is of interest in critical phenomena, since it implies $k_i \xi \to \infty$ (see Exercise 7-9). Consequently, in order to study the asymptotic region of fixed wave number and increasing correlation length, or of fixed correlation length but increasing wave number, we need only solve the homogeneous Callan–Symanzik equation. This equation has exactly the same form as the renormalization group equation, (8-11), and its solution proceeds in the same way as is indicated in Sec. 8-5.

Weinberg's theorem loses much of its effectiveness when a graph includes a part which is potentially infrared divergent, namely, a part in whose integrand there are less powers of momentum from the integration volumes, than there are in the denominators. In such cases the asymptotic behavior of the graph may be completely unchanged following a ϕ^2 insertion (see Exercise 8-28). This is just what happens below four dimensions, and corresponds to the difficulty discussed in Sec. 8-4. The situation is saved again by the expansion in $\epsilon = 4 - d$. The double series in powers of u and ϵ has similar properties to that of the power series in u at four dimensions. In this series the terms on the right-hand side are smaller than those on the left-hand side by a factor of $(k_i/m)^2$, up to powers of $\ln(k_i/m)$. It is always implicitly assumed that those do not add to a finite power $0(\epsilon^0)$ when the infinite series is summed.[6]

Finally, it should be pointed out that the functions $\beta(u)$ and $\gamma_\phi(u)$ in Eqs. (8-106) and (8-107) are not identical to those of Eqs. (8-21) and (8-22), since the normalization conditions are different. We used the same notation since these functions play a similar role (see Exercises 8-29 and 8-30). The results for all universal quantities are, of course, the same (see also Sec. 9-7).

8-12 RENORMALIZATION GROUP EQUATIONS FOR THE BARE THEORY

As was mentioned in the introduction to the present chapter, one can obtain a differential equation for the bare Green functions, by considering all bare theories which lead to the same renormalized theory.[3] We now proceed to present a brief account of this approach. The main motivations are two. The first is to show that the original ideas of Wilson, in which the high momentum components of the bare theory were integrated over, and recursion relations between theories with different values of the cutoff established, can be encompassed within the framework of renormalization in field theory. The second is that this approach provides for a particularly natural explication of universality (see also Sec. 9-4). The equations have the same general form as those studied throughout this chapter, and thus we do not discuss their solutions in any detail.

Consider again the critical theory normalized as in Sec. 7-5.

$$\Gamma_R^{(2)}(0; u, \kappa) = 0 \qquad (8\text{-}110)$$

$$\left.\frac{\partial}{\partial k^2} \Gamma_R^{(2)}(k; u, \kappa)\right|_{k^2 = \kappa^2} = 1 \qquad (8\text{-}111)$$

$$\left.\Gamma_R^{(4)}(k_i; u, \kappa)\right|_{SP} = u\kappa^\epsilon \qquad (8\text{-}112)$$

with the symmetry point chosen as in Eq. (7-58). The statement of the renormalizability of $\Gamma^{(N)}$ is that

$$\Gamma_R^{(N)}(p_i; g, \kappa) = Z_\phi^{N/2}\left(u, \frac{\kappa}{\Lambda}\right) \Gamma^{(N)}(p_i; \lambda, \Lambda) \qquad (8\text{-}113)$$

has a finite limit as $\Lambda \to \infty$. Thus, for large values of Λ the dependence of $\Gamma^{(N)}$ on Λ is cancelled by that of Z, to produce a product which is finite, at every order in u and ϵ.

But the leading term for Λ large on the left-hand side is independent of Λ, i.e.,

$$\left(\Lambda \frac{\partial}{\partial \Lambda}\right)_{u,\kappa} \Gamma_R^{(N)} = 0 \qquad (8\text{-}114)$$

which leads to the partial differential equation:

$$\left[\Lambda \frac{\partial}{\partial \Lambda} + \beta(\bar{u}_0, \epsilon, \kappa/\Lambda) \frac{\partial}{\partial \bar{u}_0} - \frac{N}{2} \gamma_\phi(\bar{u}_0, \epsilon, \kappa/\Lambda)\right] \Gamma^{(N)}(k_i; \bar{u}_0, \Lambda) = 0 \qquad (8\text{-}115)$$

The functions β and γ_ϕ are now defined by:

$$\beta(\bar{u}_0, \epsilon, \kappa/\Lambda) = \Lambda \left(\frac{\partial \bar{u}_0}{\partial \Lambda}\right)_{u,\kappa} \qquad (8\text{-}116)$$

$$\gamma_\phi(\bar{u}_0, \epsilon, \kappa/\Lambda) = -\Lambda \left(\frac{\partial \ln Z_\phi}{\partial \Lambda}\right)_{u,\kappa} \qquad (8\text{-}117)$$

with $\bar{u}_0$ given by

$$\bar{u}_0 = \Lambda^{-\epsilon}\lambda \qquad (8\text{-}118)$$

The functions are, of course, different from the ones which appear either in the renormalization group equation or in the Callan–Symanzik equation. They do, however, play the same role.

Equation (8-115) gives the variation of the bare vertex function under a change in the cutoff, a change which is effected keeping the renormalized coupling constant and the point of normalization fixed. This change must be compensated by a change in the bare coupling constant λ and in the renormalization constant Z_ϕ, if the normalization conditions (8-110)–(8-112) are to be preserved.

Next, one can show that the functions β and γ_ϕ have finite limits for large Λ, and therefore the differential equation, (8-115), has coefficients which are independent of Λ. In fact, these two functions cannot depend on Λ, since, to make them dimensionless, any dependence on Λ implies a dependence on κ. But the bare functions $\Gamma^{(N)}$, do not depend on κ, and β and γ_ϕ can be expressed in terms of $\Gamma^{(N)}$ using Eq. (8-115) (see Exercise 8-31). Hence β and γ_ϕ are independent of κ, and consequently of Λ. This is, of course, their asymptotic form, since the zero on the right-hand side of (8-115) is there only in the limit $\Lambda \to \infty$. Equation (8-115) can now be written as:

$$\left[\Lambda \frac{\partial}{\partial \Lambda} + \beta(\bar{u}_0, \epsilon) \frac{\partial}{\partial \bar{u}_0} - \frac{N}{2} \gamma_\phi(\bar{u}_0, \epsilon)\right] \Gamma^{(N)}(k_i; \bar{u}_0, \Lambda) = 0 \qquad (8\text{-}119)$$

Equations (8-111) and (8-112) can be used to obtain $\bar{u}_0$ and Z_ϕ as functions of u, ϵ and Λ, by using the results of Sec. 7-6. The functions β and γ_ϕ can then be computed directly. We leave the one-loop calculation as Exercise 8-32.

An equation of the type (8-115) implies the possibility of scaling for the bare vertex functions. For this one needs only that $\bar{u}_0$ be a zero, u_0^*, of β. If this is the case, then

$$\Gamma^{(N)}(k_i; u_0^*, \Lambda) = \Lambda^{\frac{N}{2} \gamma_\phi^*} \Phi^{(N)}(k_i)$$

In particular, for $\Gamma^{(2)}$ this reduces to

$$\Gamma^{(2)}(k; u_0^*, \Lambda) = \Lambda^\eta k^{2-\eta} \qquad (8\text{-}120)$$

which should be compared with Eq. (8-48′).

The renormalization group equation, (8-119), can be solved for any $\bar{u}_0$ by the technique presented in Sec. 8-4. The behavior under a change of length scale can then be studied. But in the present context it is particularly interesting to find what is the behavior of the bare functions under a dilatation of the cutoff. The result, whose derivation is left as Exercise 8-33, is:

$$\Gamma^{(N)}(k_i; \bar{u}_0, \rho\Lambda) = \exp\left\{\frac{N}{2} \int_1^\rho \gamma_\phi(\bar{u}_0(x)) \frac{dx}{x}\right\} \Gamma^{(N)}(k_i; \bar{u}_0(\rho), \Lambda)$$

$$(8\text{-}121)$$

The bare coupling constant, $\bar{u}_0(\rho)$, which corresponds to a given renormalized theory, flows with the scale of the cutoff ρ according to

$$\frac{d\bar{u}_0(\rho)}{d\ln\rho} = -\beta(\bar{u}_0(\rho)) \qquad (8\text{-}122)$$

$$\bar{u}_0(1) = \bar{u}_0 \qquad (8\text{-}123)$$

A comparison of Eq. (8-121) with (8-35), and of Eq. (8-122) with (8-31), reveals an effective change of sign of β. This represents nothing but the fact that a rescaling of the momenta by ρ, as was done in Eq. (8-33), scales Λ by ρ^{-1}. But the consequences of the change of sign in Eq. (8-122) are quite interesting.

If the analysis of the approach to the fixed point — Sec. 8-7 — is repeated, one finds that the roles of the different types of fixed points is reversed. If β has a zero with a positive slope it will be attractive in the infrared, namely, as the scale of momenta tends to zero the coupling constant will flow into this fixed point and the theory will scale. Since β appears with a negative sign in Eq. (8-122), $\bar{u}_0$ will flow into that same infrared-stable fixed point when $\rho \to \infty$, i.e., when the cutoff will become infinitely large. Scaling appears in this picture as a consequence of the presence of an infrared-stable fixed point, which leads to scaling at fixed momenta as the bare coupling constant goes to infinity. This happens independently of the initial value of $\bar{u}_0$, a phenomenon called universality.

8-13 RENORMALIZATION GROUP EQUATIONS AND SCALING IN THE INFINITE M LIMIT

The infinite M limit of a ϕ^4 theory with an $O(M)$ symmetry was discussed in some detail in Sec. 6-8. It can serve as a model in which the various concepts introduced in the present chapter can be explicitly exhibited. One can compute the Wilson functions β, γ_ϕ and γ_{ϕ^2}; the fixed points; the critical exponents, etc. One can see through some of the magic surrounding the renormalization group by comparing the solutions, which are known for any coupling constant, at and away from the fixed point. One can also follow the connection between the bare and the renormalized coupling constant, which makes universality somewhat less mysterious.

In Sec. 6-8-4 it was shown that in the present model $Z_\phi = 1$. Hence,

$$\gamma_\phi(u) = 0; \quad \eta = 0 \qquad (8\text{-}124)$$

In fact, if one is seeking critical exponents only, then this result, together with the value of the susceptibility exponent γ, Eq. (6-100), and the scaling relations derived in Secs. 8-8 to 8-10, is sufficient. But we want more.

In Sec. 7-10 the renormalization of the theory with an $O(M)$, symmetry was discussed. We start by rewriting Eq. (7-115) as

$$\Gamma_{SP}^{(4)} = -M^{-1}g \qquad (8\text{-}125)$$

where $\Gamma_{SP}^{(4)}$ is the coefficient of S_{ijkl} in $\Gamma_{ijklR}^{(4)}$, calculated at the momentum point SP, with zero mass.

Using Eqs. (6-92) and (6-93) one finds

$$g = \frac{\lambda}{1 + \frac{1}{6}\lambda I_{SP}} \qquad (8\text{-}126)$$

with SP defined in Sec. 7-5. When the dimensionless coupling constants u_0 and u are introduced according to (8-14), Eq. (8-126) can be solved for u_0. The result is

$$u_0 = \frac{u}{1 - \frac{1}{6}u J_{SP}} \qquad (8\text{-}127)$$

where $J_{SP} = \kappa^\epsilon I_{SP}$. If the theory was dimensionally regularized, according to Sec. 8-3, then the function $\beta(u)$ can be calculated by inserting (8-127) in Eq. (8-21). The result is:

$$\beta(u) = -\epsilon u(1 - \frac{1}{6}u J_{SP}) \qquad (8\text{-}128)$$

Another procedure would be to calculate β using Eq. (8-126) together with (8-16). This calculation in left as Exercise 8-34. Its value lies in making the discussion at the end of Sec. 8-2 more concrete. In this way one first obtains β as a function of u and κ/Λ whose limit as $\Lambda \to \infty$ is (8-128).

The normalization condition for $\Gamma^{(2,1)}$ led us to Eq. (6-109) for Z_{ϕ^2}. The same logic applied to the massless theory leads to

$$Z_{\phi^2} = \frac{1}{1 - \frac{1}{6}u J_{SP}} \qquad (8\text{-}129)$$

If J_{SP} is dimensionally regularized, γ_{ϕ^2} can be computed using Eq. (8-74). The result is simply:

$$\gamma_{\phi^2} = -\frac{1}{6}\epsilon u J_{SP} \qquad (8\text{-}130)$$

In order to calculate ν we need the value of the fixed point. From Eq. (8-128) we deduce that there are two fixed points. The Gaussian one, $u^* = 0$, and the spherical one

$$u^* = \frac{6}{J_{SP}} \qquad (8\text{-}131)$$

Substituting u^* in Eq. (8-130) leads to

$$\nu = \frac{1}{2 - \epsilon} \qquad (8\text{-}132)$$

which is exactly equal to $\frac{1}{2}\gamma$, as it should be.

The value of u^* is of order M^0, which implies, together with Eq. (8-125), that the renormalized coupling constant is $0(M^{-1})$. This result brings us back to the discussion in Sec. 6-8-2, where it was argued that the explicit M-dependence of the bare coupling constant persists in perturbation theory, leading to a non-trivial fixed point value, which also vanishes as M^{-1}.

All the above results hold at any number of space dimensions, despite the fact that they were expressed in terms of ϵ. This is a very interesting feature, since perturbation theory produces the same type of difficulties which led us to the ϵ expansion in Sec. 8-4, even in the infinite -M limit. Nevertheless, when the series is summed, one discovers a massless scale invariant theory even at three dimensions.

Using Eq. (8-25), u^* can be written as:

$$u^* = \frac{12\Gamma(d-2)}{\Gamma(\tfrac{1}{2}d)\Gamma(2-\tfrac{1}{2}d)\Gamma^2(\tfrac{1}{2}d-1)} \qquad (8\text{-}133)$$

As $\epsilon \to 0$, or $d \to 4$, u^* vanishes. In other words, at four dimensions, in the infinite M limit, there is a Gaussian fixed point only — there is asymptomic freedom.

In terms of the renormalized parameters, the renormalized vertex functions can be expressed in the form:

$$\Gamma^{(4)}_{ijkl\mathrm{R}}(k_i) = \tfrac{1}{3}[\delta_{ij}\delta_{kl}A_\mathrm{R}(k_1+k_2) + 2 \text{ permutations}] \qquad (8\text{-}134)$$

$$\Gamma^{(2,1)}_\mathrm{R}(k;p) = g^{-1}A_\mathrm{R}(p) \qquad (8\text{-}135)$$

in which:

$$A_\mathrm{R}(k) = \frac{1}{g^{-1} + \tfrac{1}{6}[I(k)-I_\mathrm{SP}]} = \frac{\kappa^\epsilon}{u^{-1} + \tfrac{1}{6}[J(k)-J_\mathrm{SP}]} \qquad (8\text{-}136)$$

and

$$J(k) = \kappa^\epsilon I(k) \qquad (8\text{-}137)$$

One can now ask when the fixed point will be reached, and with it scale invariance.

To answer this question we write

$$\lambda = \bar{u}_0 \Lambda^\epsilon \qquad (8\text{-}138)$$

as in the previous section, and expand the integral I according to

$$I(k) = Ak^{-\epsilon} - B\Lambda^{-\epsilon} + k^{-\epsilon}0(k^2/\Lambda^2) \qquad (8\text{-}139)$$

Similarly, I_SP will be given by the same expression evaluated at $k^2 = \kappa^2$. Notice that for $\epsilon > 0$ (8-139) is a veritable expansion of the integral, and thus letting $\Lambda \to \infty$ one finds that A is exactly the coefficient in Eq. (8-25).

Substitution of (8-139) in (8-126) gives:

$$u = \frac{\bar{u}_0(\Lambda/\kappa)^\epsilon}{1 + \frac{1}{6}\bar{u}_0[A(\Lambda/\kappa)^\epsilon - B] + (\Lambda/\kappa)^\epsilon 0(\kappa^2/\Lambda^2)} \qquad (8\text{-}140)$$

On the other hand, (8-131) is equivalent to $u^* = 6/A$. The only way to obtain this value on the right-hand side of Eq. (8-140) is by letting $\Lambda \to \infty$. In this limit $\bar{u}_0$ cancels, and the fixed point is reached, no matter what the coefficient $\bar{u}_0$ in Eq. (8-138) was to start with. This is universality.

But this result is obtained only in the limit $\Lambda \to \infty$. The presence of the last term in the denominator of Eq. (8-140), prevents u from reaching u^* with finite Λ (cf. Sec. 9-5 below).

How does this reflect itself in the bare theory? There, after all, κ does not appear, and the limit $\Lambda \to \infty$ must coincide with the limit $k \to 0$, since in the massless theory Λ is the only scale of momentum.

The function which has to be considered is $A(k)$ of Eq. (6-93). After (8-138) and (8-139) are substituted in it, it reads:

$$A(k) = \frac{u_0\Lambda^\epsilon}{1 + \frac{1}{6}u_0[A(\Lambda/k)^\epsilon - B] + (\Lambda/k)^\epsilon 0(k^2/\Lambda^2)} \qquad (8\text{-}141)$$

Indeed, if either $\Lambda \to \infty$ or if $k \to 0$, $A(k)$ behaves as a power, namely,

$$A(k) \sim \frac{6}{A} k^\epsilon \qquad (8\text{-}142)$$

The moral of the story is that if perturbation theory is resummed, the asymptotic behavior for $k \ll \Lambda$ can be obtained without recourse to the renormalization group, fixed points etc. If, however, one tries to unravel the asymptotic scaling behavior in perturbation theory itself by letting $\Lambda \to \infty$, then in the vicinity of four dimensions there are divergences. One must resort to the machinery of the renormalization group. A new momentum scale κ appears, as in Eq. (8-136), and scaling is rediscovered at the fixed point. A_R then appears to be a power for all values of k, but one has to keep in mind that the limit $\Lambda \to \infty$ has already been taken. Thus, it is only the asymptotic behavior which is described.

Finally, if (8-141) is expanded in powers of $\bar{u}_0$ the asymptotic behavior cannot be discerned. There is though a special value of $\bar{u}_0$ which allows for the cancellation of the dangerous dependence on Λ — namely, the Λ^ϵ, or the powers of $\ln\Lambda$ in the ϵ expansion.[14] In the present example, this value of u_0 is

$$\bar{u}_0^* = \frac{6}{B} \qquad (8\text{-}143)$$

which corresponds to the fixed point in the description of Sec. 8-12. Another way which leads to the same result is to look for a value of $\bar{u}_0$ which will resum the powers of $\ln k$ to give a power of k. The result (8-141) implies that this must again be given by (8-143). This is just the procedure used by Wilson in his original article on the Feyman graph expansion.

Appendix 8-1

GENERAL FORMULAS FOR CALCULATING FEYNMAN INTEGRALS

In the present appendix we list some formulas which are necessary for the computation of Feynman graphs in any number of dimensions.

A most useful formula for the calculation of graphs is Feynman's method for folding many denominators into one. It reads:

$$\frac{1}{a_1^{\alpha_1} a_2^{\alpha_2} \ldots a_n^{\alpha_n}} = \frac{\Gamma(\alpha_1 + \alpha_2 + \ldots + \alpha_n)}{\Gamma(\alpha_1)\Gamma(\alpha_2) \ldots \Gamma(\alpha_n)} \int dx_1 \, dx_2 \ldots dx_{n-1}$$

$$\frac{x_1^{\alpha_1 - 1} x_2^{\alpha_2 - 1} \ldots x_{n-1}^{\alpha_{n-1} - 1} (1 - x_1 - x_2 \ldots - x_{n-1})^{\alpha_n - 1}}{[x_1 a_1 + x_2 a_2 + \ldots + x_{n-1} a_{n-1} + (1 - x_1 - x_2 \ldots - x_{n-1}) a_n]^{\alpha_1 + \alpha_2 + \ldots + \alpha_n}}$$

(A8-1)

where the integration over the *Feynman parameters*, x_i, extends over the domain:

$$0 \leqslant x_i \leqslant 1; \quad x_1 + x_2 + \ldots + x_{n-1} \leqslant 1 \quad \text{(A8-2)}$$

Next, we need a prescription for computing d-dimensional momentum integrals. The only formulas required are[15]

$$\int dq F(q + k) = \int dq F(q) \qquad (A8\text{-}3)$$

$$\int dq F(\lambda q) = |\lambda|^{-d} \int dq F(q) \qquad (A8\text{-}4)$$

$$\int dq \frac{1}{(q^2 + 2kq + m^2)^\alpha} = \frac{1}{2} \frac{\Gamma(\frac{1}{2}d)\Gamma(\alpha - \frac{1}{2}d)}{\Gamma(\alpha)} (m^2 - k^2)^{\frac{d}{2} - \alpha} \qquad (A8\text{-}5)$$

These coincide with usual expressions when d is an integer. In Eq. (A8-5), and hereafter, the geometric angular factor will be divided out, and usually absorbed in a redefinition of the coupling constants, i.e.,

$$dq = d^d q / S_d \qquad (A8\text{-}6)$$

with

$$S_d = [2^{d-1} \pi^{d/2} \Gamma(\tfrac{1}{2}d)]^{-1} \qquad (A8\text{-}7)$$

See also App. 9-1.

EXERCISES

8-1 Use the renormalizability of $\Gamma^{(N,L)}$ to show that a change in the renormalization momentum induces the same change in the coupling constant as in $\Gamma^{(N)}$, the same finite scaling of the field, and an additional finite rescaling of ϕ^2.

8-2 Prove the functional equation of the renormalization group in terms of Γ. Use Eq. (7-83).

8-3 Using the results of the calculation of the massless theory to two-loop level, Sec. 7-6, write an explicit functional equation of the renormalization group to this order.

8-4 Using Eqs. (8-6) and (8-4) calculate $\bar{\beta}$ and γ_ϕ. Show that they have a finite limit as $\Lambda \to \infty$.

8-5 Using the results of Exercise 8-1 show that

$$\gamma_{\phi^2} = \left(\kappa \frac{\partial \ln Z_{\phi^2}}{\partial \kappa} \right)_{\lambda, \Lambda}$$

is finite as $\Lambda \to \infty$.

8-6 Applying the normalization conditions to the renormalization group equation, obtain expressions for $\bar{\beta}$ and γ_ϕ. Compare with the results of Exercise 8-4. Calculate β and γ_ϕ from Eq. (8-15) in the same way.

8-7 Use the functional equation of the group to obtain the differential equation, (8-11).

8-8(a) Compute β and γ_ϕ to order two loops in the massless theory.
    (b) Verify that

$$\left(\frac{\partial \ln u_0}{\partial u}\right)^{-1} \sim \epsilon^{-1}$$

    (c) What is the corresponding statement for $\partial \ln Z_\phi / \partial u$?

8-9 Derive the differential renormalization group equation for $\Gamma_R^{(N,L)}$.

8-10(a) Show that if in $I(k)$, Eq. (7-27), $m \neq 0$ and $k \neq 0$, the only poles are at $d \geqslant 4$.
    (b) Using App. 8-1 derive the expression for $I(k)$ when $m = 0$, Eq. (8-25).

8-11 Consider the dimensionally regularized forms of the graphs shown in Fig. 8-3. Using App. 8-1 perform the momentum integrals. Where are the poles of the resulting analytic functions?

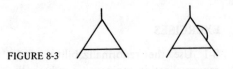

FIGURE 8-3

8-12 Prove that in a ϕ^4 theory

$$\beta(u) \sim u; \quad \gamma_\phi(u) \sim u^2$$

as $u \to 0$. How does γ_{ϕ^2} behave in this limit?

8-13 Let $\Gamma_R^{(N,L)}$ be a homogeneous function of its momenta. The dimensions d_ϕ and d_{ϕ^2} of the fields ϕ and ϕ^2, respectively, are defined via

$$\Gamma_R^{(N,L)}(\rho k_i, \rho\, p_i) = \rho^{d - Nd_\phi + Ld_{\phi^2}}\, \Gamma_R^{(N,L)}(k_i, p_i)$$

    (a) What are the canonical values of d_ϕ and d_{ϕ^2}?
    (b) What will the renormalization group equation give for d_{ϕ^2}?

8-14 Calculate $\beta(u)$ and $\gamma_\phi(u)$ in lowest order at $d = 4$.

8-15 Using the fact that

$$\Gamma_R^{(N)}(k_i; t, u, \kappa) = Z_\phi^{N/2} \Gamma_R^{(N)}(k_i; \delta\mu^2, g_0, \Lambda)$$

(see Sec. 7-7), derive the renormalization group equation for the left-hand side directly, using Eq. (7-80).

8-16 Calculate the general solution for the N-point vertex function above the critical temperature. Show that in order for scaling to hold one must have $u = u^*$. (The standard method of characteristics is rather useful for finding the solution.)

8-17 Using the relation (2-82) giving ξ^2 in terms of the two-point Green function,

    (a) write ξ^2 in terms of $\Gamma^{(2)}$;
    (b) write ξ^2 in terms of $\Gamma_R^{(2)}$;
    (c) using the renormalization group equation for $\Gamma_R^{(2)}$ above T_c, derive an equation for ξ^2; and
    (d) what is the solution? (See, e.g., Ref. 11.)

8-18 Prove that at the fixed point

$$\Gamma_R^{(2)}(k; t, \kappa) = \kappa^\eta k^{2-\eta} f(k\xi)$$

8-19 Solve the renormalization group equation for $H(t, M, u, \kappa)$.

8-20 Using the solution in Exercise 8-19, show that under a length scale transformation

$$H(t, M, u, \kappa) = \rho^{\frac{1}{2}(d+2)} H(t(\rho), M(\rho), u(\rho), \kappa) \exp\left[-\frac{1}{2}\int_1^\rho \eta(u(x)) \frac{dx}{x}\right]$$

with

$$\frac{d \ln t(\rho)}{d \ln \rho} = -\frac{1}{\nu(u(\rho))} \quad ; \quad t(1) = t$$

$$\frac{d \ln M(\rho)}{d \ln \rho} = -\frac{1}{2}[d - 2 + \eta(u(\rho))] \quad ; \quad M(1) = M$$

8-21 Study the behavior of the general solution as $\rho \to 0$ and as $\rho \to \infty$.

8-22 Show that $\Gamma_R^{(2)}(k)$ below T_c satisfies a renormalization group equation.

    (a) Use this equation to show that $\Gamma_R^{(2)}(k)$ scales below T_c if $u = u^*$.
    (b) Identify ν' and show that $\nu = \nu'$.

8-23 Show that all connected graphs of $G^{(0,N)}$ are also 1PI.

8-24 Calculate

$$Z_{\phi^2}^2 \left[\Gamma^{(0,2)}(,p,-p) - \Gamma^{(0,2)}(,p,-p) \Big|_{p^2=\kappa^2} \right]$$

to order two loops. Show that its limit $\Lambda \to \infty$ exists, when $p \neq 0$.

8-25 Show that the renormalization constants, which make $\Gamma^{(0,2)}$ finite at $T = T_c$ ($m = 0$), are sufficient for the renormalization of $\Gamma^{(0,2)}$ away from T_c.

8-26(a) Solve the renormalization group equation $\Gamma_R^{(0,2)}(,p,-p;u,\kappa)$ at T_c.
    (b) What is its behavior as $p \to 0$?
    (c) What is the relation of the solution to the one found for $p = 0$ at $T \neq T_c$?

8-27 Derive the Callan–Symanzik equations for $\Gamma^{(N,L)}$.

8-28 Using Weinberg's theorem[13] study the asymptotic behavior of the graphs shown in Fig. 8-4 and of the graphs generated by all possible ϕ^2 insertions into these graphs. Compare $d = 4$ with $d < 4$.

FIGURE 8-4

8-29(a) Using the normalization conditions for the massive theory at zero momentum, calculate u_0 and Z_ϕ to one-loop order.
    (b) The same as (a) but for the zero mass theory.
    (c) Compare β and γ_ϕ to this order.

8-30(a) Solve the homogeneous Callan–Symanzik equation.
    (b) Discuss the behavior of the solution under dilatations of the length scale.

8-31 Using the normalization conditions in Sec. 8-12, express β and γ_ϕ of Eq. (8-115) in terms of bare vertex functions. Prove that they have a limit as $\Lambda \to \infty$.

8-32 Show that in a ϕ^4 theory, if u and β are calculated up to one-loop level, the results are

$$u = \left(\frac{\Lambda}{\kappa} \right)^\epsilon \left(\bar{u}_0 - \frac{3\bar{u}_0^2}{16\pi^2} \ln \frac{\Lambda}{\kappa} \right) + 0(\bar{u}_0^3, \epsilon \bar{u}_0^2)$$

$$\beta = -\epsilon \bar{u}_0 + \frac{3\bar{u}_0^2}{16\pi^2} + 0(\bar{u}_0^3, \epsilon \bar{u}_0^2)$$

8-33 Solve the renormalization group equation for the bare theory for general $\bar{u}_0$.

(a) Study the behavior of the solution under a change of scale of the momenta.

(b) Compare with the behavior under a change of scale of the cutoff.

8-34 Calculate $\beta(u, \Lambda)$ in the infinite-M limit. Verify that the limit $\Lambda \to \infty$ is finite through $d = 4$, and gives the same result as dimensional regularization.

REFERENCES

1. M. Gell-Mann and F. E. Low, *Physical Review*, **95**, 1300 (1954); E. C. G. Stueckelberg and A. Peterson, *Helevetia Physica Acta*, **26**, 499 (1953). The classical exposition of these ideas appears in BS.
2. C. G. Callan Jr., *Physical Review*, **D2**, 1541 (1970); K. Symanzik, *Communications in Mathematical Physics*, **18**, 227 (1970).
3. J. Zinn-Justin, "Wilson Theory of Critical Phenomena and Renormalized Theory". Lectures delivered at the Cargése Summer School 1973. K. Symanzik, op. cit. and KS. See also E. Brézin, AIP Conference Proceedings, No. 18, p. 849, 19th annual conference on Magnetism and Magnetic Materials, 1973 (Americal Institute of Physics, N.Y. 1974).
4. K. G. Wilson, *Physical Review Letters*, **28**, 548 (1972).
5. C. G. Callan Jr., Lectures delivered at the Cargése Summer School 1973, unpublished.
6. K. Symanzik, *Lettere Al Nuovo Cimento*, **8**, 771 (1973). See also Zinn-Justin, "Wilson Theory of Critical Phenomena and Renormalized Theory". Lectures delivered at the Cargése Summer School 1973. K. Symanzik, op. cit. and KS.
7. S. Coleman, "Scaling Anomalies" in International Summer School "Etore Majorana (1971)" (Academic Press, N.Y. 1972).
8. K. G. Wilson, *Physical Review*, **D2**, 1473 (1970).
9. D. J. Gross and F. Wilczek, *Physical Review Letters*, **30**, 1343 (1973); H. D. Politzer, *Physical Review Letters*, **30**, 1346 (1973) and G. 't Hooft, unpublished work.
10. S. Coleman and D. J. Gross, *Physical Review Letters*, **31**, 851 (1973). See also D. J. Gross and F. Wilczek, *Physical Review*, **D8**, 3633 (1973); H. D. Politzer, *Physics Reports*, 14c, 129 (1974).
11. C. Bervillier, *Physical Review*, B14, 4964 (1976).
12. This was the approach adopted initially by E. Brézin, J. C. Le Guillou and J. Zinn-Justin Ref. 2, Chap. 4, as well as by P. K. Mitter, Ref. 6, Chap. 7.
13. S. Weinberg, *Physical Review*, 118, 838 (1960).
14. K. G. Wilson, *Physical Review Letters*, **28**, 548 (1972).
15. See G. 't Hooft and M. Veltman, Ref. 1, Chap. 7, and "Diagrammar".

9

THE COMPUTATION OF THE CRITICAL EXPONENTS

9-1 INTRODUCTION

The lesson of the last chapter is that in order to describe quantitatively the asymptotic behavior of a system near its critical point, or the deep inelastic scattering of elementary particles, one must study in detail the fixed points of the renormalization group. One has to determine their position in the space of parameters — coupling constants; to classify them according to the type of attraction they exhibit — domains of stability; and finally to compute the anomalous dimensions of various operators, which allows the determination of the asymptotic properties of functions describing experimentally accessible quantities.

The problem starts, therefore, with the attempt to find the zeros of $\beta(u)$. This function is given to us as a power series in u, and hence one can trust it only for small values of the dimensionless coupling constant. Having computed β to any given order in u, one can proceed to find the zeros of the polynomial. But there is no evident small parameter to assure us, or even to promise us, that the value found for any of those roots is small enough, so as to lie in the range in which the calculation of β is a good enough approximation to the full function.

In fact, the abovementioned difficulty leads to the rather disappointing feature that in relativistic quantum field theory in four dimensions, as well as in critical phenomena at the spatial dimensionality at which they become classical, one can draw meaningful conclusions only if the theory is asymptotically free.[†] In that case one needs to know β and the various γ's only arbitrarily close to the origin.

If one goes below the critical dimensionality to study phase transitions, one encounters another difficulty — that of infrared divergences, which was discussed in Sec. 8-4. There we saw that the only way by which the critical theory can be made meaningful (e.g., for $d < 4$ in a ϕ^4 theory) is to expand simultaneously in u and in $\epsilon = 4 - d$. This necessity frees us from the first constraint, namely, the constraint of asymptotic freedom. Now β is a function of u and ϵ, and its zeros, u^*, can be calculated as functions of ϵ. As we shall see, there are fixed points at values of the coupling constant which vanish as $\epsilon \to 0$, and hence, at least asymptotically in ϵ, the calculation is controlled. These fixed points are not free, and for finite ϵ the anomalous dimensions are finite powers.

Furthermore, one can systematically expand β in powers of u and ϵ, such that $u^*(\epsilon)$, as well as the various anomalous dimensions, are calculated up to a given order in ϵ. Higher order terms in β will not affect these results. Exact asymptotic expansions of the critical exponents, and of other properties which depend only on the fixed points — *universal properties* —[2] can be generated in this way. The fact that these asymptotic expansions are in very good agreement with experimental results ($\epsilon = 1$), as well as with high precision numerical studies, is a pleasant surprise.

In the present chapter four different ways of performing the actual calculations are illustrated, the one treated with greatest detail follows the renormalization of the critical (massless) theory. The functions β, γ_ϕ, and γ_{ϕ^2} are computed using normalization conditions imposed on the dimensionally regularized theory. Second, we show how the computation proceeds when the theory is renormalized at a finite mass—again using normalization conditions. But the β and γ_ϕ are those appropriate for use with the Callan-Symanzik equations. Third, is the computations of β and γ_ϕ which enter the equations for the bare vertices (Sec. 8-12). And fourth, is the calculation of these functions in the same context as the first calculation outlined above, but using minimal subtraction rather than normalization conditions to determine β and γ_ϕ.[3]

The renormalization constants, the functions β, γ_ϕ, etc. look quite different, since they all depend on the particular normalization conditions used. But the critical exponents, and other universal quantities, are identical: they describe the physical system.

[†]Coleman and Weinberg[1] have proposed an alternative to this constriction in the presence of spontaneous symmetry breaking. See e.g. Part II, Chapter 4.

9-2 THE SYMBOLIC CALCULATION OF THE RENORMALIZATION CONSTANTS AND WILSON FUNCTIONS

We consider a ϕ^4 theory. At this stage we do not have to restrict ourselves to a single component field, but we will keep only one coupling constant. A more general case will be discussed in the next chapter.

There are three renormalization constants which have to be calculated — u_0, Z_ϕ and Z_{ϕ^2}. They are functions of u and ϵ. Let us write them symbolically, as

$$u_0 = u(1 + a_1 u + a_2 u^2) \qquad (9\text{-}1)$$

$$Z_\phi = 1 + b_2 u^2 + b_3 u^3 \qquad (9\text{-}2)$$

$$\bar{Z}_{\phi^2} = 1 + c_1 u + c_2 u^2 \qquad (9\text{-}3)$$

where we have used the fact that the momentum dependence of $\Gamma^{(2)}$ starts at second order in the coupling constant. As we go along it will become clear that in order to obtain the critical exponents to order ϵ^2, no higher order terms in the renormalization constants are needed. We still have to determine to what order in ϵ one has to compute $a_i, b_i,$ and c_i so as to obtain the critical exponents to order ϵ^2.†

First, Eqs. (9-1)–(9-3) will be used to obtain the Wilson functions, $\beta, \gamma_\phi,$ and γ_{ϕ^2} to the corresponding order. Recall that these functions have to be expanded in powers of u and ϵ. A direct substitution of (9-1)–(9-3) in the definitions of the Wilson functions gives:

$$\beta(u) = -\epsilon \left(\frac{\partial \ln u_0}{\partial u} \right)^{-1} = -\epsilon u [1 - a_1 u + 2(a_1^2 - a_2)u^2] \qquad (9\text{-}4)$$

$$\gamma_\phi(u) = \beta(u) \frac{\partial \ln Z_\phi}{\partial u} = -\epsilon u [2b_2 u + (3b_3 - 2b_2 a_1)u^2] \qquad (9\text{-}5)$$

$$\bar{\gamma}_{\phi^2}(u) = -\beta(u) \frac{\partial \ln \bar{Z}_{\phi^2}}{\partial u} = \epsilon u [c_1 + (2c_2 - c_1^2 - a_1 c_1)u] \qquad (9\text{-}6)$$

From the general arguments in Sec. 8-2 we know that ϵa_1, $\epsilon(a_1^2 - a_2)$, and $\epsilon(3b_3 - 2b_2 a_1)$ are finite as $\epsilon \to 0$. It then follows that to find the non-trivial (non-zero) root of β to order ϵ, one needs to know only the constant term in ϵa_1, and the u^2 term is unnecessary. To obtain that same root to order ϵ^2 we need ϵa_1 to order ϵ, while in $\epsilon(a_1^2 - a_2)$ only the constant is needed. This type of consideration can be easily generalized to the following statement.

To calculate u^* to order ϵ^n the function $\beta(u, \epsilon)$ has to be calculated up to order $\epsilon^p u^q$ with $p + q = n + 1$. The proof is left as Exercise 9-1.

---

† As we shall see, the last term in Z_ϕ allows η to be calculated to $0(\epsilon^3)$.

It should be noticed that when one uses renormalization by minimal subtraction of poles in ϵ, ϵa_1 will be *exactly* constant. No terms which vanish as $\epsilon \to 0$ will be present. The same is true for the coefficients of u^2 (see Secs. 9-9—9-11, below).

The considerations of Sec. 8-2 imply also that the coefficients of u^2 in γ_ϕ, and of u and u^2 in γ_{ϕ^2} are finite as $\epsilon \to 0$. Hence, η can be obtained to order ϵ^2 from the first order term in u^* alone, while both the first and second order terms in u^* are necessary in order to obtain ν to order ϵ^2. In fact, if u^* is known to second order in ϵ, η can be computed to order ϵ^3. This is special feature of the ϕ^4 theory (see Exercise 9-2).

Next we have to calculate a_i, b_i, and c_i in terms of the integrals which enter the perturbation expansion. The three primitively divergent vertex functions at the symmetry point can be written as:

$$\frac{\partial}{\partial k^2} \Gamma^{(2)}(k) \bigg|_{k^2 = \kappa^2} = 1 - B_2 u_0^2 + B_3 u_0^3 \qquad (9\text{-}7)$$

$$\Gamma^{(4)} \bigg|_{SP} = \kappa^\epsilon [u_0 - A_1 u_0^2 + (A_2^{(1)} + A_2^{(2)}) u_0^3] \qquad (9\text{-}8)$$

$$\Gamma^{(2,1)} \bigg|_{SP} = 1 - C_1 u_0 + (C_2^{(1)} + C_2^{(2)}) u_0^2 \qquad (9\text{-}9)$$

in which a power of κ was divided out of the integrals, so as to render them dimensionless, namely,

$$B_2 = \bar{B}_2 \kappa^{2\epsilon} \frac{\partial}{\partial k^2} D_3 \bigg|_{k^2 = \kappa^2} \equiv \bar{B}_2 \kappa^{2\epsilon} D_3' \qquad (9\text{-}10)$$

$$B_3 = \bar{B}_3 \kappa^{3\epsilon} \frac{\partial}{\partial k^2} D_5 \bigg|_{k^2 = \kappa^2} \equiv \bar{B}_3 \kappa^{3\epsilon} D_5' \qquad (9\text{-}10')$$

where D_3 is given by Eq. (6-54) with $\mu^2 = 0$, and $\bar{B}_2$ is the numerical constant coming from the symmetry factor and from the tensorial contraction, if the number of components is greater than one. Comparison with Eq. (7-70) gives $\bar{B}_2 = \frac{1}{6}$ for a single component theory. D_5 is the integral corresponding to the three-loop graph in Exercise 4-10.

In $\Gamma^{(4)}$ we have

$$A_1 = \bar{A}_1 \kappa^\epsilon I_{SP} \qquad (9\text{-}11)$$

$$A_2^{(1)} = \bar{A}_2^{(1)} \kappa^{2\epsilon} I_{SP}^2 \qquad (9\text{-}12)$$

$$A_2^{(2)} = \bar{A}_2^{(2)} \kappa^{2\epsilon} I_{4SP} \qquad (9\text{-}13)$$

where I and I_4 are given by (6-59) and (6-61), respectively, and $\bar{A}_j^{(i)}$ are numerical constants.

Finally, comparing Eq. (9-9) with Eq. (7-74) one can write:

$$C_1 = \bar{C}_1 \kappa^\epsilon I_{SP} \qquad (9\text{-}14)$$

$$C_2^{(1)} = \bar{C}_2^{(1)} \kappa^{2\epsilon} I_{SP}^2 \qquad (9\text{-}15)$$

$$C_2^{(2)} = \bar{C}_2^{(2)} \kappa^{2\epsilon} I_{4SP} \qquad (9\text{-}16)$$

We can now proceed to express a_i, b_i, and c_i in terms of $A_j^{(i)}$, B_j, and $C_j^{(i)}$. This can be done in two different ways: the first uses the normalization conditions, and the second uses minimal subtraction. We leave the latter until Sec. 9-11, and proceed with the former.

Normalization conditions:

$$\left. \frac{\partial}{\partial k^2} \Gamma_R^{(2)} \right|_{k^2 = \kappa^2} = 1 = (1 + b_2 u^2 + b_3 u^3)(1 - B_2 u_0^2 + B_3 u_0^3)$$

$$= 1 + (b_2 - B_2)u^2 + (b_3 + B_3 - 2B_2 a_1)u^3 + O(u^4)$$

after u_0 has been substituted from Eq. (9-1). Hence,

$$b_2 = B_2 \qquad (9\text{-}17)$$

$$b_3 = 2B_2 a_1 - B_3 \qquad (9\text{-}17')$$

For the four-point function we have:

$$\left. \Gamma_R^{(4)} \right|_{SP} = \kappa^\epsilon u = \kappa^\epsilon (1 + 2b_2 u^2)[u_0 - A_1 u_0^2 + (A_2^{(1)} + A_2^{(2)})u_0^3]$$

Substituting u_0 from (9-1), and comparing powers of u, one finds:

$$a_1 = A_1 \qquad (9\text{-}18)$$

$$a_2 = 2(A_1)^2 - (A_2^{(1)} + A_2^{(2)}) - 2b_2 \qquad (9\text{-}19)$$

Finally, for $\Gamma^{(2,1)}$ one has:

$$\left. \Gamma_R^{(2,1)} \right|_{SP} = 1 = (1 + c_1 u + c_2 u^2)[1 - C_1 u_0 + (C_2^{(1)} + C_2^{(2)})u_0^2]$$

Again, substituting (9-1) for u_0 and comparing powers of u, leads to:

$$c_1 = C_1 \qquad (9\text{-}20)$$

$$c_2 = (a_1 + c_1)C_1 - (C_2^{(1)} + C_2^{(2)}) \qquad (9\text{-}21)$$

The eight functions $A_j^{(i)}$, B_j, and $C_j^{(i)}$ contain only four different integrals. Substituting Eqs. (9-10)–(9-16) in (9-17)–(9-21), the result is:

$$b_2 = \bar{B}_2 \kappa^{2\epsilon} D_3' \qquad (9\text{-}22)$$

$$b_3 = \kappa^{3\epsilon} [2\bar{B}_2 \bar{A}_1 I_{SP} D_3' - \bar{B}_3 D_5'] \qquad (9\text{-}22')$$

$$a_1 = \kappa^\epsilon \bar{A}_1 I_{SP} \qquad (9\text{-}23)$$

$$a_2 = \kappa^{2\epsilon} \{ [2(\bar{A}_1)^2 - \bar{A}_2^{(1)}] I_{SP}^2 - \bar{A}_2^{(2)} I_{SP} - 2\bar{B}_2 D_3' \} \qquad (9\text{-}24)$$

$$c_1 = \kappa^\epsilon \bar{C}_1 I_{SP} \qquad (9\text{-}25)$$

$$c_2 = \kappa^{2\epsilon} \{ [(\bar{A}_1 + \bar{C}_1)\bar{C}_1 - \bar{C}_2^{(1)}] I_{SP}^2 - \bar{C}_2^{(2)} I_{4SP} \} \qquad (9\text{-}26)$$

We can now determine the order in ϵ to which the various integrals in Eqs. (9-22)–(9-26) have to be calculated. The integrals coming from $\Gamma^{(4)}$, such as I_{SP} and I_{4SP}, start at order ϵ^{-L}, where L is the number of loops. The integrals in $\Gamma^{(2)}$, in a ϕ^4 theory, start at order ϵ^{-L+1} (see Apps. 9-2 and 9-3). As was mentioned above, in order to obtain u^* to order ϵ, only the ϵ^{-1} term in I_{SP} is needed, since a_1 is proportional to I_{SP}. To obtain u^* to order ϵ^2 one needs both the ϵ^{-1} and ϵ^0 terms in I_{SP}. In $a_1^2 - a_2$ we need terms up to order ϵ^{-1}. Considering Eq. (9-24), we note that I_{SP} calculated to order ϵ^0 will give the terms of order ϵ^{-1} in I_{SP}^2 correctly. On the other hand, I_{4SP}, which starts at order ϵ^{-2}, has to be calculated to order ϵ^{-1}, and in D_3 only the lowest order term – that of order ϵ^{-1} – is needed (cf. Exercise 9-3).

Turning to Eqs. (9-5) and (9-6) one sees that if the integrals were computed to the order dictated by the requirement that u^* be accurate to order ϵ^2, then γ_ϕ^* and $\gamma_{\phi^2}^*$ – or η and ν – can be obtained to order ϵ^3 and ϵ^2, respectively. First one notes that ϵb_2 is finite as $\epsilon \to 0$. Thus, if u^* starts at order ϵ, the lowest order term in D_3 will give η to order ϵ^2. As has already been mentioned, in a ϕ^4 theory, if u^* is know to order ϵ^2, one can calculate η to order ϵ^3. But, from Eq. (9-5) we see that D_3 will have to be calculated to order ϵ^0, and D_5 to order ϵ^{-1}. The discussion concerning ν is left as Exercise 9-4. We return to this discussion when the calculation is performed in the framework of minimal subtraction.

9-3 THE ϵ EXPANSION OF THE CRITICAL EXPONENTS

All that remains to be done in order to find the fixed point, and the critical exponents of an $O(M)$-symmetric ϕ^4 theory, is to collect the coefficients appearing in Eqs. (9-22)–(9-26) from Sec. 7-10, and the ϵ expansions of the various integrals from Apps. 9-2 and 9-3, and to insert them to obtain $a_i, b_i,$ and c_i. Then u^* is to be solved to order ϵ^2 from Eq. (9-4), and the resulting value of the coupling constant at the fixed point inserted in Eqs. (9-5) and (9-6) to obtain η and ν. The other exponents are calculated using the scaling relations derived in Chap. 8.

The numerical coefficients in Eqs. (9-22)–(9-26) are

$$\bar{B}_2 = \frac{M+2}{18} \qquad (9\text{-}27)$$

$$\bar{B}_3 = \frac{(M+2)(M+8)}{108} \qquad (9\text{-}27')$$

$$\bar{A}_1 = \frac{M+8}{6} \qquad (9\text{-}28)$$

$$\bar{A}_2^{(1)} = \frac{M^2 + 6M + 20}{36} \qquad (9\text{-}29)$$

$$\bar{A}_2^{(2)} = \frac{5M + 22}{9} \qquad (9\text{-}30)$$

$$\bar{C}_1 = \frac{M+2}{6} \qquad (9\text{-}31)$$

$$\bar{C}_2^{(1)} = \left(\frac{M+2}{6}\right)^2 \qquad (9\text{-}32)$$

$$\bar{C}_2^{(2)} = \frac{M+2}{6} \qquad (9\text{-}33)$$

These we read directly from Eqs. (7-121), (7-122), and (7-126), except for $\bar{B}_3$ which was left as Exercise 4-10.

In listing the integrals which appear in a_i, b_i, and c_i, the area of the d-dimensional unit sphere is divided out and absorbed in u_0 and u. We write

$$\kappa^\epsilon I_{SP} = S_d J_{SP} \qquad (9\text{-}34)$$

$$\kappa^{2\epsilon} D_3 = (S_d)^2 E_3 \qquad (9\text{-}35)$$

$$\kappa^{2\epsilon} I_{4SP} = (S_d)^2 J_{4SP} \qquad (9\text{-}36)$$

$$\kappa^{3\epsilon} D_5 = (S_d)^3 E_5 \qquad (9\text{-}36')$$

Then, using the results of App. 9-2, we have

$$J_{SP} = \frac{1}{\epsilon} \left(1 + \tfrac{1}{2}\epsilon\right) \qquad (9\text{-}37)$$

$$E_3' \big|_{k^2 = \kappa^2} = -\frac{1}{8\epsilon} \left(1 + \tfrac{5}{4}\epsilon\right) \qquad (9\text{-}38)$$

$$E_5' \big|_{k^2 = \kappa^2} = -\frac{1}{6\epsilon^2} \left(1 + 2\epsilon\right) \qquad (9\text{-}38')$$

$$J_{4SP} = \frac{1}{2\epsilon^2} \left(1 + \tfrac{3}{2}\epsilon\right) \qquad (9\text{-}39)$$

Inserting (9-27)–(9-33) and (9-37)–(9-39) in the equations for a_i, b_i, and c_i, one arrives at:

$$b_2 = -\frac{M+2}{144}\frac{1}{\epsilon}\left(1 + \tfrac{5}{4}\epsilon\right) \qquad (9\text{-}40)$$

$$b_3 = -\frac{(M+2)(M+8)}{1296}\left(1 + \tfrac{5}{4}\epsilon\right) \qquad (9\text{-}40')$$

$$a_1 = \frac{M+8}{6}\frac{1}{\epsilon}\left(1 + \tfrac{1}{2}\epsilon\right) \qquad (9\text{-}41)$$

$$a_2 = \frac{M^2 + 26M + 108}{36}\frac{1}{\epsilon^2}(1 + \epsilon) - \frac{5M + 22}{18}\frac{1}{\epsilon^2}\left(1 + \tfrac{3}{2}\epsilon\right) + \frac{M+2}{72}\frac{1}{\epsilon}$$

$$= \left(\frac{M+8}{6}\right)^2 \frac{1}{\epsilon^2} + \frac{2M^2 + 23M + 86}{72}\frac{1}{\epsilon} \qquad (9\text{-}42)$$

$$c_1 = \frac{M+2}{6}\frac{1}{\epsilon}\left(1 + \tfrac{1}{2}\epsilon\right) \qquad (9\text{-}43)$$

$$c_2 = \frac{M^2 + 7M + 10}{36}\frac{1}{\epsilon^2} + \frac{2M^2 + 11M + 14}{72}\frac{1}{\epsilon} \qquad (9\text{-}44)$$

The only point of interest, beyond the elementary algebra, is the fact that in the combinations $a_1^2 - a_2$ which appears in β, in $(3b_3 - 2b_2 a_1)$, which appears in γ_ϕ, and in $2c_2 - c_1^2 - a_1 c_1$, which appears in $\bar{\gamma}_{\phi^2}$, the $1/\epsilon^2$ terms cancel exactly. The results for β, γ_ϕ and $\bar{\gamma}_{\phi^2}$ are:

$$\beta(u) = -\epsilon u + \frac{M+8}{6}\left(1 + \tfrac{1}{2}\epsilon\right)u^2 - \frac{9M + 42}{36}u^3 \qquad (9\text{-}45)$$

$$\gamma_\phi(u) = \frac{M+2}{72} [(1 - \tfrac{5}{4}\epsilon)u^2 - \frac{M+8}{12} u^3] \qquad (9\text{-}46)$$

$$\bar{\gamma}_{\phi^2}(u) = \frac{M+2}{6} u \ (1 + \tfrac{1}{2}\epsilon - \tfrac{1}{2}u) \qquad (9\text{-}47)$$

The function $\beta(u)$ has a zero at $u = 0$ — the Gaussian fixed point — and at

$$u^* = \frac{6}{M+8} \epsilon \left\{ 1 + \epsilon \left[\frac{3(3M+14)}{(M+8)^2} - \frac{1}{2} \right] \right\} \qquad (9\text{-}48)$$

When u^* is inserted in Eq. (9-46) one finds for η:

$$\eta = \epsilon^2 \frac{M+2}{2(M+8)^2} \left[1 + \epsilon \left(\frac{6(3M+14)}{(M+8)^2} - \frac{1}{4} \right) \right] \qquad (9\text{-}49)$$

where we have used the fact that, in a ϕ^4 theory, η can be calculated to order ϵ^3 without going beyond the two-loop level in calculating the position of the fixed point.

Insertion of u^* in Eq. (9-47) gives:

$$\bar{\gamma}_{\phi^2}^* = 2 - \nu^{-1} - \eta = \epsilon \frac{M+2}{M+8} \left[1 + \frac{6(M+3)}{(M+8)^2} \epsilon \right] \qquad (9\text{-}50)$$

from which it follows that, to order ϵ^2,

$$\nu = \frac{1}{2} + \frac{M+2}{4(M+8)} \epsilon + \frac{(M+2)(M^2+23M+60)}{8(M+8)^3} \epsilon^2 \qquad (9\text{-}51)$$

Using scaling relations one can now proceed to evaluate the rest of the critical exponents. They are:

$$\gamma = \nu(2 - \eta) = 1 + \frac{M+2}{2(M+8)} \epsilon + \frac{(M+2)(M^2+22M+52)}{4(M+8)^3} \epsilon^2 \qquad (9\text{-}52)$$

$$\alpha = 2 - d\nu = \frac{4-M}{2(M+8)} \epsilon - \frac{(M+2)(M^2+32M+72)}{4(M+8)^3} \epsilon^2 \qquad (9\text{-}53)$$

$$\beta = \tfrac{1}{2}(d\nu - \gamma) = \frac{1}{2} - \frac{3}{2(M+8)} \epsilon + \frac{(M+2)(M^2+22M+52)}{4(M+8)^3} \epsilon^2 \qquad (9\text{-}54)$$

If one compares these results with high-temperature series expansions, which are quite precise, one finds a surprisingly good agreement, even at three dimensions ($\epsilon = 1$). The results are given in Table 9-1. One notices, however, that if the exponents are calculated to order ϵ^3, the agreement becomes worse.[4] This is related to the fact that the nature of the ϵ expansion is not well known. It is definitely not a convergent series, but, rather, it is an asymptotic series. Thus,

Table 9-1   Comparison of the ϵ expansion with high-temperature series

	At order ϵ	At order ϵ^2	At order ϵ^3	High-temperature series
$\eta(n = 1)$	0.019	0.037	0.029	0.041 ± 0.010
$\gamma(n = 1)$	1.167	1.244	1.195	1.250 ± 0.003
$\eta(n = 3)$	0.021	0.039	0.032	0.043 ± 0.014
$\gamma(n = 3)$	1.227	1.346	1.325	1.375 ± 0.040

the extension to higher values of ϵ has to be done by some special type of resummation, and not simply by keeping a greater number of terms in the series. A systematic way of treating the ϵ expansion has been developed.[5] The recent understanding of the nature of the ϵ expansion leads to a new way of summing the ϵ series, giving spectacularly good results with the information at order ϵ^3.

9-4   THE NATURE OF THE FIXED POINTS – UNIVERSALITY

In the previous section we have seen that $\beta(u)$ had at least two small roots. One was at $u = 0$, the other at u^* of order $\epsilon = 4 - d$. Yet the critical exponents were computed at the non-zero fixed point. The reason, of course, is that this is the stable fixed point in the infrared limit.

The function $\beta(u)$, Eq. (9-45), has the shape depicted in Fig. 9-1. We see that it has the opposite shape to that of Fig. 8-1, namely, at $u = 0$ the slope of $\beta(u)$ is negative, as long as $\epsilon > 0$, while at $u = u^*(\epsilon)$ the slope is positive. Thus, the origin is ultraviolet-stable, and is unstable in the infrared. The non-trivial fixed point, $u = u^*$, is stable in the infrared.

From the discussion in Sec. 8-6 it follows that if, in a ϕ^4 theory, one starts with a bare coupling constant however small, the renormalized coupling constant

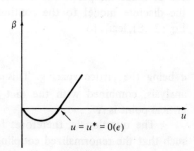

FIGURE 9-1
The β function in the ϵ expansion.

will flow away from the origin as the momenta tend to zero. Clearly, if the bare coupling constant is identically zero it will stay a Gaussian (free) theory. But, if a ϕ^4 perturbation is introduced, be it ever so small, the theory, in the low-momentum limit will behave as a scale invariant theory, with $u = u^*$. The opposite is true concerning the non-trivial fixed point. If we start with a bare coupling constant which leads to the vicinity of u^* as the momenta tend to zero, the theory will behave as a scale invariant theory with $u = u^*$, and will be stable to ϕ^4 perturbation, as well as to higher ones.

The discussion in Sec. 8-7 is limited to the symmetric theory at the critical temperature. Away from the critical point one can show, on studying the general solution of Eq. (8-65) or (8-81), that the fixed point is approached when, besides the momenta becoming small, the temperature tends to T_c and M tends to zero (see also Exercises 8-16 and 8-20). The fact that one is not at the asymptotic limit leads to corrections to the scaling behavior. These will be studied in the next chapter.

The independence of the asymptotic behavior near the critical point on the initial value of the bare coupling constant is one facet of *universality*. But the universality is wider. It covers also the fact that the critical behavior is independent of the higher momentum terms in the coefficient of ϕ^2, all momentum dependence of the coefficient of ϕ^4, and all higher powers of the field. In other words, all microscopic details of the interaction are completely suppressed, either by arguments of relevance, or by the stability domain of the fixed point.

Since in the present case there is only one relevant coupling constant, the situation is particularly simple. A somewhat more complicated case will be studied in the next chapter, when to the $O(M)$-symmetric interaction we add a term with cubic symmetry.

9-5 SCALE INVARIANCE AT FINITE CUTOFF

One may now proceed to ask the question whether there exists a value of the bare coupling constant for which the theory will be scale invariant. This question can be made sharper if one notices first that the transformation which led from the discrete model to the continuous field theory, after producing the form Eq. (2-68), leads to

$$\lambda = \bar{u}_0 a^{d-4} \approx \bar{u}_0 \Lambda^{4-d} \qquad (9\text{-}55)$$

a being the lattice spacing. This could have been arrived at by dimensional analysis, combined with the fact that the only length which remains at the critical point is Λ^{-1}.

The question is, therefore: for a finite Λ, does there exist a value of $\bar{u}_0$ such that the renormalized coupling constant is exactly u^*? In other words, can there be a scale invariant theory in which the microscopic length a is finite, and the theory is represented as a ϕ^4 theory? The answer is negative, as we proceed to show. The only way of having $u = u^*$ is to have $\Lambda \to \infty$. Then universality becomes the statement that, in the limit $\Lambda \to \infty$, one reaches u^* irrespective of the value of $\bar{u}_0$. This is the reflection of the fact that, for finite Λ, scale invariance appears only in the limit when all other length scales tend to zero. Unless $u = u^*$ the theory with finite momenta, for example, will not be scale invariant (see, e.g., Sec. 9-6).

Previously u_0 was defined via Eq. (8-19). Therefore, we have:

$$u_0 = u_0(u, \kappa/\Lambda) = (\Lambda/\kappa)^\epsilon \bar{u}_0 \qquad (9\text{-}56)$$

The relation between u_0 and u is given by:

$$-\epsilon \left(\frac{\partial \ln u_0}{\partial u} \right)^{-1} = \beta(u) \qquad (9\text{-}57)$$

where, in fact, β should depend on Λ/κ also, but here we are concerned with the leading behavior for large Λ, and so only the leading term is kept.

When u is near u^*, Eq. (9-57) can be rewritten as:

$$\frac{\partial \ln u_0}{\partial u} = -\frac{\epsilon}{\beta(u)} \approx -\frac{\epsilon}{\omega(u - u^*)} \qquad (9\text{-}58)$$

with

$$\omega = \beta'(u^*) \qquad (9\text{-}59)$$

The solution of this equation is:

$$u - u^* = u_0^{-\omega/\epsilon} = u_0^{-1 + 0(\epsilon)} \approx (\bar{u}_0)^{-1} \left(\frac{\kappa}{\Lambda} \right)^\epsilon \qquad (9\text{-}60)$$

i.e., as long as Λ remains finite $u \neq u^*$. On the other hand, in the limit $\Lambda \to \infty$, $u \to u^*$ for all values of $\bar{u}_0$.

This is an interesting result, since it contrasts strongly with the fact that if one integrates over spins, as was originally done by Wilson[6] or if one decimates spins as Niemeijer and Van Leeuwen,[7] one obtains a fixed point even in the theory with a finite cutoff. These methods have the disadvantage that one has to handle an infinite number of coupling constants — all the irrelevant ones.

The balance is that the method presented in these pages allows one to concentrate on a very limited number of parameters, but leads to scale invariance only in the limit when the cutoff becomes infinite. This is a non-negligible price, since it carries with it the restriction to the ϵ expansion. No such restriction enters the other methods and they work perfectly well even at two dimensions. There is good reason to hope that once this trade-off, between infinite cutoff to an infinite number of parameters, will become more transparent, a great deal will have been learnt about the possibility of freeing the field theory from the ϵ expansion.†

It should be emphasized that Eq. (9-60) implies not only that for finite Λ $u \neq u^*$, but also that as $\Lambda \to \infty$, $u \to u^*$ for all values of u_0. This may seem to contradict equations such as (9-1), or (7-56), in which on the right-hand side, the limit of infinite Λ is implicit in the dimensional regularization and yet one finds values of $u \neq u^*$. The apparent discrepancy stems from the fact that in (9-1), for example, u_0 is kept finite, while $\Lambda \to \infty$. From Eq. (9-56) it then follows that $\bar{u}_0 \sim (\kappa/\Lambda)^\epsilon$, which vanishes as $\Lambda \to \infty$. When $u \to u^*$ it is the infinite series on the right-hand side of (9-1) which leads to an infinite result, after it is resummed by Eq. (9-58). This restores the behavior $u_0 \sim \Lambda^\epsilon$ in the limit of infinite Λ.

The fact that infinite Λ always leads to $u = u^*$ should not cause any surprise. It simply means that in this limit there is no length scale and any value of k is asymptotically small, leading to exact scaling for all values of k. This is just what happens when $u = u^*$.

9-6 AT THE CRITICAL DIMENSION – ASYMPTOTIC INFRARED FREEDOM

The ϵ expansion of the Wilson functions gives the leading behavior of these functions for small renormalized coupling constant u at $d = 4$, which is the critical number of dimensions for the ϕ^4 theory. Taking the limit $\epsilon \to 0$ in Eqs. (9-45)–(9-47), one has:

$$\beta(u) = \frac{M+8}{6} u^2 + 0(u^3) \qquad (9\text{-}61)$$

$$\gamma_\phi(u) = \frac{M+2}{72} u^2 + 0(u^3) \qquad (9\text{-}62)$$

$$\bar{\gamma}_{\phi^2}(u) = \frac{M+2}{6} u + 0(u^2) \qquad (9\text{-}63)$$

The origin is now a double zero of β. The non-trivial fixed point u^* has merged with the Gaussian fixed point. We are faced with a situation which is similar to the one discussed in Sec. 8-7, in connection with Fig. 8-2, with a function β having the form depicted in Fig. 9-2. From the discussion in Sec. 8-7 it follows that the origin now becomes an infrared-stable fixed point, while it was ultraviolet-stable below $d = 4$.

†I am greatly indebted to Dr. Shang Ma for an enlightening conversation which stimulated these considerations.

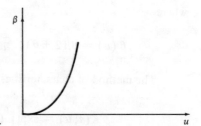

FIGURE 9-2
The form of β in four dimensions.

In other words, we expect that in four dimensions, as one approaches the limit of a spatially uniform critical theory, the behavior will become asymptotically free. This is the infrared asymptotic freedom, as has already transpired in our previous discussion of asymptotic freedom. The approach to the free theory is very slow, and traces of the interacting theory can be noticed even in the asymptotic region.

To see how this comes about we consider the temperature dependence of the inverse susceptibility. The renormalized $\Gamma^{(2)}$ at zero momentum is proportional to χ^{-1}, and it satisfies the renormalization group equation (8-65), namely:

$$\left[\kappa \frac{\partial}{\partial \kappa} + \beta(u) \frac{\partial}{\partial u} - \eta(u) - \theta(u)t \frac{\partial}{\partial t} \right] \chi_R^{-1}(t, u, \kappa) = 0 \qquad (9\text{-}64)$$

where

$$\theta(u) = -\gamma_{\phi^2}(u) = \nu^{-1}(u) - 2 \qquad (9\text{-}65)$$

Here we will introduce a variation on the *form* of the solution according to Sec. 8-5[1]. What makes this variation possible is that χ^{-1} depends on one dimensionful, physical parameter only — on t. What makes it desirable is that it exposes the dependence on t more promptly.

Since the dimension of χ^{-1} is two as it is that of t, one can write:

$$\chi_R^{-1}(t, u, \kappa) = tK\left(\frac{t}{\kappa^2}, u\right). \qquad (9\text{-}66)$$

Substituting in (9-64) one obtains an equation for K:

$$\left[\kappa \frac{\partial}{\partial \kappa} + \beta(u) \frac{\partial}{\partial u} - (\eta + \theta) - \theta t \frac{\partial}{\partial t} \right] K\left(\frac{t}{\kappa^2}, u\right) = 0. \qquad (9\text{-}67)$$

Denoting $t\kappa^{-2} = \tau$ the equation for K becomes:

$$\left[-\tau \frac{\partial}{\partial \tau} + \bar{\beta}(u) \frac{\partial}{\partial u} - (\bar{\eta} + \bar{\theta}) \right] K(\tau, u) = 0, \qquad (9\text{-}68)$$

where

$$\bar{\beta}(u) = \beta/(2+\theta) \, ; \quad \bar{\eta} = \eta/(2+\theta); \quad \bar{\theta} = \theta/(2+\theta) \, . \qquad (9\text{-}69)$$

The method of characteristics is applied to (9-68) to give:

$$K(\tau, u) = \exp\left[\int_1^\rho (\bar{\eta} + \bar{\theta}) \, \frac{dx}{x}\right] \cdot K(\tau(\rho), \, u(\rho)) \qquad (9\text{-}70)$$

with the characteristics:

$$\rho \, \frac{d\tau(\rho)}{d\rho} = -\tau(\rho) \qquad (9\text{-}71\text{a})$$

$$\rho \, \frac{du(\rho)}{d\rho} = \bar{\beta}(u(\rho)) \qquad (9\text{-}71\text{b})$$

and the initial conditions

$$\tau(\rho = 1) = \tau \, ; \, u(\rho = 1) = u.$$

Integrating (9-71a) one finds:

$$\tau(\rho) = \tau/\rho \qquad (9\text{-}72)$$

and choosing $\rho = \tau$, (9-70) becomes:

$$K(\tau, u) = \exp\left[-\int_1^\tau (\bar{\eta} + \bar{\theta}) \, \frac{dx}{x}\right] F(u(\tau))$$

where F is an arbitrary function of $u(\tau)$.

Setting $\kappa = 1$, and substituting K in (9-66), the inverse susceptibility becomes,

$$\chi_R^{-1} (t, u, k) = t \exp\left[-\int_1^t (\bar{\eta} + \bar{\theta}) \, \frac{dx}{x}\right] F(u(t)). \qquad (9\text{-}73)$$

This is the solution of the renormalization group equation.

Next we proceed to investigate the solution for small values of t. To leading order, for small u,

$$\bar{\beta}(u) = \frac{1}{2} au^2 \, ; \quad \bar{\theta} = -\frac{1}{2} bu \qquad (9\text{-}74)$$

where a and b are the coefficients of the quadratic and linear terms in β and γ_{ϕ^2} – Eqs. (9-61) and (9-63) – respectively. The solution of (9-71b), for $u(\rho)$ is

$$u(\rho) \sim \frac{2}{a|\ln \rho|} . \qquad (9\text{-}75)$$

Hence, for small t we can justifiably concentrate on small $u(t)$.

Neglecting $\bar{\eta}$ in the exponential in Eq. (9-73) and using (9-74) for $\bar{\theta}$, gives for the exponential term:

$$\exp\left[\frac{1}{2} b \int^t u(x) \frac{dx}{x}\right] \sim \exp\left[\frac{b}{a} \int^t \frac{1}{|\ln x|} \frac{dx}{x}\right]$$

$$= \exp\left[-\frac{b}{a} \int^t \frac{1}{\ln x} \frac{dx}{x}\right] = C|\ln t|^{-b/a} .$$

The asymptotic behavior of χ_R^{-1} as $t \to 0$ can now be deduced from (9-73), keeping in mind that $u(t) \to 0$ in this limit. The last factor on the right-hand-side becomes a constant and

$$\chi_R^{-1}(t) \sim t|\ln t|^{-(M+2)/(M+8)} \qquad (9\text{-}76)$$

The result of the above manipulations is that, using the renormalization group equation, we have expressed the susceptibility of the system for temperatures arbitrarily close to T_c, and any coupling constant, in terms of the susceptibility far away from T_c ($t(\rho) = 1$) and a vanishingly small coupling constant. The price one has had to pay is shown in Eq. (9-73) in the form of the coefficient which appears on the right-hand side, providing the logarithmic correction to the linear term in t of the free theory. Similar corrections appear in the equation of state (see Exercises 9-5 and 9-6). These logarithmic factors constitute deviations from scaling.

The case of a phase transition at four dimensions may not seem a very practical one, but the point here is that the logarithmic corrections are a general feature of theories at the critical number of dimensions. At least two cases are known in which this number of dimensions is three, and the logarithmic corrections can be calculated and measured. These two cases are the uniaxial dipolar ferromagnet[8] and tricritical behavior.[9]

9-7 ϵ EXPANSION FOR THE CALLAN–SYMANZIK METHOD

In this section and in the next one we rederive the results of Sec. 9-3, namely, the ϵ expansion of the critical exponents. The interesting feature to notice, since the critical exponents being universal are identical in all three procedures, is that this comes about despite the fact that at intermediate stages one obtains different expressions. The comparison of the intermediate results indicates that, even in the absence of other advantages, the renormalization at the critical point is advantageous for purely technical reasons: integrals with zero mass are simpler than integrals with a mass, even if the external momenta are non-zero. Integrals without a cutoff are much simpler than those with a cutoff, especially when they include more than one loop.

First we calculate to the order of one loop. To this end we use Eq. (8-106), in which u_0 is substituted using Eq. (6-64) together with the definitions

$$\lambda = u_0 m^\epsilon \qquad (9\text{-}77)$$

$$g = u m^\epsilon \qquad (9\text{-}78)$$

To the order of one loop, g_1 and m_1 in Eq. (6-64) can be replaced by g and m, respectively. Thus,

$$u_0 = u + \tfrac{3}{2} u^2 m^\epsilon \int^\Lambda \frac{1}{(q^2 + m^2)^2} \qquad (9\text{-}79)$$

Next, one descends below four dimensions letting $\Lambda \to \infty$. Then u_0 becomes a function of u and ϵ only, just as in Sec. 8-2 or 8-10. The form is:

$$u_0 = u + \tfrac{3}{2} u^2 \int \frac{1}{(q^2 + 1)^2} \qquad (9\text{-}80)$$

The integral has to be computed as an expansion in powers of ϵ. Notice that I_{SP} in Eq. (9-11) has been replaced here by a somewhat different integral. The value of this integral, after the geometric factor is divided out as in Sec. 9-3, is a special case of formula (A8-5). It is:

$$D_2 = \int (q^2 + 1)^{-2} = \frac{1}{\epsilon} (1 - \tfrac{1}{2}\epsilon) + O(\epsilon) \qquad (9\text{-}81)$$

The first term is the same as in Eq. (9-37). The second has the opposite sign. This implies that to the first non-trivial order in ϵ, $\beta(u)$, u^*, $\eta(\epsilon)$ etc. will all be identical to those in Eqs. (9-45), (9-48), and (9-49), respectively. Differences will start at the next order in ϵ. To calculate these differences we have to proceed to include the contributions of graphs with two loops.

The results, to the order of two loops, can be read off from Eqs. (7-70), (7-71), and (7-72), with the modification that the integrals have to be replaced by the expressions corresponding to the same graphs, but with all momenta set to zero and a finite mass. When the cutoff is made infinite the integrals become homogeneous functions of the mass which can be extracted. The result for u_0 as a function of u is:

$$u_0 = u\{1 + \tfrac{3}{2}uD_2 + u^2 \left[\tfrac{15}{4}D_2^2 - 3D_4 - \tfrac{1}{3}E_3'\right]\} \qquad (9\text{-}82)$$

where D_2 is defined in Eq. (9-81),

$$D_4 = \int \frac{1}{(q_1^2 + 1)^2(q_2^2 + 1)[(q_1 + q_2)^2 + 1]} \qquad (9\text{-}83)$$

and E_3', which comes from the renormalization of the wave function, is given by

$$E_3' = \frac{\partial}{\partial k^2} \int \frac{1}{(q_1^2 + 1)(q_2^2 + 1)[(q_1 + q_2 + k)^2 + 1]}\bigg|_{k=0} \qquad (9\text{-}84)$$

Next, using the formulas in App. 8-1, D_4 and E_2 are expanded in ϵ. The derivation is left as Exercise 9-7. The results are:

$$D_4 = \frac{1}{2\epsilon^2}\,(1 - \tfrac{1}{2}\epsilon) \qquad (9\text{-}85)$$

and

$$E_3' = -\frac{1}{8\epsilon}\,(1 - \tfrac{1}{4}\epsilon) - \tfrac{1}{8}L \qquad (9\text{-}86)$$

where L is a number given by:

$$L = \int_0^1 dx \left\{ \frac{1}{1 - x(1 - x)} + \frac{\ln\,[x(1 - x)]}{[1 - x(1 - x)]^2} \right\} \qquad (9\text{-}87)$$

To calculate β we use Eq. (8-106) and obtain:

$$\beta(u) = -u\,[\epsilon - \tfrac{3}{2}(1 - \tfrac{1}{2}\epsilon)u + \tfrac{17}{12}u^2] \qquad (9\text{-}88)$$

Comparing to Eq. (9-45) with $M = 1$, we notice that the change of sign which appeared in Eq. (9-81) persists. But the term which changed sign contributes to order ϵ^2 in u^*. Thus it will not contribute to η at order ϵ^2, only at order ϵ^3.

In order to see the disappearance of the difference we proceed to calculate η to the next order.† To this end, we need only one more graph in the calculation of Z_ϕ – the three-loop graph denoted by D_5 in Sec. 9-2. In other words,

$$\gamma_\phi(u) = -\epsilon u\,[\tfrac{1}{3}E_3'u + (D_2E_3' - \tfrac{3}{4}E_5')u^2] \qquad (9\text{-}89)$$

†Notice that we avoid calculating v, and prefer the next order in η. The reason is that in the present technique the renormalization constants are temperature dependent, and the calculation of v, though possible, is somewhat awkward (see Ref. 11).

with the new function, corresponding to E'_5 in Eq. (9-38'),

$$E'_5(\epsilon) = \frac{\partial}{\partial k^2} \int \frac{1}{(q_1 + k)^2 + 1} \left[\int \frac{1}{(q_2^2 + 1)[(q_2 + q_1)^2 + 1]} \right]^2 \Bigg|_{k=0} \qquad (9\text{-}90)$$

The ϵ expansion of E'_5 is left as Exercise 9-7. The result is

$$E'_5(\epsilon) = -\frac{1}{6\epsilon^2}(1 - \tfrac{1}{4}\epsilon) - \frac{1}{4\epsilon}L \qquad (9\text{-}91)$$

with L given again by Eq. (9-87).

The first thing to notice is that in the combination $D_2 E'_3 - \tfrac{3}{4}E'_5$ in Eq. (9-89) the ϵ^{-2} terms cancel, as they should to render γ_ϕ finite as $\epsilon \to 0$. But beyond this the number L, which is part of the term proportional to ϵ^{-1} and thus could have entered into η, cancels as well.

Furthermore, the non-trivial fixed point — the root of β in Eq. (9-88) — is:

$$u^* = \tfrac{2}{3}\epsilon[1 + (\tfrac{17}{27} + \tfrac{1}{2})\epsilon] \qquad (9\text{-}92)$$

A comparison with u^* obtained at zero mass, Eq. (9-48), shows that the $\tfrac{1}{2}$ inside the inner brackets changed sign. But γ_ϕ has also changed. Substitution of Eqs. (9-86), (9-81) and (9-91) in (9-89) leads to:

$$\gamma_\phi(u, \epsilon) = \frac{u^2}{24}(1 - \tfrac{1}{4}\epsilon - \tfrac{3}{2}u) \qquad (9\text{-}93)$$

to be compared with

$$\gamma_\phi(u, \epsilon) = \frac{u^2}{24}(1 - \tfrac{5}{4}\epsilon - \tfrac{3}{4}u) \qquad (9\text{-}94)$$

which is (9-46) for $M = 1$. Finally, substituting the value of u^* from Eq. (9-92) in (9-93) gives the same result as is obtained from Eq. (9-48) on setting $M = 1$.

The moral of the last section is that in the process of renormalization there may appear many quantities which depend on the details of the procedure. All these have to disappear in the end, i.e., in the calculation of the universal quantities. It is very convenient to be able to identify these spurious terms since much labor can be saved in the intermediate stages — such labor as might have been expanded in the evaluation of the integral L. 't Hooft has contributed much towards the general identification of the effects of normalization choices, and his technique of minimal subtraction, which avoids normalization altogether, seems to be the most efficient procedure. We describe this procedure in detail in Secs. 9-9–9-11. Some further examples of different normalization conditions leading to the same exponents are indicated in Exercises (9-8) and (9-9).

9-8 ϵ EXPANSION OF THE RENORMALIZATION GROUP EQUATIONS FOR THE BARE FUNCTIONS

To exhibit the way in which the process described in Sec. 8-11 leads to an ϵ expansion for the critical exponents, we follow this procedure to first order in ϵ in the calculation of the position of the fixed point, and to order ϵ^2 in the calculation of η. The computation of ν is left as Exercise 9-10.

In Exercise (8-30) u and β were calculated without explicitly stating how the cutoff was introduced. Universality implies, of course, that the results should be insensitive to the choice of cutoff function (see Exercise 9-11).

A convenient choice as far as further integrals are concerned is the following:

The propagator is put in the Schwinger parametrization, namely,

$$\frac{1}{q^2 + m^2} = \int_0^\infty d\alpha e^{-\alpha(q^2 + m^2)} \qquad (9\text{-}95)$$

The restriction that $|q|$ does not exceed Λ is introduced by an elimination of the low values of α. The regularized propagator is:

$$G_{0\Lambda}(q) = \int_{\Lambda^{-2}}^\infty d\alpha e^{-\alpha(q^2 + m^2)} \qquad (9\text{-}96)$$

Clearly, for $q^2 > \Lambda^2$, $G_{0\Lambda}$ falls off exponentially.

For the present calculation we need two integrals. They are

$$I_{SP} = \int G_{0\Lambda}(q) G_{0\Lambda}(q + k) \Big|_{k^2 = \kappa^2} \qquad (9\text{-}97)$$

and

$$D_3' = \frac{\partial}{\partial k^2} \int G_{0\Lambda}(q_1) G_{0\Lambda}(q_2) G_{0\Lambda}(q_1 + q_2 + k) \Big|_{k^2 = \kappa^2} \qquad (9\text{-}98)$$

These two integrals are evaluated in App. (9-1) to the order needed here. Their values are:

$$I_{SP} \sim \Lambda^{-\epsilon} \left(\frac{\Lambda}{\kappa}\right)^\epsilon \ln \frac{\Lambda}{\kappa} + 0\left(\frac{\kappa^2}{\Lambda^2}, \epsilon\right) \qquad (9\text{-}99)$$

and

$$D_3' \sim -\Lambda^{-2\epsilon} \left(\frac{\Lambda}{\kappa}\right)^{2\epsilon} \tfrac{1}{4} \ln \frac{\Lambda}{\kappa} + 0\left(\frac{\kappa^2}{\Lambda^2}, \epsilon\right) \qquad (9\text{-}100)$$

The geometric factor is divided out of the integrals and is absorbed in the coupling constant.

Using Eq. (9-99), we arrive immediately at the results listed in Exercise (8-30), namely,

$$u = \left(\frac{\Lambda}{\kappa}\right)^{\epsilon} \left(\bar{u}_0 - \tfrac{3}{2}\bar{u}_0 \ln \frac{\Lambda}{\kappa}\right) \qquad (9\text{-}101)$$

$$\beta(\bar{u}_0) = -\bar{u}_0 \left(\epsilon - \tfrac{3}{2}\bar{u}_0\right) \qquad (9\text{-}101a)$$

To first order in ϵ, the fixed point lies at

$$\bar{u}_0^* = \tfrac{2}{3}\epsilon \qquad (9\text{-}102)$$

Similarly, the normalization condition (7-54) together with Eq. (9-100) lead to

$$\gamma_\phi = -\Lambda \frac{\partial}{\partial \Lambda} \ln Z_\phi = \tfrac{1}{24}\bar{u}_0^2 \qquad (9\text{-}103)$$

which together with (9-102) gives the expected result

$$\eta = \frac{\epsilon^2}{54}$$

for the case $M = 1$.

9-9 DIMENSIONAL REGULARIZATION AND CRITICAL PHENOMENA

The process of regularization described in Sec. 8-3 amounts to exactly the same thing as the procedure for isolating the infrared singular part of a graph, which was discussed in Sec. 7-3. In that case, integrations by parts were performed until the integral in question became convergent in the ultraviolet. The surface terms were discarded, as well as the term which completed the convergent integral to infinity. Clearly, if $d < d_0$ — i.e., the original integral converges — then all those surface terms actually vanish. The original integral is equal to the term which is left over after the desired number of integrations have been performed. Since the analytic continuation in d is unique the two procedures lead to the same result.

The discussion of questions such as classical versus non-classical behavior of the theory, critical dimensionality, identification of primitively divergent functions, relevant operators etc. can now proceed as follows. First one performs a dimensional regularization. The result is that all graphs become homogeneous functions of the momentum (and mass) scales. Then one can follow the argument in Secs. 7-3 and 7-9. But there is a difficulty. This is the appearance of the poles as function of the number of dimensions. The original theory of critical phenomena, which included an intrinsic cutoff, did not have any such singularities, and here it is claimed that, as far as the low-momentum behavior is concerned, the new theory is equivalent to it.

To understand the appearance of these poles, within the context of a theory of critical phenomena with a cutoff, we consider an example:

The integral

$$I_\alpha(a) = \int_0^\Lambda \frac{dx}{(x+a)^\alpha} \qquad (9\text{-}104)$$

is finite for all α, if $a > 0$. If $\alpha > 1$ it will have singular infrared behavior as a function of a.

Dimensional regularization amounts to taking $\alpha > 1$ (this corresponds to a small number of dimensions) and letting $\Lambda \to \infty$. The regularized integral is:

$$I_\alpha(a) \to \frac{a^{1-\alpha}}{\alpha - 1} \qquad (9\text{-}105)$$

which has a single pole at $\alpha = 1$, reflecting the logarithmic ultraviolet divergence.

The natural procedure for critical phenomena is to perform a "partial p", and then

$$I_\alpha(a) = \frac{1}{1-\alpha} \frac{x}{(x+a)^\alpha} \bigg|_0^\Lambda - \frac{\alpha}{1-\alpha} \int_0^\Lambda \frac{a dx}{(x+a)^{\alpha+1}} \qquad (9\text{-}106)$$

If the surface term is dropped, which is exact for $\alpha > 1$ as $\Lambda \to \infty$, the remaining integral converges, in the wider domain $\alpha > 0$. The result is identical to (9-105).

But as far as the infrared behavior is concerned no harm has been done either in discarding the surface term or in extending $\Lambda \to \infty$ in the remaining integral. Nevertheless, as $\alpha \to 1$ a singularity develops in $I_\alpha(a)$. The source of this singularity is our attempt to perform a partial integration of a logarithmic integral – an integral whose power counting gives zero. This is reflected in the fact that the surface term becomes infinite even for $a > 0$ and finite Λ.

To recover from (9-105) the infrared singular part of the original integral, (9-104), when α is in the neighborhood of unity one performs an ϵ expansion according to Eq. (8-29). If $\alpha = 1 + \epsilon$ then

$$I_\alpha(a) = \frac{1}{\epsilon} [(\Lambda + a)^{-\epsilon} - a^{-\epsilon}] = \sum_1^\infty \frac{1}{n!} \epsilon^{n-1} (-\ln a)^n$$

$$- \sum_1^\infty \frac{1}{n!} \epsilon^{n-1} [-\ln(\Lambda + a)]^n$$

The first series on the right-hand side is singular for small values of a. The second one is analytic. Thus, in studying the singularities in the critical region, one is interested only in the first term. But, this term can easily be obtained from the dimensionally regularized form (9-105). All one has to do is to expand it in powers of ϵ, and to *subtract the pole*. This prescription coincides exactly with 't Hooft and Veltman's procedure for renormalization, to which we now turn.

9-10 RENORMALIZATION BY MINIMAL SUBTRACTION OF DIMENSIONAL POLES

It was mentioned in the introduction to the present chapter that 't Hooft and Veltman devised a method of renormalization which avoids normalization conditions altogether. This method has a few distinct advantages

- (*a*) It is most elegant.
- (*b*) Since the external momenta are left arbitrary, it allows an automatic identification of terms which should cancel those depending on the normalization point (see, e.g., Sec. 9-7 and Exercises 9-8 and 9-9).
- (*c*) It gives the coefficients appearing in the renormalization group equations a particularly simple form (see Sec. 9-11).
- (*d*) From (*b*) and (*c*), above, there follow many intrinsic checks at intermediate stages of the calculation.
- (*e*) It is especially appealing in applications to critical phenomena, since, as we have seen in the previous section, it is founded on the logic described in the last part of Sec. 7-3.

We consider, again, a critical (massless) theory. The problem of subtractions of mass corrections does not arise in the present framework, since in a dimensionally regularized theory all these terms, evaluated at zero mass, vanish. This is a direct consequence of Exercise 9-13. The proof is left as Exercise 9-14. The result is that a relation like (7-53) is trivially satisfied.

The vertex functions which will develop primitive poles at four dimensions are exactly those which have a logarithmic ultraviolet divergence. They are, of course, the ones which give rise to difficulties when integrated by parts. For a ϕ^4 theory these functions were identified in Sec. 7-3 to be $\partial/\partial k^2 \Gamma^{(2)}$, $\Gamma^{(4)}$ and $\Gamma^{(2,1)}$. But since $\Gamma^{(2)} (k = 0) = 0$, we can choose $\Gamma^{(2)}$ instead of its derivative.

Next one can assert that for this theory there exist three functions u_0, Z_ϕ and Z_{ϕ^2} which can be expanded in a power series in the variable u, according to

$$u_0 \equiv \lambda \kappa^{-\epsilon} = u \left[1 + \sum_1^\infty a_i(\epsilon) u^i\right] \qquad (9\text{-}107)$$

$$Z_\phi = 1 + \sum_1^\infty b_i(\epsilon) u^i \qquad (9\text{-}108)$$

$$Z_{\phi^2} = 1 + \sum_1^\infty c_i(\epsilon) u^i \qquad (9\text{-}109)$$

such that

$$Z_\phi \Gamma^{(2)}(k; u_0, \kappa) = \Gamma_R^{(2)}(k; u, \kappa) \qquad (9\text{-}110)$$

$$Z_\phi^2 \Gamma^{(4)}(k_i; u_0, \kappa) = \Gamma_R^{(4)}(k_i; u, \kappa) \qquad (9\text{-}111)$$

$$\bar{Z}_{\phi^2} \Gamma^{(2,1)}(k_1, k_2, p; u_0, \kappa) = \Gamma_R^{(2,1)}(k_1, k_2, p; u, \kappa) \qquad (9\text{-}112)$$

are finite when $d \to 4$, order by order in u. $\bar{Z}_{\phi^2}$ is defined in Eq. (8-74).

That this is a reasonable statement can be argued as follows: In the second part of Sec. 7-5 we stated the renormalizability of a massless theory regularized with a cutoff. Once mass renormalization has been taken care of, the three bare functions in Eqs. (9-110)–(9-112) are all finite when $\Lambda \to \infty$, as long as $d < 4$. They all have logarithmic divergences at four dimensions. Therefore, the renormalizability discussed in Sec. 7-5 is a statement about the limit $d \to 4$ and then $\Lambda \to \infty$. The statement made here is about the limit $\Lambda \to \infty$ and then $d \to 4$. Perturbation theory can now be used to show that no peculiarity arises from the interchange of the two limits. This is the discussion that was opened in Secs. 8-2 and 8-3.

Another procedure for demonstrating the renormalizability in this scheme is to show inductively that the singularities in $\epsilon (= 4 - d)$ can be removed in every order in u. In this way one runs into the very complicated combinatorics, which are also necessary for proving the renormalization statements in Sec. 7-4 or Sec. 7-5, and which we are carefully avoiding.

Notice that so far κ is a completely arbitrary parameter with the dimension of momentum. It serves only to define the dimensionless coupling constant u_0.

Next, the arbitrariness in the renormalization constant has to be eliminated. 't Hooft and Veltman suggest that $a_i(\epsilon)$, $b_i(\epsilon)$ and $c_i(\epsilon)$ be determined by the simple requirement that poles in ϵ be *minimally subtracted*. This means that in every order in u coefficients have to be chosen so as to cancel the poles in ϵ, and nothing but the poles. The momentum κ stays arbitrary. That this is a feasible project, and that it leads to a unique result, can be demonstrated inductively in perturbation theory.[3] Or, alternatively, it can be reduced to a case discussed previously.

The significance of the statement that minimal subtraction works is in its assertion that the ϵ poles in the vertex functions are of the following types:

(i) The residue of the pole of highest order in a graph is independent of the external momenta.

(ii) The residues of poles of lower order, which do depend on momentum, are cancelled by cross-products between the poles in the renormalization constants and lower order terms in the vertex function, which are non-singular. This should be true for any set of external momenta.

When we speak here of a momentum dependence of the residues we refer to singular, logarithmic, dependence. It should be remembered that graphs, such as those of $\Gamma^{(2)}$, may have an overall polynomial dependence on the external momenta (see, e.g. Eqs. (A9-20) or (A9-29)).

But both features (i) and (ii) must also be present in the previous case, in which normalization conditions were used. After all, the fact that the renormalization constants were calculated at some specified set of momenta does not make them momentum dependent. The poles in Eqs. (9-110)–(9-112) ought to cancel for arbitrary external momenta. One can then convince oneself that, given a set of a_i, b_i, and c_i in Eqs. (9-107)–(9-109), a change in these coefficients by terms which are finite as $\epsilon \to 0$ will still lead to good renormalized functions. In other words, the change from vertex functions renormalized using normalization conditions to those renormalized by minimal subtraction amounts to a finite renormalization.

Before proceeding to demonstrate the process by an example, one can draw two simple conclusions. The first is that the necessary cancellation of the momentum-dependent terms appearing in the vertex functions by momentum-independent constants, gives a check on the tensorial contractions and combinatorial coefficients which accompany the graphs. If such checks are deemed unnecessary, all terms with a logarithmic dependence on the external momenta can be discarded.

The second conclusion is that the coefficients a_i, b_i, and c_i have no finite terms when $\epsilon \to 0$. The importance of this remark will become clear in Sec. 9-11.

In order to see how the procedure works we carry it through up to the order of two loops. The three functions in question can be written as:

$$\Gamma^{(2)}(k; u_0, \kappa) = k^2(1 - B_2 u_0^2) \qquad (9\text{-}113)$$

$$\Gamma^{(4)}(k_i; u_0, \kappa) = \kappa^\epsilon u_0 [1 - A_1 u_0 + (A_2^{(1)} + A_2^{(2)})u_0^2] \qquad (9\text{-}114)$$

$$\Gamma^{(2,1)}(k_1, k_2, p; u_0, \kappa) = 1 - C_1 u_0 + (C_2^{(1)} + C_2^{(2)})u_0^2 \qquad (9\text{-}115)$$

in which a notation identical to that of Sec. 9-2 is used, but the difference should not be overlooked.

(a) The integrals appearing in the functions A, B, and C depend on the external momenta scaled by κ. This was done so as to absorb the powers of κ which appear when $u_0 \kappa^\epsilon$ is substituted for the coupling constant λ.

(b) B_2 is not the derivative of the two-loop graph in $\Gamma^{(2)}$ but the graph itself calculated at the external momentum k/κ and multiplied by $(k/\kappa)^{-2}$.

(c) The numerical factors which enter the A's and the C's are different due to the fact that we are not at a symmetry point of the external momenta.

For example

$$A_1 = \frac{M+8}{18}\left[I\left(\frac{k_1+k_2}{\kappa}\right) + I\left(\frac{k_1+k_3}{\kappa}\right) + I\left(\frac{k_1+k_4}{\kappa}\right)\right] \qquad (9\text{-}116)$$

which reduces at SP to A_1 in Eq. (9-8), together with (9-11) and (9-28). Similarly there are now six distinct integrals contributing to $A_2^{(2)}$, namely,

$$A_2^{(2)} = \frac{5M+22}{54}\left[I_4\left(\frac{k_1}{\kappa},\frac{k_2}{\kappa},\frac{k_3}{\kappa},\frac{k_4}{\kappa}\right) + 5 \text{ permutations}\right] \qquad (9\text{-}117)$$

We can now proceed to perform minimal subtraction. Consider first $\Gamma^{(2)}$. Since we calculate to $0(u^2)$, u_0^2 can be replaced by u^2, and we have to require that the poles of

$$\Gamma_R^{(2)} = k^2(1 + b_1 u + b_2 u^2)(1 - B_2 u^2) = k^2[1 + b_1 u + (b_2 - B_2)u^2 + 0(u^3)]$$

be minimally cancelled to $0(u^2)$.

There are no poles whose residue is linear in u. Thus, $b_1 = 0$. The coefficient b_2 must be:

$$b_2 = [B_2]_s \qquad (9\text{-}118)$$

Where $[E]_s$ should be read as "the singular part of E". The value of b_2 can now be read from Eq. (A9-31) together with the numerical coefficient of the graph, given by Eq. (9-27). It is:

$$b_2 = -\frac{M+2}{144\epsilon} \qquad (9\text{-}119)$$

and

$$Z_\phi = 1 - \frac{M+2}{144\epsilon}u^2 \qquad (9\text{-}120)$$

which should be compared with (9-40). The difference between (9-119) and (9-40) consists of a term which is not singular in ϵ. Another point to notice is that on this level the singular term is independent of $\ln(k^2)$.

Next we consider $\Gamma^{(4)}$ to order u^3 :

$$
\begin{aligned}
\kappa^{-\epsilon}\,\Gamma_R^{(4)}\,(k_1,\ldots,k_4\,;u,\kappa) &= (1+2b_2 u^2)(u+a_1 u^2 +a_2 u^3) \\
&\quad -(u^2 +2a_1 u^3)\left(\frac{M+8}{18}\right)\left[I\!\left(\frac{k_1+k_2}{\kappa}\right)+2 \text{ permutations}\right] \\
&\quad +u^3\left\{\left(\frac{M^2+6M+20}{108}\right)\left[I^2\!\left(\frac{k_1+k_2}{\kappa}\right)+2 \text{ permutations}\right]\right. \\
&\quad \left.+\left(\frac{5M+22}{54}\right)\left[I_4\!\left(\frac{k_1}{\kappa},\ldots,\frac{k_4}{\kappa}\right)+5 \text{ permutations}\right]\right\} \\
&= u+u^2\left\{a_1 -\frac{M+8}{18}\left[I\left(\frac{k_1+k_2}{\kappa}\right)+2 \text{ permutations}\right]\right\} \\
&\quad +u^3\left\{a_2 +2b_2 -2a_1\left(\frac{M+8}{12}\right)\left[I\left(\frac{k_1+k_2}{\kappa}\right)+2 \text{ permutations}\right]\right. \\
&\quad +\left(\frac{M^2+6M+20}{108}\right)\left[I^2\!\left(\frac{k_1+k_2}{\kappa}\right)+2 \text{ permutations}\right] \\
&\quad \left.+\frac{5M+22}{54}\left[I_4\!\left(\frac{k_i}{\kappa}\right)+5 \text{ permutations}\right]\right\}
\end{aligned}
$$

The term of order u^2, together with Eq. (A9-17) gives a_1

$$
a_1 =\frac{M+8}{18}\left[I\!\left(\frac{k_1+k_2}{\kappa}\right)+2 \text{ permutations}\right]_s =\frac{M+8}{6\epsilon} \qquad (9\text{-}121)
$$

to be compared with a_1 of Eq. (9-41). Notice that to this order the residue of the pole is still independent of $\ln(k^2)$.

Next, the coefficient of u^3 is used to determine a_2. We have:

$$
\begin{aligned}
a_2 =\Bigg[&-2b_2 +2a_1\frac{M+8}{18}\left[I\!\left(\frac{k_1+k_2}{\kappa}\right)+2 \text{ permutations}\right] \\
&-\frac{M^2+6M+20}{108}\left[I^2\!\left(\frac{k_1+k_2}{\kappa}\right)+2 \text{ permutations}\right] \\
&-\frac{5M+22}{54}\left[I_4\!\left(\frac{k_i}{\kappa}\right)+5 \text{ permutations}\right]\Bigg]_s \qquad (9\text{-}122)
\end{aligned}
$$

The term with $\ln(k_1+k_2)^2$ in I is finite as $\epsilon\to0$. But $a_1\alpha\epsilon^{-1}$ and hence in $a_1 I$ there are terms of the form

$$
\epsilon^{-1}\left[\ln(k_1+k_2)^2 +2 \text{ permutations}\right]
$$

These must exactly cancel against terms coming from I^2 and I_4, or else a_2 will depend on the external momenta, which is nonsensical.

THE COMPUTATION OF THE CRITICAL EXPONENTS

There are two sources of concern:

(a) I_4 depends on all k_i while I and I^2 depend only on one pair.
(b) The coefficients must match exactly to give rise to the desired cancellation.

A glance at Eq. (A9-41) reveals that the terms of I_4, which are $0(\epsilon^{-1})$, depend only on pairs of external momenta. In fact the $L(k)$ which appears in Eq. (A9-41) is identical to that which appears in I. The terms of $0(\epsilon^{-2})$ are independent of $\ln(k^2)$, as they should be.

Substituting (9-119), (A9-17) and (A9-41) in Eq. (9-122) one finds that all momentum-dependent terms cancel, and that:

$$a_2 = \frac{(M+8)^2}{36\epsilon^2} - \frac{3M+14}{24\epsilon} \qquad (9\text{-}123)$$

(cf. Eq. 9-42). This, together with (9-121), gives:

$$u_0 = u \left\{ 1 + \frac{M+8}{6\epsilon} u + \left[\frac{(M+8)^2}{36\epsilon^2} - \frac{3M+14}{24\epsilon} \right] u^2 \right\} \qquad (9\text{-}124)$$

Finally, c_1 and c_2 of $\overline{Z}_{\phi^2}$ are calculated by requiring a minimal subtraction of $\Gamma^{(2,1)}$. The derivation is left as Exercise (9-15). The result is

$$\overline{Z}_{\phi^2} = 1 + \frac{M+2}{6\epsilon} u + \left[\frac{(M+2)(M+5)}{36\epsilon^2} - \frac{M+2}{24\epsilon} \right] u^2 \qquad (9\text{-}125)$$

The cancellation of the momentum-dependent term in D_3, which enters in $\Gamma^{(2)}$, happens only at the level of three loops. The demonstration that this cancellation does in fact take place is left as Exercise (9-16).

9-11 THE CALCULATION OF EXPONENTS IN MINIMAL SUBTRACTION

Having calculated u_0, Z_ϕ and Z_{ϕ^2} as functions of u and ϵ, the Wilson functions β, γ_ϕ and γ_{ϕ^2} can be obtained using Eqs. (8-21), (8-22), and (8-24), respectively. The present method allows us to deduce some general properties of these functions.

The functions u_0, Z_ϕ and Z_{ϕ^2} contain poles of arbitrary order in ϵ. Still, β, γ_ϕ and γ_{ϕ^2} must have a finite limit as $\epsilon \to 0$. This implies that the expression for $(\partial \ln u_0/\partial u)^{-1}$ can have at most simple poles in ϵ, at every order in u. Otherwise, the explicit ϵ in Eq. (8-21) will not suffice to give a finite β in four dimensions. The higher order poles must cancel at every order in u. These considerations follow from dimensional regularization, and not especially from minimal subtraction. They have been mentioned already in Sec. 8-2 and 9-2. What is specific to the present technique is the fact that since, apart from the lowest order terms in the renormalization constants, there are no regular terms in ϵ, all coefficients in $(\partial \ln u_0/\partial u)^{-1}$ must be exactly proportional to ϵ^{-1}. Hence β must have the form:

$$\beta(u, \epsilon) = -\epsilon u + \beta_1(u) \qquad (9\text{-}126)$$

where β_1 is independent of ϵ (see also Exercise 9-17).

Similarly, γ_ϕ and γ_{ϕ^2} have to be independent of ϵ. The general proof is left as Exercise 9-18. Here we will see this occurring to the order of two loops.

Elementary algebra shows that when the expression for u_0 is inserted in Eq. (8-21), the coefficients so conspire as to give

$$\beta(u, \epsilon) = -u\left(\epsilon - \frac{M+8}{6}u + \frac{3M+14}{12}u^2\right) \qquad (9\text{-}127)$$

Similarly for γ_ϕ and $\overline{\gamma}_{\phi^2}$ one finds, respectively,

$$\gamma_\phi(u, \epsilon) = \frac{M+2}{72}u^2 \qquad (9\text{-}128)$$

$$\overline{\gamma}_{\phi^2} = \frac{M+2}{6}u\left(1 - \tfrac{1}{2}u\right) \qquad (9\text{-}129)$$

The calculation of the term of order u^3 in γ_ϕ is left as Exercise 9-19.

Comparison of Eqs. (9-127)–(9-129) with Eqs. (9-45)–(9-47) reveals that the former can be obtained from the latter by simply setting $\epsilon = 0$ and adding a term $-\epsilon u$ to β. This is a general consequence of minimal subtraction. It is nothing but the statement made above about the dependence of β, γ_ϕ and γ_{ϕ^2} on ϵ.

Finally, Eq. (9-127) can be solved to obtain the fixed point. One finds

$$u^* = \frac{6}{M+8}\epsilon + \frac{18(3M+14)}{(M+8)^3}\epsilon^2 \qquad (9\text{-}130)$$

which is somewhat different from u^* of Eq. (9-48). But when it is inserted in the expressions for γ_ϕ and γ_{ϕ^2}, (9-128) and (9-129), respectively, η and ν of Sec. 9-3 are reprodued to $0(\epsilon^2)$. Using the results of Exercise (9-20) one can check that η agrees with (9-49) to order ϵ^3.

Appendix 9-1

CALCULATION OF SOME INTEGRALS WITH CUTOFF[10]

In this appendix we compute the leading terms of the integrals I_{SP} and D'_3 defined, respectively, in Eqs. (9-97) and (9-98). The propagators are regularized according to Eq. (9-96). The first integral is:

$$I_{SP} = \int_{\Lambda^{-2}} d\alpha_1 \, d\alpha_2 \int dq \exp\left[-\alpha_1 q^2 - \alpha_2 (q+k)^2\right]\Bigg|_{k^2 = \kappa^2}$$

The integration over q is performed after a completion of the square, and using the analytic continuation of the Gaussian integral

$$\int dq e^{-Aq^2} = \frac{1}{(2\pi)^d} \left(\frac{\pi}{A}\right)^{d/2} \qquad (A9\text{-}1)$$

to non-integer numbers of dimensions. After S_d, Eq. (A7-5), is divided out of the integral, we use (A9-1) in the form:

$$\int dq \, e^{-Aq^2} = \tfrac{1}{2}\Gamma\left(\tfrac{1}{2}d\right) A^{-d/2} \qquad (A9\text{-}2)$$

I_{SP} becomes:

$$I_{SP} = \tfrac{1}{2}\Gamma(\tfrac{1}{2}d) \int_{\Lambda^{-2}} d\alpha_1 \, d\alpha_2 (\alpha_1 + \alpha_2)^{-d/2} \exp\left[-\frac{\alpha_1\alpha_2}{\alpha_1 + \alpha_2}\kappa^2\right]$$

$$= \tfrac{1}{2}\Gamma(\tfrac{1}{2}d) \, \Lambda^{-\epsilon}\left(\frac{\Lambda}{\kappa}\right)^\epsilon \int_{(\kappa/\Lambda)^2} dx_1 \, dx_2 (x_1 + x_2)^{-2+\frac{\epsilon}{2}} \exp\left[-\frac{x_1 x_2}{x_1 + x_2}\right] \quad (A9\text{-}3)$$

In the last integral we need the leading term for large Λ and small ϵ. We set $\epsilon = 0$ and leave the proof, that keeping ϵ finite but small leads to higher order terms, as Exercise 9-12. We concentrate on

$$J = \int_u dx_1 \, dx_2 (x_1 + x_2)^{-2} \exp\left[-\frac{x_1 x_2}{x_1 + x_2}\right] \quad (A9\text{-}4)$$

A useful trick is to compute $\partial J/\partial u$. This reads:

$$\frac{\partial J}{\partial u} = -2\int dx(u+x)^{-2}\exp\left[-u\frac{x}{u+x}\right] = -\frac{2}{u}\int_1^\infty dx(1+x)^{-2}\exp\left[-u\frac{x}{1+x}\right]$$

The integral is analytic in u and the leading term for small values of u is simply:

$$\frac{\partial J}{\partial u}\underset{u\to 0}{\sim} -u^{-1} \quad (A9\text{-}5)$$

Coming back to J we can ignore the integration constant, since it is not singular as $u \to 0$, and write

$$J \sim 2\ln\frac{\Lambda}{\kappa} \quad (A9\text{-}6)$$

when $\Lambda \gg \kappa$. Inserting (A9-6) in (A9-3), and expanding $\Gamma(\tfrac{1}{2}d)$ in ϵ, leads to Eq. (9-99).

The second integral we need is

$$D_3' = \frac{\partial}{\partial k^2} \int_{\Lambda^{-2}} d\alpha_1 \, d\alpha_2 \, d\alpha_3 \int dq_1 \, dq_2 \exp\left[-\alpha_1 q_1^2 - \alpha_2 q_2^2 - \alpha_3(q_1 + q_2 + k)^2\right]\Big|_{k^2 = \kappa^2}$$

The integration over many momenta is performed by a further generalization of the Gaussian integral, (A9-2). If q_i $(i = 1, \ldots, L)$ are d-dimensional vectors which are integrated over, v_i $(i = 1, \ldots, L)$ are d-dimensional constant vectors and M_{ij} is an $L \times L$ matrix, then

$$\int \prod_{i=1}^L dq_i \exp\left[-(M_{ij}q_i q_j + 2v_i q_i)\right] = \left[\frac{\Gamma(\tfrac{1}{2}d)}{2}\right]^L \frac{1}{(\text{Det } M)^{\frac{1}{2}d}} \exp[(M^{-1})_{ij}v_i v_j]$$

$$(A9\text{-}7)$$

Using this result we can rewrite D_3' in the form:

$$D_3' = [\tfrac{1}{2}\Gamma(\tfrac{1}{2}d)]^2 \left.\frac{\partial}{\partial k^2}\right|_{k^2 = \kappa^2} \int_{\Lambda^{-2}} d\alpha_1\, d\alpha_2\, d\alpha_3 \frac{1}{(\alpha_1\alpha_2 + \alpha_1\alpha_3 + \alpha_2\alpha_3)^{d/2}}$$

$$\times \exp\left[-\frac{\alpha_1\alpha_2\alpha_3}{(\alpha_1\alpha_2 + \alpha_1\alpha_3 + \alpha_2\alpha_3)} k^2\right] = -\left[\tfrac{1}{2}\Gamma\left(\frac{d}{2}\right)\right]^2 \Lambda^{-2\epsilon} \left(\frac{\Lambda}{\kappa}\right)^{2\epsilon}$$

$$\times \int_{(\frac{\kappa}{\Lambda})^2} dx_1\, dx_2\, dx_3 \frac{x_1 x_2 x_3}{(x_1 x_2 + x_1 x_3 + x_2 x_3)^{3 - \epsilon/2}} \exp\left[-\frac{x_1 x_2 x_3}{x_1 x_2 + x_1 x_3 + x_2 x_3}\right]$$

$$(A9\text{-}8)$$

As in the case of I_{SP} we are interested in the leading part of the integral in (A9-8) as κ/Λ and ϵ become small. The integral diverges in this double limit.

Denoting the integral by J, we compute again its derivative with respect to the lower limit. We have

$$\frac{\partial J}{\partial u} = -3u \int_u dx_1\, dx_2 \frac{x_1 x_2}{[x_1 x_2 + u(x_1 + x_2)]^{3 - \epsilon/2}} \exp\left[-\frac{u x_1 x_2}{x_1 x_2 + u(x_1 + x_2)}\right]$$

$$\underset{\epsilon \to 0}{\sim} -\frac{3}{u} \int_1^\infty dx_1 dx_2 \frac{x_1 x_2}{[x_1 x_2 + x_1 + x_2]^3} \exp\left[-\frac{u x_1 x_2}{x_1 x_2 + x_1 + x_2}\right]$$

$$\underset{u \to 0}{\sim} -\frac{3}{u} \int_1^\infty dx_1\, dx_2 \frac{x_1 x_2}{[x_1 x_2 + x_1 + x_2]^3} + 0(u^0) \qquad (A9\text{-}9)$$

The last integral is easily evaluated, leading to

$$\frac{\partial J}{\partial u} \sim -\frac{1}{2u}$$

and since $u = (\kappa/\Lambda)^2$, one finds:

$$J = \ln\frac{\Lambda}{\kappa} + 0\left(\left(\frac{\Lambda}{\kappa}\right)^0\right) \qquad (A9\text{-}10)$$

Inserting J in Eq. (A9-8) and expanding the Γ functions in ϵ one arrives at Eq. (9-100).

Appendix 9-2

ONE-LOOP INTEGRALS IN DIMENSIONAL REGULARIZATION

In the calculating integrals in this appendix and the next, we will not aim at the most complete expressions. Rather, we will be after the first few terms of the expansion of these integrals in powers of the difference from some given number of dimensions. On the other hand we will give the external momenta generic values. This is required by the method of minimal subtraction. The values of the integrals at special symmetry points can be simply read off from the resulting expressions.

First we consider the graph in Fig. 6-6b:

$$I(k) = \int dq\, \frac{1}{q^2(q+k)^2} = \int_0^1 dx \int dq\, \frac{1}{(q^2 + 2xkq + xk^2)^2} \qquad (A9\text{-}11)$$

in which Eq. (A8-1) was used and the mass was set equal to zero. Integrating over the momentum using Eq. (A8-5) one finds:

$$I(k) = \tfrac{1}{2}\Gamma(\tfrac{1}{2}d)\Gamma(2 - \tfrac{1}{2}d)\int_0^1 dx\,[x(1-x)k^2]^{\frac{1}{2}d - 2} \qquad (A9\text{-}12)$$

The graph in Eq. (A9-11) can be viewed as a second order contribution to $\Gamma^{(4)}$ in a ϕ^4 theory, or as a second order term of $\Gamma^{(2)}$ in a ϕ^3 theory.[13] In the first case we are interested in the neighborhood of four dimensions. In the second, the neighborhood of $d = 6$ is of interest.

$$\text{(i)} \quad d = 4 - \epsilon$$

$$I(k) = \tfrac{1}{2}\Gamma(2 - \tfrac{1}{2}\epsilon)\Gamma(\tfrac{1}{2}\epsilon) \int_0^1 dx\,[x(1-x)k^2]^{-\epsilon/2} \quad \text{(A9-13)}$$

To obtain the two leading terms the integrand is expanded using Eq. (8-29). In addition we use the following properties of the Γ functions:

$$\Gamma(x+1) = x\Gamma(x) \quad \text{(A9-14)}$$

and

$$\frac{\Gamma(1 + \alpha_1\epsilon)\Gamma(1 + \alpha_2\epsilon)\ldots\Gamma(1 + \alpha_n\epsilon)}{\Gamma(1 + \beta_1\epsilon)\ldots\Gamma(1 + \beta_m\epsilon)} = 1 + 0(\epsilon^2) \quad \text{(A9-15)}$$

if

$$\sum_1^n \alpha_i - \sum_1^m \beta_i = 0 \quad \text{(A9-16)}$$

Using (A9-14) and (A9-15), one finds:

$$I(k) = \frac{1}{\epsilon}[1 - \tfrac{1}{2}\epsilon - \tfrac{1}{2}\epsilon L(k)] + 0(\epsilon) \quad \text{(A9-17)}$$

with

$$L(k) = \int dx\, \ln[x(1-x)k^2] \quad \text{(A9-18)}$$

Recall that the external momenta have been made dimensionless by factorizing out κ. Hence, at the symmetry point, SP, $k^2 = 1$. The integral in (A9-18) can be evaluated to be

$$L(\text{SP}) = -2$$

and

$$I_{\text{SP}} = \frac{1}{\epsilon}(1 + \tfrac{1}{2}\epsilon) + 0(\epsilon) \quad \text{(A9-19)}$$

$$\text{(ii)} \quad d = 6 - \epsilon$$

$$I(k) = \tfrac{1}{2}\Gamma(3 - \tfrac{1}{2}\epsilon)\Gamma(-1 + \tfrac{1}{2}\epsilon) \int_0^1 dx\,[x(1-x)k^2]^{1 - \tfrac{1}{2}\epsilon}$$

$$= -\frac{k^2}{3\epsilon}[1 - \tfrac{1}{4}\epsilon - 3\epsilon L_1(k)] \quad \text{(A9-20)}$$

with

$$L_1(k) = \int_0^1 x(1-x)\ln[x(1-x)k^2] \qquad \text{(A9-21)}$$

As was discussed in the text $\Gamma^{(2)} \propto k^2$ in a dimensionally regularized massless theory. This is seen explicitly in (A9-20). If $\partial/\partial k^2 \Gamma^{(2)}$ is desired, it can be obtained from (A9-20). Finally, at the special point $k^2 = 1$

$$I(k) = -\frac{k^2}{3\epsilon}(1 + \tfrac{7}{12}\epsilon) \qquad \text{(A9-22)}$$

Another integral which appears in a ϕ^3 theory at the level of one loop is the contribution to the three-point vertex, Fig. 9-3.

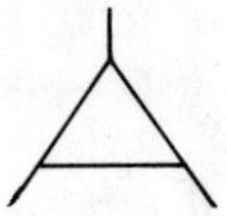

FIGURE 9-3
A one-loop graph in a ϕ^3 theory.

$$J(k_1, k_2) = \int dq \, \frac{1}{q^2(q - k_1)^2(q + k_2)^2}$$

$$= 2\int dx_1 \, dx_2 \int dq \, \frac{1}{[q^2 - 2(x_1 k_1 - x_2 k_2)q + x_1 k_1^2 + x_2 k_2^2]^3} \qquad \text{(A9-23)}$$

The parameters x_1 and x_2 satisfy (A8-2).

Using formula (A8-5) one arrives at:

$$J(k_1, k_2) = \tfrac{1}{2}\Gamma(\tfrac{1}{2}d)\Gamma(3 - \tfrac{1}{2}d)\int dx_1 \, dx_2 \, [x_1(1-x_1)k_1^2 + x_2(1-x_2)k_2^2$$

$$+ 2x_1 x_2 k_1 k_2]^{\frac{1}{2}d - 3} \qquad \text{(A9-24)}$$

Expanding in $\epsilon(= 6 - d)$ one arrives at

$$J(k_1, k_2) = \frac{1}{\epsilon}[1 - \tfrac{3}{4}\epsilon - \epsilon L_2(k_1 k_2)] \qquad \text{(A9-25)}$$

where

$$L_2(k_1, k_2) = \int_0^1 dx_1 \int_0^1 dx_2 \theta(1 - x_1 - x_2)$$

$$\ln[x_1(1-x_1)k_1^2 + x_2(1-x_2)k_2^2 + 2x_1 x_2 k_1 k_2] \qquad \text{(A9-26)}$$

Even at a symmetric point, L_2 is an unpleasant integral. But renormalization by minimal subtraction assures us that it does not have to be calculated.

Appendix 9-3

TWO-LOOP INTEGRALS IN DIMENSIONAL REGULARIZATION

Consider the second order contribution to $\Gamma^{(2)}$ in a ϕ^4 theory near four dimensions. Again we keep only the first two terms in the ϵ expansion.

$$D_3(k) = \int dq_1 \, dq_2 \frac{1}{q_1^2 q_2^2 (q_1 + q_2 + k)^2} \quad \text{(A9-27)}$$

Using Eq. (A9-12) we have:

$$D_3(k) = \tfrac{1}{2}\Gamma(2 - \tfrac{1}{2}\epsilon)\Gamma(\tfrac{1}{2}\epsilon) \int_0^1 dx \, [x(1-x)]^{-\frac{1}{2}\epsilon} \int dq \frac{1}{q^2[(q+k)^2]^{\frac{1}{2}\epsilon}}$$

$$\text{(A9-28)}$$

Using (A8-1) and (A8-5) the last integral can be written as:

$$\int dq \frac{1}{q^2[(q+k)^2]^{\frac{1}{2}\epsilon}} = \frac{\Gamma(1 + \tfrac{1}{2}\epsilon)}{\Gamma(\tfrac{1}{2}\epsilon)} \frac{1}{2} \frac{\Gamma(\tfrac{1}{2}d)\Gamma(1 + \tfrac{1}{2}\epsilon - \tfrac{1}{2}d)}{\Gamma(1 + \tfrac{1}{2}\epsilon)}$$

$$\times \int_0^1 dy \, y^{\frac{1}{2}\epsilon - 1} [y(1-y)k^2]^{\frac{1}{2}d - 1 - \frac{1}{2}\epsilon} = -\frac{k^2}{8}[1 - \tfrac{1}{4}\epsilon - 2\epsilon L_3(k)]$$

$$\text{(A9-29)}$$

with

$$L_3(k) = \int dy(1-y)\ln[y(1-y)k^2] \qquad \text{(A9-30)}$$

Substituting (A9-29) in (A9-28) one finds:

$$D_3(k) = -\frac{k^2}{8\epsilon}(1 + \tfrac{1}{4}\epsilon - 2\epsilon L_3) + 0(\epsilon) \qquad \text{(A9-31)}$$

and when $k^2 = 1, D_3$ reduces to

$$\overline{D_3}(k^2 = 1) = -\frac{1}{8\epsilon}(1 + \tfrac{9}{4}\epsilon) \qquad \text{(A9-32)}$$

Noting that k^2 appears with a power $1 - \epsilon$ in (A9-29) one can compute D_3'. Namely,

$$D_3' = \frac{\partial}{\partial k^2} D_3 \bigg|_{k^2=1} = -\frac{1}{8\epsilon}(1 + \tfrac{5}{4}\epsilon) \qquad \text{(A9-33)}$$

There is one single three-loop graph which was used in Chap. 9. This is E_5, given by the second graph in Exercise 4-10. Its derivative with respect to k^2, at $k^2 = 1$, is

$$E_5' = \frac{\partial}{\partial k^2} E_5 \bigg|_{k^2=1} = -\frac{1}{6\epsilon^2}(1 + 2\epsilon) + 0(1) \qquad \text{(A9-34)}$$

The derivation is left as Exercise (9-16).

Finally, we calculate the two-loop graph of $\Gamma^{(4)}$, Fig. 6-6e.

$$I_4(k_i) = \int dq_1 \, dq_2 \frac{1}{q_1^2(P-q_1)^2 q_2^2(q_1 - q_2 + k_3)^2} \qquad \text{(A9-35)}$$

in which we denote $k_1 + k_2 = P$.

First, using Eq. (8-25) we perform the integral over the internal bubble, i.e., we integrate over q_2. The result is:

$$I_4(k_i) = \tfrac{1}{2}\Gamma(2 - \tfrac{1}{2}\epsilon)\Gamma(\tfrac{1}{2}\epsilon)\frac{[\Gamma(1 - \tfrac{1}{2}\epsilon)]^2}{\Gamma(2 - \epsilon)}$$

$$\times \int dq \frac{1}{q^2(P-q)^2[(q+k_3)^2]^{\epsilon/2}} \qquad \text{(A9-36)}$$

The remaining integral we treat by introducing, consecutively, two Feynman parameters:

$$\dot{\text{/}}. = \int_0^1 dz \int dq \frac{1}{(q^2 - 2zPq + zP^2)^2 [(q + k_3)^2]^{\epsilon/2}}$$

$$= \frac{\Gamma(2 + \frac{1}{2}\epsilon)}{\Gamma(\frac{1}{2}\epsilon)} \int_0^1 dy (1 - y)^{\frac{1}{2}\epsilon - 1} y \int_0^1 dz$$

$$\times \int dq \int \frac{1}{\{q^2 - 2[yzP + (1-y)k_3]q + yzP^2 + (1-y)k_3^2\}^{2 + \frac{1}{2}\epsilon}} .$$

$$= \frac{1}{2} \frac{\Gamma(\frac{1}{2}d)\Gamma(\epsilon)}{\Gamma(\frac{1}{2}\epsilon)} \int_0^1 dy (1 - y)^{\frac{1}{2}\epsilon - 1} y$$

$$\times \int_0^1 dz [yz(1-yz)P^2 + y(1-y)k_3^2 - 2yz(1-y)k_3 P]^{-\epsilon} \qquad \text{(A9-37)}$$

where the integration over the remaining momentum q was already performed.

Next we proceed to the ϵ expansion. The products of the numerical factor in front of the integrals in (A9-36) and in (A9-37) is $[1 + 0(\epsilon^2)]/4\epsilon$. In the integral in Eq. (A9-37) we cannot simply set $\epsilon = 0$, because of the singularity at $y = 1$. We therefore add and subtract the value of the quantity in square brackets at the point $y = 1$, i.e., we write:

$$[\ ]^{-\epsilon} = [z(1-z)P^2]^{-\epsilon} + \{[\ ]^{-\epsilon} - [z(1-z)P^2]^{-\epsilon}\}$$

$$= [z(1-z)P^2]^{-\epsilon} - \epsilon \ln \left\{ \frac{[\ ]}{z(1-z)P^2} \right\} + 0(\epsilon^2) \qquad \text{(A9-38)}$$

The important point to notice is that the two leading terms in I_4 will be $0(\epsilon^{-2})$ and $0(\epsilon^{-1})$. As $y \to 1$ the logarithm in (A9-38) will vanish, thus rendering the integral over y convergent when $\epsilon \to 0$. But there is a factor of ϵ in front of the logarithm, which cancels the $1/\epsilon$ from the numerical prefactor. Hence the complicated integral over the logarithm contributes to order ϵ^0. This is beyond our present concern.

We are left with the task of calculating

$$J = \int_0^1 dy (1 - y)^{\frac{1}{2}\epsilon - 1} y \int_0^1 dz [z(1-z)P^2]^{-\epsilon}$$

Using the formula:

$$\int_0^1 dx \, x^a (1-x)^b = \frac{\Gamma(a+1)\Gamma(b+1)}{\Gamma(a+b+2)} \qquad \text{(A9-39)}$$

J can be evaluated as:

$$J = \frac{\Gamma(\tfrac{1}{2}\epsilon)\Gamma(2)}{\Gamma(2 + \tfrac{1}{2}\epsilon)} \; [1 - \epsilon L(P)] = \frac{2}{\epsilon}[1 - \tfrac{1}{2}\epsilon - \epsilon L(P)] + 0(\epsilon) \qquad \text{(A9-40)}$$

Notice that L is the same integral that appeared in I, Eq. (A9-17). Introducing the numerical prefactor one arrives at

$$I_4(k_1, \ldots, k_4) = \frac{1}{2\epsilon^2} \; [1 - \tfrac{1}{2}\epsilon - \epsilon L(k_1 + k_2)] \qquad \text{(A9-41)}$$

which at the symmetry point is:

$$I_{4SP} = \frac{1}{2\epsilon^2}(1 + \tfrac{3}{2}\epsilon) \qquad \text{(A9-42)}$$

Some further integrals are left as Exercise (9-20).

EXERCISES

9-1   Prove that to obtain $u^*(\epsilon)$ to $0(\epsilon^n)$, $\beta(u, \epsilon)$ has to be known up to $0(\epsilon^p u^q)$, with $p + q = n + 1$.

9-2   Evaluate symbolically the renormalization constants and the Wilson functions to order two loops in a symmetric ϕ^3 theory near six dimensions.

  (a) What will be the statement corresponding to Exercise 9-1?
  (b) Can η be computed to $0(\epsilon^2)$ if u^* is known to the lowest non-vanishing order?

A realistic case of this type is the Potts model.[12]

9-3   Consider the leading ϵ dependence of the one- and two-loop integrals of $\Gamma^{(2)}$ and $\Gamma^{(3)}$ in a symmetric ϕ^3 theory. Compare with the case of ϕ^4. To what order in ϵ do the integrals have to be calculated so as to obtain η and ν to order ϵ^2?

9-4(a)   Study the renormalization group equation for H as a function of M at T_c and of M as a function of t at $H = 0$, using the fact that each contains only one dimensional variable. Derive the equations corresponding to Eq. (9-68) and solve them.

  (b) Analyze the asymptotic dependence of H on M and of M on t at four dimensions.

9-5 Using the renormalization group equation for the equation of state, analyze the dependence of H on M at T_c, and of M on t at $H = 0$, at four dimensions.

9-6 Analyze the behavior of the two-point function at the critical point in four dimensions as a function of momentum.

9-7 Compute the ϵ expansion of the integrals

$$E_4 = \int \frac{1}{(q_1^2 + 1)^2 (q_2^2 + 1)[(q_1 + q_2)^2 + 1]}$$

$$E_3 = \int \frac{1}{(q_1^2 + 1)(q_2^2 + 1)[(q_1 + q_2 + k)^2 + 1]}$$

$$E_5 = \int \frac{1}{[(q_1 + k)^2 + 1](q_2^2 + 1)[(q_1 + q_2)^2 + 1](q_3^2 + 1)[(q_1 + q_3)^2 + 1]}$$

Compare with the integrals at zero mass.

9-8(*a*) Following the procedure outlined in Sec. 7-6 calculate the renormalization constants in a massless theory to the order of two loops with $\kappa^2 \to v^2 \kappa^2$.

(*b*) Calculate $\beta(u)$, $\gamma_\phi(u)$, $\gamma_{\phi^2}(u)$ and $u^*(\epsilon)$. Compare with the results of Sec. 9-3.

(*c*) Compute $\gamma(\epsilon)$ and $\nu(\epsilon)$.

9-9 The same as Exercise 9-8, but with the following normalization conditions:

$$\frac{\partial^2}{\partial k^2} \Gamma_R^{(2)} \Big|_{k^2 = \kappa^2} = 1$$

$$\Gamma_R^{(4)} \Big|_{SP} = u \kappa^\epsilon$$

$$\Gamma_R^{(2,1)} \Big|_{\overline{SP}} = 1$$

where SP is defined by:

$$k_i k_j = \frac{\kappa^2}{3} (4\delta_{ij} - 1)$$

and $\overline{SP}$ by

$$k_1^2 = k_2^2 = p^2 = \kappa^2$$

9-10 Using the renormalization of the massless theory, with the cutoff introduced as in Sec. 9-8, calculate γ_{ϕ^2}, which appears in the equation for the bare function, to the accuracy necessary to obtain ν to order ϵ.

9-11 Calculate I_{SP} and D'_3 with the regularized propagator

$$G_{0\Lambda}(k) = \frac{\theta(\Lambda^2 - k^2)}{k^2 + m^2}$$

Compare β and γ_ϕ with (9-101) and (9-103).

9-12 Carry out the procedure following Eq. (A9-3) keeping ϵ finite. What are the resulting corrections to the integral?

9-13 Show that the dimensional regularization of an integral of a power yields zero.

9-14 Prove that in any massless theory all mass correction terms vanish if the theory is dimensionally regularized.

9-15 Calculate $Z_{\phi^2}(\epsilon)$ to order u^2 by minimal subtraction. Compare with Eqs. (9-25) and (9-43)–(9-44).

9-16(a) Calculate the first two terms in an expansion in ϵ of $E_5(k)$, Fig. 9-4.

FIGURE 9-4

(b) Derive Eq. (A9-34)
(c) Show that in the computation of Z_ϕ by minimal subtraction this graph will cancel the singular momentum-dependent term arising from $L_3(k)$ in D_3.

9-17 What is the general form of β in a ϕ^3 theory renormalized by minimal subtractions?[13]

9-18 Prove that if a theory is renormalized by minimal subtraction, γ_ϕ and γ_{ϕ^2} are functions of u only.

9-19 Using the results of Exercise (9-16) calculate the contribution of order u^3 to γ_ϕ.

FIGURE 9-5

9-20 Calculate the integrals corresponding to the graphs shown in Fig. 9-4 for general values of the external momenta, to $O(\epsilon^{-1})$. The results are given in Ref. 13.

REFERENCES

1. S. Coleman and E. Weinberg, *Physical Review,* **D7,** 1888 (1973).
2. K. G. Wilson and M. E. Fisher, *Physical Review Letters,* **28,** 240 (1972) an extensive review see WK. See also the review of D. J. Wallace in DG.
3. G. 't Hooft and M. Veltman, *Nuclear Physics,* **B44,** 189 (1972) and "Diagrammar". In the context of statistical physics see, e.g., J. D. Lawrie *Journal of Physics,* **A9,** 961 (1975) and D. J. Amit, *Journal of Physics,* **A9,** 1441 (1976).
4. See, e.g., Chap. IX of BLZ. and, E. Brézin, J. C. Le Guillou, J. Zinn-Justin, and B. G. Nickel, *Physics Letters,* **44A,** 227 (1973).
5. E. Brézin, J. C. Le Guillou, and J. Zinn-Justin, *Physical Review* **D15,** 1544 and 1588 (1977). This work is an extension of the original ideas of L. N. Lipatov, *Zh. Eksp. Teor. Fiz.* **25,** 116 (1977). The new numerical results for the exponents in three dimensions: J. C. Le Guillou and J. Zinn-Justin, *Physical Review Letters,* **39,** 95 (1977).
6. K. G. Wilson, *Physical Review,* **B4,** 3174 and 3184 (1971).
7. T. J. Niemeijer and J. M. J. Van Leeuwen, *Physica,* **71,** 17 (1974); *Physical Review Letters,* **31,** 1411 (1973), and the review by these authors in DG.
8. Experiment: G. Ahlers, A. Kornblit and H. Guggenheim: *Proceedings of the International Conference on Low Temperature Physics,* Finland 1975 (North-Holland, Amsterdam, 1975) Theory: A. Aharony, *Physical Review* **B8,** 3363 (1973); E. Brézin, *Journal de Physique-Lettres,* **36,** L51 (1975), C. Bervillier, *Journal de Physique-Lettres,* **36,** L225 (1975).
9. M. Vohrer, These de Troixieme Cycle, Ecole Normale Superieure (unpublished) and M. Vohrer and E. Brèzin, *Physical Review* B (to be published).
10. We follow here IIM.
11. E. Brezin, J. C. Le Guillou and K. Zinn-Justin, *Physical Review,* **D8,** 2418 (1973).
12. G. R. Golner, *Physical Review,* **A8,** 3419 (1973); D. J. Amit and A. Scherbakov, *Journal of Physics C,* **7,** L96 (1974) and D. J. Amit, *Journal of Physics,* **A9,** 1441 (1976). See also R. G. Priest and T. C. Lubensky, *Physical Review,* **B13,** 4159 (1976).
13. See, e.g., D. J. Amit, Ref. 12.

PART II

FURTHER APPLICATIONS AND DEVELOPMENTS

PART II

FURTHER APPLICATIONS AND DEVELOPMENTS

1

INTRODUCTION

As was mentioned in the preface, the application of field theoretic methods, and in particular of the renormalization group analysis, to critical phenomena and to other problems is far from being a closed subject. Part of the effort in this field, in addition to the natural search for new horizons in the depth of understanding of field theory and of its possible new applications, is devoted to the assimilation of the immense culture that has developed around the theory of critical phenomena in the last few years using a variety of techniques.

It is important to find out whether all the results, which are often being discovered by other techniques, can be incorporated within the very aesthetic and unified framework described in the earlier chapters. The answer is that this integration always succeeds, and often leads to easier and more general ways of arriving at the results. Part of this simplicity follows from the fact that the computation of integrals in a massless theory without a cutoff is much easier. This becomes a weighty consideration as one reaches for higher and higher order terms in ϵ.

But more important perhaps is the fact that one is dealing with the properties of the solutions of a standard, and well-defined, set of partial differential equations. All physical quantities are expressed in terms of these solutions, and hence questions about their behavior at, or away from, the fixed point; about their behavior beyond asymptotic terms; identification of all universal quantities, etc. can again be reduced to the discussion of these equations.

Part II is dedicated to a few such topics. It is by no means exhaustive of the very rich culture which has developed in this domain. The approach to scaling is discussed in greater detail, by considering the effects of the finite size of the system of irrelevant operators and of high wave-vectors. Then, universality is re-examined and extended. In particular it is shown that not only exponents are universal, but also certain scaling functions and combinations of critical amplitudes. The richness opened by the presence of more than one coupling constant is glanced at in Chapter 4, exposing such phenomena as dynamic restoration of symmetry of runaway trajectories and of second order phase transitions becoming first order – otherwise known as the Coleman-Weinberg mechanism. In Chapter 5 we describe some elements of the study of crossover phenomena – the way a system interpolates between two competing, closely spaced, different critical behaviors.

Finally, in Chapter 6, we raise another curtain. It is shown that systems with a continuous symmetry can be described by a field theory near their lower critical dimension – that number of dimensions at which Goldstone modes destroy long-range order. An independent ϵ-expansion ensues.

BEYOND LEADING SCALING

2-1 CORRECTIONS TO SCALING IN A ϕ^4 THEORY

The non-trivial fixed point is infrared-stable. One safe way of reaching it is for all the length scales — momenta, temperature t, magnetization — to tend to zero. Another is to have a bare coupling constant which lands exactly on u^* when renormalized. But this can happen only if the cutoff is infinite (see I-9-5). Since in any theory of statistical physics Λ is large but finite, scaling can come only at the asymptotic limit.

For any finite values of the momenta, the temperature difference from T_c, or of the magnetization, there will be corrections to the homogeneous scaling behavior. It is to these corrections that we now turn our attention.

Consider, for example, the vertex function $\Gamma_R^{(N)}(p_i; u, \kappa)$, at the critical temperature. If $u = u^*$, then from Eq. (I-8-43) it follows that $\Gamma_R^{(N)}$ is a homogeneous function of the scale of its momentum variables, namely:

$$\Gamma_R^{(N)}(\rho p_i; u^*, \kappa) = \rho^{N+d-\frac{1}{2}Nd-\frac{1}{2}N\eta} \Gamma_R^{(N)}(p_i; u^*, \kappa) \qquad (2-1)$$

This is the scaling form of $\Gamma^{(N)}$.

If $u \neq u^*$, but close to it, then the deviation of $\Gamma_R^{(N)}(p_i, u, \kappa)$ from its form at the fixed point can be described by:

$$\Gamma_R^{(N)}(p_i; u, \kappa) = \exp\left[\frac{N}{2}\int_{u^*}^{u}\frac{\eta(u') - \eta}{\beta(u')}\,du'\right]C^{(N)}(p_i; u, \kappa)\Gamma_R^{(N)}(p_i; u^*, \kappa) \qquad (2\text{-}2)$$

The integrand in the exponential is, of course, finite at $u = u^*$, and thus, taking the limit $u \to u^*$, one finds that

$$C^{(N)}(p_i; u^*, \kappa) = 1 \qquad (2\text{-}3)$$

On the other hand, inserting (2-2) in the renormalization group equation satisfied by $\Gamma_R^{(N)}$, $C^{(N)}$ is found to obey the equation:

$$\left[\kappa\frac{\partial}{\partial\kappa} + \beta(u)\frac{\partial}{\partial u}\right]C^{(N)}(p_i; u, \kappa) = 0 \qquad (2\text{-}4)$$

for which (2-3) serves as a boundary condition. This last equation can be used to calculate $C^{(N)}$ as a power series in $u - u^*$. To obtain $C^{(N)}$ to first order in $u - u^*$ we write

$$\beta(u) = \omega(u - u^*) + 0[(u - u^*)^2] \qquad (2\text{-}5)$$

where $\omega = \beta'(u^*)$. The solution of Eq. (2-4) with this β is

$$C^{(N)}(p_i; u, \kappa) = 1 + D_1(p_i; (u - u^*)\kappa^{-\omega}) \qquad (2\text{-}6)$$

Expanding again to first order in $u - u^*$, one finds:

$$C^{(N)}(p_i; u, \kappa) = 1 + (u - u^*)\kappa^{-\omega}D(p_i) \qquad (2\text{-}7)$$

But since $C^{(N)}$ is dimensionless, we must have

$$D(\rho p_i) = \rho^\omega D(p_i) \qquad (2\text{-}8)$$

Inserting it all back in Eq. (2-2) we can study the behavior of $\Gamma_R^{(N)}$ under a change of scale of the momenta. The result is:

$$\Gamma_R^{(N)}(\rho p_i; u, \kappa) = \exp[\ \ ]C^{(N)}(\rho p_i; u, \kappa)\rho^{N+d-\frac{1}{2}Nd-\frac{1}{2}N\eta}\Gamma_R^{(N)}(p_i; u^*, \kappa)$$

$$= \exp[\ \ ]\Gamma_R^{(N)}(p_i; u^*, \kappa)\rho^{N+d-\frac{1}{2}Nd-\frac{1}{2}N\eta}$$

$$\times\left[1 + (u - u^*)\left(\frac{\rho}{k}\right)^\omega D(p_i)\right] \qquad (2\text{-}9)$$

The fact that the fixed point is infrared-stable is tantamount to the saying that $\omega > 0$. As $\rho \to 0$, the exponential prefactor tends to unity, the correction vanishes, and scaling is approached asymptotically. This result should be compared with the behavior of the coupling constant, as derived in Sec. I-9-5. It should be noticed that since the integrand in the prefactor is finite as $u \to u^*$, the prefactor is essentially independent of ρ.

The new exponent ω, which describes the deviation from scaling, can be computed in the ϵ expansion. Using Eqs. (I-9-45) and (I-9-48) one obtains

$$\omega = \beta'(u) = \epsilon + O(\epsilon^2) \qquad (2\text{-}10)$$

This exponent was first calculated by Wegner[1].

The deviations from scaling can also be expressed in terms of the variables t or M. One has, for the correction function

$$C^{(N)}(p_i; t, M, u, \kappa) = 1 + (u - u^*)t^{\omega \nu} D(p_i t^{-1/\beta}) \qquad (2\text{-}11)$$

The proof is left as Exercise 2-1. See also Exercise 2-2.

Notice that the exponent of the correction is, again, dependent on the fixed point only i.e., it is universal. Another important point is that close to four dimensions this exponent is very small — of order ϵ. Other corrections to scaling such as those which would be induced by a ϕ^6 operator, will have powers of order unity near four dimensions. Thus the corrections discussed above are the most important ones, and the ones which disappear most slowly as ρ, or t, tends to zero (see Sec. 2-3 and 2-4).

Another role of these corrections is to bridge the gap between the Gaussian behavior and the critical behavior. Clearly, for large enough t the correlation function become Gaussian, i.e., the Ginzburg criterion is satisfied. (see Sec. I-6-4). As t increases these corrections add up to change the behavior from the anomalous critical behavior to the Gaussian one. This is a *crossover* phenomenon, in which for fixed momenta, for example, the behavior of the correlation function will cross from being dominated by the non-trivial fixed point over to the behavior dominated by the Gaussian fixed point.

2-2 FINITE-SIZE SCALING

A very important tool in the practical application of the renormalization group to specific systems follows from the realization that the size of the system is itself a variable in terms of which thermodynamic quantities scale[2]. Following Brézin[3] we will show that the idea is quite naturally incorporated in the field-theoretic framework, within which it can also be theoretically examined[3].

Consider a finite system of linear size L† and let $P_L(t)$ be a thermodynamic quantity, which becomes singular as $L \to \infty$ and $t \to 0$. It may be a

†Partially infinite geometries can also be considered[2].

susceptibility, a correlation length etc.[†] Defining

$$\frac{P_L(t)}{P(t)} = g(L, t) \qquad (2\text{-}12)$$

where $P(t)$ is the bulk value of $P_L(t)$, namely its value in the limit $L \to \infty$, the statement of finite-size scaling is:

$$g(L, t) = f(L/\xi(t)). \qquad (2\text{-}13)$$

From the fact that $P_L(t)$ is finite as $t \to 0$, and from the definition of P as the limit of P_L as $L \to \infty$, one deduces immediately the asymptotic limits of $f(x)$. Namely

$$f(x) \sim 1 \qquad\qquad \text{as } x \to \infty \qquad (2\text{-}14)$$

$$f(x) \sim x^{\rho/\nu} \qquad\qquad \text{as } x \to 0 \qquad (2\text{-}15)$$

where ρ is the critical exponent associated with $P(t)$.

The power of (2-13) is better appreciated when one notices that this scaling form, when applied to $P(t) = \xi(t)$, implies

$$\frac{\xi_{L'}(t')}{\xi_L(t)} = \frac{L'}{L} \qquad (2\text{-}16)$$

in which $(L, t) \to (L', t')$ is a scale transformation defined by

$$L'/L = \xi(t')/\xi(t) . \qquad (2\text{-}17)$$

The proof of (2-16) is left as Exercise 2-3.

On the one hand (2-17) is an exact real-space renormalization group transformation, which has $t = 0 (T = T_c)$ for a fixed point. On the other hand (2-16) is a powerful computational tool, since all the quantities are defined on finite systems. In particular one has

$$(1 + \nu^{-1})\ln(L'/L) = \ln[\dot{\xi}_{L'}(0)/\dot{\xi}_L(0)] , \qquad (2\text{-}18)$$

where $\dot{\xi}(t) = d\xi/dt$. See Exercise 2-4.

The existence of the simple renormalization group transformation (2-17) depends on the scaling assumption (2-13). It is this relation which we proceed to derive within the field theoretic framework.

For simplicity consider a single component, ϕ^4-theory in its symmetric phase. The system is contained in a d-dimensional box of linear dimension $L = Na$, where a is the lattice spacing, regularizing the theory — i.e. the cutoff momentum is $\Lambda = \pi/a$. Again, without limiting the generality of the study, periodic boundary conditions are chosen.

[†] A correlation length in a finite system will be defined by (I-2-81).

Any function $F(r)$, defined on the above lattice, has a Fourier decomposition

$$F(\mathbf{r}) = L^{-d} \sum_{\mathbf{q}} \widetilde{F}(\mathbf{q}) e^{-i q \cdot \mathbf{r}}; \qquad q_\alpha = \frac{2\pi}{L} n_\alpha \qquad (2\text{-}19)$$

where $0 < n_\alpha < N - 1$ are integers. The function $\widetilde{F}(\mathbf{q})$ is defined on the interval $(0, \frac{2\pi}{a})$ in each of the d dimensions. Such a function satisfied a Poisson identity of the type:

$$L^{-1} \sum_{p=0}^{N-1} \widetilde{F}(q) = \sum_{n=-\infty}^{\infty} \int_0^{2\pi/a} \frac{dq}{2\pi} \widetilde{F}(q) e^{iqnL} \qquad (2\text{-}20)$$

in each of the of the d directions, where on the left hand side $q = 2\pi p / L$. The importance of the identity (2-20) is in the fact that the full asymptotic behavior of the left hand side, as $L \to \infty$, is contained in the term with $n = 0$ on the right hand side. The corrections are exponentially small. This will now be used to make the central argument.

For the ϕ^4-theory, on the finite lattice, one can define Green functions $G_L^{(N)}$ and vertex functions $\Gamma_L^{(N)}$, in complete analogy with the usual case. Their limits as $L \to \infty$ are our usual functions of Chapters 2–5 of Part 1. These functions have ultra-violet divergences as $a \to 0$ even in the finite box. The crucial point is that: *the divergences of the functions in the finite volume are identical to the divergences of the same functions in the thermodynamic limit.*

To convince ourselves of this statement let us observe that the functions computed in the finite-size lattice have the same diagramatic expansion as those we have studied in Chapters I-4 and I-5. The only difference is that integrals over internal momenta are replaced by sums, such as the one appearing on the left hand side of (2-20). In the thermodynamic limit the spacing between the discrete momenta vanishes. Momentum conservation at interaction vertices carries over, and hence all considerations concerning loops carry over as well.

Every sum over a loop momentum can be replaced using the Poisson identity (2-20). If in all loops one takes the term with $n \doteq 0$, the thermodynamic limit is recovered. Hence, to prove our assertion, it suffices to show that even if a single n is non-zero, the graph is finite. Clearly, only primitive divergences are of importance. The others are cancelled by insertions.

A primitively divergent graph is one which diverges only after the last loop integration is performed. In configuration space this implies that, in *all* internal $G_0(x)$, $|x| \sim a$. The presence of a factor e^{iqL} in any loop integral will force at least two G_0's to be a distance L away. Therefore, as all G_0's in the graph will approach their short-distance singularity, there will be one (at least) which will be $G_0(L)$, and the graph will be finite. See Exercises 2-5 – 2-7.

The above considerations imply that the *same* multiplicative renormalizations required to make $\Gamma^{(N)}$ finite will eliminate the divergences of $\Gamma_L^{(N)}$ as well. Consequently, the two renormalized functions will satisfy the same renormalization group equation, and the ratio (of the renormalized functions)

$$\Phi_L^{(N)} = \Gamma_L^{(N)}/\Gamma^{(N)}$$

satisfies:

$$\left[\kappa \frac{\partial}{\partial \kappa} + \beta(u) \frac{\partial}{\partial u} + \gamma_{\phi^2}(u) t \frac{\partial}{\partial t} \right] \Phi_L^{(N)} = 0 \quad . \quad (2\text{-}21)$$

If the $\Gamma^{(N)}$'s are at zero external momenta then

$$\Phi_L^{(N)} = \Phi_L^{(N)}(t, u, \kappa) \; . \qquad (2\text{-}22)$$

The fact that $\Phi_L^{(N)}$ is dimensionless and satisfies (2-21) implies, in the notation of Chapter I-9, that

$$\Phi_L^{(N)}(t, u, 1) = \Phi_{L\rho}^{(N)}(t(\rho), u(\rho), 1). \qquad (2\text{-}23)$$

where $t(\rho)$ is given by Eq. (I-9-70).
   Choosing ρ via

$$t(\rho) = 1$$

gives $\rho = \rho(t) = \xi^{-1}(t)$, which tends to zero at $t \to 0$ (or $T \to T_c$). Hence, as $t \to 0$, $u(\rho) \to u^*$ and

$$\Phi_L^{(N)}(t, u) \sim F(L\rho(t)) \sim F(L\xi^{-1}(t)),$$

which is the desired result. Notice that we have also obtained that the function expressing the finite-size scaling is universal — it does not depend on the initial value of u nor on the renormalization procedure. But, not all is well, this universal function has no ϵ-expansion. It is singular at four dimensions[3].

2-3 ANOMALOUS DIMENSIONS OF HIGH COMPOSITE OPERATORS[5]

In Sec. I-7-9 it was argued, on the basis of naive power counting, that operators with a dimension higher than the lowest non-trivial one are irrelevant. They were subsequently discarded. These considerations leave a few questions unanswered.

(i) The ultimate effect of an operator is determined by the renormalization group equations, not by naive power counting. Thus, the consistency of the claim that the theory is dominated by the interaction with lowest dimension has to be checked after renormalization.

(ii) If consistency is verified, how do corrections to the dominant behavior induced by the irrelevant operators compare with the corrections discussed in the previous section?

(iii) Is it possible that the next operator would become dominant as the number of space-dimensions is lowered well below the critical number for the most relevant operator?

It is beyond the scope of this work to answer all these questions. These questions do indicate, as will be seen below, the importance of information about the anomalous dimensions of composite operators. We shall construct the tools necessary for the study of such operators. Then, in the next section, these tools will be used to give some answers to the questions raised above.

By a composite operator we mean an operator constructed from a product of the elementary field and its derivatives at the same point. In general it has a form like:

$$A(p) = \int dx \, \exp(ipx) T_{abc...}^{ijk...} \, \partial_i \partial_j \partial_k \ldots \phi_a(x) \phi_b(x) \phi_c(x) \ldots$$

$$= \int f_{abc...}(p_1, \ldots, p_l) \phi_a(p_1) \phi_b(p_2) \phi_c(p_3) \ldots \delta(\Sigma p_i - p) dp_1 \ldots dp_l$$

$$(2\text{-}24)$$

where T is a tensor which makes A invariant under spatial rotations, and under a global symmetry group of the field components.

The function f is rotation invariant, homogenous and symmetric in the p_i. For example, in an $O(M)$ symmetric theory we may have

$$A(p) = \frac{1}{4!} \int dx \, \exp(ipx) (\nabla \phi)^2 (\phi)^2$$

$$= \sum_{p_1 \ldots p_4} \left(\sum_{i \neq j} p_i \cdot p_j \right) S_{abcd} \phi_a(p_1) \phi_b(p_2) \phi_c(p_3) \phi_d(p_4) \delta(\Sigma p_i - p) \quad (2\text{-}25)$$

as an operator of dimension 6 in four dimensions, with S given by Eq. (I-4-36), as well as

$$A_1(p) = \frac{\kappa^{2\epsilon}}{6!} \, dx \, \exp(ipx) (\Phi^2)^3$$

$$(2\text{-}26)$$

$$= \frac{\kappa^{2\epsilon}}{6!} \sum_{p_1 \ldots p_6} \phi_a(p_1) \phi_a(p_2) \phi_b(p_3) \phi_b(p_4) \phi_c(p_5) \phi_c(p_6) \delta(\Sigma p_i - p)$$

Given a Lagrangian of the form:

$$\mathcal{L} = \mathcal{L}_1(\phi) + \lambda_A A(0) \qquad (2\text{-}27)$$

in which $\mathcal{L}_1$ is the part which includes the most relevant terms, one can express the effect of the extra term on a vertex part, to first order in λ_A, as:

$$\Gamma^{(N)}(\mathbf{p}_1, \ldots, \mathbf{p}_N; \lambda_A) = \Gamma^{(N)}(\mathbf{p}_1, \ldots, \mathbf{p}_N) + \lambda_A \Gamma_A^{(N)}(\mathbf{p}_1, \ldots, \mathbf{p}_N, 0) \qquad (2\text{-}28)$$

On the left-hand side stands the vertex calculated with $\mathcal{L}$ given by (2-27). The first term on the right is the original vertex calculated with $\mathcal{L}_1$. The second term is a vertex with an insertion of $A(0)$ calculated with the same Lagrangian. This is the expression for a regularized bare theory.

Before studying the question of how (2-28) is renormalized, we note that it is the relative behavior of the first and second terms on its right-hand side as the scale of the momenta tends to zero which will become relevant. That is, as the theory becomes scale invariant, $\Gamma_{AR}^{(N)}$ will scale. We will have:

$$\Gamma_{AR}^{(N)}(\lambda p_i, 0) \sim \lambda^D \Gamma_{AR}^{(N)}(p_i, 0)$$

The exponent D can be written as:

$$D = d - N d_\phi + d_A \qquad (2\text{-}29)$$

and d_A is called the dimension of the composite operator A. The expression for $\Gamma_R^{(N,1)}$, Exercise I-8-13, is a special case in point.

The canonical dimension of the composite operator can be obtained by dimensional analysis. It is

$$d_A^0 = m + l(\tfrac{1}{2}d - 1) - d \qquad (2\text{-}30)$$

where m is the degree of the function $f(p_i)$ in Eq. (2-24), and l is the number of factors of the field. The dimension of a vertex with an insertion of the operator A is:

$$[\Gamma_A^{(N)}(p_1, \ldots, p_N, p)] = \Lambda^{m + (l-N)(\frac{1}{2}d - 1)} \qquad (2\text{-}31)$$

The question as to whether a higer composite operator begins to dominate the asymptotic behavior of the correlation, is equivalent to the question of the stability of the original fixed point with respect to perturbation by this operator. Equations (2-28) and (2-29) imply that the original behavior is stable as long as $d_A > 0$. A becomes marginal when $d_A = 0$, and relevant for $d_A < 0$. However, as the operators which determined the original asymptotic behavior had a canonical dimension equal to zero at the critical number of space dimensions, the next lowest operator will start with a term $d_A^0 = 2$. If it is to become relevant, the corrections due to renormalization have to overpower this large value.

The next question is the renormalization of $\Gamma_A^{(N)\dagger}$. The introduction of the composite operator A into a renormalized vertex $\Gamma^{(N)}$ gives rise to new singularities – either new divergences in Λ, or new poles in ϵ – which cannot be eliminated by the renormalization of the field and of the coupling constant. This was already seen, in the case of the ϕ^2 insertion, in Chap. I-6.

FIGURE 2-1
Some low order terms in $\Gamma_{\phi^6}^{(4)}$.

(a)   (b)

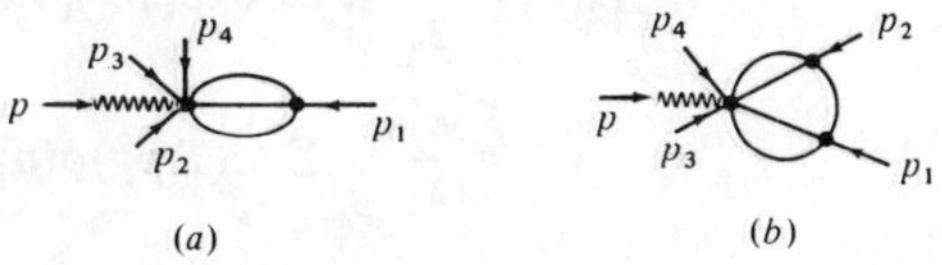

For example an insertion of ϕ^6 into $\Gamma^{(4)}$ leads to terms such as the graphs in Fig. 2-1. The wiggly line indicates the point of insertion. Graph 2-1a is quadratically divergent; it behaves like the two-loop term in $\Gamma^{(2)}$. Obviously neither a multiplication of the propagators by Z_ϕ nor a replacement of the interaction λ by g will render this graph finite.

In a theory which is regularized by a cutoff a graph like Fig. 2-1a has a term proportional to Λ^2 – independent of the external momenta, and in addition a term $\ln \Lambda$ – quadratic in the external momenta. Usually, the quadratic term has to be subtracted, and the logarithmic divergence is renormalized by multiplication. On the other hand, in a dimensionally regularized massless theory no momentum-independent terms appear. The graph Fig. 2-1a will therefore be proportional to p_1^2, the coefficients having poles corresponding to the $\ln \Lambda$'s. This should be compared with the appearance of the k^2 in Eq. (I-9-113) – see also Exercise 2-8.

But here there is a difference. If $\Gamma_{\phi^6}^{(4)}(p_1, \ldots, p_4, p)$ has to be quadratic in the p_i and symmetric, there are three different combinations which are allowed:

$$\sum_1^4 p_i^2, \quad \sum_{i \neq j} p_i p_j; \quad \left(\sum_i p_i\right)^2 = p^2 \qquad (2\text{-}32)$$

Only two of them are independent since

$$\sum_{i=1}^4 p_i^2 + \sum_{i \neq j} p_i \cdot p_j = p^2$$

After symmetrization, the graph in Fig. 2-1a is proportional to Σp_i^2 only, since this graph, with the particular distribution of momenta appearing in the figure, is equal to the second order term in $\Gamma^{(2)}(p_1)$ – Eq. (I-9-113).

$\dagger$The discussion will follow the presentation of Jug[4] which is much more streamlined than the treatment of the first edition.

On the other hand, the graph in Fig. 2-1b depends on p_1^2 and p_2^2 as well as on $\boldsymbol{p_1} \cdot \boldsymbol{p_2}$ (cf. Exercise 2-8). This fact implies that a single, momentum-independent renormalization constant will not make $\Gamma_{\phi^6}^{(4)}$ finite.

The situation is saved by noting that there are other composite operators, which at four dimensions have canonical dimension $d_A^0 = 6$:

$$A_2(p) = \frac{\kappa^\epsilon}{3!} \int dx \, \exp(ipx)(\nabla^2 \phi)\phi^3$$

$$= \frac{\kappa^\epsilon}{4!} \sum_{p_1 \dots p_4} (\Sigma \, p_i^2)\phi(p_1) \dots \phi(p_4)\delta(\Sigma \, p_i + p) \qquad (2\text{-}33)$$

$$A_2'(p) = \frac{\kappa^\epsilon}{2!2!} \int dx \, \exp(ipx)(\nabla\phi)^2 \phi^2 =$$

$$= \frac{\kappa^\epsilon}{4!} \sum_{p_1 \dots p_4} \left(\sum_{i \neq j} p_i p_j \right)\phi(p_1) \dots \phi(p_4)\delta(p_i + p) \qquad (2\text{-}34)$$

$$A_3 = \frac{\kappa^\epsilon}{4!} \int dx \, \exp(ipx)\nabla^2\phi^4 = \frac{\kappa^\epsilon p^2}{4!} \sum_{p_1 \dots p_4} \phi(p_1) \dots \phi(p_4)\delta(p_i + p) \qquad (2\text{-}35)$$

Here the discussion has been restricted to a single-component field for the sake of clarity.

The three operators (2-33) $-$ (2-35) correspond, of course, to the three momentum combinations in (2-32). And, similarly, A_2' can be replaced by the difference of A_3 and A_2 everywhere. When A_2 and A_3 are inserted in $\Gamma^{(4)}$ they give rise to graphs such as those depicted in Fig. 2-2. The stroke on a propagator stands for a factor of q^2, where q is the momentum carried by the line. Since the theory is massless a stroke on an internal line eliminates the propagator and, consequently, the graph Fig. 2-2a becomes momentum

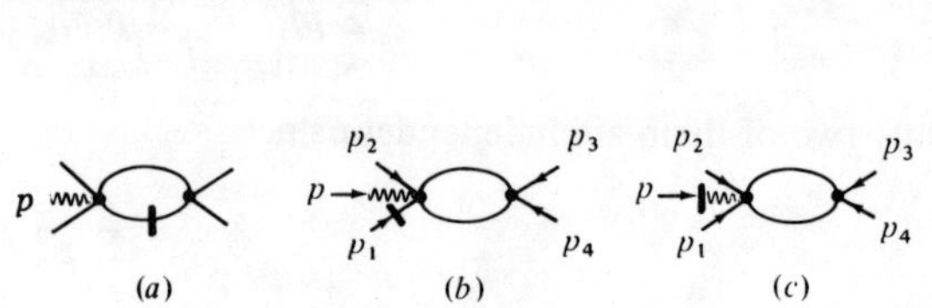

FIGURE 2-2
One loop graphs of $\Gamma_2^{(4)}$ and $\Gamma_3^{(4)}$.   (a)   (b)   (c)

independent, and it vanishes when dimensionally regularized. Graph 2-2b is proportional to Σp_i^2, and 2-2c is proportional to

$$p^2 = (\Sigma p_i)^2 = \sum_i p_i^2 + \sum_{i \neq j} p_i p_j$$

Thus, in order to renormalize $\Gamma_1^{(4)} \equiv \Gamma_{\phi_2^4}^{(4)}$ we have to include $\Gamma_2^{(4)}$ and $\Gamma_3^{(4)}$. But then A_2 and A_3 have to be treated as well. Consider therefore $\Gamma_2^{(2)}$. The lowest order divergent term is given by Fig. 2-3a, which is proportional to $p_1^2 p_2^2$. This divergence can be absorbed by the Born term of $\Gamma_4^{(2)}$, where

$$A_4(p) = \frac{1}{2!} \int dx \exp(ipx)(\nabla^2 \phi)^2$$

$$= \frac{1}{2!} \sum_{p_1 p_2} p_1^2 p_2^2 \phi(p_1)\phi(p_2)\delta(p_1 + p_2 + p) \qquad (2\text{-}36)$$

which is represented in Fig. 2-3b.

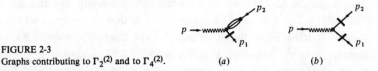

FIGURE 2-3
Graphs contributing to $\Gamma_2^{(2)}$ and to $\Gamma_4^{(2)}$. $\qquad\qquad$ (a) $\qquad\qquad\qquad$ (b)

The conclusion is that in order to renormalize $\Gamma^{(4)}$ with an insertion of an operator of dimension 6, at four dimensions, we have to include all operators which have the same dimension at $d = 4$. Operators of lower dimension are avoided by dimensional regularization of a massless theory.

There are four independent momentum combinations of degree four.

$$p_1^2 p_2^2;\ p_1^4 + p_2^4;\ (\mathbf{p}_1 + \mathbf{p}_2)^2 (p_1^2 + p_2^2);\ p^4 = (\Sigma \mathbf{p}_i)^4 \qquad (2\text{-}37)$$

A_4 in Eq. (2-36) corresponds to the first of these combinations. Corresponding to the other three one has:

$$A_5(p) = \int dx \exp(ipx)\phi \nabla^4 \phi$$

$$= \frac{1}{2!} \sum_{p_1 p_2} (p_1^4 + p_2^4)\phi(p_1)\phi(p_2)\delta(p_1 + p_2 + p) \qquad (2\text{-}38)$$

$$A_6(p) = \int dx \exp(ipx)\nabla^2(\phi \nabla^2 \phi)$$

$$= \frac{p^2}{2!} \sum_{p_1 p_2} (p_1^2 + p_2^2)\phi(p_1)\phi(p_2)\delta(p_1 + p_2 + p) \qquad (2\text{-}39)$$

$$A_7(p) = \frac{1}{2!} \int dx \exp(ipx)\nabla^4 \phi^2$$

$$= \frac{p^4}{2!} \sum_{p_1 p_2} \phi(p_1)\phi(p_2)\delta(p_1 + p_2 + p) \qquad (2\text{-}40)$$

(See also Exercise 2-9). Note that the powers of κ multiplying A_1 through

A_7 insure that these operators have equal canonical dimensions when the number of space dimensions decreases below four. In fact, they are all of canonical dimension two.

The renormalization equation will have a matrix form, namely:

$$\Gamma_{iR}^{(N)}(p_1, \ldots, p_N, p; u, \kappa) = Z_\phi^{\frac{1}{2}N} Z_{ij} \Gamma_j^{(N)}(p_1, \ldots, p_N, p; u_0) \qquad (2\text{-}41)$$

In order to determine the matrix $\bar{Z}$, $(7)^2$ conditions are needed. These can be obtained from the coefficients of 1 in $\Gamma_i^{(6)}$, from those of Σp_i^2 in $\Gamma_i^{(4)}$, and from those of the coefficients of the four momentum combinations, (2-37), in $\Gamma_i^{(2)}$.

Equation (2-41) leads to a renormalization group equation for the $\Gamma_{iR}^{(N)}$. The only κ-dependence in the bare $\Gamma_i^{(N)}$ is that dependence which was introduced explicitly when the dimensions of the inserted operators were equalized, namely, in $\Gamma_j^{(N)}$ there is a factor $\kappa^{-\frac{1}{2}\epsilon(2-l_j)}$, where l_j is the number of ϕ's in A_j. Taking this into account one derives the renormalization group equations:

$$\left\{ \left[\kappa \frac{\partial}{\partial \kappa} + \beta \frac{\partial}{\partial u} - \frac{N}{2}\eta(u) \right] \delta_{ij} + \gamma_{ij}(u) \right\} \Gamma_{jR}^{(N)} = 0 \qquad (2\text{-}42)$$

with

$$\gamma_{ij} = \tfrac{1}{2}\epsilon Z_{ik}(2 - l_k)Z_{kj}^{-1} + Z_{ik}\kappa \frac{\partial}{\partial \kappa} Z_{kj}^{-1} \qquad (2\text{-}43)$$

(see Exercise 2-10.)

Now we are ready to define the anomalous dimensions of the composite operators. They do not correspond to the individual operators $A_1 \ldots A_7$, but to linear combinations thereof. These are the linear combinations corresponding to the eigenvectors of the matrix γ_{ij}.

Let $u = u^*$, and let $V^{(\alpha)}$ be the left eigenvectors of $\gamma(u^*)$, namely:

$$\sum_i V_i^{(\alpha)}\gamma_{ij}^* = \lambda_\alpha V_j^{(\alpha)} \qquad (2\text{-}44)$$

Then

$$\Gamma_{\alpha R}^{(N)} = \sum_j V_j^{(\alpha)}\Gamma_{jR}^{(N)} \qquad (2\text{-}45)$$

satisfies the equation:

$$\left[\kappa \frac{\partial}{\partial \kappa} - \frac{N}{2}\eta + \lambda_\alpha \right]\Gamma_{\alpha R}^{(N)} = 0 \qquad (2\text{-}46)$$

Consequently, at the fixed point, these functions depend on κ as

$$\Gamma_{\alpha R}(p_i,\ p;\ u^*,\ \kappa) = \kappa^{\frac{1}{2}N\eta - \lambda_\alpha} F(p_i,\ p)$$

And using dimensional analysis one finds that they scale with the overall momentum scale ρ according to:

$$\Gamma_{\alpha R}^{(N)}(p_i,\ p,\ u^*,\ \kappa) = \rho^{d - N d_\phi + 2 - 2\epsilon + \lambda_\alpha}\Gamma_{\alpha R}^{(N)}(p_i/\rho\ ,p/\rho) \qquad (2\text{-}47)$$

The canonical dimension of A_α is 2, so its anomalous dimension is λ_α. As for the total dimension:

$$d_{A\alpha} = 2 + \lambda_\alpha \qquad (2\text{-}48)$$

(cf. Eq. (2-29)).

What is still lacking is a determination of the matrix Z, of renormalization constants. As usual, there is much freedom left at this stage. We will proceed as follows: first the theory is regularized by continuation in the number of dimensions. Hence, divergences of integer powers will automatically vanish. We then observe that only $\Gamma_i^{(2)}$, $\Gamma_i^{(4)}$ and $\Gamma_i^{(6)}$ are primitively divergent (the verification is left as Exercise 2-11). Dimensional analysis leads to the conclusion that the logarithmic divergences of $\Gamma_i^{(6)}$ are momentum independent; those of $\Gamma_i^{(4)}$ are proportional to second order polynomials in the momenta, and those of $\Gamma_i^{(2)}$ to fourth order polynomials in the momenta.

As we have argued above, there are two independent second order terms in the momenta, and four fourth order terms. Hence, the dimensionally regularized, primitively divergent vertices can be decomposed as follows:

$$\Gamma_i^{(6)} \equiv \Gamma_i^{\{1\}} \qquad (2\text{-}49)$$

$$\Gamma_i^{(4)}(p_1,\ldots,p_4;p) \equiv (\sum_{j=1}^{4} P_j^2)\Gamma_i^{\{2\}} + p^2 \Gamma_i^{\{3\}} \qquad (2\text{-}50)$$

$$\Gamma_i^{(2)}(p_1,p_2;p) \equiv p_1^2 p_2^2\,\Gamma_i^{\{4\}} + (p_1^4 + p_2^4)\Gamma_i^{\{5\}} + p^2 (p_1^2 + p_2^2)\Gamma_i^{\{6\}} + p^4\Gamma_i^{\{7\}}$$

$$(2\text{-}51)$$

One can then easily verify that the Born term of $\Gamma_i^{\{k\}}$ is $\kappa^{\frac{1}{2}\epsilon(l_i-2)\delta_i^k}$. Hence we can choose as a normalization condition:

$$\hat{\Gamma}_{iR}^{\{k\}}\big|_{SP} \equiv \kappa^{\frac{1}{2}\epsilon(2 - l_i)}\,\Gamma_{iR}^{\{k\}}\big|_{SP} = \delta_i^k \qquad (2\text{-}52)$$

where SP is chosen with momenta of size κ, symmetric under permutations. The renormalization of $\Gamma_i^{\{k\}}(p_i;p)$ is achieved by

$$\hat{\Gamma}_{iR}^{\{k\}}(p_i;p) = Z_\phi^{\frac{1}{2}lk} Z_{ij} \hat{\Gamma}_j^{\{k\}}(p_i;p) \qquad (2\text{-}53)$$

These normalization conditions can be inverted to give:

$$Z_{ik}^{-1} = Z_\phi^{\frac{1}{2}lk} \hat{\Gamma}_i^{\{k\}}\big|_{SP} \qquad (2\text{-}54)$$

From this, as well as from minimal subtraction, one can compute Z to any given number of loops, and obtain γ_{ij} as a power series in u and ϵ.

The considerations given above all concern the special case of operators of canonical dimension 6 in a ϕ^4 theory in four dimensions. The technique is, of course, quite general. It has been applied to operators of dimension 4 in a Heisenberg model in two dimensions[6] and to operators of dimension 8 in a ϕ^3 theory in six dimensions[7].

2-4 CORRECTIONS DUE TO IRRELEVANT OPERATORS

In the scaling region, $\Gamma_R^{(N)}$ scales like $\rho^{d-Nd\phi}$. Hence, the question of the relevance of the higher composite operators discussed in the previous section reduces to the sign of $d_{A\alpha}$. If the dimension of A_α is positive the operator is irrelevant since, as $\rho \to 0$, the first order correction in Eq. (2-28) will vanish faster than the leading term. Very close to four dimensions

$$d_{A\alpha} \approx 2$$

Hence, the corrections induced become smaller by two powers of ρ. These should be compared with the correction of order ρ^ϵ induced by the finite cutoff, or by the fact that $u \neq u^*$, which was the subject of Sec. 2-1.

In fact, one can study the corrections to scaling due to operators of dimension 4 at four dimensions – operators such as ϕ^4, $\phi\nabla^2\phi$, $\nabla^2\phi^2$. The result is exactly the same as that arrived in Sec. 2-1. This calculation, which runs along lines completely analogous to Sec. 2-3, is left as Exercise 2-12.

Here the procedure will be illustrated by the computation of the

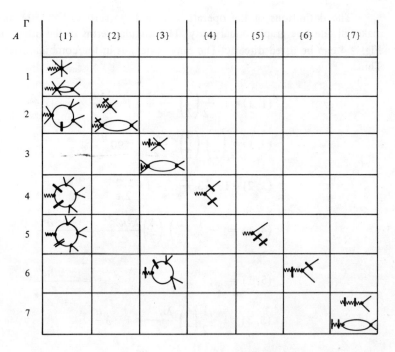

FIGURE 2-4
Graphs of $\Gamma_i^{\{k\}}$ at one-loop order.

anomalous dimensions of the operators of dimension 6 to order ϵ. The results are not very exciting but the intermediate steps do bring out many general features of the technique.

To determine Z_{ij} we apply the method of minimal subtraction to Eq. (2-52). The ϵ expansion is generated by keeping graphs up to a certain number of loops. Here only one-loop graphs are needed, and since no field renormalization occurs at this level, $Z_\phi = 1$. Some of them – the off-diagonal ones – contribute to orders higher than ϵ.

In Fig. 2-4 the one-loop graphs contributing to $\Gamma_l^{\{k\}}$ are represented. There are 49 entries, but at this level many of them vanish. Only graphs which lead to poles in ϵ are drawn, as these are the only ones which will contribute to $Z_{ij}(u, \epsilon)$. Thus, graph such as those in Fig. 2-5 will not have poles, and are consequently dropped. Again, the stroke on a propagator implies a factor of q^2, where q is the momentum carried by the line. The result is that all the graphs in Fig. 2-4, which are not trees, have integrals equal to the familiar $I - (I\text{-}7\text{-}27)$ with $m = 0$. They are all proportional to ϵ^{-1}.

FIGURE 2-5
One-loop graphs which do not
contribute to Z_{ij}.

The definitions of the operators A_i and the vertices $\hat{\Gamma}^{\{k\}}$ are such as to make all the tree graphs equal unity. The singular terms in the other graphs in Fig. 2-4 can be listed directly. The only variety is in the combinatorial factors. Thus:

$$(1, 1) = 1 - \frac{1}{2} \binom{6}{2} \frac{\lambda \kappa^{-\epsilon}}{\epsilon} = 1 - \frac{15}{2} \frac{u}{\epsilon}$$

$$(2, 1) = \binom{6}{2} \binom{4}{2} \frac{\lambda^2 \kappa^{-2\epsilon}}{\epsilon} = 90 \frac{u^2}{\epsilon}$$

$$(2, 2) = 1 - \frac{1}{3} 3 \frac{\lambda \kappa^{-\epsilon}}{\epsilon} = 1 - \frac{3}{2} \frac{u}{\epsilon}$$

$$(4, 1) = -\frac{1}{2} \binom{6}{2} \binom{4}{2} \frac{\lambda^3 \kappa^{-3\epsilon}}{\epsilon} = \frac{-15 u^3}{\epsilon}$$

$$(5, 1) = \qquad\qquad = \frac{-90 u^3}{\epsilon}$$

$$(3, 3) = 1 - \frac{1}{2} \binom{4}{2} \frac{\lambda \kappa^{-\epsilon}}{\epsilon} = 1 - 3 \frac{u}{\epsilon}$$

$$(6, 3) = \binom{4}{2} \frac{\lambda^2 \kappa^{-2\epsilon}}{\epsilon} = 6 \frac{u^2}{\epsilon}$$

$$(7, 7) = 1 - \frac{1}{2} \frac{\lambda \kappa^{-\epsilon}}{\epsilon} = 1 - \frac{1}{2} \frac{u}{\epsilon}$$

We ignore the fact that the matrix $\Gamma_i^{\{k\}}$ is triangular, which implies that all its functions $- Z_{ij}, \gamma_{ij}$ etc. $-$ are triangular as well. In this case the eigenvalues lie on the diagonal, and there is no coupling between the various operators. But this is not true beyond the one-loop level. Also, at this level one can replace $\lambda \kappa^{-\epsilon}$ by u (see, e.g., Eq. (I-9-1)).

Let us now denote by M_{ik} the singular part of $\Gamma_i^{\{k\}}|_{\mathrm{SP}}$, namely the poles in ϵ. Clearly, any Z's satisfying the renormalization equation (2-52) will also render

$$N_{ij} = \delta_{ij} + M_{ij}$$

finite, and vice versa. Hence N_{ij}^{-1} will render $\hat{\Gamma}$ and all other Γ's finite. This would amount to employing minimal subtraction, rather than the normalization condition (2-52).

At the level of one loop $Z_\phi = 1$, and one has

$$Z_{ij}^{-1} = N_{ij} = \delta_{ij} + M_{ij} \qquad (2\text{-}55)$$

Since M_{ij} vanishes with u, we can write

$$Z_{ij} = \delta_{ij} - M_{ij}$$

Next we compute the two terms in γ_{ij}, Eq. (2-43). The second term can be transformed in the same way as γ_ϕ was transformed by Eq. (I-8-22); namely:

$$Z_{ik} \kappa \frac{\partial}{\partial \kappa} Z_{kj}^{-1} = \beta(u) Z_{ik} \frac{\partial}{\partial u} Z_{kj}^{-1} = -\epsilon u \frac{\partial}{\partial u} M_{ij} \qquad (2\text{-}56)$$

where the last equality is true only at the one-loop level, and $\beta(u)$ was substituted from Eq. (I-9-45).

From (2-55) and the form of the matrix M it follows that $M \propto \epsilon^{-1}$. Hence, (2-56) is independent of ϵ. For the first term in γ_{ij} it implies:

$$\tfrac{1}{2} \epsilon Z_{ik} (2 - l_k) Z_{kj}^{-1} = \tfrac{1}{2} \epsilon [(2 - l_j)\delta_{ij} - (l_i - l_j)M_{ij}] \qquad (2\text{-}57)$$

The first term is linear in ϵ, and the second is independent of ϵ but is at least linear in u. At the fixed point u itself is proportional to ϵ.

When (2-56) and (2-57) are evaluated as functions of u and ϵ, substituted in Eq. (2-43) for γ_{ij}, and $u^* = \tfrac{2}{3}\epsilon$ is substituted for u, one arrives at:

$$\gamma_{ij} = \begin{matrix}
3\epsilon & 0 & 0 & 0 & 0 & 0 & 0 \\
-40\epsilon^2 & 0 & 0 & 0 & 0 & 0 & 0 \\
0 & 0 & \epsilon & 0 & 0 & 0 & 0 \\
\frac{40}{3}\epsilon^3 & 0 & 0 & 0 & 0 & 0 & 0 \\
\frac{80}{3}\epsilon^3 & 0 & 0 & 0 & 0 & 0 & 0 \\
0 & 0 & 0 & 0 & 0 & 0 & 0 \\
0 & 0 & 0 & 0 & 0 & 0 & \tfrac{1}{3}\epsilon
\end{matrix}$$

The eigenvalues are the terms in the diagonal. None of them is negative. For all of them the dimension, Eq. (2-48), will be greater than 2, and the fixed point will stay stable against perturbation by the corresponding operators.

Clearly, at higher orders the matrix becomes much more complicated. One then uses some simplifying features which reduce the order of the final matrix that has to be diagonalized. The two most general ones are

(i) *The dimension of every operator which is a total derivative is simply related to the dimension of a lower operator, an operator which, at the critical number of dimensions, has a dimension lower by an integer.* For example, in our case when A_3 is inserted in a vertex it gives simply p^2 times a vertex in which ϕ^4

is inserted. Similarly if A_7 is inserted it gives p^4 times the vertex with a ϕ^2 insertion. In the first case one finds that

$$d_{A_3} = 2 + d_{\phi^4}$$

Then, using the result of Exercise 2-12, or of Ref. 9, namely that

$$d_{\phi^4} = \omega = \beta'(u^*)$$

(see also Sec. 2-1), one finds that

$$d_{A_3} = 2 + \epsilon = 2 + \lambda_3 + 0(\epsilon^2)$$

as is implied by Eq. (2-48).

For A_7 one has

$$d_{A_7} = 4 + d_{\phi^2} = 2 + \lambda_7 + 0(\epsilon^2)$$

as it should. The verification is left as Exercise 2-13.

(ii) *For every independent equation which follows from the classical equations of motion there is an eigenvalue of γ_{ij} which can be expressed in terms of dimensions of lower operators.*

In the ϕ^4 theory one has the classical equation:

$$(-\nabla^2 + \mu^2)\phi + \frac{\lambda}{3!}\phi^3 = 0 \qquad (2\text{-}58)$$

To this equation there correspond two independent relations between our operators: If (2-58) is multiplied by ϕ^3 one obtains a relation between A_1 and A_2, and if it is multiplied by $\nabla^2\phi$, a relation between A_2 and A_4 is obtained. Here only the first instance will be discussed. Multiplying Eq. (2-58) by ϕ^3 leads, in the renormalized massless theory to an equation of the form

$$\sum_i a_i(u)\Gamma_{iR}^{(N)}(p_1 \ldots p_N, p) = N\kappa^{-\epsilon}p_N^2 \Gamma_{\phi^3 R}^{(N-1)}(p_1, \ldots, p_{N-1}, p_N + p) \qquad (2\text{-}59)$$

The origin of such equations is discussed in App. 2-1. The relation between A_2 and A_4 leads to a simpler equation, given in App. 2-1. Its simplicity leaves it in the scope of the cases discussed in Ref. 8. Eq. (2-59) brings out some new features.

The $a_i(u)$ are a set of dimensionless coefficients, which are generated from the equation of motion in the process of renormalization. They depend on u only. At the fixed point the behavior of the right-hand side of (2-59) can be expressed in terms of the anomalous dimensions of operators such as $\phi^3(x)$. This is a lower operator than the insertions on the left-hand side, which have the same dimension as ϕ^6. The operator

$$\left[\kappa\frac{\partial}{\partial\kappa} - \tfrac{1}{2}(N-1)\eta + \epsilon + \gamma_{\phi^3}^* \right]$$

when applied to the right-hand side of (2-59) at the fixed point, gives zero. Therefore one has:

$$\sum_i a_i(u)\left[\kappa\frac{\partial}{\partial\kappa}-\tfrac{1}{2}(N-1)\eta+\epsilon+\gamma^*_{\phi^3}\right]\Gamma^{(N)}_{iR}=0 \qquad (2\text{-}60)$$

where the anomalous dimension of ϕ^3, $\gamma^*_{\phi^3}$, is defined by:

$$\left[\kappa\frac{\partial}{\partial\kappa}-\tfrac{1}{2}N\eta+\gamma^*_{\phi^3}\right]\Gamma^{(N)}_{\phi^3R}=0 \qquad (2\text{-}61)$$

The vertices $\Gamma^{(N)}_i$ satisfy Eq. (2-42). When this is substituted in (2-60) one finds the equation:

$$\sum_i a_i(u^*)\left[-\gamma_{ij}+(\epsilon-\tfrac{1}{2}\eta+\gamma^*_{\phi^3})\delta_{ij}\right]\Gamma^{(N)}_{jR}(p_1\ldots p_N,p)=0$$

from which it follows that $a_i(u^*)$ is a left eigenvector of γ_{ij} namely:

$$a_i\gamma_{ij}=a_j(\epsilon-\tfrac{1}{2}\eta+\gamma^*_{\phi^3}) \qquad (2\text{-}62)$$

so that

$$\lambda=\epsilon-\tfrac{1}{2}\eta+\gamma^*_{\phi^3}$$

is an eigenvalue.

The anomalous dimension of ϕ^3 can be expressed in terms of that of ϕ, i.e., η. This follows again from the equation of motion. The result is:

$$\gamma^*_{\phi^3}=\epsilon-\tfrac{1}{2}\eta \qquad (2\text{-}63)$$

The derivations is given in App. 2-1, or alternatively in Ref. 9.

The result is that γ_{ij} has 2ϵ as an eigenvalue to all orders.

2-5 NEXT-TO-LEADING TERMS IN THE SCALING REGION

In Sec. I-8-8 it was shown that at the fixed point the two-point function in the symmetric state (above T_c) behaves as[†]

$$\Gamma^{(2)}(p;t,\kappa)=\kappa^\eta p^{2-\eta}f(p\xi)$$

with $\xi=t^{-\nu}$. The knowledge that at the critical point itself $\Gamma^{(2)}_R$ is finite, implies that $f(x)$ has a finite limit when $x\to\infty$ – namely, when $\xi\to\infty$ at a fixed value of p.

This behavior characterizes the function when the momentum p is much smaller than the cutoff (see Sec. I-9-5). This condition we keep. The corrections

---

[†]Throughout this section the subscript "R", denoting that the functions are renormalized, will be dropped.

due to deviations from the limit $p/\Lambda \to 0$, which imply that $u \neq u^*$, were discussed in Sec. 2-1. Next one can ask the question: given that in the scaling region

$$\Gamma^{(2)}(p; t, \kappa) \to C\kappa^\eta p^{2-\eta} \qquad (2\text{-}64)$$

when $t^\nu/p \to 0$, what are the next terms in an expansion of $\Gamma^{(2)}$ in powers of t^ν/p?

As we shall see, the result is that the first correction to (2-64) consists of two terms, which are of the same order of magnitude near $d = 4$, namely:

$$\Gamma^{(2)}(p; t, \kappa) \sim \kappa^\eta p^{2-\eta} [C + C_1 t p^{-1/\nu} + C_2 (t p^{-1/\nu})^{1-\alpha}] + 0(t^2 p^{-2\nu}) \qquad (2\text{-}65)$$

It is interesting to mention that historically the two correction terms were discovered separately, in different contexts, by thermodynamic arguments. The last term can be shown to be necessary if the connection between the two-point correlation function and the specific heat is to be consistent.[10] The term proportional to t was introduced in order to explain anomalies in the resistivity of metals.[11]

Here it will be shown how both terms arise in a systematic way within the framework of renormalized field theory.[12]

We start by writing the equation for $\Gamma^{(2)}(p; t, \kappa)$, Eq. (I-8-67), with $N = 2$, in the form:

$$\left(\kappa \frac{\partial}{\partial \kappa} - \eta\right) \Gamma^{(2)}(p; t, \kappa) = \theta t \frac{\partial}{\partial t} \Gamma^{(2)}(p; t, \kappa) \qquad (2\text{-}66)$$

with $\theta = \nu^{-1} - 2$. The assertion that $\Gamma^{(2)}$ has the limit (2-64) as $t \to 0$ for fixed p is equivalent to the statement that

$$\lim_{t \to 0} t \frac{\partial}{\partial t} \Gamma^{(2)} = 0 \qquad (2\text{-}67)$$

From Eq. (I-7-82) it follows that:

$$\frac{\partial}{\partial t} \Gamma^{(2)}(p; t, \kappa) = \Gamma^{(2,1)}(p, -p, 0; t, \kappa) \qquad (2\text{-}68)$$

Hence, in order to obtain the next-to-leading terms in $\Gamma^{(2)}$ it is sufficient to calculate the leading term of $\Gamma^{(2,1)}$ on the right-hand side of (2-68).

The vertex $\Gamma^{(2,1)}$ also satisfies a renormalization group equation. The derivation of this equation was the subject of Exercise I-8-9. At the fixed point this equation can be written as:

$$\left[\kappa \frac{\partial}{\partial \kappa} - (\theta + \eta)\right] \Gamma^{(2,1)}(p, -p, 0; t, \kappa) = \theta t \frac{\partial}{\partial t} \Gamma^{(2,1)} = \theta t \Gamma^{(2,2)}(p, -p, 0, 0; t, \kappa)$$

$$(2\text{-}69)$$

The last equality follows again from Eq. (I-7-82).

In this case is faced with a new situation, namely, the right-hand side of Eq. (2-69) diverges as $t \to 0$. Therefore, the leading term of $\Gamma^{(2,1)}$ cannot be obtained by solving the homogeneous equation. The reason for the divergence is, of course, the vanishing of two of the external momenta — those of the two ϕ^2 insertions. It is not simply that $\Gamma^{(2,2)}$ diverges as $t \to 0$, $\Gamma^{(2,1)}$ in Eq. (2-68) diverges as well. It is $t\Gamma^{(2,2)}$ that diverges, implying a rather strong divergence of the vertex for $t \to 0$.

FIGURE 2-6
A first order graph of $\Gamma^{(2,2)}$.

A simple way of noticing this divergence is to consider a low order graph of $\Gamma^{(2,2)}$, as shown in Fig. 2-6. Clearly, if this graph is calculated with zero momentum insertions and zero mass, it is infinite. The expansion of vertices in t implies finite external momenta until after the series in t has been resummed. Then the momenta can be set equal to zero. Resuming (I-7-82) implies that t enters as a mass squared. Therefore,

$$\Gamma^{(2,2)}(p, -p, 0, 0; t, \kappa) \underset{t \to 0}{\sim} t^{(d-6)/2} = t^{-1-\frac{1}{2}\epsilon} \qquad (2\text{-}70)$$

By the same token

$$\Gamma^{(2,1)}(p, -p, 0; t; \kappa) \underset{t \to 0}{\sim} t^{-\frac{1}{2}\epsilon} \qquad (2\text{-}71)$$

assuring us of (2-67).

In order to obtain the asymptotic behavior of $\Gamma^{(2,2)}$ on the right-hand side of Eq. (2-64) a new tool is required. This is the *Operator Product Expansion,* otherwise known as the *Short Distance Expansion.* We now make a detour to discuss this technique.

2-6 THE OPERATOR PRODUCT EXPANSION

It was postulated independently by Wilson[13] and by Kadanoff[14] that a product of two fields at two different, but close, points can be expanded according to

$$\phi(x)\phi(y) = \sum_i c_i(x - y) A_i\left(\frac{x+y}{2}\right) \qquad (2\text{-}72)$$

when $|x - y| \sim 0$. The c_i are coefficients, and the A_i are operators: The statement (2-72) acquires a meaning when it is substituted in a correlation function or in a vertex. Namely, it implies that

$$\Gamma^{(N)}\left(\frac{p}{2} + k, \frac{p}{2} - k, p_3 \ldots p_N\right) = \sum_i c_i(k)\Gamma_{A_i}^{(N-2)}(p_3, \ldots, p_N, p) \qquad (2\text{-}73)$$

where p is the momentum carried by the insertion A_i, and k is much greater than all other momenta.

In general the unit operator will be present among the operators A_i in Eq. (2-72). It does not contribute, however, when substituted in a vertex function since it represents graphs which are not connected (see Exercise 2-14 and 2-15).

The proof of the expansion in the context of renormalized perturbation theory is due to Zimmermann. It will not be reproduced here. The important feature is that the terms on the right-hand side of Eq. (2-73) can be classified by their engineering (naïve) dimensions.

The operators A_i are composite operators with the internal symmetry of the expanded product. In our case they are even powers of ϕ and even powers of derivatives. Near four dimensions each additional pair of ϕ's or of ∇'s adds 2 units to the dimension of A_i in units of momentum. To compensate, the dimension of c_i must decrease. Thus, if

$$A_i(x) = (\nabla)^{m_i} \phi^{l_i}$$

then

$$[A_i(x)] = \Lambda^{m_i + l_i(d/2 - 1)} \qquad (2\text{-}74)$$

Correspondingly,

$$[c_i(k)] = \Lambda^{-(l_i - 2)(d/2 - 1) - m_i + \epsilon} \qquad (2\text{-}75)$$

(see Exercise 2-16), from which we see that an increase in m_i or in l_i decreases the dimension of c_i by integers.

The result is that the leading contribution, when k is large, comes from the coefficient of the operator with lowest dimension — in our case from $\phi^2(x)$. The correction will be smaller by a factor of $k^{-2+\delta}$. It will correspond to the operators $\phi^4(x)$ and $[\nabla\phi(x)]^2$, where $\delta \to 0$ as $d \to 4$. Since in the case discussed in Sec 2-5 all momenta except k are zero, this extra power of k^{-2} is accompanied by a factor t. Thus, the next term beyond the first one will be smaller by a factor t/k^2, roughly. So this is just the desired expansion.

Each of the coefficients $c_i(k)$ satisfies a renormalization group equation. The one we are concerned with satisfies an equation in which all the coefficients are given in terms of $\eta(u)$ and $\nu(u)$. This is not true for the higher coefficients,[15] which satisfy equations in which there appear anomalous dimensions of higher composite operators (see, e.g., Sec. 2-3).

As was already mentioned, the term we need in order to obtain the leading behavior of $\Gamma^{(2,2)}$ is the one proportional to $\phi^2(x)$. The corresponding relation between vertices follows from Eq. (2-73), namely:

$$\Gamma^{(N)}\left(\frac{p}{2}+k,\frac{p}{2}-k,p_3\ldots p_N\right)\sim c(k)\Gamma^{(N-2,1)}(p_3,\ldots,p_N,p) \qquad (2\text{-}76)$$

The vertices on both sides of this equation satisfy a renormalization group equation. This leads to an equation for $c(k)$ which reads:

$$\left[\kappa\frac{\partial}{\partial\kappa}+\beta(u)\frac{\partial}{\partial u}-\eta(u)+(\nu^{-1}(u)-2)\right]c(k)=0 \qquad (2\text{-}77)$$

(The derivation is left as Exercise 2-17). At the fixed point this equation reduces to:

$$\left[\kappa\frac{\partial}{\partial\kappa}-(\eta-\theta)\right]c(k)=0 \qquad (2\text{-}78)$$

From (2-75) it follows that the dimension of $c(k)$ is ϵ. If in addition one assumes that it has a limit as $t\to 0$, then Eq. (2-78) implies:

$$c(k)\equiv A\kappa^{\eta-\theta}k^{\epsilon+\theta-\eta} \qquad (2\text{-}79)$$

2-7 COMPUTATION OF NEXT-TO-LEADING TERMS IN ϵ-EXPANSION

Now we return to the problem raised in Sec. 2-5. On the right-hand side of Eq. (2-69) we have $\Gamma^{(2,2)}$, and all momenta except p, $-p$ are zero. Therefore, p is a large momentum in the sense in which k was large to justify an operator product expansion.

The analogue of Eq. (2-73) is

$$\Gamma^{(2,2)}(p,-p,0,0)\sim c(p)\Gamma^{(0,3)}(0,0,0) \qquad (2\text{-}80)$$

with $c(p)$ given by Eq. (2-79) (see, e.g., Exercise 2-18). One may wonder why this factorization was not performed on $\Gamma^{(2,1)}$ in Eq. (2-66). The reason is that we are dealing with renormalized vertices, and $\Gamma^{(0,2)}$, which would have appeared on the right-hand side of the equation corresponding to (2-80), is not multiplicatively renormalizable (see, e.g., Sec. I-8-10).

To obtain the leading behavior of $\Gamma^{(0,3)}$ as a function of κ and t we turn to the renormalization group equation satisfied by this function at the fixed point, namely,

$$\left[\kappa \frac{\partial}{\partial \kappa} - \theta t \frac{\partial}{\partial t} - 3\theta\right]\Gamma^{(0,3)} = 0 \qquad (2\text{-}81)$$

Taking into account that the dimension of $\Gamma^{(0,3)}$ is $(-2 - \epsilon)$, the solution can be written down as:

$$\Gamma^{(0,3)}(0, 0, 0; t, \kappa) = B\kappa^{-2-\epsilon} \left(\frac{t}{\kappa^2}\right)^{-1-\alpha} \qquad (2\text{-}82)$$

That this is indeed the solution can be verified by substitution (see also Exercise 2-19). The index α is the index of the specific heat, which enters here through the scaling relation

$$d\nu = 2 - \alpha \qquad (2\text{-}83)$$

Combining Eq. (2-69) with (2-80), (2-79), and (2-82) one arrives at:

$$\left[\kappa \frac{\partial}{\partial \kappa} - (\theta + \eta)\right]\Gamma^{(2,1)}(p, -p, 0; t, \kappa) \sim D\left(\frac{p}{\kappa}\right)^{\epsilon+\theta-\eta} \left(\frac{t}{\kappa^2}\right)^{-\alpha} \qquad (2\text{-}84)$$

The solution of this equation consists of two parts. One is the solution of the homogeneous equation. This part would have been obtained had we treated Eq. (2-69) ignoring its right-hand side, as we did with the equation for $\Gamma^{(2)}$. The second part is the solution of the inhomogeneous equation. Thus:

$$\Gamma^{(2,1)}(p, -p, 0; t, \kappa) \sim E\left(\frac{p}{\kappa}\right)^{-\theta-\eta} + F\left(\frac{p}{\kappa}\right)^{\epsilon+\theta-\eta} \left(\frac{t}{\kappa^2}\right)^{-\alpha} \qquad (2\text{-}85)$$

with

$$F = \frac{D}{\epsilon - 2\eta}$$

Clearly, the two terms in (2-85) do not differ by a finite power of a small parameter close to four dimensions.

When (2-85) is inserted back into (2-66) the solution for $\Gamma^{(2)}$ will include three terms. One — the solution of the homogeneous equation — is just (2-64). The other two — the solution of the inhomogeneous equation — are just the second and third terms in the square brackets in Eq. (2-65). Written with explicit κ-dependence, $\Gamma^{(2)}$ reads:

$$\Gamma^{(2)}(p; t, \kappa) \sim \kappa^\eta p^{2-\eta}[C + C_1'\kappa^\theta tp^{-1/\nu} + C_2'\kappa^{\theta(1-\alpha)}(tp^{-1/\nu})^{1-\alpha}] \qquad (2\text{-}86)$$

To obtain this result in a direct ϵ expansion in perturbation theory would be rather difficult unless it is assumed in advance that the correction is made of exactly two terms[16]. In the present method no such apriori knowledge is required. It is also interesting to note that, had we neglected the right-hand side of Eq. (2-69), only the term regular in t would have been obtained. In fact, going down the chain of vertices one can generate an infinite series of terms of the form

$$(tp^{-1/v})^n$$

in $\Gamma^{(2)}$.

The next correction to the two-point correlation function — the one smaller again by a factor t/p^2 near four dimensions — has also been obtained by the technique described above[15], as well as the first correction in the state with broken symmetry[17]. These results have also been extended to interpolate between the region $p\xi < 1$ and $p\xi > 1$[18].

Appendix 2-1

RENORMALIZED EQUATIONS OF MOTION

In this appendix three special renormalized equations of motion will be derived, in a ϕ^4-theory, at its critical point. These will serve to justify some of the results derived in Secs. 2-3 and 2-4, as well as to exemplify a very powerful general tool. A variety of such relations are derived in the appendices to G. Jug's article ref. (4), who also applied them very creatively[19]. We will follow his presentation below.

Consider a regularized, symmetric ϕ^4-theory. Since the integral of a derivative of a function, which vanishes on the boundary, is zero, we have:

$$0 = \int \mathcal{D}\phi \; \frac{\delta}{\delta\phi(x)} \; \exp\left\{-\int [\mathcal{L}(\phi) - J\phi] \, dx\right\}$$

$$= \int \mathcal{D}\phi \left[\frac{\partial \mathcal{L}(\phi)}{\partial \phi(x)} - J(x)\right] \exp\left\{-\int [\mathcal{L}(\phi) - J\phi] \, dx\right\}$$

But

$$\frac{\partial \mathcal{L}}{\partial \phi} = \mathcal{L}'(\phi)$$

can be replaced by $\mathcal{L}'(\delta/\delta J)$, which leads to the functional identity:

$$[\mathcal{L}'(\delta/\delta J(x)) - J(x)]\, Z\{J\} = 0 \quad \text{(A2-1)}$$

This is a functional differential equation for the partition function, or for the generating functional of the Green functions.

It will be assumed that the theory is dimensionally regularized, and hence, at the critical point the bare mass is zero. Eq. (A2-1) can then be explicitly written as:

$$\left[-\nabla_x^2 \frac{\delta}{\delta J(x)} + \frac{\lambda}{3!} \left(\frac{\delta}{\delta J(x)} \right)^3 \right] Z\{J\} = J(x) Z\{J\} \quad \text{(A2-2)}$$

in which

$$Z_{\phi^3(x)}\{J\} \equiv \frac{1}{3!} \left(\frac{\delta}{\delta J(x)} \right)^3 Z\{J\} \quad \text{(A2-3)}$$

is the generating functional for Green functions with an insertion of the operator $(1/3!)\phi^3(x)$.

Eq. (A2-2) can be written as an equation for connected functions. Denoting by $W_{\phi^3}\{J\}$ the generating functional for connected Green functions with an insertion of $(1/3!)\phi^3(x)$, one has

$$-\nabla_x^2 \frac{\delta W\{J\}}{\delta J(x)} + \lambda W_{\phi^3(x)}\{J\} = J(x) \quad \text{(A2-4)}$$

See Exercise 2-20.

The Legendre transform, with respect to J, of this equation leads to an equation for the generating functionals of the vertex parts, namely:

$$-\nabla_x^2 \phi(x) + \lambda \Gamma_{\phi^3(x)}\{\phi\} = (\delta/\delta\phi(x))\Gamma\{\phi\} \quad \text{(A2-5)}$$

Either of the last two equations can be used to generate relations between renormalized Green functions, or vertex functions, with an without insertions.
Case A The anomalous dimension of ϕ^3

Operating on Eq. (A2-5) with $N(>1)$ derivatives $\delta/\delta\bar\phi(x_i)$ and Fourier transforming one finds:

$$\Gamma^{(N+1)}(p_1,\ldots,p_N;p) = \lambda \Gamma_{\phi^3}^{(N)}(p_1,\ldots,p_N;p) \quad \text{(A2-6)}$$

where p is the momentum associated with the explicit coordinate in (A2-5). The insertion on the right hand side of (A2-6) is of the operator

$$\phi^3(p) = \frac{1}{3!} \int dx\, \phi^3(x) \exp(ipx) \quad \text{(A2-7)}$$

The first term in (A2-7) is renormalized by multiplication by $Z_\phi^{(N+1)/2}$, which removes the poles from the second term as well. If we define Z_{ϕ^3} via

$$\Gamma_{\phi^3 R}^{(N)} = Z_\phi^{N/2} Z_{\phi^3} \Gamma_{\phi^3}^{(N)} \qquad \text{(A2-8)}$$

then the renormalized version of Eq. (A2-7) will read:

$$\Gamma_R^{(N+1)}(p_1, \dots, p_N, p) + \kappa^\epsilon f(u)\Gamma_{\phi^3 R}^{(N)}(p_1, \dots, p_N, p) = 0 \qquad \text{(A2-9)}$$

It is important to notice that in the process of renormalization ϕ^3 does not mix with other operators, as there are no other operators except ∇_ϕ^2 which have the same dimension at $d = 4$. But this operator is a total derivative, and it renormalizes by itself, as was discussed in Sec. 2-4. This allows one to identify the anomalous dimension of ϕ^3, rather than just an eigenvalue of an unknown combination of operators, as is the case in the examples which will be considered below.

The function $f(u)$ is given by:

$$f(u) = \kappa^{-\epsilon} \lambda(u) Z_\phi^{1/2} Z_{\phi^3}^{-1}$$

which must be finite at every order in u, as $\epsilon \to 0$.

At the fixed point Eq. (A2-9) implies that $\Gamma_{\phi^3 R}^{(N)}$ satisfies the equation:

$$\left(\kappa \frac{\partial}{\partial \kappa} - \frac{N+1}{2}\eta + \epsilon \right)\Gamma_{\phi^3 R}^{(N)} = 0 \qquad \text{(A-10)}$$

Comparing with Eq. (2-61) one arrives at (2-63). See Exercise 2-21.

Case B The eigenvalue of γ_{ij} for an operator of dimension 6 in a multi-component ϕ^4-theory[4].

If instead of the single component theory of (A) above, one considers a theory with N fields and

$$\mathscr{L}_{\text{Int}} = \frac{1}{4!}\lambda F_{ijkl}\phi_i\phi_j\phi_k\phi_l \qquad \text{(A2-11)}$$

it is straight-forward to show that (A2-2) is replaced by:

$$\left[-\nabla_x^2 \frac{\delta}{\delta J_i(x)} + \frac{\lambda}{3!}F_{ijkl}\frac{\delta^3}{\delta J_j(x)\delta J_k(x)\delta J_l(x)} \right] Z\{J\} = J_i(x)Z\{J\}$$

$$\text{(A2-12)}$$

The interaction tensor F is assumed to be symmetric in all indices Eqs. (A2-4) and (A2-5) are, respectively, generalized to:

$$-\nabla_x^2 \frac{\delta W\{J\}}{\delta J_i(x)} + \lambda W_{\phi_i^3(x)} J = J_i(x) \qquad \text{(A2-13)}$$

and

$$-\nabla_x^2 \bar{\phi}_i(x) + \lambda \Gamma_{\phi_i^3(x)} \{\bar{\phi}\} = (\delta/\delta \bar{\phi}_i(x)) \Gamma \{\bar{\phi}\} \quad \text{(A2-14)}$$

The inserted operator is now

$$\phi_i^3(x) \equiv \frac{1}{3!} F_{ijkl} \phi_j \phi_k \phi_l \quad \text{(A2-15)}$$

The classical equation of motion (2-58), written for a multi-component critical theory, reads

$$-\nabla_x^2 \phi_i(x) + \frac{\lambda}{3!} F_{ijkl} \phi_j(x) \phi_k(x) \phi_l(x) = 0 \quad \text{(A2-16)}$$

Multiplying by $-\nabla_x^2 \phi_i(x)$ one produces a classical equation connecting operators of dimension 6. This equation can be directly translated to a functional equation for generating functionals, by applying to (A2-12) the operator

$$-\nabla_y^2 \frac{\delta}{\delta J_i(y)}$$

One finds, corresponding to (A2-12), (A2-13) and (A2-14), the following equations:

$$\left[-\nabla_x^2 \frac{\delta}{\delta J_i(x)} \nabla_y^2 \frac{\delta}{\delta J_i(y)} + \frac{\lambda}{3!} F_{ijkl} \frac{\delta^3}{\delta J_j(x) \delta J_k(x) \delta J_l(x)} \nabla_y^2 \frac{\delta}{\delta J_i(y)} \right.$$

$$\left. - \nabla_y^2 \delta(x - y) - J_i(x) \nabla_y^2 \frac{\delta}{\delta J_i(y)} \right] Z\{J\} = 0 \quad \text{(A2-17)}$$

$$-W_4\{J\} + \frac{1}{2} u_0 W_2\{J\} = \frac{1}{2} J_i(x) \nabla_x^2 (\delta/\delta J_i(x)) W\{J\} \quad \text{(A2-18)}$$

$$-\Gamma_4\{\bar{\phi}\} + \frac{1}{2} u_0 \Gamma_2\{\bar{\phi}\} = \frac{1}{2} \left[\nabla_x^2 \bar{\phi}_i(x) \right] [\delta/\delta \bar{\phi}_i(x)] \Gamma\{\bar{\phi}\} \quad \text{(A2-19)}$$

where A_2 and A_4 are the obvious generalizations of (2-21) and (2-25). They are:

$$A_2(x) = \frac{\kappa^\epsilon}{3!} \left[\nabla^2 \phi_i(x) \right] F_{ijkl} \phi_j(x) \phi_k(x) \phi_l(x) \quad \text{(A2-20)}$$

and

$$A_4(x) = \frac{1}{2!} \left[\nabla^2 \phi_i(x) \right]^2 \quad \text{(A2-21)}$$

with $u_0 = \kappa^{-\epsilon} \lambda$. Recall that all these operators, written in momentum space, have naive dimension 2.

Operating on (A2-19) with N derivatives with respect to $\bar{\phi}_{i_\alpha}(x_i)$ and setting $\bar{\phi} = 0$ one arrives at:

$$-\Gamma^{(N)}_{i_1,\ldots,i_N;4}(x_i,\ldots,x_N;x) + \frac{1}{2}\,u_0\Gamma^{(N)}_{i_1,\ldots,i_N}(x_1,\ldots,x_N;x)$$

$$= \frac{1}{2}\sum_{j=1}^{N}\nabla_x^2\delta(x-x_j)\Gamma_{i_1,\ldots,i_N}(x_1,\ldots x\ldots x_N) \qquad \text{(A2-22)}$$

which reads in momentum space:

$$-\Gamma^{(N)}_{i_1,\ldots,i_N;4}(p_1,\ldots,p_N;p) + \frac{1}{2}\,u_0\Gamma^{(N)}_{i_1,\ldots,i_N;2}(p_1,\ldots,p_N;p)$$

$$= -\frac{1}{2}\sum_{j=1}^{N}p_j\,\Gamma^N_{i_1,\ldots,i_N}(p_1,\ldots,p_j+p_1,\ldots,p_N) \qquad \text{(A2-23)}$$

where p is the momentum of the inserted operator.

The right-hand side of Eq. (A2-23) is renormalized by $Z_\phi^{N/2}$. This renormalizes the left-hand side as well. But the insertions of dimension 6 mix to express the renormalized left-hand side. What we can conclude is that

$$\sum_{i=1}^{7} a_i(u)\Gamma^N_{i_1,\ldots,i_N;iR}(p_i;p)$$

$$= \frac{1}{2}\sum_{j=1}^{N}p_j\Gamma^N_{i_1,\ldots,i_NR}(p_1,\ldots,p_j+p,\ldots p_N) \qquad \text{(A2-24)}$$

which implies that the left-hand side satisfies the same renormalization group equation as a usual $\Gamma^{(N)}$ namely,

$$\sum_{j=1}^{7} a_i(u)\left[\kappa\frac{\partial}{\partial\kappa} + \beta(u)\left(\frac{\partial\ln a_i(u)}{\partial u} + \frac{\partial}{\partial u}\right) - \frac{1}{2}N_\gamma(u)\right]\Gamma^{(N)}_{iR} = 0$$

$$\text{(A2-25)}$$

where the internal indices on $\Gamma^{(N)}$ have been suppressed.

At the fixed point Eq. (A2-25), together with Eq. (2-39), leads to the conclusion that γ_{ij} has $a_i(u)$ as a left eigenvector, with eigenvalue zero. The proof is left as Exercise 2-22.

Case C The eigenvalue connected with the equation

$$\phi^3(x)\left[-\nabla_x^2\phi(x) + \frac{\lambda}{3!}\phi^3(x)\right] = 0 \qquad \text{(A2-26)}$$

We restrict the discussion to a single field again. The generalizations are straightforward[4]. Applying $\delta^3/[\delta J(y)]^3$ to (A2-2) leads to the following functional equation for $W\{J\}$ — the generating functional of the connected Green functions:

$$-W_{A_2(x)}\{J\} + 20u_0 W_{A_1(x)}\{J\} = \kappa^\epsilon J(x)W_{\phi^3(x)}\{J\} \qquad \text{(A2-27)}$$

which can also be converted into an equation for the bare Γ's:

$$-\Gamma_{A_2(x)} \{\bar{\phi}\} + 20u_0 \Gamma_{A_1(x)} \{\bar{\phi}\} = \kappa^\epsilon \Gamma_{\phi^3(x)} \{\bar{\phi}\} \frac{\delta \Gamma\{\bar{\phi}\}}{\delta \bar{\phi}(x)} \qquad (A2\text{-}28)$$

The innovation here is that the equation connecting the Γ's is non-linear. Hence it is easier to use (A2-27) in deriving eigenvalues. After all, using the same renormalization constants which render the $\Gamma^{(N)}$'s finite one can renormalize the $G_c^{(N)}$'s – see e.g. Sec. I-7-8. The only difference between the renormalization group equations satisfied by $G_c^{(N)}$ and $\Gamma^{(N)}$ is a change in sign of γ_ϕ.

Applying N derivative $\delta/\delta J(x_i)$ to (A2-27) and setting $J = 0$, leads to:

$$-G_2^{(N)}(p_1, \ldots, p_N; p) + 20u_0 G_1^{(N)}(p_1, \ldots, p_N; p)$$

$$= \kappa^\epsilon \sum_{j=1} G_{\phi^3}^{(N-1)}(p_1, \ldots, p_j \ldots, p_N) \qquad (A2\text{-}29)$$

where the subscript c has been dropped. We now proceed recursively. According to the Case A above, the right-hand side of (A2-29) is renormalized by $Z_{\phi^3} Z_\phi^{(N-1)/2}$, and the anomalous dimension associated with ϕ^3 is known. This combination renormalizes the right-hand side as well. The $G_{jR}^{(N)}$'s satisfy renormalization group equations corresponding to (2-42), namely:

$$\left\{ \left[\kappa \frac{\partial}{\partial \kappa} + \beta \frac{\partial}{\partial u} + \frac{1}{2} N \gamma_\phi(u) \right] \delta_{ij} + \gamma_{ij}(u) \right\} G_{jR}^{(N)}(p_1, \ldots, p_N; p) = 0$$

$$(A2\text{-}30)$$

with the same matrix γ_{ij} as the one entering the equation for $\Gamma_{jR}^{(N)}$. The right hand side of (A2-29), renormalized, satisfies the equation

$$\kappa \left[\frac{\partial}{\partial \kappa} + \beta \frac{\partial}{\partial u} + \frac{1}{2}(N-1) \gamma_\phi(u) + \gamma_{\phi^3}(u) - \epsilon \right] (\text{r.h.s.})_R = 0$$

$$(A2\text{-}31)$$

As usual the renormalization of the left-hand side of (A2-29) introduces a mixture of all renormalized insertions. One has:

$$\sum_{i=1}^7 b_i(u) G_{iR}^{(N)}(p_1, \ldots, p_N; p) = \kappa^\epsilon \sum_{j=1}^N G_{\phi^3 R}^{(N-1)} \qquad (A2\text{-}32)$$

Combining (A2-32) with (A2-31) and (A2-30), and setting $u = u^*$ one arrives at the eigenvalue equation

$$\sum_{i=1}^7 b_i(u^*) [(-\tfrac{1}{2}\eta + \gamma_{\phi^3}^* - \epsilon) \delta_{ij} - \gamma_{ij}(u^*)] G_{jR}^{(N)} = 0 \qquad (A2\text{-}33)$$

which implies that $b_i(u^*)$ is an eigenvector of γ_{ij} with eigenvalue

$$\lambda = \gamma_{\phi^3}^* - \frac{1}{2}\eta - \epsilon \qquad \text{(A2-34)}$$

Finally, substituting $\gamma_{\phi^3}^*$ from (2-63), leads to

$$\lambda = -\eta \qquad \text{(A2-35)}$$

to all orders in ϵ. The details of the derivation are left to Exercises 2-23 and 2-24.

EXERCISES

2-1 Derive the partial differential equation satisfied by the function which describes the deviations from scaling of $\Gamma_R^{(N)}(p_i; t, M, u, \kappa)$. Choose your variables in such a way that at $u = u^*$ this function is 1. Solve for this function, and describe the deviations from scaling, to first order in $u - u^*$, as a power of t, and as a power of M.

2-2 Calculate correction to scaling to the specific heat.

2-3 Show that if

$$\xi_L(t)/\xi(t) = f(L/\xi(t))$$

and a scale transformation is defined via (2-17) then (2-16) follows.

2-4 Linearizing (2-17) around $t = t' = 0$, recalling that $\xi_{L'}(0)/\xi_L(0) = L'/L$, and that $t'/t \equiv [\xi(t')/\xi(t]^{-\nu^{-1}}$, deduce (2-18). How should $t = 0$ be determined?

2-5 Show that the graphs in Fig. I-7-6a and Fig. I-7-6c are finite when a factor e^{iqL} is inserted. (use the techniques of Appendix I-9-1).

2-6 The same as (2-5) but carry the argument in configuration space.

2-7 Consider a three loop graph, contributing to a primitive divergence of $\Gamma^{(4)}$, and show in configuration space that any loop with $n \neq 0$ will make it finite.

2-8 Calculate by dimensional regularization the graph in Fig. 2-1. Show that they produce in $\Gamma_{\phi^6}^{(4)}$ terms like

$$f_1(\Sigma p_i^2) + f_2(\Sigma p_i)^2$$

with independent coefficients f_1 and f_2.

2-9 Consider a theory with a cubic most relevant interaction. It is renormalizable in six dimensions. Assume that it has a symmetric state. What operators are needed in order to renormalize ϕ^4? (Motivate by considering the insertion in vertices.)

2-10(*a*) Derive the renormalization group equations for $\Gamma_{jR}^{(N)}$ with A_j operators of dimension 6 at $d = 4$.

(*b*) Derive the renormalization group equations for $\Gamma_{jR}^{(N)}$ with A_j operators of dimension 4 at $d = 4$.

(*c*) Derive the equations for $\Gamma_{jR}^{(N)}$ with A_j operators of dimensions 8 in a ϕ^3 theory at $d = 6$.

2-11 Show that only $\Gamma_i^{(2)}$, $\Gamma_i^{(4)}$ and $\Gamma_i^{(6)}$ are primitively divergent, and that the logarithmic parts of their divergences are, respectively, momentum independent, second order and fourth order in the external momenta.

2-12(*a*) List all the operators of dimension 4 in a ϕ^4 theory at $d = 4$.

(*b*) Equalize the dimensions of the operators.

(*c*) Define dimensionless vertices with insertions.

(*d*) Derive the relevant renormalization group equations.

(*e*) Discuss the eigenvalues, and compare with Sec. 2-1.

2-13(*a*) Show that the dimension of the operator ϕ^2 is, according to Eq. (2-29)

$$d_{\phi^2} = -\nu^{-1}$$

(*b*) Show that to $0(\epsilon)$

$$d_{A_7} = 4 + d_{\phi^2}$$

2-14 Consider the free theory. Show that there the only operator which gives rise to singularities, as $x \sim y$ in $\phi(x)\phi(y)$, is the constant. What are the corresponding $c(x - y)$ and $c(k)$? (Study the N-point correlation $G^{(N)}$.)

2-15 Show that, in general, the constant does not contribute to the short distance expansion of a vertex function, Eq. (2-73).

2-16 Using the expansion (2-72) show that if the dimension of A_i is d_i, then the dimension of the expansion coefficient c_i is

$$[c_i(k)] = \Lambda^{2-d_i}$$

starting once from Eq. (2-72) and once from (2-73).

2-17 Derive a renormalization group equation for the first coefficient in the operator product expansion.

2-18 Draw the graphs of $\Gamma^{(2,2)}$ and of $\Gamma^{(0,3)}$ up to the order of two loops. Show that, up to this order,

$$\Gamma^{(2,2)}(p, -p, 0, 0; t, \kappa) = c(p)\Gamma^{(0,3)}(0, 0, 0; t, \kappa)\left[1 + 0\left(\frac{t}{p^2}\right)\right]$$

where

$$c(p) = \Gamma^{(4)}(p, -p, 0, 0).$$

All vertices are renormalized.

2-19 Solve the equation for $\Gamma^{(0,3)}(0, 0, 0; t, \kappa)$ using the technique of Sec. I-8-8.

2-20 Show that if $A(\phi(x))$ is a monomial in $\phi(x)$, then $Z_A\{J\}/Z\{J\}$ is a generating functional for connected Green functions with an insertion of A.

2-21 Use Eq. (A2-4) to arrive at the anomalous dimension of ϕ^3.

2-22(a) Derive the equation connecting the vertices with the insertions of A_2 and A_4, to the vertex with no insertions, Eq. (A2-22).

(b) Using the relation between the renormalized vertices show that $\lambda = 2\epsilon$ is an eigenvalue of γ_{ij}.

2-23(a) Derive the relation between the vertices with the insertion of A_1 and A_2, Eq. (A2-29).

(b) Using Eq. (A2-32) show that

$$\sum_i b_i(u^*)\left(\kappa\frac{\partial}{\partial\kappa} - \frac{N}{2}\eta + 2\epsilon\right)\Gamma_{iR}^{(N)} = 0$$

and from it that $\lambda = 2\epsilon$ is an eigenvalue.

2-24(a) Derive Eq. (A2-27) and from it (A2-29).

(b) Show that combining (A2-30) – (A2-32), at the fixed point, one finds (A2-32).

(c) Show that the same result can be arrived at starting from the non-linear equation (A2-28).

REFERENCES

1. F. W. Wegner, *Physical Review*, **B5** 4529 (1972), **B6** 1891 (1972) and FW. In the present context, see E. Brezin, J. C. Le Guillou and J. Zinn-Justin, *Physical Review*, **B8** 5330 (1973).
2. M. E. Fisher and M. N. Barber, *Physical Review Letters*, **28**, 1516 (1972); M. P. Nightingale, *Physica* **83**, A561 (1976); M. Suzuki, *Progress in Theoretical Physics*, **58**, 1143 (1977); B. Derrida, *Journal of Physics* **A14**, 145 (1981).
3. E. Brezin, *Journal de Physique* (Paris), **43**, 15 (1982).
4. G. Jug, *Annals of Physics*, **142**, 140 (1982).

5. See e.g., Zimmerman; E. Brezin, C. De Dominicis and J. Zinn-Justin, *Lettere al Nuovo Cimento,* **9,** 483 (1974) and **10,** 849 (1974); P. K. Mitter, *Physical Review,* **D7,** 2927 (1973).

6. E. Brézin, J. Zinn-Justin and J. C. Le Guillou, *Physical Review,* **D14,** 4976 (1976).

7. D. J. Amit, D. J. Wallace and R. K. P. Zia, *Physical Review,* **B15,** 4657 (1977).

8. E. Brézin, C. De Dominicis and J. Zinn-Justin, *Lettere al Nuovo Cimento,* **9,** 483 (1974).

9. E. Brézin, C. De Dominicis and J. Zinn-Justin, Ref. 8 above and Chap. III of BLZ.

10. M. E. Fisher and R. J. Burford, *Physical Review,* **156,** 583 (1967). See also M. E. Fisher in *Critical Phenomena,* M. S. Green and J. V. Sengers, eds., (Washington D. C.: National Bureau of Standards, 1966).

11. M. E. Fisher and J. S. Langer, *Physical Review Letters,* **20,** 665 (1968).

12. E. Brézin, D. J. Amit and J. Zinn-Justin, *Physical Review Letters,* **32,** 151 (1974). All these results are implicitly contained in Symanzik (KS) and even in G. Mack and K. Symanzik, *Communications in Mathematical Physics,* **27,** 247 (1972).

13. K. G. Wilson, *Physical Review,* **179,** 1499 (1969) and in Zimmerman.

14. L. P. Kadanoff, *Physical Review Letters,* **23,** 1430 (1969).

15. See, e.g., E. Brézin, C. De Dominicis and J. Zinn-Justin, Ref. 8 above.

16. M. E. Fisher and A. Aharony, *Physical Review Letters,* **31,** 1238 (1973).

17. E. Brézin, J. C. Le Guillou and J. Zinn-Justin, *Physical Review Letters,* **32,** 473 (1974).

18. D. R. Nelson, *Physical Review,* **B14,** 1123 (1976); Y. Achiam and J. M. Kosterlitz, *Journal of Physics,* **C10,** 4559 (1977).

19. G. Jug and G. Rickayzen, *Journal of Physics,* **A14,** 1357 (1981).

3

UNIVERSALITY REVISITED

3-1 RENORMALIZATION SCHEME INDEPENDENCE OF CRITICAL EXPONENTS

To complete the observation made at the end of Sec. I-9-7, we present a general proof of the statement that critical exponents are independent of the various arbitrary choices made in regularizing or in renormalizing the theory. The argument follows closely the Les Houches lectures of Gross.[1]

Clearly, a different regularization, or a different subtraction procedure, will result in a different renormalized coupling constant, as well as different functional forms for β and for the various anomalous dimension functions γ. Furthermore, the value of the coupling constant at the fixed point will differ.

Let the dimensionless, renormalized coupling constant, in two different procedures, be denoted by u_1 and u_2. Using arguments of the type which led to Eq. (I-8-6) one concludes that:

$$u_2 = G(u_1) \tag{3-1}$$

and usually G will be $O(u_1)$. Similarly, arguments like those leading to Eq. (I-8-4) together with Eq. (3-1) imply that any renormalization constant Z, satisfies:

$$Z_2(u_2) = F(u_1)Z_1(u_1) \ , \qquad (3\text{-}2)$$

where the subscripts on the Z's refer to the two procedures.

First we show that if u_1^* and u_2^* are the fixed points in the two schemes, then

$$u_2^* = G(u_1^*) \ . \qquad (3\text{-}3)$$

The flow functions β are related via:

$$\beta_2(u_2) = \kappa \left. \frac{\partial u_2}{\partial \kappa} \right|_{\lambda,\Lambda} = \beta_1(u_1) \frac{\partial G(u_1)}{\partial u_1} \ . \qquad (3\text{-}4)$$

Hence, while u_1^* may differ from u_2^*, if $\beta(u_1^*) = 0$, $\beta_2(G(u_1^*)) = 0$.

Next we turn to the anomalous dimensions, or critical exponents. The typical γ is given by

$$\gamma_i(u_i) = \kappa \left. \frac{\partial \ln Z_i(u_i)}{\partial \kappa} \right|_{\lambda,\Lambda} \ . \qquad (3\text{-}5)$$

Hence, using Eq. (3-2),

$$\gamma_2(u_2) = \gamma_1(u_1) + \frac{\partial \ln F}{\partial u_1} \beta(u_1) \ . \qquad (3\text{-}6)$$

Consequently, while the functions γ_1 and γ_2 will be different, at the fixed point they obtain the same value.

Finally, it turns out that the slope of β at the fixed point is independent of the scheme. This again should come as no surprise. After all, as was discussed in Sec. I-8-7 it is this value which determines the asymptotic behavior of the theory, and is of physical significance. Moreover, in Sec. 2-1 it is shown that $\beta'(u^*)$ is the exponent ω describing corrections to scaling.

The proof is, again, straightforward. Using Eq. (3-4) one has

$$\frac{\partial \beta_2(u_2)}{\partial u_2} = \frac{\partial}{\partial u_2} \left(\frac{\partial u_2}{\partial u_1} \right) \beta_1(u_1) + \frac{\partial \beta_1(u_1)}{\partial u_1} \left(\frac{\partial u_1}{\partial u_2} \right) \left(\frac{\partial u_2}{\partial u_1} \right)$$

at $u_1 = u_1^*$ and $u_2 = u_2^*$ the first term on the right-hand-side vanishes, and the result follows.

3-2 THE UNIVERSAL FORM OF THE EQUATION OF STATE

As was mentioned at the end of Sec. I-8-9, the form of the equation of state is universal, i.e., it depends only on the fixed point. We have already seen that the critical exponents are universal. But other quantities are usually not universal, in the sense that they depend on the value of the renormalized coupling constant u, and not only on u^*. One comes across factors such as (I-8-57), which depend explicitly on u. In this section and in the next one we examine other quantities beside critical exponents which are universal, and hence can be computed in the ϵ expansion.

Consider the renormalization group equation for the equation of state, Eq. (I-8-81). The behavior of the general solution of this equation under a change in the scale of length is given by:

$$H(t,M,u,\kappa) = \rho^{\frac{1}{2}(d+2)} \exp\left[-\frac{1}{2}\int_1^\rho \eta(u(x))\,\frac{dx}{x}\right] H(t(\rho), M(\rho), u(\rho), \kappa)$$

(3-7)

where, as usual, $u(\rho)$ is the solution of

$$\rho\frac{du(\rho)}{d\rho} = \beta(u(\rho))$$

(3-8)

$t(\rho)$ satisfies

$$\rho\frac{d\ln t(\rho)}{d\rho} = -\nu^{-1}(u(\rho))$$

(3-9)

and

$$\rho\frac{d\ln M(\rho)}{d\rho} = -\frac{1}{2}[d-2+\eta(u(\rho))]$$

(3-10)

with the initial conditions:

$$M(1) = M; \qquad t(1) = t \ ,$$

(See Exercises I-8-20 and 2-1).

The value of ρ is arbitrary. We fix it by requiring that

$$M(\rho) = 1$$

(3-11)

We could as well have used $t(\rho) = 1$ to fix ρ (see Exercise 3-2). The solution of Eq. (3-10) is

$$M(\rho) = M \exp\left\{-\frac{1}{2}\int_1^\rho [d-2+\eta(u(x))]\,\frac{dx}{x}\right\}$$

(3-12)

The condition (3-11) can therefore be rewritten as

$$\rho^{\frac{1}{2}(d-2+\eta)} = M \exp\left\{\frac{1}{2}\int_1^\rho [\eta(u(x)) - \eta]\,\frac{dx}{x}\right\}$$

(3-13)

where $\eta = \eta(u^*)$.

The coefficient of the function H in Eq. (3-7) can also be rewritten in terms of η. It becomes:

$$\rho^{\frac{1}{2}(d+2-\eta)} \exp\left\{-\frac{1}{2}\int_1^\rho [\eta(u(x)) - \eta]\frac{dx}{x}\right\} . \qquad (3-14)$$

Inserting (3-13) in (3-14) and making use of the scaling relations (I-8-88) and (I-8-89) this factor can be put in the form

$$M^\delta \exp\left\{-\frac{d\nu}{2\beta}\int_1^\rho [\eta(u(x)) - \eta]\frac{dx}{x}\right\} \qquad (3-15)$$

The solution of Eq. (3-9) for $t(\rho)$ reads:

$$t(\rho) = t\exp\left\{-\int_1^\rho \nu^{-1}(u(x))\frac{dx}{x}\right\} , \qquad (3-16)$$

and when ρ is fixed by (3-11) it becomes:

$$t(\rho) = tM^{-\beta^{-1}} \exp\int_1^\rho\left\{\frac{1}{2}\beta^{-1}[\eta(u(x)) - \eta] - [\nu^{-1}(u(x)) - \nu^{-1}]\right\} \qquad (3-17)$$

The derivation is left as Exercise 3-3. Notice that in Eq. (3-15) and (3-17) β is the exponent, not the flow function.

Finally, we arrive at the following result for the equation of state:

$$H(t, M, u, \kappa) = \kappa^{\frac{1}{2}(d+2)}\left(\frac{M}{\kappa^{(d-2)/2}}\right)^\delta A(u, \rho)h\left[\frac{t}{\kappa^2}\left(\frac{M}{\kappa^{(d-2)/2}}\right)^{-1/\beta} B(u, \rho), u(\rho)\right]$$

$$(3-18)$$

in which $\rho = \rho(M)$, according to (3-13). The functions A and B are the exponentials appearing in Eqs. (3-14) and (3-17), respectively. The explicit κ dependence was extracted by dimensional analysis.

As $\rho \to 0, u(\rho) \to u^*, M \to 0$ and $t \to 0$. The proof we leave as Exercise 3-4. The only carriers of the dependence on u in Eq. (3-18) are the functions A and B. In the asymptotic region these functions become respectively $A(u, 0)$ and $B(u, 0)$; all the other quantities in (3-18) tend to their values at u^*.

It is possible to eliminate this non-universality by absorbing it in the definitions of the amplitudes of H and t. At the critical temperature we have, after setting $\kappa = 1$,

$$H = AM^\delta h(0) \equiv Ah(0)\bar{H} \qquad (3-19)$$

where $h(0)$ is a universal constant, and on the coexistence curve, where $h = 0$ and $t < 0$

$$M = \left(-\frac{Bt}{C}\right)^\beta \equiv (-\bar{t})^\beta \qquad (3-20)$$

Here $(-C)$ is a universal constant, being the position of the zero of the function $h(x, u^*)$.

In terms of $\bar{H}$ and $\bar{t}$ the equation of state has the form:

$$\bar{H}(t, M) = M^\delta h(C\bar{t}M^{-1/\beta}, u^*) \qquad (3\text{-}21)$$

The meaning of this result is that if the equation of state is calculated with the coupling constant at its fixed value, and H and t are normalized in such a way that at T_c

$$H = M^\delta$$

asymptotically, and on the coexistence curve

$$M = t^\beta$$

then the form of the relationship between these variables H, M and t is universal.

3-3   THE EQUATION OF STATE TO ORDER ϵ

As an example of the application of the results of the previous section, we calculate the equation of state to first order in ϵ. For this purpose one needs the renormalized equation of state to the order of one loop. We will consider the case of a field with a single component. The $0(M)$ symmetric theory[2] will be taken up in Chap. 6.

In Sec. I-6-5 a renormalized form of the effective potential $U(M)$ was derived – Eq. (I-6-39). Here this expression will not do, since the renormalization was carried out at finite mass. When the theory is renormalized at zero mass as in Sec. I-7-6, the result is:

$$U(M) = \tfrac{1}{2} t M^2 + \frac{1}{4!} u^* M^4 + \frac{1}{2} \int dp \left[\ln\left(p^2 + t + \frac{u^*}{2} M^2 \right) - \ln p^2 - \tfrac{1}{2} u^* M^2 \frac{1}{p^2} \right]$$
$$+ \tfrac{1}{4}(u^* t M^2 + \tfrac{1}{4} u^{*2} M^4) I_{SP} \qquad (3\text{-}22)$$

In deriving this result, κ^2 was set equal to unity. The details are left as Exercise 3-5.

It is important to notice that the mere replacement of u by u^* does not make this form universal, it is only after H and t are normalized via (3-19) and (3-20) that the resulting relation becomes universal.

Another important consideration is that of the relative orders of magnitude of the terms in $U(M)$. From the first two terms on the right-hand side of Eq. (3-22), one concludes that if $u^* \sim \epsilon$ then $M^2 \sim \epsilon^{-1}$. The terms including the one-loop contribution are of order unity. Therefore, all the integrals have to be calculated with $\epsilon = 0$, or $d = 4$.

The equation of state reads:

$$H = \frac{\partial U}{\partial M} = tM + \frac{1}{6}u^*M^3 + \frac{1}{2}u^*M(t + \frac{1}{2}u^*M^2)\left(I_{SP} - \int dp \frac{1}{p^2(p^2 + t + \frac{1}{2}u^*M^2)}\right)$$

(3-23)

$$= tM + \frac{1}{6}u^*M^3 + \frac{1}{4}u^*M(t + \frac{1}{2}u^*M^2)[\ln(t + \frac{1}{2}u^*M^2) + 1]$$

(3-24)

where the area of the four-dimensional unit sphere is again absorbed in u^*, and in y which is defined by

$$y = u^*M^2 \qquad (3\text{-}25)$$

In terms of y, H can be written as:

$$H = M\left[(t + \frac{1}{6}y) + \frac{\epsilon}{6}(t + \frac{1}{2}y)\ln(t + \frac{1}{2}y)\right] \qquad (3\text{-}26)$$

where the value of u^* at order ϵ was substituted. But from (3-21) we know that H should be written as M multiplied by a function of

$$x = ty^{-1/2\beta} \qquad (3\text{-}27)$$

This requirement suffices to determine β and δ to order ϵ. The proof is left as Exercise 3-6. In terms of M and x, H has the form:

$$H = My^{\frac{1}{2}(\delta - 1)}\left[(x + \frac{1}{6}) + \frac{\epsilon}{6}(x + \frac{1}{2})\ln(x + \frac{1}{2})\right] \qquad (3\text{-}28)$$

Finally, to arrive at the universal form we have to normalize H and x so that the conditions $H = M^\delta$ for $t = 0$ and $M = t^\beta$ when $H = 0$ be satisfied.

It can be easily checked that if H and x are transformed according to:

$$H \to \frac{1}{6}(u^*)^{\frac{1}{2}(\delta - 1)}(1 - \frac{1}{2}\epsilon\ln 2)H \qquad (3\text{-}29)$$

and

$$x \to \frac{1}{6}(1 - \frac{1}{3}\epsilon\ln 3)x \qquad (3\text{-}30)$$

then the equation of state will read:

$$H = M^\delta\{(x + 1) + \frac{1}{6}\epsilon[(x + 3)\ln(x + 3) - 3(x + 1)\ln 3 - 2x\ln 2]\} \qquad (3\text{-}31)$$

This is the universal form to order ϵ. The coefficients in Eqs. (3-29) and (3-30) are not universal. They contain, in general, the functions A and B, appearing in Eq. (3-18), and hence they depend on u.

3-4 TWO SCALE FACTOR UNIVERSALITY – UNIVERSAL RATIOS OF AMPLITUDES

Ever since Kadanoff introduced the idea of scaling,[3] it has been known that out of all the critical exponents of interest, of which one lists 12, only 2 are independent. Given η and ν, for example, one can obtain all other exponents from simple algebraic relations – scaling relations. The underlying reason is already contained in Kadanoff's paper, namely, that all those quantities in whose critical behavior one is interested, are constructed from two basic operators. In our language these are ϕ and ϕ^2.

The above is summarized, within the formalism described here, by the statement that the general $\Gamma_R^{(N,L)}$ is governed by a renormalization group equation of the type.

$$\left[\kappa \frac{\partial}{\partial \kappa} + \beta(u) \frac{\partial}{\partial u} - \tfrac{1}{2}\eta(u)\left(N + M \frac{\partial}{\partial M} \right) - (\nu^{-1}(u) - 2)\left(L + t \frac{\partial}{\partial t} \right) \right] \Gamma_R^{(N,L)}$$

$$= \delta_{N,0}\,\delta_{L,2}\,\kappa^{-\epsilon}B(u) \tag{3-30}$$

in the whole critical region (see, e.g., Exercise I-8-9). Only η and ν enter this equation. They are, of course, related to the anomalous dimensions of ϕ and ϕ^2.

After the discovery of the universal nature of the exponents, it became clear that the amplitudes of the asymptotic terms governing the behavior of the various quantities near the critical point were not universal. This is due to the appearance of factors, such as (I-8-57), in the amplitudes.

But just as the fact that all the quantities of interest are constructed from ϕ and ϕ^2 brings in only two anomalous dimensions, could it not bring also a reduced number of non-universal amplitudes? This idea was first put forth as a conjecture for one such relationship.[4] Further instances were then found,[5] but the general origin of these relations, and therefore also the direct and systematic derivation of them all, was left to the present formalism.[6]

This approach shows clearly that the relations between the non-universal parts of the amplitudes of different physical quantities, follow indeed from the presence of only two length scales – ϕ and ϕ^2 – alternatively, of the magnetization and the temperature. Thus, there are as many relations between amplitudes as there are between critical exponents.

The difference between exponents and amplitudes is in the fact that *while the two independent anomalous dimensions are universal, the two remaining amplitudes are not.* Hence, in contrast to the situation in which all critical exponents can be computed at the fixed point, only universal combinations of amplitudes can be computed.

The vertex functions $\Gamma_R{}^{(N,L)}$, with $N(L-2) \neq 0$, containing ϕ and ϕ^2 operators only, satisfy the renormalization group equation:

$$\left[\kappa\frac{\partial}{\partial\kappa}+\beta(u)\frac{\partial}{\partial u}-\tfrac{1}{2}\eta(u)\left(N+M\frac{\partial}{\partial M}\right)-\theta(u)\left(L+t\frac{\partial}{\partial t}\right)\right]\Gamma_R^{(N,L)}(k_i,p_i;t,M,u,\kappa)=0$$

$$(3\text{-}31)$$

the derivation of which was left as Exercise I-8-9. The functions η and θ are such that as $u\to u^*$, $\eta(u)\to\eta$, and $\theta(u)\to\nu^{-1}-2$.

Equation (3-31) can be solved in the (by now) standard way. The solution has the property that

$$\Gamma_R^{(N,L)}(q_i;t,M,u,\kappa)=\rho^{d-\frac{1}{2}N(d-2)-2L}$$

$$\times\exp\left[-\frac{N}{2}\int_1^\rho\eta(u(x))\frac{dx}{x}-L\int_1^\rho\theta(u(x))\frac{dx}{x}\right]$$

$$\Gamma_R^{(N,L)}(\rho^{-1}q_i;t(\rho),M(\rho),u(\rho),\kappa)\qquad(3\text{-}32)$$

where q_i is a shorthand notation for (k_i,p_i). The functions $u(\rho)$, $t(\rho)$ and $M(\rho)$ satisfy Eqs. (3-8)–(3-10). A simple reshuffling of the exponentials in Eq. (3-32) leads to:

$$\Gamma_R^{(N,L)}(q_i;t,M,u,\kappa)=\rho^{d-\frac{1}{2}N(d-2+\eta)-L\nu^{-1}}[Y(u,\rho)]^N[X(u,\rho)]^L$$

$$\Gamma_R^{(N,L)}(\rho^{-1}q;t(\rho),M(\rho),u(\rho),\kappa)\qquad(3\text{-}33)$$

with the functions X and Y, given by:

$$Y(u,\rho)=\exp-\frac{1}{2}\int_1^\rho[\eta(u(x))-\eta]\frac{dx}{x}\qquad(3\text{-}34)$$

$$X(u,\rho)=\exp-\int_1^\rho[\nu^{-1}(u(x))-\nu^{-1}]\frac{dx}{x}\qquad(3\text{-}35)$$

Notice that these two functions have smooth limits as $\rho\to0$, $u\to u^*$, and that these limits depend on the initial value u.

Before studying the effect of X and Y we first choose ρ as a function of t via the condition

$$t(\rho)=1\qquad(3\text{-}36)$$

It then follows from (3-16) that

$$\rho=(Xt)^\nu\qquad(3\text{-}37)$$

and from (3-12) and (I-8-89) that,

$$M(\rho)=(YM)(Xt)^{-\beta}\qquad(3\text{-}38)$$

The correlation function can now be written as:

$$\Gamma_R^{(N,L)}(q_i; t, M, u, \kappa) = (Xt)^{d\nu - N\beta - L} Y^N X^L$$
$$\Gamma_R^{(N,L)}(q_i(Xt)^{-\nu}; 1, YM(Xt)^{-\beta}, u(\rho)) \qquad (3\text{-}39)$$

The variable κ was suppressed. Its value has been set to unity. The dependence on κ can be easily reconstituted by dimensional analysis.

To repeat, as $\rho \to 0$, $u(\rho) \to u^*$, and X and Y tend to finite limits which depend on u, and, consequently, are not universal. But all of the non-universality enters through only two scale factors, which are clearly associated with M and t.

One conventionally defines the following notation for the asymptotic behavior near a critical point of the 12 functions of interest:

Table 3-1 Definitions of the critical amplitudes

(a) $T > T_c; H = 0$ (critical isochore)	(b) $T < T_c; H = 0$ (critical isochore)
$\xi = \xi_0^+ t^{-\nu}$	$\xi = \xi_0^-(-t)^{-\nu'}$
$\chi = C^+ t^{-\gamma}$	$\chi = C^-(-t)^{-\gamma'}$
$C_s = \dfrac{A^+}{\alpha} t^{-\alpha}$	$C_s = \dfrac{A^-}{\alpha'}(-t)^{-\alpha'}$
	$M = B(-t)^\beta$

(c) $T = T_c; H \neq 0$ (critical isotherm)	(d) $T = T_c; H = 0$ (critical point)
$\xi = \xi_0^c \lvert H \rvert^{-\nu_c}$	$\chi(p) = \hat{D} p^{\eta - 2}$
$C_s = A^c/\alpha^c \lvert H \rvert^{-\alpha_c}$	
$H = DM^\delta$	
$\chi = C^c \lvert H \rvert^{-\gamma_c}$	

Then, for example, C^+ and C^- can be expressed in terms of X and Y. Taking the limit $q \to 0$ and $M \to 0$ of $\Gamma_R^{(2)}$ one has:

$$(C^+)^{-1} = X^\gamma Y^2 \Gamma_R^{(2)}(0; 1, 0, u^*) \qquad (3\text{-}40)$$

While setting M to its value on the coexistence curve, gives:

$$(C^-)^{-1} = X^\gamma Y^2 \Gamma_R^{(2)}(0; 1, z, u^*) \qquad (3\text{-}41)$$

where z is the position of the zero of the equation of state, as was discussed in the previous section. From the last two equations it follows immediately that the ratio C^+/C^- is universal. In a completely analogous way one can show that the ratio of the amplitudes of the specific heat, above and below the transition C_s^+/C_s^-, and that of the correlation lengths ξ_0^+/ξ_0^-, are universal quantities as well (see Exercise 3-7).

At the critical temperature it is more convenient to proceed by fixing ρ via the condition (3-11), namely $M(\rho) = 1$. Then $\Gamma_R^{(N,L)}$ takes on the form:

$$\Gamma_R^{(N,L)} = Y^N X^L (YM)^{\delta+1-N-L\beta^{-1}}$$
$$\times \Gamma_R^{(N,L)}(q_i(YM)^{-\nu/\beta}; (Xt)(YM)^{-\beta^{-1}}, 1, u(\rho)) \qquad (3\text{-}42)$$

The derivation is left as Exercise 3-8. For momentum-dependent quantities at the critical point one can factorize the q-dependence by choosing $\rho = q$, where q is an overall scale of the set of momenta q_i. This we leave as Exercise 3-9.

There are relations between amplitudes which are completely trivial. For example, the relation between D and C^c in Table 3-1 follows directly from the fact that

$$\chi^{-1} = \frac{\partial H}{\partial M}$$

and hence

$$\delta C^c D^{1/\delta} = 1 \qquad (3\text{-}43)$$

Much less trivial are the universal combinations of amplitudes of thermodynamic quantities with amplitudes of correlation functions. For example, using Eq. (3-42), the amplitude D mentioned above is given by:

$$D = Y^{\delta+1} \Gamma_R^{(1)}(0; 0, 1, u^*) \qquad (3\text{-}44)$$

On the other hand, choosing the scale variable $\rho = q$, one obtains for $\hat{D}$ – the coefficient of $q^{2-\eta}$ in $\Gamma^{(2)}$ – the expression:

$$(\hat{D})^{-1} = Y^2 \Gamma_R^{(2)}(1; 0, 0, u^*) \qquad (3\text{-}45)$$

Elimination of Y between (3-44) and (3-45) leads to a non-trivial universal combination of amplitudes

$$R_D \equiv (\hat{D})^{\frac{1}{2}(\delta+1)} D = \Gamma_R^{(1)}(0; 0, 1, u^*)[\Gamma_R^{(2)}(1; 0, 0, u^*)]^{-\frac{1}{2}(\delta+1)} \qquad (3\text{-}46)$$

Similarly, one can show that

$$Q_2 \equiv \frac{C^+}{C^c}(\xi_0^c/\xi_0^+)^{2-\eta} \qquad (3\text{-}47)$$

Table 3-2 The ten universal combinations of critical amplitudes

Among thermodynamic amplitudes	Among correlation amplitudes	Mixing thermodynamic and correlation amplitudes
C^+/C^-		$R_\xi^+ = \xi_0^+(A^+)^{1/d}$
A^+/A^-	ξ_0^+/ξ_0^-	$Q_2 = \dfrac{C^+}{C^-}(\xi_0^c/\xi_0^+)^{2-\eta}$
$R = C^+DB^{\delta-1}$		$R_D = D^{(\delta+1)/2}D$
$R_C = \dfrac{A^+C^+}{B^2}$		$R_{Ac} = [(\xi_0^+)^2 A_c^\nu]^d C_c^\alpha$

and

$$R_{Ac} \equiv [(\xi_0^+)^2 A_c^\nu]^d (C^c)^\alpha \qquad (3\text{-}48)$$

are universal.

The complete list of the universal ratios of amplitude which hold among the quantities defined in Table 3-1 is given in Table 3-2. The derivations are left as Exercises 3-10 and 3-11.

Not only are the combinations in Table 3-2 independent of u, they are also independent of κ, and of any further finite renormalizations. The proofs of these two statements, which are straightforward, are left as Exercises 3-11 and 3-12.

Finally, the various combinations of amplitudes, being universal, can be computed in the ϵ expansion. No details will be presented here. The results can be found in Bervillier's article.[6]

EXERCISES

3-1 The form (3-7) is a somewhat different representation of the solution of the renormalization group equation than the one presented in chapter I-8.
   (a) Prove directly that it satisfies the equation for H, if $u(\rho)$, $t(\rho)$ and $M(\rho)$ are defined to satisfy Eqs. (3-8)–(3-10).
   (b) Solve the equation in the old style and describe how it can be transformed to this form.

3-2 Fixing ρ, in the solution for H – Eq. (3-7), via

$$t(\rho) = 1$$

derive the dependence of H on t and M.

3-3   Derive Eq. (3-17).

3-4(a) Show that if $M(\rho) = 1$, Eq. (3-11), then as $\rho \to 0$, $M \to 0$ and $t \to 0$.

(b) Show that the same limits are approached if ρ is fixed as in Exercise 3-2.

3-5   Using the expression for the effective potential in terms of the bare parameters on the one-loop level, derive the renormalized form. Remember that when renormalizing at zero mass the renormalization of $\Gamma^{(2,1)}$ enters through relation (I-7-81) between t and $\mu^2 - \mu_c^2$.

3-6   Show that the requirement that the equation of state, Eq. (3-26), be of the form $M^\delta f(tM^{-1/\beta})$ to order ϵ, implies

$$\delta = 3 + \epsilon$$

$$\beta = \frac{1}{2} - \frac{\epsilon}{6}$$

and that (3-28) follows.

3-7(a) Show that the ratio of coefficients of the singular part of the specific heat above and below T_c is universal.

(b) Show the same for the ratio of the amplitudes of the correlation length. Remember that $\xi(t, M, u, \kappa)$ also satisfies a renormalization group equation (see Exercise I-8-17).

3-8   Derive the solution for $\Gamma^{(N,L)}$ when ρ is fixed normalizing $M(\rho) = 1$.

3-9   Derive $\Gamma^{(N,L)}$ when ρ is fixed by the requirement $\rho = q$, where q is a scale of all q_i.

3-10   Using the results of Exercises (3-8) and (3-9) express the remaining amplitudes in Table 3-1 in terms of X, Y, and universal quantities.

3-11   Using the results of Exercise 3-10, complete Table 3-2.

3-12   Prove that if the explicit dependence of $\Gamma^{(N,L)}$ on κ is reconstituted, the universal combinations of amplitudes, appearing in Table 3-2, will not be affected.

3-13   Prove that if the theory is renormalized by imposing two different sets of normalization conditions, the universal combinations in Table 3-2 will be the same.

REFERENCES

1. D. J. Gross, "Applications of the Renormalization Group to High-Energy Physics" in *Methods in Field Theory*, R. Balian and J. Zinn-Justin Eds., (North-Holland Publishing Co. and World Scientific Publishing Co. Pte. Ltd., 1981).
2. E. Brezin, D. J. Wallace and K. G. Wilson, *Physical Review Letters,* **29**, 591 (1972), *Physical Review*, **B7**, 232 (1973) and BLZ.
3. L. P. Kadanoff, *Physics,* **2**, 263 (1966).
4. D. Stauffer, M. Ferrer and M. Wortis, *Physical Review Letters*, **29**, 345 (1972).
5. M. E. Fisher and H. B. Tarko, *Physical Review*, **B11**, 1131 (1975).
6. C. Bervillier, *Physical Review*, **B14**, 4964 (1976).

4

CRITICAL BEHAVIOR WITH SEVERAL
COUPLINGS

4-1 INTRODUCTION

In theories with a single coupling constant the flow patterns of the coupling and
consequently the domains of universality of each fixed point, are rather simple.
The typical situation is discussed in Sec. I-8-7. As the number of parameters –
coupling constants – is increased the possibilities rapidly become much more
varied.

For statistical mechanics the most striking new features are:

(a) In the space of parameters there may be regions corresponding to different
symmetries of the system. In Sec. 4-2 below we will investigate a case with two
coupling constants. The two-dimensional space of coupling constants describes
systems which have a discrete symmetry (a change of sign of each field × permutation of the fields). It contains one line on which the system has a continuous
symmetry (rotations in field space).

The remarkable feature is that one may find situations in which there is a
two-dimensional domain of attraction of a fixed point (infrared stable), with a
symmetry that is higher than the generic symmetry of systems in the domain[1,2].
The field theorist will say that *at large distances the symmetry is dynamically
restored.* In the theory of critical phenomena the translation would be: *fluctuations restore the symmetry.*

(b) There may be regions in the space of coupling constants, which are not in the domain of any of the fixed points within the range of our approximations. Such is the case for the superconductor (scalar electrodynamics[3]) for all non-zero values of the charge[4]. The couplings may flow, as one penetrates the infrared region, to parts of the coupling constant space in which the classical approximation is unstable.

In those cases, discussed in Secs. 4-3 and 4-4 the system undergoes a first order phase transition, despite the fact that the classical approximation indicates a second order transition. The first order transition is induced by fluctuations.

Clearly, the first order transition takes place above the temperature at which the correlation is infinite (zero mass). Otherwise a second order transition would have taken place first. Hence, the symmetric zero-mass theory, in the abovementioned cases, is deeply inside the broken symmetry phase. This observation is the *Coleman-Weinberg mechanism*[3] of *dimensional transmutation* as viewed with the perspective of critical phenomena.

The particle theorist's version of the same underlying scene is the following[3]. The massless classical theory indicates no symmetry breaking, and is scale invariant in four dimensions, where the couplings are dimensionless. As soon as quantum effects (fluctuations) are taken into account, one finds that the symmetry is already broken, and the massless symmetric theory is irrelevant.

The equation giving the expectation value of the field — the extremum of the free energy — is an equation involving all the coupling constants and the value of the field. When the latter is non-zero, one can eliminate one of the *dimensionless* coupling constants in terms of the *dimensionful* parameter — the expectation value of the field. This is *dimensional transmutation*.

4-2 MORE THAN ONE COUPLING CONSTANT – CUBIC ANISOTROPY

As was mentioned in Sec. I-7-10, when the field has more than one component there may be any number of independent ϕ^4 coupling constants, all of which become relevant at the same number of spatial dimensions. The situation can become very rich and very complex. In the present section a very simple extension beyond the case of a single coupling constant will be described. Beside the $0(M)$-symmetric interaction we include an additional ϕ^4 interaction which possesses cubic symmetry. Much more complex cases have been discussed,[5] mainly for the treatment of specific physical systems. Some general conclusions can be drawn, the most striking of which is that under very general conditions, if the number of components M satisfies:

$$M \leqslant 4 - 0(\epsilon) \qquad (4-1)$$

out of the multiplicity of fixed points, the $O(M)$-symmetric one — often called the Heisenberg fixed point — is the only stable one. A special case of this general statement will be discussed below. Here we will follow the presentation of ref. 2.

The Lagrangian we consider has a quartic term of the form

$$\mathscr{L}_{\text{Int}} = \frac{1}{4!}\left[\lambda_1 \left(\sum_{i=1}^{M} \phi_i^2\right)^2 + \lambda_2 \sum_{i=1}^{M} \phi_i^4\right] \tag{4-2}$$

$$= \frac{1}{4!}\, g_{ijkl}\phi_i\phi_j\phi_k\phi_l$$

with,

$$g_{ijkl} = \lambda_1 S_{ijkl} + \lambda_2 F_{ijkl} \tag{4-3}$$

The tensors S and F are defined by Eqs. (I-4-36) and (I-4-41), respectively.

This interaction has the following simplifying features. The symmetry $\phi_i \to -\phi_i$ and of the permutations of ϕ_i's among themselves implies immediately that a function with two indices is proportional to the unit matrix, namely,

$$\Gamma_{ij}^{(2)} = \Gamma^{(2)}\delta_{ij} \tag{4-4}$$

The field can be renormalized with a single number Z_ϕ as before. This simplification will not be used here as the calculation will be carried to first order in ϵ only.

The same symmetry allows for only two independent invariants with four indices. Thus, a four-point function, symmetric in its spatial variables, must be a linear combination of S and F.

Renormalization will therefore consist of introducing three constants $Z_\phi(u_1, u_2)$, $\lambda_1(u_1, u_2, \kappa)$, $\lambda_2(u_1, u_2, \kappa)$ — leaving the renormalization of ϕ^2 aside — such that

$$\Gamma_{i_1}^{(N)} \cdots {}_{i_N R}(k_i; u_1, u_2, \kappa) = [Z_\phi(u_1, u_2)]^{N/2}\Gamma_{i_1}^{(N)} \cdots {}_{i_N}(k_i; \lambda_1, \lambda_2, \Lambda) \tag{4-5}$$

and the left-hand side is the finite limit of the right-hand side, as $\Lambda \to \infty$, order by order in u_1, u_2 and ϵ. These renormalization constants are determined either from normalization conditions, such as:

$$\Gamma_{ijR}^{(2)}(k = 0) = 0 \tag{4-6}$$

$$\frac{\partial}{\partial k^2}\Gamma_{ijR}^{(2)}(k = 0) = \delta_{ij} \tag{4-7}$$

$$\Gamma_{ijklR}^{(4)}\Big|_{SP} = \kappa^\epsilon u_1 S + \kappa^\epsilon u_2 F \tag{4-8}$$

or, alternatively, by minimal subtraction of poles in ϵ.

In a calculation to order ϵ, $Z_\phi = 1$ and Eq. (4-8) has to be considered up to one loop only. Defining,

$$u_{10} = \kappa^{-\epsilon}\lambda_1; \quad u_{20} = \kappa^{-\epsilon}\lambda_2 \qquad (4\text{-}9)$$

Equation (4-8) reads:

$$u_1 S + u_2 F = \left[u_{10} - \left(\frac{M+8}{6}u_{10}^2 + u_{10}u_{20}\right)J_{SP}\right]S + \left[u_{20} - (2u_{10}u_{20} + \tfrac{3}{2}u_{20}^2)J_{SP}\right]F \qquad (4\text{-}10)$$

and hence

$$u_1 = u_{10} - \left(\frac{M+8}{6}u_{10}^2 + u_{10}u_{20}\right)J_{SP} \qquad (4\text{-}11)$$

$$u_2 = u_{20} - (2u_{10}u_{20} + \tfrac{3}{2}u_{20}^2)J_{SP} \qquad (4\text{-}12)$$

(J_{SP} is defined in Eq. (I-9-39).)

Before solving these last two equations let us note that Eq. (4-5) implies a renormalization group equation for $\Gamma_R^{(N)}$ of the form:

$$\left[\kappa\frac{\partial}{\partial\kappa} + \sum_{i=1}^{2}\beta_i(u_1, u_2)\frac{\partial}{\partial u_i} - \frac{N}{2}\gamma_\phi(u_1, u_2)\right]\Gamma_{i_1 \cdots i_N R}^{(N)}(k_i; u_i, \kappa) = 0 \qquad (4\text{-}13)$$

The functions β_i, of which there are as many as there are independent relevant coupling constants, are given by:

$$\beta_i = \left(\kappa\frac{\partial u_i}{\partial\kappa}\right)_{\lambda_1, \lambda_2} \qquad i = 1, 2 \qquad (4\text{-}14)$$

With u_i expressed in the form (4-11)–(4-12) this direct definition of β_i is rather convenient, though an equivalent of the form (I-8-21) can be constructed (see Exercise 4-1).

From (4-14) and (4-11)–(4-12) one derives:

$$\beta_1 = -\epsilon\left[u_1 - \left(\frac{M+8}{6}u_1^2 + u_1 u_2\right)\frac{1}{\epsilon}\right] \qquad (4\text{-}15)$$

$$\beta_2 = -\epsilon\left[u_2 - (2u_1 u_2 + \tfrac{3}{2}u_2^2)\frac{1}{\epsilon}\right] \qquad (4\text{-}16)$$

Clearly, scale invariance will appear at the fixed points, at which all β's vanish. To order ϵ we find four such fixed points. They are:

      (1) The Gaussian fixed point $u_1 = u_2 = 0$

      (2) The Heisenberg fixed point $u_1 = \dfrac{6}{M+8}\epsilon; \quad u_2 = 0$

(3) The Ising fixed point $\quad u_1 = 0; \quad u_2 = \frac{2}{3}\epsilon$

(4) The cubic fixed point $\quad u_1 = \frac{2}{M}\epsilon; \quad u_2 = \frac{2(M-4)}{3M}\epsilon$

The asymptotic behavior will, of course, depend on which of these four fixed points will be approached in the infrared limit.

Following the standard argument one finds that the coupling constants flow with the scale of length ρ according to:

$$\rho \frac{\partial u_i(\rho)}{\partial \rho} = \beta_i(u_j(\rho)) \qquad (4\text{-}17)$$

with

$$u_i(1) = u_i \qquad (4\text{-}18)$$

A simple generalization of the considerations which led to Eq. (I-8-53) leads to the conclusion that a fixed point is attractive in the infrared if all the eigenvalues of the matrix

$$B_{ij} = \frac{\partial \beta_i}{\partial u_j} \qquad (4\text{-}19)$$

at that fixed point, have a positive real part. Using (4-15) and (4-16) we find:

$$B = \begin{pmatrix} -\epsilon + \frac{M+8}{3}u_1 + u_2 & u_1 \\ 2u_2 & -\epsilon + 2u_1 + 3u_2 \end{pmatrix} \qquad (4\text{-}20)$$

Obviously at the Gaussian fixed point both eigenvalues are negative. This point is doubly unstable. At the Heisenberg fixed point the eigenvalues are

$$b_1 = \epsilon; \qquad b_2 = \frac{4-M}{M+8}\epsilon \qquad (4\text{-}21)$$

Thus, as long as $M < 4$, this point is completely stable. The third fixed point is, to order ϵ, identical in value to the case $M = 1$. In fact, if $u_1 = 0$ then the whole theory is simply equivalent to a product of M independent Ising models. It is referred to as the Ising fixed point.

At this fixed point

$$b_1 = -\tfrac{1}{3}\epsilon \; ; \qquad b_2 = \epsilon \qquad (4\text{-}22)$$

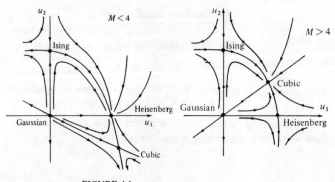

FIGURE 4-1
Flow patterns of the coupling constants for $M < 4$ and $M > 4$.

It is always stable in one direction and unstable in a second one. The last fixed point has as eigenvalues:

$$b_1 = M\epsilon \, ;$$

$$b_2 = \tfrac{1}{3}(M - 4)\epsilon \tag{4-23}$$

When $1 < M < 4$ one of these eigenvalues is positive and the other is negative. Thus, the Heisenberg fixed point is the only stable fixed point. Namely, in the long-wavelength limit the $0(N)$-symmetry is restored. On the other hand when $M > 4$ the Heisenberg fixed point becomes unstable, and the cubic fixed point becomes completely stable. These flow patterns are represented in Fig. 4-1, with the arrows indicating the directions in which the two coupling constants stream as the infrared limit is approached.

The calculation of the exponents to order ϵ is left as Exercise 4-2. Another example of a theory described by two ϕ^4 coupling constants, but which has a different structure, is described in Exercise 4-3.

4-3 RUNAWAY TRAJECTORIES

A short reflection over the two flow diagrams in Fig. 4-1 may lead to the following query. The topography, in both cases, is that of two ridges — connecting the origin at a summit, to the 'extreme' fixed points which are saddles — enclosing a basin with a fixed point at its bottom. This stable fixed point — of spherical symmetry or cubic symmetry — attracts all flows starting on the 'inner' slopes of the two ridges. But what are the physical properties of a system with small coupling constants, which finds itself on the 'outer' slope of a ridge?

These trajectories will surely not flow to any of the four fixed points. The diagrams indicate that in all four instances the flow runs away towards regions where one of the coupling constants becomes ever more negative. This can be

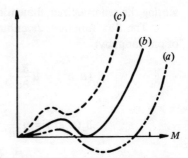

FIGURE 4-2
The free energy as a function of the order parameter (*a*) below (*b*) at (*c*) above a first order transition.

verified, to order ϵ, using Eqs. (4-15)–(4-17). Namely, one may suspect that the system will become unstable for large, negative values of a four-point coupling. An instability may, in turn, suggest a first order transition.

While the above naive expectations will stand the test of more sophisticated inquiry, they remain naive. Firstly, because all theories along a flow trajectory describe the same system, and if it were stable for small values of the couplings, it will remain stable as we observe the system with coarser and coarser probes. What provides for stability are higher order terms in the free energy, which are generated by the resummation, introduced by the solution of the renormalization group equation. Second, if the system undergoes a first order transition, one should be able to construct an expression for the free energy, which would be as accurate as the flow equations, and which exhibits such a transition. Namely, the free energy should have the property that at some value of the parameters it develops a second minimum, a finite distance away from the symmetric one (in field space), but of equal free energy – Fig. 4-2.

Before proceeding with the analysis which lays the above doubts at rest, let us mention another physical system where another variant of the same mechanism appears, and in which it was first explicitly discovered. This system is the superconductor,[3] or scalar electrodynamics.[4] The Lagrangian is given by Eq. (I-2-9), and it will be rewritten here in the form:

$$\mathcal{L}_{SC} = \frac{1}{2}\mu^2|\psi|^2 + \frac{\lambda}{4!}|\psi|^4 + \frac{1}{4}(\nabla \times A)^2 + \frac{1}{2}|(\nabla - iqA)\psi|^2 ,$$
$$(4\text{-}24)$$

where ψ is a complex (two-component) scalar field and A is the electromagnetic potential.

One easily verifies that q^2 has the same dimension as λ at all values of the spatial dimensions, and that four is the critical dimension, at which both couplings become dimensionless. The flow diagram for these two coupling constants, to order $\epsilon(=4-d)$, is represented in Fig. (4-3), with u and e^2 representing the renormalized, dimensionless couplings, corresponding to λ and q^2.

The flow functions describing the diagram in Fig. 4-3 are given, at the level of one loop, by:

$$\beta_u(u, e^2) = \mu \frac{\partial u}{\partial \mu}\Big|_{\lambda, q^2} = -\epsilon u + \frac{5}{3}u^2 - 6e^2 u + 18e^4$$

$$\beta_e(u, e^2) = \mu \frac{\partial e^2}{\partial \mu}\Big|_{\lambda, q^2} = -\epsilon e^2 + \frac{e^4}{3}$$

What the flow pattern in Fig. 4-3 represents is a situation in which there is only one ridge – the u axis. On this ridge there is one peak – at the origin, and one saddle point – the $0(2)$ symmetric fixed point. None are stable, and all trajectories, which are not restricted precisely to the ridge, run away towards negative values of u.

Both cases, as well as many others, are instances of first order transitions induced by fluctuations.

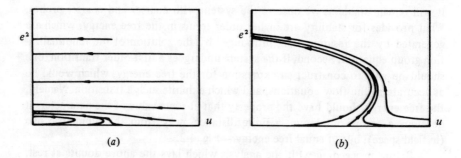

(a) (b)

FIGURE 4-3
The flow diagram of the coupling constants in a superconductor at $d = 4 - \epsilon$. (a) the large picture (b) near the $0(2)$-fixed point[4b].

4-4 FIRST ORDER TRANSITIONS INDUCED BY FLUCTUATIONS: THE COLEMAN-WEINBERG MECHANISM

In order to clarify the situations described in the previous section we will concentrate on the first case – the one with a cubic anisotropy.[6] We will have to step back to the Landau-Ginzburg level, or the classical level, of the theory. The reason is that if a first order transition takes place then our standard logic has it that no renormalization group is necessary, since no correlation length diverges. Typically, at a first order transition (Fig. 4-2) the mass at the symmetric minimum does not vanish.† The considerations concerning flows of coupling constants seem somewhat out of place.

The introduction of renormalization and of the renormalization group follows, usually, the discovery that the Landau-Ginzburg theory predicts a second order transition, hence divergent correlation lengths. Thus we go back to the bare theory described by (4-2) to investigate its predictions, namely, to consider a free energy of the form

$$F_{c1} = \frac{1}{2}\mu^2 \, \bar{\phi}^2 + \frac{\lambda_1}{4!}(\bar{\phi}^2)^2 + \frac{\lambda_2}{4!} \sum_{i=1}^{M} \bar{\phi}_i^{\,4} \, , \qquad (4\text{-}25)$$

where $\bar{\phi}$ is the average of the M-component field ϕ.

Clearly, as long as the quartic part in (4-25) is positive definite, F will describe a second order transition, at $\mu^2 = 0$. On the other hand, if (λ_1, λ_2) is such that the quartic part can become negative in some directions in $\bar{\phi}$-space, then F will describe an unstable system as $\bar{\phi}$ will tend to increase in amplitude indefinitely in any of the negative directions.

What are these directions, and what are the dangerous values of (λ_1, λ_2)? Clearly, only the cubic term – proportional to λ_2 – is sensitive to the direction in $\bar{\phi}$-space. We may have two cases

(a) $\lambda_2 > 0$; F is minimized by ϕ in the direction of the diagonals of the $\bar{\phi}$-hypercube, or the $(\pm 1, \pm 1, \pm 1, \ldots, \pm 1)$ directions. For a given amplitude $|\bar{\phi}|$ of $\bar{\phi}$ in one of these directions

$$F_{\text{diag}} = \frac{1}{2}\mu^2 \, |\phi|^2 + \frac{1}{4!}(\lambda_1 + \frac{\lambda_2}{N})|\phi|^4 \, . \qquad (4\text{-}26)$$

The free energy stops being positive definite if

$$\lambda_1 + \frac{\lambda_2}{N} < 0 \, . \qquad (4\text{-}27)$$

(b) $\lambda_2 < 0$; F is *minimized* by ϕ in the direction of a hyper-cubic axis, or $(0, 0, 1, \ldots, 0)$ direction. For a given amplitude $|\bar{\phi}|$

$$F_{\text{axis}} = \frac{1}{2}\mu^2 \, |\bar{\phi}|^2 + \frac{1}{4!}(\lambda_1 + \lambda_2)|\bar{\phi}|^4 \, . \qquad (4\text{-}28)$$

The system becomes unstable when

$$\lambda_1 + \lambda_2 < 0 \, . \qquad (4\text{-}29)$$

†There are exceptions, such as the situation at a critical end-point.[7]

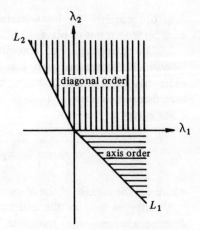

FIGURE 4-4

The "stability wedge" of the classical theory with cubic anisotropy. The boundaries of the stability wedge are $L_1 : \lambda_1 + \lambda_2 = 0$ and $L_2 : \lambda_1 + \frac{1}{N}\lambda_2 = 0$.

This situation is depicted in Fig. 4-4. Outside the hatched region – the stability wedge – the system is unstable. Inside, it undergoes a second order transition, as μ^2 (or T) is lowered through $\mu^2 = 0$. Above the λ_1-axis the symmetry breaks in a diagonal direction, below it breaks along a cube's axis. If λ_2 passes through zero, for $\mu^2 < 0$, the system undergoes a first order transition, in which the order parameter flips discontinuously from one direction to the other. This transition will not concern us here.

Since the classical theory predicts a second order transition in the entire stability wedge, it implies large fluctuations and divergent correlation lengths, hence the renormalization group is called for. Suppose, for concreteness, that $M > 4$. If $\lambda_1 > 0$ and $\lambda_1 \gg \lambda_2 > 0$, then u_1 and u_2 will be in the same region in the (u_1, u_2)-plane, and the phase-transition will be of second order, of the cubic type, as described in Fig. 4-1.

On the other hand, if $\lambda_1 > 0$, but $\lambda_2 < 0$ and $|\lambda_2| \ll \lambda_1$, the classical theory still predicts a continuous transition, and infrared divergences will necessitate a renormalization group. As long as λ_1 and λ_2 are very small, u_1 and u_2 have very nearly the same values (apart from a factor of $(\Lambda/\kappa)^\epsilon$). Hence the system, with these values of the *bare* parameters, will be on a runaway trajectory.

A systematic study of Eqs. (4-15)–(4-17) shows that any such trajectory will cross the line $u_1 + u_2 = 0$ and flow into the region $u_1 + u_2 < 0$.[8,9] Points in the (λ_1, λ_2) plane, corresponding to points in the region $u_1 + u_2 < 0$, have $\lambda_1 + \lambda_2 < 0$, and describe unstable systems on the classical level. Yet, when the trajectory in the (u_1, u_2)-plane crosses the boundary of the stability wedge, no instability is implied, since the entire trajectory is a description of the same system.

We shall now proceed to show that the following statements hold:

(a) The renormalized free energy exhibits a first order transition when $u_1 + u_2 = 0$.
(b) There is no problem of stability.
(c) The calculation is systematic as an ϵ-expansion.

First we need an expression for the *bare* free energy, which is a generalization of Eq. (I-6-25) to the case of a Lagrangian (4-25), with M fields. To derive a closed expression we restrict $\bar{\phi}$ to be uniform in space, to ensure translational invariance, and then we apply Eq. (I-A6-20). The result to order one loop is:

$$F_B(\bar{\phi}) = F_{c1}(\bar{\phi}) + \frac{1}{2} Tr \ln \left\{ \frac{\delta^2 F_{c1}\{\bar{\phi}(x)\}}{\delta\phi_i(x)\delta\phi_i(y)} \Bigg|_{\phi(x) = \bar{\phi}} \right\} \qquad (4\text{-}30)$$

In the special case under consideration, the symmetry breaking will occur along an axis in $\bar{\phi}$-space, hence

$$\bar{\phi} = (\bar{\phi}, 0, \ldots, 0)$$

and

$$F_B(\bar{\phi}) = \frac{1}{2}\mu^2 \bar{\phi}^2 + \frac{\lambda_1 + \lambda_2}{4!} \bar{\phi}^4 + \frac{1}{2} \int dp \left\{ \ln[p^2 + \mu^2 + \tfrac{1}{2}(\lambda_1 + \lambda_2)\bar{\phi}^2] \right.$$

$$\left. + (M-1) \ln[p^2 + \mu^2 + \tfrac{1}{6}\lambda_1 \bar{\phi}^2] \right\}. \qquad (4\text{-}31)$$

The details of derivation are left as Exercise 4-4.

Next the free energy must be renormalized to remove the different divergences contained in the integral. Expressed in terms of renormalized temperature t, magnetization ϕ and couplings u_1 and u_2 one has:

$$F = \frac{1}{2}t\phi^2 + \frac{\kappa^\epsilon}{4!}(u_1 + u_2)\phi^4 + \frac{1}{2}\int dp \left\{ \ln[p^2 + t + \frac{\kappa^\epsilon}{2}(u_1 + u_2)\phi^2] \right.$$

$$+ (M-1)\ln[p^2 + t + \frac{\kappa^\epsilon}{6}u_1 \phi^2]$$

$$- M\ln p^2 - \frac{[t + \frac{\kappa^\epsilon}{2}(u_1 + u_2)\phi^2] + (M-1)[t + \frac{\kappa^\epsilon}{6}u_1 \phi^2]}{p^2}$$

$$\left. + \frac{[t + \frac{1}{2}\kappa^\epsilon(u_1 + u_2)\phi^2]^2 + (M-1)[t + \frac{1}{6}\kappa^\epsilon u_1 \phi^2]^2}{2p^2(p+q)^2} \right\}_{q^2 = \kappa^2}$$

$$(4\text{-}32)$$

See Exercises (4-5)–(4-6).

The integrals can be computed by continuation in the number of dimensions (see e.g. Sec. I-9-9 and App. 9-3). Recalling that integrals of powers vanish, and keeping only leading terms in ϵ, one finds:

$$F = \tfrac{1}{2}t\phi^2 + \tfrac{1}{4}(u_1 + u_2)\phi^4 + f(t + \tfrac{1}{2}(u_1 + u_2)\phi^2) + (M-1)f(t + \tfrac{1}{6}u_1\phi^4)$$

(4-33)

where κ has been set to unity and

$$f(x) = \tfrac{1}{8}x^2(\ln x + \tfrac{1}{2})$$ (4-34)

See Exercise 4-7.

Let us first make a few remarks about orders of magnitude. The u's are of $0(\epsilon)$, and we will choose the value of t to be of $0(\epsilon)$. As we shall see below, when the symmetry breaks, $\phi^2 = 0(\epsilon^{-1})$. Hence $t\phi^2 = 0(1)$. Now, on the special line $u_1 + u_2 = 0$, the second term on the right-hand side of (4-33) is absent, and the first f is $0(\epsilon^2)$. On the other hand, the last term on the right-hand side of (4-33) is $0(1)$, since $u_1\phi^2 = 0(1)$. Thus, symmetry breaking can take place as the $t\phi^2$ is balanced against this last term, and for consistency the solution must satisfy

$$\phi^2 = 0(\epsilon^{-1}).$$

Next, note that there is no problem of stability. As $u_1 + u_2$ vanishes, or even becomes slightly negative, the free energy will be dominated by the last f. For large values of ϕ this term behaves as $\phi^4\ln\phi^2 \gg \phi^4$. This confirms assertion (b) above.

To convince ourselves that on the boundary, $u_1 + u_2 = 0$, F describes a system which undergoes a first order transition notice that $f(x)$ in (4-34), has the form drawn in Fig. 4-5.

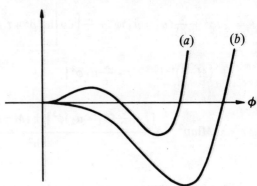

FIGURE 4-5
(a) The function $f(x)$ is also the free energy at zero mass as in Coleman-Weinberg,
(b) the free energy on the boundary $u_1 + u_2 = 0$, for $T < T_c$ and non-zero mass.

It is quite clear that as $t\phi^2$ is added to f, to give the free energy on the boundary, one goes through a sequence like the one depicted in Fig. 4-5, which indicates a first order transition at some $t > 0$.

Formally, one would detect a first order transition as a minimum of the free energy with $\phi_1 \neq 0$, at which

$$F(\phi_1) = F(0) . \qquad (4\text{-}35)$$

Hence one has two equations, which determine the values of t_1 and ϕ_1 at the transition. The equations can be solved explicitly. If one denotes:

$$u_1 = 6a\epsilon , \qquad t_1 = b\epsilon , \qquad \phi_1^2 = c\epsilon^{-1} \qquad (4\text{-}36)$$

one finds

$$b = \frac{a^2}{4}(M-1) , \qquad c = a^{-1} e^{-3/2} . \qquad (4\text{-}37)$$

The fact that such a solution exists, with a, b and c of order unity implies that indeed the *free energy, with renormalized parameters on the boundary of the region in which the quartic term is positive, exhibits a first order phase transition as one varies the temperature.* This is the expression of point (a), above.

In fact, since our solution satisfies (4-36), we have already one part of point (c), namely, this is a development in ϵ. The remaining question is about the higher order terms. These, one can argue, must be at least of order $u_1^2\,\phi_1^2\,\ln(t_1)$, which in the neighborhood of the first order transition is of order $\epsilon \ln \epsilon$, while the terms that were kept were all of order one.

But all the above considerations have concerned a theory for which the renormalized parameters $u_1 + u_2 = 0$. The physical description starts with bare couplings $\lambda_2 < 0$, $\lambda_1 > 0$, with $|\lambda_2| \ll \lambda_1$. This last condition ensures that there is an initial, fast increase of the correlation length, as the system will tend to flow along the ridge towards the Heisenberg fixed point, which helps repress any undersirable irrelevant operators. See Fig. 4-1 with $M > 4$. In fact, the ridge from the origin to this fixed point is a line of tri-critical points — each point on it represents a second order transition point sitting at the top of a line of transitions of first order.

To the initial bare couplings correspond renormalized couplings u_1, u_2. Again $0 < -u_2 \ll u_1$. One then uses the renormalization group, because initially the correlation length grows as t is reduced and it appears that there are infrared difficulties in perturbation theory. The renormalization group implies, as usual, that t or ϕ can be rolled out of the infrared dangerous region, via

$$F(t, \bar{\phi}, u_1, u_2, \kappa) = \rho^d F(t(\rho), \bar{\phi}(\rho), u_1(\rho), u_2(\rho), \kappa) \qquad (4\text{-}38)$$

choosing ρ by the temperature condition

$$t(\rho) = \kappa^2 = 1$$

gives $\rho(t) = \xi^{-1}(t)$, when $t \to 0$. As ρ decreases u_1 and u_2 flow, and always hit the boundary, at some $\rho_1 > 0$. One has

$$u_1(\rho_1) + u_2(\rho_1) = 0 \qquad (4\text{-}39)$$

It is for this value of ρ_1 that we have been able to deduce a first order transition, at:

$$t_1 = t(\rho_1) = b\epsilon$$

$$\phi_1 = \phi(\rho_1) = c\epsilon^{-1}$$

What are then the values of the initial t and ϕ? This can be answered by first expressing $t(\rho_1)$ and $\phi(\rho_1)$ in terms of t and ϕ, and then introducing ρ_1. The solution of the characteristic equations for $t(\rho)$ and $\phi(\rho)$, with initial values t and ϕ, are given by (3-9) and (3-10). One has

$$t(\rho_1) = tf(\rho_1)$$

$$\phi(\rho_1) = \phi g(\rho_1)$$

Thus the values of the initial t and ϕ at which the transition occurs are

$$t_1^{(i)} = \frac{b\epsilon}{f(\rho_1)} \quad , \qquad \phi_1^{(i)} = \frac{c\epsilon^{-1}}{g(\rho_1)}$$

The value of ρ_1 can be expressed in terms of the initial u_1 and u_2 by solving the flow equations for the couplings from (u_1, u_2) to (4-39). The equations to be solved are, of course, Eqs. (4-15)−(4-17). The most interesting feature is that[7]

$$\rho_1 \sim e^{-D/\epsilon}$$

which is a result of the fact that u's must cross a distance of order ϵ with speed ϵ^2, on a logarithmic scale of ρ. Thus, for example,

$$f(\rho_1) \sim \rho_1^{-2/\epsilon}$$

and therefore

$$t_1^{(i)} \sim e^{-2D/\epsilon}$$

A similar result holds for $\phi_1^{(i)}$. It should, therefore, not be surprising that the power of the renormalization group was required to arrive at such a highly non-analytic result.

4-5 GEOMETRICAL DESCRIPTION OF THE COLEMAN-WEINBERG PHENOMENON

Using the technique introduced in Sec. I-9-6, to solve the renormalization group equation for quantities depending on a single dimensionful parameter, one can derive (following Yamagishi[10]) a very beautiful geometrical description of the symmetry breaking at zero mass – the Coleman-Weinberg phenomenon. In particular we shall discover that the entire question of whether fluctuations induce symmetry breaking in this case resides in the flow functions β.

Returning to the discussion in Sec. 4-4 above, we will assume that $\lambda_2 < 0$, and hence if symmetry is to break it will be along an axis in ϕ-space. Taking the renormalized mass to be zero, the amplitude ϕ remains the only dimensionful parameter in the free energy (the effective potential).

Using dimensional analysis the free energy can be written as

$$U(\phi, u_1, u_2, \kappa) = \phi^{2d/(d-2)} \, V(\mu, u_1, u_2) \qquad (4\text{-}40)$$

with

$$\mu = \phi/\kappa^{(d-2)/2} \qquad (4\text{-}41)$$

The renormalization group equation for U:

$$\left[\kappa \frac{\partial}{\partial \kappa} + \beta_1(u_1, u_2) \frac{\partial}{\partial u_1} + \beta_2(u_1, u_2) \frac{\partial}{\partial u_2} - \frac{1}{2} \eta \phi \frac{\partial}{\partial \phi} \right] U(\phi, u_1, u_2, \kappa) = 0$$

$$(4\text{-}42)$$

becomes the following equation for V:

$$\left[\mu \frac{\partial}{\partial \mu} + \bar{\beta}_1 \frac{\partial}{\partial u_1} + \bar{\beta}_2 \frac{\partial}{\partial u_2} - \frac{d}{d-2} \, \bar{\eta} \right] V(\mu, u_1, u_2) = 0 \qquad (4\text{-}43)$$

in analogy with Sec. I-9-6. The new functions with bars are related to the barless ones via

$$\bar{\gamma} = \frac{2\gamma}{d-2+\eta} \qquad (4\text{-}44)$$

See Exercise 4-8.

The solution of Eq. (4-43) is

$$V(\mu, u_1, u_2) = F(u_1(\mu), u_2(\mu)) \exp\left[-\frac{d}{d-2} \int_1^\mu \bar{\eta}(u_i(x)) \frac{dx}{x} \right] \qquad (4\text{-}45)$$

with F an arbitrary function of $u_i(\mu)$ and the initial conditions $u_i(\mu = 1) = u_i$. Inserting (4-45) in (4-40) gives the free energy of the massless theory as a function of a single symmetry breaking parameter ϕ.

The arbitrary function F can be eliminated by a judicious choice of *normalization*, which effects the coupling constants.[3] Choosing:

$$V(\phi = \kappa^{(d-2)/2}) = \frac{u_1 + u_2}{4!} \kappa^d \qquad (4\text{-}46)$$

in which we have expressed our preference for symmetry breaking along a cube's axis, we find from (4-40) and (4-45) that

$$F(u_1(1), u_2(1)) = F(u_1, u_2) = u_1 + u_2$$

From which it follows that

$$F(u_1(\mu), u_2(\mu)) = u_1(\mu) + u_2(\mu) \qquad (4\text{-}47)$$

The free energy along the axis can be finally written as:

$$U = \frac{1}{4!}[u_1(\mu) + u_2(\mu)] \phi^{2d/(d-2)} \exp\left[-\frac{d}{d-2} \int_1^\mu \bar{\eta} \frac{dx}{x}\right] \qquad (4\text{-}48)$$

See Exercise 4-9.

The Coleman-Weinberg phenomenon is the statement that U possesses a minimum at $\phi = \phi_0 \neq 0$, which is lower than the symmetric minimum $U(\phi = 0) = 0$. The function U must satisfy the conditions:

$$\frac{\partial U}{\partial \phi_0} = 0 \qquad (4\text{-}49)$$

$$\frac{\partial^2 U}{\partial \phi_0^2} > 0 \qquad (4\text{-}50)$$

$$U(\phi_0) < 0 \qquad (4\text{-}51)$$

The last condition implies that

$$u_1(\mu_0) + u_2(\mu_0) < 0 \qquad (4\text{-}52)$$

Namely, the couplings at the scale of symmetry breaking must be beyond the *classical* stability wedge. The first condition — (4-49) — reduces to

$$\beta_1(u_i(\mu_0)) + \beta_2(u_i(\mu_0)) + d[u_1(\mu_0) + u_2(\mu_0)] = 0 \qquad (4\text{-}53)$$

This equation gives the geometric description of the phenomenon. It states that symmetry breaking can and will take place if the trajectory of the coupling constants $u_i(\mu)$ intersects the curve

$$\beta_1(u_i) + \beta_2(u_i) + d(u_1 + u_2) = 0 \qquad (4\text{-}54)$$

in a region of parameters where $u_2 < 0$ and $U'' > 0$. The point of intersection gives $\mu_0 = \phi_0 / \kappa^{(d-2)/2}$.

Thus the full information about the symmetry breaking is contained in the flow functions, including the condition $U''(\phi_0) > 0$, which was not written explicitly.

When the ordered state requires more than one amplitude of symmetry breaking the situation becomes considerably more complex. Such may be the case for a He^4 super-solid, a phase in which both crystaline and superfluid order are present. In statistical mechanics one encounters a *tetra-critical point*.[11] In particle physics such situations are just beginning to be considered,[12] in the context of super-symmetry. The bridge is yet to be constructed.

EXERCISES

4-1 Show that if the theory can be renormalized by a set of coupling constants $u_{i0}(u_i, \epsilon)$, then the functions

$$\beta_i = \left(\kappa \frac{\partial u_i}{\partial \kappa} \right)_{\text{bare}}$$

satisfy:

$$\frac{\partial \ln u_{i0}}{\partial u_j} \beta_j(u_k) = -\epsilon$$

4-2 Calculate ν, γ and α to order ϵ for general values of M in a model with an interaction of the form Eq. (4-2).

4-3 Consider the case of the Potts model with the additional symmetry $\phi_i \to -\phi_i$. Its interaction Lagrangian can be defined as:

$$\mathcal{L}_{\text{Int}} = \frac{1}{4!} (\lambda_1 S_{ijkl} + \lambda_2 F_{ijkl}) \phi_i \phi_j \phi_k \phi_l$$

with

$$F_{ijkl} = \sum_a e_i e_j e_k e_l$$

The set of vectors α is the hypertetrahedral set, satisfying:

$$\sum_{i=1}^{M+1} e_i^\alpha e_i^\beta = (M+1)\delta^{\alpha\beta} - 1 ; \qquad \sum_{\alpha=1}^{M+1} e_i^\alpha = 0$$

$$\sum_{\alpha=1}^{M+1} e_i^\alpha e_i^\alpha = (M+1)\delta_{ij}$$

Calculate the β functions, the fixed points with their domains of stability, and the critical exponents, at order ϵ (See, e.g., Ref. 13 Chap. I-2).

4-4 If the interaction term in tne Lagrangian is

$$\mathscr{L}_{\text{Int}} = \frac{1}{4!} \lambda_{ijkl}\, \phi_i\, \phi_j\, \phi_k\, \phi_l$$

The free energy to one loop, in a translationally invariant field, is

$$F = F_{c1}(\bar{\phi}) + \frac{1}{2}\text{Tr}_{ij}\int dp \ln\left[(p^2 + \mu^2)\delta_{ij} + \frac{1}{2}\lambda_{ijkl}\,\bar{\phi}_k\,\bar{\phi}_l\right]$$

show that if $\bar{\phi}$ is along an axis (4-31) results. What is the result for $\bar{\phi}$ on a diagonal?

4-5 Show that for a general quartic interaction as in Exercise 4-4,

$$F = \frac{1}{2}t\phi^2 + \frac{\kappa^\epsilon}{4!}u_{ijkl}\,\phi_i\,\phi_j\,\phi_k\,\phi_l + \frac{1}{2}\text{Tr}_{ij}\int dp \left\{ \ln(p^2 + a_{ij}) - \ln p^2 - \frac{a_{ij}}{p^2} \right.$$

$$\left. + \frac{(a^2)_{ij}}{2p^2(p+q)^2} \Bigg|_{q^2 = \kappa^2} \right\}$$

where

$$a_{ij} = t\delta_{ij} + \frac{1}{2}\kappa^\epsilon u_{ijkl}\phi_k\phi_l$$

is finite, as the regularization is removed.

4-6 Show what F of the previous exercise satisfies the following normalization conditions:

$$\Gamma_{ij}^{(2)}(p=0, t=0, \phi=0) = 0$$

$$\frac{\partial}{\partial p^2}\Gamma_{ij}^{(2)}(p, t=0, \phi=0)\Big|_{p^2 = \kappa^2} = \delta_{ij}$$

$$\Gamma_{ijkl}^{(4)}\Big|_{\text{SP}} = \kappa^\epsilon u_{ijkl}$$

4-7 Show that in dimensional regularization F, of Exercise 4-5, becòmes to leading order

$$F = \frac{1}{2}t\phi^2 + \frac{1}{4}u_{ijkl}\,\phi_i\,\phi_j\,\phi_k\,\phi_l + \sum_i f(t + v_i)$$

where v_i are the eigenvalues of $B_{ij} = \frac{1}{2}u_{ijkl}\phi_k\phi_l{}^9$.

4-8 Starting from Eq. (4-42) derive Eq. (4-43). Show that (4-45) is a solution of this equation.

4-9 Derive the form of the free energy for the case $\lambda_2 > 0$. What are the conditions for the appearance of a Coleman-Weinberg phenomenon.

4-10 Investigate geometrically the flow functions for u_1 and u_2 at order ϵ and verify that Yamagishi's conditions are satisfied.

REFERENCES

1. D. J. Wallace, *Journal of Physics*, **C6**, 1390 (1973); I. J. Ketley and D. J. Wallace, *Journal of Physics*, **A6**, 1667 (1973) and A. Aharony, *Physical Review*, **B8**, 3349 (1973) and *Physical Review Letters*, **31**, 1494 (1973).
2. E. Brezin, J. C. LeGuillou and J. Zinn-Justin, *Physical Review*, **B10**, 892 (1974).
3. S. Coleman and E. Weinberg, Ref. 1 Ch. I-9; see also J. Iliopoulos and N. Papanicolaou, *Nuclear Physics*, **B105**, 77 (1976) and **B111** 209 (1976).
4. B. I. Halperin, T. C. Lubensky and S. K. Ma, *Physical Review Letters*, **32**, 292 (1974); Jing-Huei Chen, T. C. Lubensky, and D. R. Nelson, *Physical Review*, **B17**, 4274 (1978).
5. Extensive lists are presented by Aharony in DG and in M. Kerszberg, *Symmetry Fluctuations and Multicritical Phase Diagrams*, Ph. D. thesis, Weismann Institute of Science, 1980.
6. The early studies of the phase-structure of this system have been by D. J. Wallace, *Journal of Physics*, **C6**, 1390 (1973); T. Natterman and S. Trimper, *Journal of Physics*, **A8**, 2000 (1975); I. F. Lyuksutsov and V. Pokrovskii, *JETP Letters*, **21**, 9 (1975).
7. V. J. Emery, *Physical Review*, **B11**, 3397 (1975).
8. J. Rudnick, *Physical Review*, **B18**, 1406 (1978).
9. H. Iacobson and D. J. Amit, *Annals of Physics*, **133**, 57 (1981).
10. H. Yamagishi, *Physical Review*, **D23**, 1880 (1981).
11. K. S. Liu and M. E. Fisher, *Journal of Low Temperature Physics*, **10**, 655 (1973); M. E. Fisher and D. R. Nelson, *Physical Review Letters*, **32**, 1350 (1974); D. R. Nelson, J. M. Kosterlitz and M. E. Fisher, *Physical Review Letters*, **33**, 817 (1974); A. Aharony and A. D. Bruce, *Physical Review Letters*, **33**, 427 (1974).
12. M. B. Einhorn and D. R. T. Jones, *Nuclear Physica*, **B** [FS] in press.

5

CROSSOVER PHENOMENA

5-1 INTRODUCTION

The main effort in the theoretical developments described in this volume has been directed towards the extraction of the asymptotic behavior of various correlation functions and thermodynamic quantities as relevant parameters, such as temperature, external field or wave-number move slightly off their critical values. But as the number of parameters increases one is led into ever richer situations. One often encounters a number of different types of critical behavior — fixed points — within reach of given approximation techniques.

The flow diagrams in Fig. 4-1, for example, have four fixed points each, within reach of the ϵ-expansion. Considering the case $M < 4$, if $u_1 = 0$, the system has an Ising critical point. For small $u_1 > 0$, as the temperature decreases towards the critical point, $t \ll \Lambda^2$, one would expect to observe Ising critical behavior, until t becomes of the order of u_1^{2/d_1}, where d_1 is the anomalous dimension of u_1 at the Ising point. Then deviations will start and the system will cross-over to the Heisenberg fixed point, namely the asymptotic behavior in the critical region ($t \ll \Lambda^2$) will not be monotonic, and will continuously change from Ising exponents to Heisenberg exponents. This is a *cross-over* phenomenon, and the function interpolating between the two asymptotic behaviors is the *cross-over function*[1]. But this cross-over will occur only provided that $d_1 > 0$, and will be faster the larger the *cross-over exponent* (See Secs. 2 and 3).

Figure 4-1 itself already presents a variety of cross-overs. The phenomenon is very general, and quite varied. Changing the wave-vector, k at a temperature t slightly above its critical values will induce a cross-over from critical to Gaussian behavior as k^2/t changes from very large to very small values, while both are very small compared to Λ^2. Asymmetric masses in an M-vector model will induce a cross-over from a higher to a lower symmetry Heisenberg behavior, as t crosses the value of the mass-difference, etc.

Some cross-over phenomena will be discussed in the present chapter. Another one will appear in Chapter 6.

5-2 CROSSOVER IN MAGNETIC SYSTEMS INTERACTING QUADRATICALLY AND THE HARRIS CRITERION FOR RELEVANCE OF RANDOM DILUTION

Let us now observe the system with a cubic anisotropy from another angle, making use of the powerful tools developed in Secs. 2-3, 2-4 and the related appendices. We will be able to show that the topography of flows in the space of coupling constants may be richer than what we found at first order in ϵ. Specifically, it will transpire that:

The Ising fixed point is stable if the specific heat exponent of the corresponding Ising model is negative.

that is if the specific heat does not diverge. In other words, the sign of b_1 in (4-22) is not definite. Eq. (4-22) is the lowest order term of the result[2]:

$$b_1 = -\alpha/\nu \qquad (5\text{-}1)$$

Compare Eqs. (I-9-53) and (I-9-51).

As we shall show below, following Jug and Carneiro[3], is that this result holds to all orders in ϵ. As will be also briefly indicated, a particular case of the general result (5-1) is the important consequence that *the critical behavior of an Ising model is insensitive to a random dilution of its sites, if and only if the specific heat of the pure system does not diverge.* This criterion discovered phenomenologically by Harris[4], is proved to all orders in ϵ by a continuation of (5-1) in the number of components, M, to $M = 0$.

To be more specific let us reformulate the problem discussed in Sec. 4-1, following the remark made at the end of that section, namely that when $u_1 = 0$, the system is a product of M Ising models. Hence, the interaction (4-2) is written as

$$\mathscr{L}_{\text{Int}} = \frac{1}{4!}[\sigma_1 \sum_{i=1}^{N} \phi_i^4 + \sigma_2 \sum_{i \neq j} \phi_i^2 \phi_j^2] \qquad (5\text{-}2)$$

The new couplings are related to the old ones via:

$$\lambda_1 = \sigma_2; \quad \lambda_2 = \sigma_1 - \sigma_2 \qquad (5\text{-}3)$$

and the analysis of Sec. 4-1 can be rephrased in terms of the σ's. The details are left as Exercise 5-I.

In the formulation (5-2) one can pose the problem of the relevance of σ_2 with respect to the Ising fixed point. $\mathscr{L}_{\text{Int}}$ describes an assembly of Ising models, interacting quadratically — through their energy densities. Hence we are asking about the relevance of that interaction.

Another way of asking the same question is to inquire about the *crossover exponent* at the Ising critical point. After all for $\sigma_2 = 0$ the critical behavior of the system is dominated by the Ising fixed point. On the other hand for $\sigma_2 \neq 0$, which implies $\lambda_1 \neq 0$, the system may *crossover* to a critical behavior dominated by either the cubic or the Heisenberg fixed points.

The scaling behavior of any thermodynamic quantity $f(t, \sigma_2)$, can be written as:[1]

$$f(t, \sigma_2) = t^{\Delta} \bar{f}(\sigma_2/t^{\psi}) \qquad (5\text{-}4)$$

where Δ is the critical exponent of the quantity f in the pure Ising system — $\sigma_2 = 0$. For finite σ_2, as $t \to 0$, one may have either

 (a) $\psi < 0$, and as $t \to 0$ we recover
 $f \propto t^{\Delta}$
 even for finite σ_2.

 (b) $\psi > 0$, and the argument of f tends to infinity as $t \to 0$ and $\sigma_2 \neq 0$, the interaction is relevant and causes a *crossover*.

The exponent ψ is called the *crossover exponent*.

The quantitative result of this section is[2,3] that to all orders

$$\psi = \alpha \qquad (5\text{-}5)$$

where α is the specific heat exponent of the pure Ising system.

Before proceeding to the actual demonstration we need one more logical connection: if d_2 is the dimension of A_2 — the operator multiplying σ_2, then

$$\psi = -\nu d_2 \qquad (5\text{-}6)$$

the proof is left as Exercise 5-2. The relation (5-1) is therefore a statement that b_1 is the dimension of A_2. In other words, if

$$\beta_2(v_1, v_2) = \kappa \left. \frac{\partial v_2}{\partial \kappa} \right|_{\text{bare}}$$

where v_1 and v_2 are dimensionless, renormlized interactions corresponding to σ_1 and σ_2, then

$$\left. \frac{\partial \beta_2(v_1, v_2)}{\partial v_2} \right|_{\text{Ising fixed point}} = d_2 \qquad (5\text{-}7)$$

This can be proved directly, but is left as Exercise 5-3.

We shall now proceed to show that the dimension of A_2 is $-\alpha/\nu$, at the Ising fixed point. First notice that the naive dimension of $A_2(p)$ is, like that of $\phi^4(p)$, $d-4(=-\epsilon)$. Next, we observe that the operator A_2, when inserted into any Green function of the product of non-interacting Ising models, leads to a factorization. The anomalous dimension of the operator can then be read off. According to (2-48) the sum of the naive dimension and the anomalous dimension is the total dimension of the operator.

The factorization is very simple. Consider the vertex $\Gamma_2^{(N+M)}$ with N fields of index α and M fields of index β, and out of the sum over $i \neq j$ in A_2 choose the term $\phi_\alpha^2 \phi_\beta^2$. Clearly, since there are no mixing terms when $\sigma_2 = 0$, the ϕ_α^2 can only contract with fields of index α among the external legs and in the statistical weight. See also Exercise 5-3. Therefore:

$$\Gamma_2^{(N+M)}(p_1, \ldots, p_N, q_1, \ldots, q_M; p)$$

$$= \Gamma_{\phi_\alpha^2}^{(N)}(p_1, \ldots, p_N)\, \Gamma_{\phi_\beta^2}^{(M)}(q_1, \ldots, q_M) \qquad (5\text{-}8)$$

with

$$\sum_1^N p_i + \sum_1^M q_i + p = 0$$

The above factorization implies that $Z_\phi^{\frac{1}{2}(N+M)} \, Z_{\phi^2}^2$ will renormalize $\Gamma_2^{(N+M)}$, and hence the anomalous dimension of $\phi_\alpha^2 \phi_\beta^2$ is $2\gamma_{\phi^2}^*$, (see e.g. Sec. I-8-8.) In turn,

$$2\gamma_{\phi^2}^* = 2(2 - \nu^{-1}) = 4 - d - \alpha/\nu$$

which leads to the desired result

$$d_2 = -\alpha/\nu$$

and via (5-6) to (5-5).

Finally, we mention that an Ising model whose sites are populated with probability p can be described by a field theory with a Lagrangian of the form[5]:

$$\mathscr{L} = \sum_{\alpha=1}^{n} \left[\frac{1}{2} \mu^2 \phi_\alpha^2 + \frac{1}{2} (\nabla\phi_\alpha)^2 + \frac{\lambda}{4!} \phi_\alpha^4 \right] - \frac{\Delta}{4!} \left(\sum_{\alpha=1}^{n} \phi_\alpha^2 \right)^2 \qquad (5\text{-}9)$$

where $\mu^2 \propto T - T_c(p)$, $\Delta \propto 1 - p = c$ (the concentration of impurity sites), and after any thermodynamic quantity is computed, the limit $n \to 0$ has to be taken. This is the famous *replica trick,* which is introduced to deal with quenched randomness[5].

The relation to the previous discussion should be evident. As long as $\Delta > \lambda$ the coupling between the different fields is quadratic and constitutes a perturbation on a pure Ising model, for all values of n. The mixing of the replicas is proportional to Δ and is the potential source for a crossover. The previous discussion shows that in this case as well the relevance of the disorder depends on the sign of the specific heat exponent of the pure system, just as is expected by the Harris criterion.

5-3 THE CROSSOVER EXPONENT AT A BICRITICAL POINT : SCALE INVARIANCE WITH QUADRATIC SYMMETRY BREAKING

We consider a system which is described by a bare Lagrangian of the form:

$$\mathscr{L} = \tfrac{1}{2}(\nabla\phi)^2 + \tfrac{1}{2}\mu_1^2\phi_1^2 + \tfrac{1}{2}\mu_2^2\phi_2^2 + \frac{\lambda}{4!}(\phi^2)^2 \qquad (5\text{-}10)$$

where the notation is defined by Eq. (7-151). This form may be obtained in mean-field theory from a microscopic problem of an M-component Heisenberg model with anisotropy. If $\mu_1^2 < \mu_2^2$ then, as the temperature is lowered, the K components inside ϕ_1^2 will become unstable first and the system will behave as a critical K-component model. If $\mu_1^2 > \mu_2^2$ then $(M - K)$-models become unstable and the behavior will be that of an $(M - K)$-component model. Finally, if $\mu_1^2 = \mu_2^2$ it is an M-component model.[6]

The critical temperature will depend on the magnitude of the anisotropy. The lower the number of components becoming unstable the higher T_c. Furthermore, at least for small anisotropies, T_c increases with increasing absolute value of the anisotropy, since the effect of the non-critical components, which tend to lower T_c, becomes smaller. A qualitative picture of the phase diagram is depicted in Fig. 5-1. In drawing this qualitative picture it was assumed that $K < \tfrac{1}{2}M$. The dark line separating the two ordered states is a line of first order transitions.

If the anisotropy is denoted by g then in the critical region the inverse

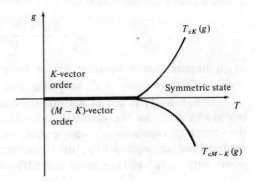

FIGURE 5-1
Phase diagram at a bicritical point.

longitudinal susceptibility should have the scaling form[1]:

$$\chi_L^{-1}(t,g) = t^\gamma f\left(\frac{g}{t^\varphi}\right) \qquad (5\text{-}11)$$

where $t = (T - T_{cM})/T_{cM}$, T_{cM} is the critical temperature of a Heisenberg system with M components, and $\gamma = \gamma(M)$, the critical exponent of the susceptibility of this system. For $g = 0$, χ_L^{-1} behaves as t^γ. For fixed $g \neq 0$, as t decreases f will vanish for some positive values of its argument. In other words, for small g there is a value of $t > 0$

$$t = \alpha g^{1/\varphi} \qquad (5\text{-}12)$$

where α is a zero of f, and φ is the *crossover exponent*, describing the departure of the two critical lines from T_{cM} in Fig. 5-1. Near this temperature t^γ tends to a constant, and the critical behavior is given by

$$\chi_L^{-1} \propto \tau^\gamma \qquad (5\text{-}13)$$

where $\tau = t - \alpha g^\varphi$, is the distance from the critical temperature corresponding to this value of g, and $\gamma = \gamma(K)$, or $\gamma(M-K)$ – the critical exponent of the susceptibility of K-, or $(M-K)$-vector model. The study of the *crossover function* f we leave to the following sections. Here we concentrate on the computation of φ, the exponent which describes the dependence of the critical temperature on the anisotropy.

First notice that the quadratic term in (5-10) can be rewritten as:

$$\mathscr{L}_{SB} = \tfrac{1}{2}(\mu^2 \, \Phi^2 - gB)$$

with

$$B = \frac{1}{M}\,[(M-K)\phi_1^2 - K\phi_2^2] \qquad (5\text{-}14)$$

μ^2 and g can be expressed in terms of μ_1^2 and μ_2^2 of (5-10), namely,

$$\mu^2 = \frac{K\mu_1^2 + (M-K)\mu_2^2}{M}; \qquad g = \mu_2^2 - \mu_1^2 \qquad (5\text{-}15)$$

which implies that a variation of the temperature at a fixed anisotropy is equivalent to a variation of μ^2, keeping g fixed.

In Sec. I-7-12 it was shown that the quadratic operators ϕ^2 and B each reproduces itself in the counterterms which it generates. This implies that the coupling constants μ^2 and g can be multiplicatively and separately renormalized. Or, equivalently, that if the bare vertices are expanded in a double power series in $\delta\mu^2$ and in g about the $0(M)$-symmetric critical theory as:

$$\Gamma^{(N)}(p_i; \mu^2, g, \lambda, \Lambda) = \sum_{L,M=0}^{\infty} \frac{1}{L!M!} (\delta\mu^2)^L (g)^M \Gamma^{(N,L,M)}(p_i, 0, 0; \mu_c^2, \lambda, \Lambda)$$

$$(5\text{-}16)$$

where on the right-hand side $\Gamma^{(N,L,M)}$ are vertices with L ϕ^2-insertions and M B-insertions, computed in the critical $0(M)$-symmetric theory (cf. Eq. (I-7-78). From the counterterms one can derive two constants, Z_{ϕ^2} and Z_B, such that

$$\Gamma_R^{(N,L,M)}(p_i, q_i, r_i; u, \kappa) = Z_\phi^{N/2} Z_{\phi^2}^L Z_B^M \Gamma^{(N,L,M)}(p_i, q_i, r_i; \mu_c^2, \lambda, \Lambda) \qquad (5\text{-}17)$$

are finite as $\Lambda \to \infty$. The details are left as Exercise 5-5 (see also Exercise 5-6). Following the logic leading to Eq. (I-7-82) one arrives at the renormalized form of $\Gamma^{(N)}$ in the anisotropic case away from the critical temperature. It is:

$$\Gamma_R^{(N)}(p_i; t, y, u, \kappa) = \sum_{M,L} \frac{1}{M!L!} (t)^M (y)^L \Gamma_R^{(N,L,M)}(p_i, 0, 0; u, \kappa) \qquad (5\text{-}18)$$

in which

$$\mu^2 = Z_{\phi^2} t; \qquad g = Z_B y \qquad (5\text{-}19)$$

Using Eq. (5-18) in conjunction with Eq. (5-17) one arrives at a renormalization group equation:

$$\left[\kappa \frac{\partial}{\partial \kappa} + \beta \frac{\partial}{\partial u} - \tfrac{1}{2} N \gamma_\phi(u) + \gamma_{\phi^2}(u) t \frac{\partial}{\partial t} + \gamma_B(u) y \frac{\partial}{\partial y} \right] \Gamma_R^{(N)}(p_i; t, y, u, \kappa) = 0 \qquad (5\text{-}20)$$

The steps leading to this equation are analogous to those followed in the derivation of Eq. (I-8-65) (see also Exercise 5-7). The coefficient functions are the β, δ_ϕ and γ_{ϕ^2} of the $0(M)$-symmetric theory. The only new function is γ_B, defined by:

$$\gamma_B(u) = -\kappa \left. \frac{\partial \ln Z_B}{\partial \kappa} \right|_{\lambda, \Lambda} = -\beta(u) \frac{\partial \ln Z_B}{\partial u} \qquad (5\text{-}21)$$

In the special case $N = 2$, $p_i = 0$, Eq. (5-20) reads:

$$\left[\kappa\frac{\partial}{\partial\kappa} + \beta(u)\frac{\partial}{\partial u} - \gamma_\phi(u) + \gamma_{\phi^2}(u)t\frac{\partial}{\partial t} + \gamma_B(u)y\frac{\partial}{\partial y}\right]\chi^{-1}(t, y, u, \kappa) = 0 \qquad (5\text{-}22)$$

The solution of this equation follows a well-trodden path (see, e.g., Sec. 3-4). In the asymptotic region ($t \to 0$ and hence $u(\rho) \to u^*$) it reads:

$$\chi^{-1}(t, y, u, \kappa = 1) = ZX^\gamma t^\gamma \Phi\left(YX^{-\nu(2-\gamma_B^*)}\frac{y}{t^{\nu(2-\gamma_B^*)}}\right) \qquad (5\text{-}23)$$

where ν and γ are the usual critical exponents of the $O(M)$-symmetric theory;

$$\gamma_B^* = \gamma_B(u^*)$$

and u^* is the $O(M)$-symmetric fixed point. The functions X, Y and Z depend on the initial value of u – they are non-universal. These are the analogues of Y and X in Eqs. (3-34) and (3-35).

Equation (5-23) has precisely the form of an equation of state. It should be compared with Eq. (3-16). Following the treatment of the equation of state (Sec. 3-2) one concludes that, apart from a normalization of the susceptibility and of the temperature, the form of the *crossover function* is universal. We return to the calculation of this function later on.

To conclude the present section we indicate a few of the steps involved in the computation of the crossover exponent φ. The expression to be calculated can be read off Eq. (5-23) when the latter is compared with Eq. (5-11), namely,

$$\varphi = \nu(2 - \gamma_B^*) \qquad (5\text{-}24)$$

First we show that φ depends on M only to all orders in perturbation theory. To see this consider, for example, the determination of Z_B via a normalization condition of the form:

$$\Gamma^{(2)}_{11,\,BR}\Big|_{SP} = 1 \qquad (5\text{-}25)$$

Using the form of B, Eq. (5-14), this can be written as:

$$\frac{1}{M}Z_B Z_\phi[(M-K)\Gamma^{(2)}_{11,1} + (M-K)(K-1)\Gamma^{(2)}_{11,2} - K(M-K)\Gamma^{(2)}_{11,2}] = 1$$

in which $\Gamma^2_{11,j}$ is the vertex $\Gamma^{(2)}_{11}$ with an insertion of $\frac{1}{2}\phi_j^2$, and where we have used the fact that the insertions of ϕ_j^2 with $j \neq 1$ in $\Gamma^{(2)}_{11}$ are all equal. Combining the terms inside the brackets, the normalization equation becomes:

$$Z_B Z_\phi\frac{M-K}{M}[\Gamma^{(2)}_{11,1} - \Gamma^{(2)}_{11,2}] = 1 \qquad (5\text{-}26)$$

The brackets are, of course, independent of K, as is Z_ϕ, and the explicit K-dependence in Eq. (5-26) will disappear when the logarithmic derivative in Eq. (5-21) is affected.

The graphs which enter $\Gamma^{(2)}_{11,1}$ and $\Gamma^{(2)}_{11,2}$ – the bare ones – are given in Figs. 5-2 and 5-3, respectively.

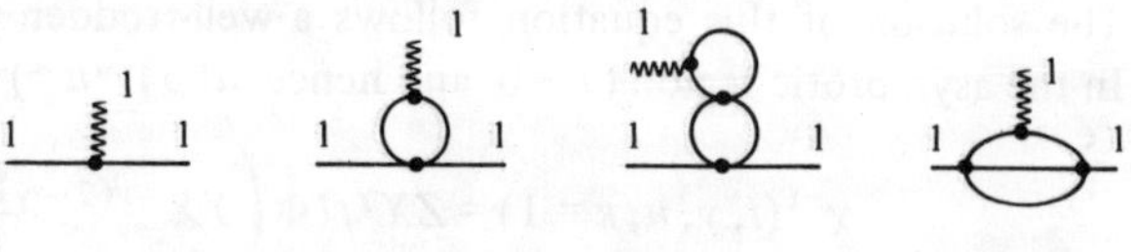

FIGURE 5-2
Graphs of $\Gamma^{(2)}_{11,1}$.

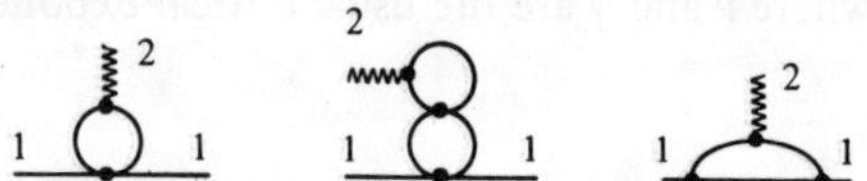

FIGURE 5-3
Graphs of $\Gamma_{11,j}, j \neq 1$.

The corresponding expressions, including the combinatorial factors, are:

$$\Gamma^{(2)}_{11,1} = 1 - \tfrac{1}{2}\lambda I_{SP} + \frac{M+8}{36}\lambda^2 I^2_{SP} + \frac{M+8}{18}\lambda^2 I_{4SP}$$

$$\Gamma^{(2)}_{11,2} = -\tfrac{1}{6}\lambda I_{SP} + \frac{M+4}{36}\lambda^2 I^2_{SP} + \tfrac{1}{9}\lambda^2 I_{4SP}$$

The integrals are defined in Eqs. (I-6-59) and (I-6-61).

Inserting the ϵ expansions for the integrals, expressing λ as $\lambda(u, \epsilon)$ – Eq. (I-9-1) – and substituting $Z_\phi(u, \epsilon)$ from Eq. (I-9-2), and u^* from Eq. (I-9-48), one arrives at:

$$\gamma^*_B = \frac{2}{M+8}\epsilon + \frac{-M^2 + 18M + 88}{2(M+8)^3}\epsilon^2 \qquad (5\text{-}27)$$

This leads to

$$\varphi = 1 + \frac{M}{2(M+8)}\epsilon + \frac{M^3 + 24M^2 + 68M}{4(M+8)^3}\epsilon^2 + 0(\epsilon^3) \qquad (5\text{-}28)$$

in agreement with previous calculations.

5-4 THE CROSSOVER FUNCTION AT A BICRITICAL POINT: A CASE STUDY OF RENORMALIZATION GROUP ANALYSIS IN THE PRESENCE OF TWO LENGTHS

The problem of calculating the crossover function – Eq. (5-11) – differs quite significantly from the calculation of the equation of state which was presented in Sec. 3.3. One can, of course, make a one-loop calculation of χ_L^{-1} and obtain this function to $O(\epsilon)$. But the objective is different, since what one seeks is a change from a behavior such as (5-11) to one described by Eq. (5-13). For a fixed value of g (or y), if

$$\nu \ll t \ll \Lambda^2,$$

one expects a behavior of the type (5-11). But, when t becomes smaller than g the behavior is dominated by another fixed point — the K-component one, relative to a new critical temperature, Eq. (5-13).

The expansion about the symmetric theory is an expansion in g/t, and for finite g the $O(M)$-symmetric fixed point is never reached. An expansion like that of the equation of state can at best describe corrections to scaling about this fixed point, as well as φ which is the analogue of β in the equation of state, but not the critical behavior which becomes dominant when t approaches $T_{cK}(g) - T_{cM}$. Once t becomes of the same order as g, a technique which takes into account the full effect of g to a given order in ϵ is called for.

As will be shown below it is possible, in the framework of renormalized field theory, to treat the problem in a way which renders τ — the temperature difference from the critical temperature for a given non-zero value of the anisotropy — as the natural variable. To achieve this one has to treat the renormalization group in a situation with two underlying masses. This we discuss first, and it is shown how the effects of the shift in the critical temperature is separated from the description of the crossover.

The resulting renormalization group equations are more complex since there is now more than one length scale, and new dimensionless variables enter the Wilson functions β, γ_ϕ, γ_{ϕ^2} etc. The solution of these equations is no longer a mere repetition of Sec. I-8-5, where the method of characteristics was particularly simple due to the fact that all functions depended on u only. Here we generalize these solutions and exhibit the results. We will not enter into great detail which can be found in the literature.[7]

In the previous section it was shown that the natural framework for the computation of the crossover exponent is the expansion around the symmetric theory. Once this has been done the course is shifted and the anisotropy is absorbed into the free Lagrangian. The theory can then be expanded relative to the critical temperature for a given anisotropy.

To accomplish this we consider the bare Lagrangian:

$$\mathcal{L} = \tfrac{1}{2}(\nabla\phi)^2 + \tfrac{1}{2}\mu_{1c}^2\phi_1^2 + \tfrac{1}{2}\mu_2^2\phi_2^2 + \frac{\lambda}{4!}(\phi^2)^2 + \tfrac{1}{2}\tau_0\phi^2 \qquad (5\text{-}29)$$

All but the last two terms are considered in the free part. In it we have chosen the K-components to be critical by setting $\mu_1^2 = \mu_{1c}^2$. As will be shown below the value of μ_{1c}^2 depends on μ_2^2, apart from its obvious dependence on λ and Λ.

The Lagrangian (5-29) should be compared with *the same* Lagrangian written to emphasize the expansion about the critical $0(M)$-symmetric theory, namely:

$$\mathscr{L} = \tfrac{1}{2}(\nabla\phi)^2 + \tfrac{1}{2}\mu_c^2\phi^2 + \frac{\lambda}{4!}(\phi^2)^2 + \tfrac{1}{2}\delta\mu^2\phi^2 - \tfrac{1}{2}gB \qquad (5\text{-}30)$$

in the notation of the previous section. The transformation of the bare parameters can then be identified as:

$$\mu_c^2 + \delta\mu^2 - \frac{M-K}{M}g = \mu_{1c}^2 + \tau_0$$

$$\mu_c^2 + \delta\mu^2 + \frac{K}{M}g = \mu_2^2 + \tau_0 \qquad (5\text{-}31)$$

where

$$\tau_0 \propto T - T_{cK}(g); \quad g > 0$$

Considerations such as those of the previous section, especially the utilization of expansion of the type (5-16) to prove renormalization, lead to the conclusion that the replacement

$$\tau_0 = Z_{\phi^2}\tau \qquad (5\text{-}32)$$

with Z_{ϕ^2} of the critical $0(M) -$ symmetric theory, together with a replacement of μ_2^2 by m^2 renormalize the τ_0-dependent theory by writing

$$\Gamma_R^{(N)}(p_i; m^2, \tau, u, \kappa) = Z_\phi^{N/2} \Gamma_b^{(N)}(p_i; \mu_2^2, \tau_0, \lambda, \Lambda) \qquad (5\text{-}33)$$

Z_ϕ also is calculated in the $0(M)$-symmetric critical theory. The renormalized Lagrangian corresponding to (5-29) is

$$\mathscr{L} = \tfrac{1}{2}(\nabla\phi)^2 + \tfrac{1}{2}m^2\phi_2^2 + \frac{\lambda}{4}(\phi^2)^2 + \tfrac{1}{2}\tau\phi^2 + \text{counterterms} \qquad (5\text{-}34)$$

For finite m the counterterms can be chosen to be the same as those of (5-30). But the massless renormalization constants are not very useful for the description of the crossover phenomenon. They would lead again to the $0(M)$-symmetric fixed point, which is the wrong behavior. After all, one knows that as m^2 — the anisotropy — grows very large all graphs with internal lines of type 2 will vanish, and the theory will become an $0(K)$-symmetric theory. This effect is not picked up by the symmetric renormalization process, since as $m^2 \to \infty$ many regularized terms in the perturbation theory vanish. But their subtraction counterparts which are independet of m^2 survive, and in the limit one arrives at a theory which is not finite.

This may appear as an academic question since one is concerned with a situation in which m^2 remains fixed and finite, and τ, or p_i, *tends* to zero. But the difficulty remains, as one would intuitively guess. If, for example, in the longitudinal susceptibility

$$\chi_L^{-1}(\tau, m^2, u, \kappa) = \Gamma_{11}^{(2)}(p = 0; \tau, m^2, u, \kappa) \quad (5\text{-}35)$$

one scales the temperature by a factor ρ^2, dimensional analysis implies that:

$$\chi_L^{-1}(\rho^2\tau, m^2, u, \kappa) = \rho^2 \exp[\ ]\chi_L^{-1}\left(\tau, \frac{m^2}{\rho^2}, u(\rho), \kappa\right) \quad (5\text{-}36)$$

Hence, as $\rho \to 0$, the theory is equivalent to one with a divergent mass. Small ρ being the region of interest, we are forced to renormalize the theory in a way which will persist in the limit $m^2 \to \infty$.

The statement (5-33), though, is still valuable since it implies that for finite m^2 the theory is renormalizable and we can shift from m^2-independent renormalization constants to m^2-dependent ones by what amounts to a finite renormalization. If the new renormalization constants tend to the $O(K)$ ones as $m^2 \to \infty$, we are sure that the theory stays renormalized in that limit. Below, two ways of pursuing this program will be indicated, and one of them will be carried out.

The first way is to impose normalization conditions on the theory with $\tau = 0$. We shall write them down and then comment on them.

$$\Gamma_{11}^{(2)}(p = 0; m^2, u, \kappa) = 0 \quad (5\text{-}37)$$

$$\Gamma_{22}^{(2)}(p = 0; m^2, u, \kappa) = m^2 \quad (5\text{-}38)$$

$$\left.\frac{d}{dp^2}\Gamma^{(2)}(p; m^2, u, \kappa)\right|_{p^2=\kappa^2} = 1 \quad (5\text{-}39)$$

$$\left.\frac{d}{dp^2}\Gamma_{22}^{(2)}(p; m^2, u, \kappa)\right|_{p=0} = 1 \quad (5\text{-}40)$$

$$\left.\Gamma_{1111}^{(4)}(p; m^2, u, \kappa)\right|_{SP} = u\kappa^\epsilon \quad (5\text{-}41)$$

The first condition is the statement that $\tau = 0$ in Eq. (5-34), i.e., the first K-components are critical. Since Z_ϕ cancels out of this equation it can be considered as an equation for μ_{1c}^2 − Eq. (5-29) − in terms of μ_2^2, λ and Λ.

The second condition is more problematic since we would like to treat the theory at a fixed value of the anisotropy while we vary κ to obtain the renormalization group equation. The field renormalization constants usually depend on κ, which enters when one tries to avoid infrared divergences in a massless theory (see e.g., Secs. I-7-5 and I-7-6). But here the $(M-K)$ components of type 2 are massive, and the normalization of $d\Gamma_{22}^{(2)}/dp^2$ can be performed at $p = $ Eq. (5-40). Then $Z_\phi^{(2)}$ can be solved as a function of μ_2^2, λ and Λ only. Thus, Eqs. (5-37), (5-39), and (5-40) imply:

$$\mu_{1c}^2 = \mu_{1c}^2(\mu_2^2, \lambda, \Lambda) \qquad (5\text{-}42)$$

$$Z_\phi^{(1)} = Z_\phi^{(1)}(\mu_2^2, \lambda, \Lambda, \kappa) \qquad (5\text{-}43)$$

$$Z_\phi^{(2)} = Z_\phi^{(2)}(\mu_2^2, \lambda, \Lambda) \qquad (5\text{-}44)$$

This is a significant result, since now Eq. (5-38) can be viewed as an equation for m^2, thus giving:

$$m^2 = m^2(\mu_2^2, \lambda, \Lambda)$$

Thus, a variation which keeps the bare theory fixed will keep m^2 – the anisotropy – fixed as well. Furthermore, m^{-1} is immediately identified as the transverse correlation length along the anisotropic phase-transition line (see, e.g., Exercise I-7-9). This is a very natural parameter for measuring the anisotropy.

As far as the four-point functions are concerned, the condition (5-41) suffices to make all four-vertices with finite m finite. This follows from the considerations of Secs. I-7-11 and I-7-12. Finally, all the equations can be inverted to give $Z_\phi^{(i)}$, and λ as functions of m^2, u, κ and $\epsilon = (4 - d)$.

Coming back to the m^2-dependence of the renormalization constants, it is clear that the constants derived from Eqs. (5-37) – (5-41) will indeed depend on m^2. For finite m they will differ by a finite renormalization from the $0(M)$-symmetric ones. It is also clear that as $m^2 \to \infty$ all bare functions *with external legs of type 1*, on the left-hand side of the normalization equations, will become those of the $0(K)$-symmetric theory. Consequently, the renormalization constants tend to their correct value as $m^2 \to \infty$ and if one restricts oneself to vertices with external legs of type 1 only, the theory remains finite in the asymptotic region of interest.

In the limit $m^2 \to \infty$ the vertices with external legs of type 2 will diverge. This seems to be in contrast with Symanzik's theorem[8] which states that an $0(M)$-symmetric counterterm of four fields will renormalize the whole theory when the symmetry is quadratically broken (see, Sec. I-7-12). This theorem holds only for finite m^2. One can still render all vertex functions finite but the quartic counterterm will no longer have the $0(M)$ symmetry.

Given that the theory has been renormalized in such a proper way we will have an equation just like (5-33), except that we have not yet prescribed the new Z_{ϕ^2}. One obvious way of doing it would be to add to the list of normalization conditions

$$\Gamma_{11R}^{(2,1)}(p_1, p_2, q_1; m^2, u, \kappa)\big|_{SP} = 1 \qquad (5\text{-}45)$$

leading to Z_{ϕ^2} which depends on m, or rather on m/κ. The same qualifying remarks as apply to $\Gamma^{(4)}$ apply here as well. Namely, as $m^2 \to \infty$ only ϕ^2 – insertions into vertices with legs of type 1 will remain finite.

This completes the definition of the framework, and all quantities can be computed, using Eqs. (5-37) – (5-41) together with (5-45), which we leave as Exercise 5-8. Another method will be used below, but first we turn to the derivation of the renormalization group equations.

The renormalization is expressed by:

$$\Gamma_{1R}^{(N)}(p_i; m^2, \tau, u, \kappa) = Z_\phi^{N/2} \Gamma_1^{(N)}(p_i; \mu_2^2, \tau_0, \lambda, \Lambda) \qquad (5\text{-}46)$$

where in $\Gamma^{(N)}$ all external legs are of type 1. Applying $\kappa \partial/\partial\kappa$ at a constant bare theory; and hence at constant m^2, one finds:

$$\left[\kappa \frac{\partial}{\partial\kappa} + \beta\left(u, \frac{m}{\kappa}\right) \frac{\partial}{\partial u} - \tfrac{1}{2} N \gamma_\phi\left(u, \frac{m}{\kappa}\right) + \gamma_{\phi^2}\left(u, \frac{m}{\kappa}\right) \tau \frac{\partial}{\partial\tau} \right] \Gamma_R^{(N)} = 0 \qquad (5\text{-}47)$$

This equation should be compared with Eq. (I-8-65). The coefficient functions are defined as before, with m^2 kept fixed when the renormalization functions are differentiated with respect to κ.

In order to discuss the solution we will restrict our attention to the case $N = 2$, $p = 0$. Equation (5-47) becomes and equation for the longitudinal (or easy) susceptibility χ_L^{-1}, namely:

$$\left[\kappa \frac{\partial}{\partial\kappa} + \beta\left(u, \frac{m}{\kappa}\right) \frac{\partial}{\partial u} - \gamma_\phi\left(u, \frac{m}{\kappa}\right) + \gamma_{\phi^2}\left(u, \frac{m}{\kappa}\right) \tau \frac{\partial}{\partial\tau} \right] \chi_L^{-1}(\tau, m^2, u, \kappa) = 0$$

$$(5\text{-}48)$$

The solutions of this equation requires a somewhat more sophisticated application of the method of characteristics than has been used so far – Sec. I-8-5 or 3-2 – since the coefficient functions depend on more than one variable.

The characteristic equation are:

$$\kappa \frac{du}{d\kappa} = \beta\left(u, \frac{m}{\kappa}\right) \qquad (5\text{-}49)$$

$$\kappa \frac{d \ln\tau}{d\kappa} = - \gamma_{\phi^2}\left(u, \frac{m}{\kappa}\right) \qquad (5\text{-}50)$$

$$\kappa \frac{d \ln\chi_L^{-1}}{d\kappa} = \gamma_\phi\left(u, \frac{m}{\kappa}\right) \qquad (5\text{-}51)$$

When there is only one length in the problem all these equations are solved by quadratures. Here we take a different course. Eq. (5-49) cannot be explicitly integrated. Hence we define the solution of this differential equation as:

$$\Phi\left(u, \frac{m}{\kappa}\right) = C(m) \qquad (5\text{-}52)$$

which can also be written as:

$$u = F\left(\Phi, \frac{m}{\kappa}\right) \qquad (5\text{-}53)$$

This u can be substituted in Eqs. (5-50) and (5-51), which are then integrated over κ along a curve of fixed Φ.

For example, the solution of Eq. (5-50) is:

$$\tau = \bar{C} \exp\left(\int^{\kappa} \frac{dx}{x} \gamma_{\phi^2}\left\{F\left[\Phi\left(u, \frac{m}{\kappa}\right), \frac{m}{x}\right], \frac{m}{x}\right\}\right) \qquad (5\text{-}54)$$

Similarly

$$\chi_L^{-1} = \exp\left(\int^{\kappa} \frac{dx}{x} \gamma_{\phi}\left\{F\left[\Phi, \frac{m}{x}\right], \frac{m}{x}\right\}\right) \Omega(p_i; m^2, \Phi) \qquad (5\text{-}55)$$

It is now easy to check that under a change in the scale of length the solution of Eq. (5-48) behaves as:

$$\chi_L^{-1}(\tau, m^2, u, \kappa) = \rho^2 \chi_L^{-1}\left(\tau(\rho), m^2, u(\rho), \frac{\kappa}{\rho}\right)$$

$$\times \exp\left(\int_{\kappa}^{\kappa/\rho} \frac{dx}{x} \gamma_{\phi}\left\{F\left[\Phi, \frac{\overline{m}}{x}\right], \frac{m}{x}\right\}\right) \qquad (5\text{-}56)$$

where $\overline{m} = m/\rho$, and the flowing coupling constant $u(\rho)$ and temperature $\tau(\rho)$ are generalizations of their counterparts in Sec. 3-2. Namely, $u(\rho)$ is defined via:

$$\Phi\left(u, \frac{m}{\kappa}\right) = \Phi\left(u(\rho), \frac{\overline{m}}{\kappa}\right) \qquad (5\text{-}57)$$

which implies, together with the fact that Φ is a solution of Eq. (5-49), that

$$\rho \frac{du(\rho)}{d\rho} = \beta\left(u(\rho), \frac{\overline{m}}{\kappa}\right), \quad u(1) = u \qquad (5\text{-}58)$$

(Cf. Eq. (I-8-37), $\tau(\rho)$ in Eq. (5-56) is given by:

$$\tau(\rho) = \frac{\tau}{\rho^2} \exp\left(-\int_{\kappa\rho}^{\kappa} \frac{dx}{x} \gamma_{\phi^2}\left\{F\left[\Phi\left(u(\rho), \frac{\overline{m}}{\kappa}\right), \frac{m}{x}\right], \frac{m}{x}\right\}\right) \qquad (5\text{-}59)$$

following a change of variable $x \to x/\rho$. This should be compared with Eq. (I-9-69), keeping in mind that $d\kappa/\kappa = du/\beta$ is just one of our characteristic equations.

Next, one uses these results to move the temperature out of the critical region by choosing the parameter ρ. This choice is made as in Sec. 3-4, namely:

$$\tau(\rho) = \kappa^2 \qquad (5\text{-}60) \cdot$$

Equation (5-56) then becomes

$$\chi_L^{-1}(\tau, m^2, u, \kappa) = \rho^2(\tau)\chi_L^{-1}\left(\kappa^2, \frac{m^2}{\rho^2(\tau)}, u(\rho(\tau)), \frac{\kappa}{\rho(\tau)}\right)$$

$$\times \exp\left(\int_{\kappa\rho}^{\kappa} \frac{dx}{x} \gamma_\phi \left[F\left(\Phi, \frac{\overline{m}}{x}\right), \frac{\overline{m}}{x}\right]\right) \tag{5-61}$$

where $\rho(\tau)$ is the solution of Eq. (5-59), together with (5-60) and (5-61).

Before proceeding with the calculation this is a good point to stop and notice that there is a better way of choosing Z_{ϕ^2} than (5-45),[9] namely:

$$\chi_L^{-1}(\tau = \kappa^2) = \Gamma_1^{(2)} \ (p = 0; \ \tau = \kappa^2, m^2, u, \kappa) = \kappa^2 \tag{5-62}$$

The fact that this actually renormalizes the ϕ^2-insertions was discussed in Sec. I-7-12. Here the special advantage of this normalization condition is that as long as $Z_\phi = 1$ it reduces (5-61) to:

$$\chi_L^{-1}(\tau, m^2, u, \kappa) = \kappa^2 \rho^2(\tau) \tag{5-63}$$

Other choices can be made, but then the calculation of $\chi_L^{-1}(\tau)$ becomes more complicated (see, e.g., Exercise 5-9).

To conclude, the *crossover function* is obtained by calculating γ_{ϕ^2} and $u(\rho)$ to order ϵ; inserting them in (5-59) − (5-60) to obtain $\rho(\tau)$, which according to (5-63) is the answer. At higher orders one has, of course, to compute γ_ϕ as well.

The crossover phenomenon is represented by defining an effective critical exponent γ_{eff}

$$\gamma_{\text{eff}}(\tau) = \frac{d \ln\chi_L^{-1}}{d \ln\tau} \tag{5-64}$$

As $\tau \to 0$, $\gamma_{\text{eff}} \to \gamma \ (K)$. As τ grows larger than m^2 the behavior comes closer and closer to the $0(M)$ one, namely, $\gamma_{\text{eff}} \to \gamma(M)$. As long as τ is kept much smaller than κ^2, the whole region in τ is in the infrared asymptotic domain, and is consequently universal.

Finally, a few words on the form of the results. A simple way to proceed is by calculating the coupling constant renormalization using generalized minimal subtraction[7], i.e., by choosing the subtractions to remove the poles in ϵ from vertices of type 1 for *all* values of m^2. In our conventional notation, to the order of one loop, we have:

$$u_0 = \kappa^{-\epsilon}\lambda = u\left[1 + \frac{K+8}{6\epsilon}u + \frac{M-K}{6\epsilon}\left(1 + \frac{m^2}{\kappa^2}\right)^{-\epsilon/2}u\right] \tag{5-65}$$

The corresponding β is:

$$\beta\left(u, \frac{\kappa}{m}\right) = -\epsilon u + \frac{K+8}{6}u^2 + \frac{M-K}{6}\frac{u^2}{1+m^2/\kappa^2} + 0(u^3) \tag{5-66}$$

It is easily checked that in the limits $m^2 \to 0$ and $m^2 \to \infty$ these functions tend to their expressions, calculated by minimal subtraction, in the $0(M)$- and $0(K)$-symmetric theories, respectively (cf. Sec. I-9-10). We leave the derivation to Exercise 5-10.

In order to compute γ_{ϕ^2} using (5-62) we write down χ_L^{-1} to order one loop. After the mass renormalization it reads:

$$\chi_L^{-1} = \tau \left[Z_{\phi^2} - \frac{K+2}{6} u\kappa^\epsilon \int \frac{1}{q^2(q^2+\tau)} - \frac{M-K}{6} u\kappa^\epsilon \int \frac{1}{(q^2+m^2)(q^2+m^2+\tau)} \right]$$

(5-67)

On calculating the ϵ expansion of the two integrals, one finds from (5-67) and (5-62) that:

$$Z_{\phi^2} = 1 + \frac{K+2}{6\epsilon} u + \frac{M-K}{6\epsilon} u \left[\left(1 + \frac{m^2}{\kappa^2}\right)^{1-\epsilon/2} - \left(\frac{m^2}{\kappa^2}\right)^{1-\epsilon/2} \right]$$

(5-68)

and

$$\gamma_{\phi^2} = \kappa \frac{\partial \ln Z_{\phi^2}}{\partial \kappa} = \frac{M+2}{6} u - \frac{M-K}{6} u \frac{m^2}{\kappa^2} \ln\left(1 + \frac{\kappa^2}{m^2}\right)$$

(5-69)

both of which have the correct limits as $m^2 \to 0$ and ∞.

The next task is to calculate $u(\rho)$. When β from (5-66) is substituted in Eq. (5-49) one obtains a Bernoulli differential equation for $u^{-1}(\kappa)$. Its solution is:

$$u^{-1}(\kappa) = \frac{K+8}{6\epsilon} - \frac{M-K}{12} \int_{\kappa_0^2/\kappa^2}^1 \frac{y^{-\epsilon/2}}{y+m^2/\kappa^2} dy + C\kappa^\epsilon$$

(5-70)

which defines for us the function Φ of (5-52), and hence given $u(\rho)$ via Eq. (5-57). It is:

$$u^{-1}(\rho) = \rho^\epsilon u^{-1} + \frac{K+8}{6\epsilon}(1-\rho^\epsilon) - \frac{M-K}{12} \rho^\epsilon \int_1^{\rho^2} \frac{x^{-\epsilon/2}}{x+m^2/\kappa^2} dx$$

$$\underset{\epsilon \to 0}{\sim} \frac{K+8}{6\epsilon} - \frac{M-K}{12} \ln\left(1 + \frac{\kappa^2 \rho^2}{m^2}\right) + \rho^\epsilon \left[u^{-1} - \frac{K+8}{6\epsilon} + \frac{M-K}{12} \ln\left(1 + \frac{\kappa^2}{m^2}\right) \right]$$

(5-71)

If ϵ is not so small one has to use somewhat more complicated forms of $u(\rho)$, which will not be discussed here.[7]

We now have all the ingredients which are needed for the calculation of $\tau(\rho)$ – Eq. (5-59). The only problem is the computation of the integral in the exponent on the right-hand side. But this turns out to be unnecessary, due to the fact that the crossover is described in terms of the logarithmic derivative of $\chi_L(\tau)$.

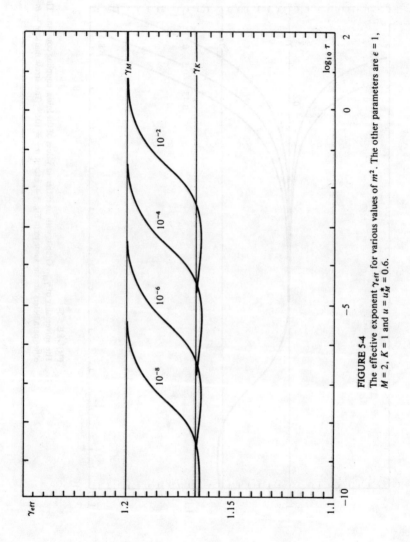

FIGURE 5-4

The effective exponent γ_{eff} for various values of m^2. The other parameters are $\epsilon = 1$, $M = 2$, $K = 1$ and $u = u_M^* = 0.6$.

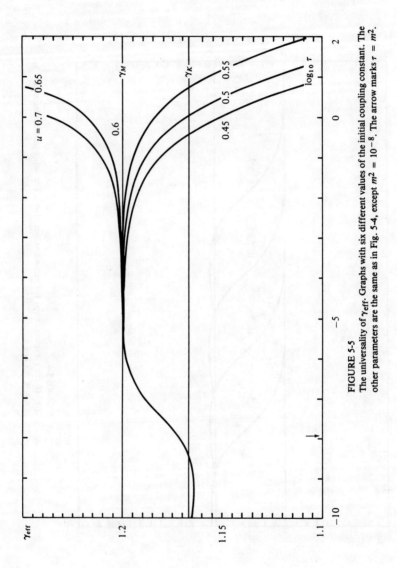

FIGURE 5-5
The universality of γ_{eff}. Graphs with six different values of the initial coupling constant. The other parameters are the same as in Fig. 5-4, except $m^2 = 10^{-8}$. The arrow marks $\tau = m^2$.

Consider an expression of the form:

$$A = \exp \left(\int_{\rho}^{1} \frac{dx}{x} \gamma \left\{ F \left[\Phi(u(\rho), \bar{m}), \frac{m}{x} \right], \frac{m}{x} \right\} \right) \tag{5-72}$$

where we have set $\kappa = 1$. According to Eq. (5-57), Φ in the above equation, and hence all of the integrand, is independent of ρ. Taking the logarithmic derivative of A with respect to ρ gives:

$$\frac{d \ln A}{d \ln \rho} = - \gamma \{ F [\Phi(u, m), \bar{m}], \bar{m} \} = - \gamma \{ u(\rho), \bar{m} \} \tag{5-73}$$

After substituting, according to (5-53).

$$F[\Phi(u,m), \bar{m}] = F[\Phi(u(\rho), \bar{m}), \bar{m}] = u(\rho) \tag{5-74}$$

Taking the logarithmic derivative of Eq. (5-64) one has:

$$\gamma_{\text{eff}} = \frac{d \ln \chi_L^{-1}}{d \ln \tau} = \frac{d \ln \rho^2(\tau)}{d\tau}$$

$\rho^2(\tau)$ is the solution of Eqs. (5-63) and (5-64). Thus, using (5-73), one finds:

$$\gamma_{\text{eff}} = 1 + \tfrac{1}{2} \gamma_{\phi^2} \frac{d \ln \rho^2(\tau)}{d \ln \tau} \tag{5-75}$$

But γ_{ϕ^2} is already of order ϵ, hence $d\ln\rho^2/d\ln\tau$ on the right-hand side can be replaced by 1, leading to

$$\gamma_{\text{eff}} = 1 + \tfrac{1}{2} \gamma_{\phi^2} \{ u(\rho), m/\rho \}.$$

To same order, $\tau^{1/2}$ can be substituted for ρ giving finally,

$$\gamma_{\text{eff}} = 1 + \tfrac{1}{2} \gamma_{\phi^2} \{ u(\tau^{1/2}), m/\tau^{1/2} \} \tag{5-76}$$

with γ_{ϕ^2} given by Eq. (5-69) and $u(x)$ given by Eq. (5-71).

A few examples of γ_{eff} for $M = 2$, $K = 1$, $\epsilon = 1$, for various values of m^2 are drawn in Fig. 5-4. In Fig. 5-5 the various graphs of γ_{eff} have different values of the initial coupling constant u. This is a spectacular demonstration of the universality of the whole crossover region if both $m^2 (= 10^{-8})$ and τ are very small compared with κ^2.

EXERCISES

5-1 Analyze the flow equations, the fixed points and their stability properties, in the space of the renormalized couplings, corresponding to σ_1 and σ_2. Show that to first order order in ϵ, the stability of the Ising fixed point is governed by the same eigenvalues as Eq. (4-22).

5-2 Using Eq. (2-28) at zero external momenta, and choosing the arbitrary momentum scale, ρ, of the renormalization group, via $t(\rho) = 1$, derive Eq. (5-6).

5-3 Let the theory described by (5-2) be renormalized in terms of the couplings v_1 and v_2 and the wave-function renormalization $Z(v_1, v_2)$. Let $\beta_1(v_1, v_2)$, $\beta_2(v_1, v_2)$ and $\gamma(v_1, v_2)$ be the flow functions and the field anomalous dimension function.

  (a) Show $\partial \beta_1 / \partial v_2 \to 0$ and $\partial \gamma / \partial v_2 \to 0$ at the Ising fixed point.

  (b) From the renormalization group equation for $\Gamma_R^{(N)}(p_i; t, v_1, v_2)$ derive an equation for $\Gamma_2^{(N)}$, which is $\Gamma^{(N)}$ with an insertion of A_2.

  (c) At the Ising fixed point, show that the dimension of this operator is
$$\frac{\partial \beta_2}{\partial v_2} .$$

5-4 Run through the argument leading to Eq. (5-8) when only one, or none of α and β coincide with the indices of the external legs in $\Gamma_2^{(N+M)}$.

5-5 Show that if the counterterms generated by ϕ^2 and B are proportional to $t\phi^2$ and yB, respectively, in the notation of Sec. I-7-12, then one can construct from the proportionality constants the functions $Z_{\phi^2}(u)$ and $Z_B(u)$, which multiplicatively renormalize $\Gamma^{(N, L, M)}$.

5-6 Using the statement about the counterterms, show that if in $\Gamma^{(N)}$ the variables μ^2 and g are replaced by t and y according to Eq. (5-19), then $[Z_\phi^{N/2} \Gamma^{(N)}(p_i; \mu^2, g, \lambda, \Lambda)]$ is finite.

5-7 Using the result of Exercise 5-6 derive the renormalization group equation, (5-20), directly, i.e., without using Eq. (5-18).

5-8 Using the normalization conditions (5-37) − (5-41) and (5-45), calculate Z_ϕ, Z_{ϕ^2} and λ as functions of m^2, u and ϵ to the order of two loops. Show that the limits $m^2 \to 0$ and $m^2 \to \infty$ are, correspondingly, the renormalization constants of the $0(M)$- and $0(K)$-symmetric theories of Sec. I-7-10 (see e.g., Ref. 7).

5-9 Calculate Z_{ϕ^2} using Eq. (5-45) to the level of two loops. Compare with the Z_{ϕ^2} of (5-62) and with the $0(M)$- and $0(K)$-symmetric ones. See also Ref. 7.

5-10 Show that u_0 of (5-65) renders the soft components of $\Gamma^{(4)}$ finite at the one-loop level for all values of m^2. Check that it eliminates the singular momentum-dependent terms at the two-loop level.[7]

REFERENCES

1. E. K. Riedel and F. J. Wegner, *Zeitschrift fur Physik,* **225,** 195 (1969).
2. J. Sak, *Physical Review,* **B10,** 3957 (1974); A Aharony, in DG, Sec. 5A.
3. G. Jug and C. E. I. Carneiro, Oxford University preprint 64/82.
4. A. B. Harris, *Journal of Physics,* **C7,** 1671 (1974).
5. G. Grinstein, Ph.D. Thesis, Harvard University (1974); G. Grinstein and A. Luther, *Physical Review,* **B13,** 1329 (1976); V. J. Emery, *Physical Review,* **B11,** 239 (1975).
6. The physical realizations of this model are discussed in M. E. Fisher and D. R. Nelson, *Physical Review Letters,* **32,** 1350 (1974); A. Aharony and A. D. Bruce, *Physical Review Letters,* **33,** 427 (1974), and D. R. Nelson and E. Domany, *Physical Review,* **B13,** 236 (1976).
7. D. J. Amit and Y. Goldschmidt, *Annals of Physics,* **114,** 356 (1978), and Y. Y. Goldschmidt Ph.D. thesis, Hebrew University (unpublished). The same problem was previously treated by D. R. Nelson and E. Domany, *Physical Review,* **B13,** 236 (1976) and by H. Horner, *Zeitschrift fur Physik,* **B23,** 183 (1976).
8. See, e.g., KS.
9. Such a procedure was used by D. J. Gross, in Methods in Field Theory, Ref. 1, ch. 3.

6

CRITICAL PHENOMENA NEAR
TWO DIMENSIONS

6-1 AN ALTERNATIVE FIELD THEORY FOR THE HEISENBERG MODEL — THE LOW TEMPERATURE PHASE

In Sec. I-8-9 we have presented a discussion of that part of the critical region which lies below the critical temperature. What has been established is that scaling laws connecting exponents above and below the transition hold and that the equation of state has a scaling form.

In the equations manipulated in Sec. I-8-9 no indices appear on either M or H, yet it has not been explicitly stipulated that any of the discussion is limited to the Ising model. On the other hand, the computation of the ϵ-expansion of the universal form of the equation of state was limited to a single component field. This was not accidental.

There is an intrinsic difficulty involved in describing the coexistence curve of an $0(M)$-symmetric system. The apparatus of the renormalization group is set up to deal with the complications introduced by a mass which tends to zero as one approaches the critical point. But for an $0(M)$-symmetric system there are $M-1$ masses which are identically zero everywhere on the coexistence curve. These are the Goldstone bosons of Sec. I-5-6.

The renormalization group, as such, does not cure the infrared divergences associated with the Goldstone modes, hence one must introduce some additional devices. The difficulty involved is indicated by the distinguished efforts which have not quite resolved the problem.[1] It seems that it has been put to rest recently in a *tour de force* by Lawrie,[2] who extended the ideas discussed in Sec. 5-3 to deal with the fact that if one approaches the coexistence curve at $T < T_c$, with a diminishing external field, one has two different masses — one which will vanish — that of the Goldstone modes, the other — the longitudinal one — will remain finite as $H \to 0$.[3]

Here we will not discuss any of these attempts. Their complexity indicates that there is something unnatural about the formulation of the problem. Even after the dust has settled down on the computation of the equation of state, little progress has been achieved concerning the way in which a Goldstone boson becomes a critical mode as $T \to T_c^-$. Namely, the calculation near four dimensions is ill-suited to describe this crossover, which is an interpolation between the critical fixed point and a zero-temperature fixed point.

An original approach to this interpolation has been suggested by Polyakov[4] and applied and extended by Nelson and Pelkovitz[5] and especially by Brézin and Zinn-Justin.[6] The underlying observation is that a system has a lower critical dimension, as well as an upper one. The lower critical dimension is the number of dimensions of space at and below which the system can no longer sustain long-range-order. For a system with a global continuous symmetry this dimension is two — this is the content of the Mermin-Wagner-Coleman[7] theorem. For a system with a discrete symmetry the lower critical dimension is one.

By now the reader should not feel ill at ease if the problem is shifted to a space of continuous number of dimensions. One can then expect that the M-W-C theorem is a continuous limit in which a sequence of $O(M)$-symmetric models in d-dimensions — $d > 2$ — has a phase transition at $T_c(d)$ which vanishes as $d \to 2$. If these were indeed the case then one would further expect that in proximity to two dimensions — $d = 2 + \epsilon$ — a low temperature expansion may lead to a $T_c = 0(\epsilon)$, within the reach of an ϵ-expansion.

The way to effect a low temperature expansion is to develop in fluctuations about a fully ordered zero temperature state. Furthermore, one had many indications[8] that the major agent destroying the order (or restoring the symmetry) in two dimensions is the fluctuating phase, rather than the amplitude.

The natural starting point would therefore be the system described in Exercise 2-3, with M-dimensional vectors of fixed magnitude placed on the sites of a d-dimensional lattice, and interacting via a rotationally invariant interaction:

$$\mathcal{A} = - \sum_{i,j}' J_{ij} \, \mathbf{S}_i \cdot \mathbf{S}_j \qquad (6\text{-}1)$$

with a J_{ij} of short range. Exercise I-2-3 intended to convey the idea that via a Gaussian transformation the theory defined by Eq. (6-1) can be transformed into an $O(M)$-symmetric polynomial field theory, in which the local part is a polynomial of ϕ^2. Then the interaction could be truncated to leave behind an $O(M)$-symmetric ϕ^4-theory.

In the truncated theory the constraint, fixing the magnitude of the field vector, is absent and amplitude fluctuations mix with phase fluctuations. These changes are consequently shown to be irrelevant near four dimensions. Since the constraint has been removed, all field components are independent and the $O(M)$-symmetry is implemented linearly. The theory is sometimes referred to as the *linear σ-model*, in contrast with the *non-linear σ-model* to be described below.

A more direct approach to the thermodynamics of the system described by the action (6-1) would have been to write the partition function in the form:

$$Z = \int \prod_{i=1}^{N} \delta(S_i^2 - 1) \, d^M S_i \, e^{-(1/kT)\mathcal{A}} \qquad (6\text{-}2)$$

in which the constraint is explicitly enforced, and to look for an expansion in powers of T. There are N sites in the lattice.

We assume a short range interaction, one with a finite second moment, and then $\mathcal{A}$ can be approximated by

$$\mathcal{A} = \text{Const.} + J \int dx [\nabla S(x)]^2 + \dots \qquad (6\text{-}3)$$

where ... stands for terms with more than two derivatives. These terms turn out to be irrelevant. The integral is just a shorthand notation for the lattice sum, which is still needed to regularize the theory.

The constant J/k is absorbed into a rescaling of the temperature units before we turn our attention to the elimination of one of the components of $\mathbf{S}$, at every point, in terms of the $(M-1)$ independent components. In other words one integrates over the δ-functions. Denoting

$$\pi^\alpha(x) \equiv S_i^\alpha \qquad \alpha = 1, \dots, M-1 \qquad (6\text{-}4a)$$

$$\sigma(x) \equiv S_i^M = [1 - \pi^2(x)]^{\frac{1}{2}} \qquad (6\text{-}4b)$$

the action can be written as

$$\mathcal{A} = \frac{1}{2} \int dx [(\nabla \pi)^2 + (\nabla \sqrt{1 - \pi^2})^2] \qquad (6\text{-}5)$$

The integration over σ produces a change in the measure of the π's. It becomes:

$$\prod_{i=1}^{N} \frac{\mathrm{d}^{M-1}\pi_i}{[1-\pi_i^2]^{\frac{1}{2}}} = \mathcal{D}\pi \exp[-\tfrac{1}{2}\sum_i \ln(1-\pi_i^2)]$$

$$= \mathcal{D}\pi \exp\left\{-\tfrac{1}{2}a^{-d}\int \mathrm{d}x \ln[1-\pi^2(x)]\right\} \qquad (6\text{-}6)$$

where a is the lattice spacing. Correspondingly, in order to render $T^{-1}\mathcal{A}$ of (6-5) dimensionless T must absorb a factor of a^{d-2} leaving T with dimension $2-d$, in units of momentum. See e.g. Exercise 6-1.

Finally, the partition function reads:

$$Z = \int \mathcal{D}\pi \exp\left\{-\frac{1}{8T}\int[\tfrac{1}{2}(\nabla\pi)^2 + \tfrac{1}{2}(\nabla\sqrt{1-\pi^2})^2]\,\mathrm{d}x\right.$$

$$\left. -\tfrac{1}{2}a^{-d}\int \mathrm{d}x \ln[1-\pi^2(x)]\right\} \qquad (6\text{-}7)$$

This form deserves a few comments.

(a) The ln term in the action — the Jacobian — insures the $O(M)$-invariance of the measure of the functional integral, which has become $d^{M-1}\pi$, at every point.

(b) The rotation invariance in the internal field space is still linearly implemented in the $M-1$ dimensional π-subspace. Rotations in the π-σ directions are implemented in a non-linear fashion, since the σ had been eliminated. This class of rotations forms the quotient group $O(M)/O(M-1)$ and a rotation by an infinitesimal ω induces the changes:

$$\delta\pi(x) = [1-\pi^2(x)]^{\frac{1}{2}}\omega \qquad (6\text{-}8a)$$

$$\delta[1-\pi^2(x)]^{\frac{1}{2}} = -\omega\cdot\pi(x) \qquad (6\text{-}8b)$$

Hence the name *non-linear σ-model*.

(c) Clearly, as long as the π-fields fluctuate with small absolute values the symmetry is broken. There is a non-zero expectation value for σ. At $T=0$ all π's vanish and $\sigma(x)=1$. (See Exercise 6-2).

(d) For the symmetry to be restored the amplitude of the π's must increase until $1-\pi^2$ vanishes. Since anyway the π's are constrained to lie inside an $(M-1)$-dimensional unit hypersphere, symmetry is restored when π lies on the surface of this sphere and (π,σ) is on the "equator". See Fig. 6-1.

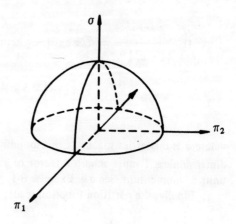

FIGURE 6-1
The domain of π and range of σ. The arrow is (π, σ).

6-2   PERTURBATION THEORY FOR THE NON-LINEAR SIGMA MODEL

As was indicated in the previous section the action in the exponent of (6-7) is to provide us with a low temperature expansion. As T appears explicitly one can conclude, on the basis of the discussion in Sec. I-6-2, that a low T expansion is an expansion in the number of loops. The only proviso is that the term introduced by the measure is linear in T, and with equal number of loops contributes to a higher order in T than the first two terms. This will not be a serious complication, since, as we shall see, this term plays a subservient role.

The action in (6-7) is unusual in that it is not polynomial in the fields. It therefore has to be expanded in powers. As has already been mentioned we will be working in the neighborhood of two dimensions, and at two dimensions the fields are dimensionless. Hence, one cannot dispose of all the high powers of π's by resorting to arguments of irrelevance. They are all equally marginal. Only additional powers of momentum lead to operators irrelevant by power counting.

Nevertheless we are spared having to deal with all the powers at once. The point being that interactions with more fields leave behind more loops, and consequently contribute to higher orders in T. Thus we shall see that to first order in T one needs at most terms with four π's, to second order at most six π's etc.

When the expansion of the action is started one finds

$$\mathcal{A} = \int dx \left\{ \tfrac{1}{2} (\nabla \pi)^2 + \tfrac{1}{8} (\nabla \pi^2) \cdot (\nabla \pi^2) \right.$$

$$\left. + \tfrac{1}{16} (\nabla \pi^2) \cdot \nabla (\pi^2)^2 + \ldots + \tfrac{1}{2} Ta^{-d} \pi^2 - \tfrac{1}{4} Ta^{-d} (\pi^2)^2 + \ldots \right\} \qquad (6\text{-}9)$$

6-2-1 The Free Propagator and Infrared Regularization

From (6-9) we can read off the free propagator. It is a Goldstone mode

$$G^0_\alpha(p) \equiv \langle \pi^\alpha(p) \, \pi^\alpha(-p) \rangle = \frac{T}{p^2} \qquad (6\text{-}10)$$

which is massless and hence creates, at two dimensions, infrared problems in perturbation theory. These difficulties can be avoided by computing expectation values of $0(M)$-invariant operators[9] only. Here we will not take this route, but instead proceed as in Brézin and Zinn-Justin[10] to regularize the theory in the infrared by introducing an external field in the direction of σ.

To the action (6-9) we add the term

$$-H\sigma(x) = -H[1 - \pi^2(x)]^{1/2} = H[-1 + \tfrac{1}{2}\pi^2 + \tfrac{1}{8}(\pi^2)^2 + \dots] \qquad (6\text{-}11)$$

which provides a mass h, and another infinite chain of interactions. One can regularize also by adding a mass term to the π's directly, this procedure comes with its own complications.[11]

The free propagator will therefore be

$$G^0_\alpha(p) = \frac{T}{p^2 + H} \qquad (6\text{-}12a)$$

and the corresponding two-point vertex

$$\Gamma^0_\alpha(p) = T^{-1}(p^2 + H) \ . \qquad (6\text{-}12b)$$

6-2-2 Disposing of the Measure

Expression (6-9) may give the impression that the π's have acquired a mass, whose square is $(-Ta^{-d})$, namely, negative. This, of course, is not the case, the symmetry is broken and Goldstone modes are Goldstone modes. This term is of first order in T and must be reckoned with together with all other terms of that order.

Notice first that the factor a^{-d} can be written as

$$a^{-d} = \int^\Lambda \frac{d^d q}{(2\pi)^d}$$

which vanishes if dimensionally regularized. This is the fast way of disposing of the interactions induced by the measure. What underlies it is the fact that the role of the measure is to ensure the $0(M)$-invariance of the theory. In the absence of this term this symmetry is broken and mass terms will appear in perturbation theory. The interactions induced by the ln serve precisely to cancel these mass terms. Dimensional regularization, which eliminates the ln, will eliminate mass terms generated by the interactions coming from the expansion of the square root. See Exercises (6-3)–(6-5).

6-2-3 The Interactions

After having disposed of the measure and having adopted dimensional regularization we can read the interaction terms off (6-9) and (6-11). The first will include two derivatives, the latter will be proportional to H. The four-point interaction will read, in momentum space

$$\frac{1}{8T} \sum_{q_1 q_2 q} (q^2 + H) \, \pi^\alpha_{q_1} \, \pi^\alpha_{q-q_1} \, \pi^\beta_{-q_2} \, \pi^\beta_{q_2-q} \tag{6-13}$$

which is represented in Fig. 6-2.

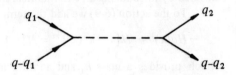

FIGURE 6-2
The four-point interaction. Lines meeting at a point have equal internal index. Dashed line is a factor $(q^2 + H)/8T$.

The six point interaction will be

$$\frac{1}{16T} \sum'_{q q_1, \ldots, q_s} (q^2 + H) \, \pi^\alpha_{q_1} \, \pi^\alpha_{q-q_1} \, \pi^\beta_{-q_2} \, \pi^\beta_{-q_3} \, \pi^\gamma_{-q_4} \, \pi^\gamma_{q_2+q_3+q_4-q} \tag{6-14}$$

for which one can draw the diagram in Fig. 6-3.

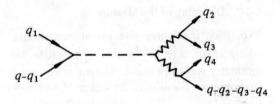

FIGURE 6-3
The six-point interaction. The wiggly lines serve only to identify pairs of π with equal internal index.

6-2-4 The Expansion of $\Gamma^{(2)}_\alpha$

The vertex functions Γ are, as usual, the one-particle irreducible parts of G. The rules for constructing graphs out of the free propagator (6-12) and the interactions (6-13), (6-14) etc. undergo no change. The graphs entering $\Gamma^{(2)}_\alpha$ to the order of two loops are therefore those depicted in Fig. 6-4.

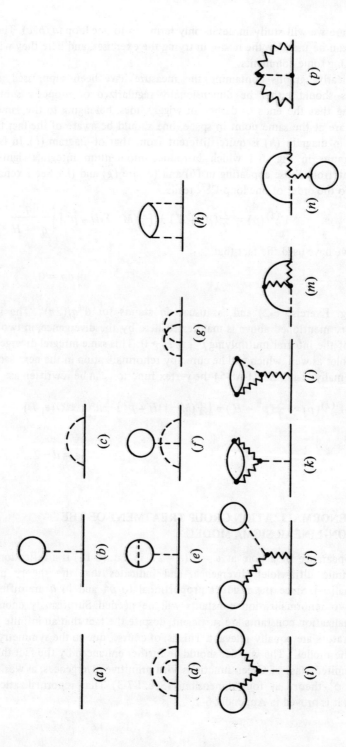

FIGURE 6-4
The two-point vertex to order two loops.

Here we will study in detail only terms up to one loop (a, b, c). The other graphs can be used by the reader in trying the exercises, and here they will serve for making some comments.

Clearly, graphs containing the measure have been suppressed, and all integrals should either be dimensionally regularized or properly subtracted. Recalling that the ends of dashed or wiggly lines, belonging to the same inter-action, are at the same point in space, one should be aware of the fact that the bubble in diagram (h) is quite different from that of diagram (l). In fact, the only graphs in Fig. 6-4 which introduce momentum integrals significantly different from those appearing in (b) and (c) are (g) and (h). See Exercise 6-6.

To the order of one loop $\Gamma^{(2)}$ reads:

$$\Gamma_\alpha^{(2)}(p) = \frac{1}{T}(p^2 + H) + [\tfrac{1}{2}(M-1)H + p^2]\int \frac{dq}{q^2 + H} \quad (6\text{-}15)$$

where we have used the fact that

$$\int dq = 0 \quad .$$

(See e.g. Exercise 6-2) and, as usual dq stands for $d^d q/(2\pi)^d$. The infrared difficulty mentioned above is manifested here by the divergence, in two dimensions, of the integral multiplying p^2, as $H \to 0$. This same integral diverges in the ultra-violet as well, which will be cured by renormalization in the next section.

Finally, using Eq. (I-A8-5) the vertex function can be rewritten as:

$$\Gamma_\alpha^{(2)}(p) = \frac{1}{T}(p^2 + H) - [\tfrac{1}{2}(M-1)H + p^2]\,\frac{1}{\epsilon}h^{\epsilon/2} + O(\epsilon, T) \quad (6\text{-}16)$$

where

$$\epsilon = d - 2 \quad .$$

6-3 RENORMALIZATION GROUP TREATMENT OF THE NON-LINEAR SIGMA MODEL

The appearance of a pole at $\epsilon = 0(d=2)$, in Eq. (6-16) is a reflection of the logarithmic ultra-violet divergence, and indicates that the theory must be renormalized. Since the residues proportional to p^2 and to h are different, at least two renormalization constants will be needed. Surprisingly enough two renormalization constants are sufficient, despite the fact that an infinite number of operators are equally relevant. This is, of course, due to the symmetry under-lying the model.[6] The wonder should be further enhanced by the fact that there is no limited class of Green functions with primitive divergences, as was the case in the ϕ^4-theory at four dimensions (Sec. I-7-3). That renormalization is so simple, it is proved in Appendix 6-1.

The fact that two dimensions is a critical dimension can be deduced from the fact that the coupling T has naive dimension $2-d$, which vanishes at two dimensions. The presence of h does not affect the renormalization. It is a soft insertion (see e.g. Exercise 6-7). Moreover, since H multiplies an elementary field, rather than a composite operator, it does not carry a renormalization of its own, just like in the usual ϕ^4-theory. See also Appendix 6-1.

According to Appendix 6-1, renormalization is affected by the following procedure:

First, a dimensionless renormalized coupling constant, t, is defined, via

$$T = \kappa^{-\epsilon} Z_t t \qquad (6\text{-}17)$$

with $\epsilon = d-2$. Then the field amplitude is rescaled through.

$$\pi^\alpha = Z_\pi^{1/2} \pi_R^\alpha \qquad (6\text{-}18)$$

where π_R is the renormalized π-field. The two renormalization constants are functions of t and ϵ, if the theory had been dimensionally regularized.

Since the σ field is related by the symmetry to the π's it also carries a factor of Z_π, which can be absorbed into the external field. The renormalization statement can therefore be phrased in terms of the Green functions as follows:

$$G_{\pi R}^{(N)}(p_i; t, h, \kappa) = Z_\pi^{-N/2} G_\pi^{(N)}(p_i; \kappa^{-\epsilon} Z_t t, Z_t Z_\pi^{-1/2} h, \Lambda) \qquad (6\text{-}19\text{a})$$

$$\Gamma_{\pi R}^{(N)}(p_i; t, h, \kappa) = Z_\pi^{N/2} \Gamma_\pi^{(N)}(p_i; \kappa^{-\epsilon} Z_t t, Z_t Z_\pi^{-1/2} h, \Lambda) \qquad (6\text{-}19\text{b})$$

with

$$H = Z_t Z_\pi^{-1/2} h \qquad (6\text{-}20)$$

which is equivalent to the statement (A6-13) in terms of the generating functional. The derivation of the equivalence is left as Exercise 6-8.

As usual, the statement implies that when Z_t and Z_π are expanded in powers of t, the power series on the right hand sides of (6-19) are finite, order by order in t, as $\epsilon \to 0$.

Turning back to Eq. (6-16) and performing an expansion in ϵ one easily finds:

$$Z_t = 1 + \frac{M-2}{\epsilon} t + O(t^2) \qquad (6\text{-}21)$$

$$Z_\pi = 1 + \frac{M-1}{\epsilon} t + O(t^2) \qquad (6\text{-}22)$$

These lead to a finite two-point function at the level of one loop:

$$\Gamma_{\pi R}^{(2)}(p; t, \kappa = 1) = \frac{1}{t}(p^2 + h) - \frac{1}{2}[p^2 + \frac{1}{2}(M-1)h] \ln h + O(t, \epsilon) \qquad (6\text{-}23)$$

That other functions are made finite by Z_t and Z_π can be verified by performing Exercises (6-9) and (6-10).

Next we study the flow of the coupling constant – the temperature – under changes of scale. The β-function is defined, as usual, by:

$$\beta(t, \epsilon) = \kappa \frac{\partial t}{\partial \kappa}\Big|_T \qquad (6\text{-}24)$$

Inserting (6-17) and (6-21), gives

$$\beta(t, \epsilon) = \epsilon t - (M-2)t^2 + O(t^3) \qquad (6\text{-}25)$$

to one loop. Minimal subtraction insures, once more, that the only ϵ dependence is the explicit ϵ in (6-25).

The function β is plotted in Fig. 6-5, for $d > 2$ ($\epsilon < 0$) and for $d < 2$ ($\epsilon > 0$). Recalling the discussion in Sec. I-8-7 one concludes from the form of β that

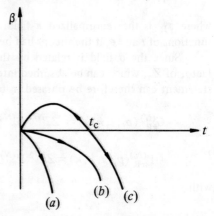

FIGURE 6-5
The flow function (a) $d < 2$, (b) $d = 2$, (c) $d > 2$.
The arrows indicate the direction of flow in the infra-red.

(a) *below two dimensions*   the theory is ultra-violet free and has no fixed point in the asymptotic behavior in the infrared. In an imprecise sense, the infrared behavior of the theory, for any non-zero temperature, is like its behavior at high temperature, where the system is disordered.

(b) *at two dimensions*   the theory is asymptotically free in the ultra-violet, just like a non-abelian gauge theory, which makes it of interest to particle physicists.

(c) *above two dimensions*   the theory has an ultra-violet stable fixed point at

$$t_c = \frac{\epsilon}{M-2} \qquad (6\text{-}26)$$

This fixed point separates the infrared behavior into two domains.
For $t < t_c$ the asymptotic behavior is free – zero temperature.
For $t > t_c$ the infrared behavior is high temperature.

From the field theoretical point of view a very interesting consequence of the form of β, above two dimensions, is that the theory is renormalizable despite the fact that it appears to be non-renormalizable by power counting. Power counting indicates that for $d > 2$, the coupling is dimensionful, and will run away from zero as the lattice spacing is decreased. This will happen, of course, for a ϕ^4-theory above four dimensions as well. But here the situation is special.

The question of whether the mass, or the inverse correlation length, can have a finite limit in the continuum, can be approached as follows: the mass m is a function of t and κ. Since it is a physical quantity it has no anomalous dimensions (Exercise I-8-17) and will therefore obey the following scaling relation:

$$\xi^{-1}(t) = m(t, \kappa) = \rho m(t(\rho), \kappa) \qquad (6\text{-}27)$$

The parameter ρ is the new scale of κ, and hence an inverse of the new lattice spacing. Thus the question boils down to the behavior of m as $\rho \to \infty$.†

The form of β insures that for $d > 2$, $t(\rho) \to t_c$ in this limit. Moreover, since t_c is the critical point, $m(t_c) = 0$, (see also Sec. 6-4). Hence, the right-hand side will remain finite as the lattice spacing vanishes for all $t < t_c$.

Next we observe that the cross-over from Goldstone-like behavior to critical behavior, at $t < t_c$, will take place naturally, as the length-scale changes. At long distances all the π's will behave as Goldstone modes, since their Green functions will be dominated by the free – zero temperature – fixed point. At short distances – shorter than $\xi(= m^{-1})$ – the π's will be governed by the fixed point at T_c, where $m = 0$, but anomalous dimensions appear. It is just this cross-over which gives meaning to a correlation length in a regime where the Green function falls off as a power throughout.[13]

The fact that the non-trivial fixed point is unstable in the infrared may appear odd if compared naively to the ϕ^4-theory. There the fixed point is stable. But the crucial difference is that here the coupling constant is the temperature, and the temperature is naturally a relevant variable at the critical point.

Let us turn to the renormalization group equations. The anomalous dimension function associated with the π-field is, as usual:

$$\gamma_\pi(t) = \kappa \left.\frac{\partial \ln Z_\pi}{\partial \kappa}\right|_{\text{bare}} = (M-1)t + O(t^2) \qquad (6\text{-}28)$$

The extreme right-hand side follows using Eq. (6-22). $G_{\pi R}^{(N)}$ then satisfies the equation:

$$\left\{ \kappa \frac{\partial}{\partial \kappa} + \beta(t)\frac{\partial}{\partial t} + \tfrac{1}{2}N\gamma_\pi(t) + \left[\tfrac{1}{2}\gamma_\pi(t) + \frac{\beta(t)}{t} - \epsilon\right] h\frac{\partial}{\partial h} \right\} G_{\pi R}^{(N)}(p_i; t, h, \kappa) = 0$$

$$(6\text{-}29)$$

†A systematic study of the renormalization of the non-linear σ-model above two dimensions has been carried out by Arefe'eva.[12]

the details of the derivation should be considered as an exercise. The same equation holds for Green functions which include σ-fields as well.

6-4 SCALING BEHAVIOR AND CRITICAL EXPONENTS

We now turn to the solution of the equations. First let us consider the zero field correlation length. It satisfies the equation:

$$\left[\kappa\frac{\partial}{\partial\kappa} + \beta(t)\frac{\partial}{\partial t}\right]\xi(t,\kappa) = 0 \qquad (6\text{-}30)$$

Dimensional analysis implies that

$$\xi(t,\kappa) = \kappa^{-1}\bar{\xi}(t) \qquad (6\text{-}31)$$

Inserting in Eq. (6-30) gives an ordinary differential equation for $\bar{\xi}$, which is solved with the initial condition $\bar{\xi}(0) = 0$, to give:

$$\xi(t,\kappa) = \kappa^{-1}t^{1/\epsilon}\exp\left\{\int_0^t dt'\left[\frac{1}{\beta(t')} - \frac{1}{et'}\right]\right\} \qquad (6\text{-}32)$$

See e.g. Exercise 6-11.

Here ν can be identified. If

$$\beta(t_c) = 0$$

the integral in (6-32) diverges as $t \to t_c$, and if $\beta'(t_c) \neq 0$, then the asymptotic behavior near t_c is:

$$\xi(t) \sim (t_c - t)^{-1/\beta'(t_c)} \qquad (6\text{-}33)$$

Hence

$$\nu = -\frac{1}{\beta'(t_c)} = \epsilon^{-1} + O(1) \qquad (6\text{-}34)$$

Next we turn to the spontaneous magnetization $-\sigma(t)$. It is simply a $G^{(1)}$, and is clearly translationally invariant. Furthermore, it is dimensionless and therefore independent of κ. Writing Eq. (6-29) for $N = 1$, $h = 0$ and no κ dependence, it reduces to

$$\left[\beta(t)\frac{\partial}{\partial t} + \tfrac{1}{2}\zeta(t)\right]\sigma(t) = 0 , \qquad (6\text{-}35)$$

which is an ordinary equation again.

The solution, with initial conditions $\sigma(0) = 1$, is

$$\sigma(t) = \exp\left[-\tfrac{1}{2}\int_0^t dt'\,\zeta(t')/\beta(t')\right] . \qquad (6\text{-}36)$$

Now one can identify β — the magnetization critical exponent. The integral diverges as $t \rightarrow t_c$, and the asymptotic behavior of $\sigma(t)$ near t_c is,

$$\sigma(t) \sim (t_c - t)^{-\zeta(t_c)/2\beta'(t_c)} \qquad (6\text{-}37)$$

and hence

$$\beta = -\frac{\zeta(t_c)}{2\beta'(t_c)} = \frac{M-1}{2(M-2)} + O(\epsilon). \qquad (6\text{-}38)$$

Finally, to compute the exponent η one sets $t = t_c$, $h = 0$, and $N = 2$ in Eq. (6-29). The solution is

$$G_\pi^{(2)}(p) \sim \kappa^{-\zeta(t_c)} p^{\zeta(t_c)-d} \qquad (6\text{-}39)$$

from which one concludes that

$$\eta = \zeta(t_c) - \epsilon = \frac{\epsilon}{M-2} + O(\epsilon^2) \qquad (6\text{-}40)$$

The scaling properties implied by the renormalization group equation (6-29) can be expressed, in the most general form, using $\xi(t)$ and $\sigma(t)$, in the form:

$$G^{(N)}(p_i; t, h) = [\xi(t)]^{(N-1)d} [\sigma(t)]^N F^{(N)} [p_i \xi, h\sigma(t) \xi^d(t) t^{-1}] \qquad (6\text{-}41)$$

The derivation is left as Exercise 6-11. See also Ref. (6).

At two dimensions the exponent ν diverges and η vanishes, as a result of the fact that the fixed point arrives at the origin. In accordance with the Mermin-Wagner-Coleman theorem the ordered phase disappears, and the entire expansion becomes meaningless. Yet, if as $\epsilon \rightarrow 0$, $M \rightarrow 2$ the situation becomes ambiguous and one cannot exclude a fixed point at a finite temperature.

Perturbation theory for $M = 2$ at $d = 2$ vanishes term by term. Nevertheless the theory is not without interest. Exponentially small terms ($\sim \exp \cdot t^{-1}$) become dominant, and via topological excitations — vortices — lead to a very special phase transition — the Kosterlitz-Thouless transition — which exhibits no long range order.[14] This transition can also be treated by field theoretic methods using the renormalization group,[15] but this will take us too far afield.

Appendix 6–1

RENORMALIZATION OF THE NON-LINEAR SIGMA MODEL

The proof that the non-linear σ-model is renormalized as simply as has been indicated in Sec. 6-3, is based on Ward-Takahashi identities, which in turn follow from the underlying $0(M)$-symmetry. Brézin, Zinn-Justin and Le Guillou[16] have used a non-linear version of the Ward-Takahashi identities, introduced by Zinn-Justin in the study of Gauge theories,[17] to prove the renormalizability of the theory in two dimensions. Here we will use a slight variation on their theme to reach the same result.[18]

Introducing J_i as sources for the π_i and H for σ, a rotation in the (π_i, σ)-plane leads to the identity:

$$\int d^2x \left(J_i(x) \frac{\delta}{\delta H(x)} - H(x) \frac{\delta}{\delta J_i(x)} \right) Z\{\mathbf{J}, H\} = 0 \qquad (A6\text{-}1)$$

and a similar identity for W, the generating functional for the connected Green functions. We are assuming, of course, that the regularization preserves the $0(M)$-symmetry.

Since only the π's are left as independent variables the Legendre transform is performed on the J_i's only. The generating functional for the vertex functions *of the π's*, $\Gamma\{\pi, H\}$, will satisfy the identity:

$$\int d^2 x \left(\frac{\delta\Gamma}{\delta H(x)} \cdot \frac{\delta\Gamma}{\delta\pi_i(x)} + H(x)\pi_i(x) \right) = 0 \qquad \text{(A6-2)}$$

in which $\pi_i(x)$ stands for the classical field:

$$\pi_i(x) = \frac{\delta W\{\mathbf{J}, H\}}{\delta J_i(x)} \qquad \text{(A6-3)}$$

Equation (A6-2) is the central tool, and its non-linearity will be turned to our advantage.

First we note that the divergent part of Γ must also satisfy the identity. Denoting it by $\Gamma_{\mathrm{div}}(\pi, H)$, one uses dimensional analysis to affect an expansion in H. Since H is of dimension 2 the expansion reads:

$$\Gamma_{\mathrm{div}}\{\pi\} = \frac{1}{T}\int d^2 x\, \Gamma^{(0)}(\pi, \nabla\pi) + \frac{1}{T}\int d^2 x\, H(x)\, \Gamma^{(1)}(\pi(x)) \qquad \text{(A6-4)}$$

where $\Gamma^{(0)}$ includes two derivatives of π's and σ and $\Gamma^{(1)}$ includes no derivatives. Substituting (A6-4) in (A6-2) and comparing powers of H one obtains the following equations for $\Gamma^{(0)}$ and $\Gamma^{(1)}$:

$$\int d^2 x\, \Gamma^{(1)}(x)\, \frac{\delta\mathcal{A}^{(0)}}{\delta\pi_i(x)} = 0 \qquad \text{(A6-5)}$$

$$\Gamma^{(1)}(x)\, \frac{\delta\Gamma^{(1)}(\pi(x))}{\delta\pi_i(x)} + \pi_i(x) = 0 \qquad \text{(A6-6)}$$

where

$$\mathcal{A}^{(0)} = \int d^2 x\, \Gamma^{(0)}(\pi, \nabla\pi) \qquad \text{(A6-7)}$$

Since $\Gamma^{(1)}$ is a local function of $\pi(x)$, (A6-6) is solved directly to give:

$$\Gamma^{(1)}(\pi(x)) = [B - \pi^2(x)]^{\frac{1}{2}} \qquad \text{(A6-8)}$$

with B an arbitrary constant of integration.

To solve Eq. (A6-5) for $\mathcal{A}^{(1)}$, or $\Gamma^{(0)}$, one observes first that this part is the $H = 0$ part, and hence must be invariant under the full $O(M)$ group. Since it includes two derivatives it is of the form

$$\Gamma^{(0)}(\pi, \nabla\pi) = A\left\{\tfrac{1}{2}(\nabla\pi)^2 + \tfrac{1}{2}[\nabla(C - \pi^2)^{\frac{1}{2}}]^2\right\} , \qquad \text{(A6-9)}$$

with A and C arbitrary. The constant C defines the new rotation transformation

$$\delta\pi_i = \omega_i(C - \pi^2)^{\frac{1}{2}} \qquad \text{(A6-10)}$$

But $\Gamma^{(0)}$ must still satisfy (A6-5), which gives

$$C = B \ .$$

leaving us with two arbitrary constants A and B. The final form of the divergent part of Γ is:

$$\Gamma_{\text{div}} = \frac{1}{T}\int d^2x \left\{ A\left[\tfrac{1}{2}(\nabla\pi)^2 + \tfrac{1}{2}(\nabla(B-\pi^2)^{1/2})^2\right] + H(B-\pi^2)^{1/2}\right\} \qquad \text{(A6-11)}$$

The divergences are, of course, contained in A and B. We can, therefore, eliminate them by absorbing A and B into a redefinition of the parameters, appearing in the action. Rewriting Γ_{div} in the form:

$$\Gamma_{\text{div}} = \frac{AB}{T}\int d^2x \left\{\tfrac{1}{2}(\nabla B^{-\frac{1}{2}}\pi)^2 + \tfrac{1}{2}(\nabla[1-(B^{-\frac{1}{2}}\pi)^2]^{1/2})^2\right.$$

$$\left. + HA^{-1}B^{-\frac{1}{2}}[1-(B^{-\frac{1}{2}}\pi)^2]\right\} \qquad \text{(A6-12)}$$

leads to the renormalization (6-17) through (6-20) via Exercise 6-7. It implies that writing the full generating functional in terms of an action

$$\mathcal{A} = \frac{\kappa^{-\epsilon}}{t}\int d^2x \left\{\tfrac{1}{2}(\nabla\pi_{\text{R}})^2 + \tfrac{1}{2}[\nabla(1-\pi_{\text{R}}^2)^{1/2}]^2 + h(1-\pi_{\text{R}}^2)^{1/2}\right\} \qquad \text{(A6-13)}$$

where π_{R}, t and h are related to π, T and H in an obvious way, eliminates the divergences. One part, the primitive one, is eliminated explicitly in (A6-11). That the finite parts do not become infinite in the process, is again left to induction about insertions etc.[16]

EXERCISES

6-1 Verify the powers of the lattice spacing appearing in the final form of the action, and check the dimensions of T and π in Eq. (6-7).

6-2 Prove once for the S variables and once for Z of (6-7) that at $T = 0$, $\pi = 0$, $\sigma = 1$.

6-3 Compute $\Gamma_\alpha^{(2)}$ to first order in T (up to terms $0(1)$), with momentum cutoff Λ and show that the mass terms cancel with the measure. What happens at the next order?

6-4 Show that to second order in T (up to terms $0(T)$) mass terms in $\Gamma^{(2)}$ vanish in dimensional regularization.

6-5 Show that all mass terms will vanish in dimensional regularization.

6-6 Write the algebraic expressions for graphs $(i)-(p)$ of Fig. 6-4. Express them in terms of (b) and (c). Keep in mind that the measure has been eliminated.

6-7 Prove, using power counting, that there are h independent renormalization constants.

6-8 Starting from the expression for the relation between the bare and renormalized generating functions, show that (6-19) give finite left-hand sides.

6-9 Calculate the connected four point Green functions of the π's to one loop, and show that (6-19a) with (6-21) and (6-22) render it finite.

6-10 Same as Exercise 6-9 for the σ-σ Green function.

6-11 Show that ξ of (6-32) satisfies the scaling (6-27).

REFERENCES

1. E. Brézin and D. J. Wallace, *Physical Review*, **B7**, 1967 (1973); D. J. Wallace and R. K. P. Zia, *Physical Review*, **B12**, 5340 (1975); D. R. Nelson, *Physical Review*, **B13**, 2222 (1976).
2. I. D. Lawrie, *Journal of Physics*, **A14**, 2489 (1980).
3. L. Schafer and H. Horner, *Zeitschrift fur Physik*, **B29**, 251 (1978).
4. A. M. Polyakov, *Physics Letters*, **59B**, 79 (1975).
5. D. R. Nelson and R. A. Pelcovits, *Physical Reivew*, **B16**, 2191 (1977).
6. E. Brézin and J. Zinn-Justin, *Physical Review*, **B14**, 3110 (1976).
7. See e.g. Ref. 11, Ch. 1.
8. T. M. Rice, *Physical Review*, **140**, 1889 (1966) and J. W. Kane and L. P. Kadanoff, *Physical Review*, **155**, 80 (1967).
9. A. Jewicki, *Physics Letters*, **71B**, 327 (1977); S. Elitzur, Institute of Advanced Study preprint (1979); D. J. Amit and G. B. Kotliar, *Nuclear Physics*, **B170[FS1]**, 187 (1980); F. David, *Physics Letters*, **69B**, 371 (1980).
10. See e.g. Ref. 6 above.
11. W. A. Bardeen, B. W. Lee and R. E. Shrock, *Physical Review*, **D14**, 985 (1976); D. J. Amit, Y. Y. Goldschmidt and L. Peliti, *Annals of Physics*, **116**, 1 (1978).
12. I. Ya. Aref'eva, E. R. Nissimov, S. J. Pacheva, *Communications in Mathematical Physics*, **71**, 213 (1980); I. Ya. Aref'eva, S. I. Azakov, *Nuclear Physics*, **B162**, 298 (1980).
13. B. D. Josephson, *Physics Letters*, **21**, 608 (1966).
14. V. L. Berezinskii, *ZhETF* (USSR), **59**, 907 (1970), (English translation *JETP*, **32**, 493 (1971)); J. M. Kosterlitz and D. J. Thouless, *Journal of Physics*, **C6**, 1181 (1973) and J. M. Kosterlitz, *op. cit.*, **C7**, 1046 (1974).
15. P. B. Wiegmann, *Journal of Physics*, **C11**, 1583 (1978); T. Ohta, *Progress in Theoretical Physics*, **60**, 968 (1978); D. J. Amit, Y. Y. Goldschmidt and G. Grinstein, *Journal of Physics*, **A13**, 484 (1980).
16. E. Brézin, J. Zinn-Justin and J. C. Le Guillou, *Physical Review*, **D10**, 2615 (1976).
17. J. Zinn-Justin, in *Trends in Elementary Particle Theory*, H. Rollnik and K. Dielz, eds. (Springer, Berlin, 1975).
18. D. J. Amit, Y. Y. Goldschmidt and L. Peliti, ref. 11 and Y. Y. Goldschmidt, Ph. D. Thesis, Hebrew University, unpublished.

AUTHOR INDEX

SUBJECT INDEX